POLYTECHNIC INSTITUTE OF BROOKLYN

MICROWAVE RESEARCH INSTITUTE

SYMPOSIA SERIES

I	Modern Network Synthesis	April 1952
II	Nonlinear Circuit Analysis	April 1953
III	Information Networks	April 1954
IV	Modern Advances in Microwave Techniques	November 1954
V	Modern Network Synthesis II	April 1955
VI	Nonlinear Circuit Analysis II	April 1956
VII	The Role of Solid State Phenomena in Electric Circuits	April 1957
VIII	Electronic Waveguides	April 1958
IX	Millimeter Waves	March-April 1959
X	Active Networks and Feedback Systems	April 1960
XI	Electromagnetics and Fluid Dynamics of Gaseous Plasma	April 1961
XII	Mathematical Theory of Automata	April 1962

Sponsored by
The Polytechnic Institute of Brooklyn
Microwave Research Institute
Aerodynamics Laboratory

In Cooperation with
The Institute of Radio Engineers
Professional Group on Electron Devices
Professional Group on Microwave Theory and Techniques
Professional Group on Nuclear Science
The Institute of the Aerospace Sciences

Co-Sponsored by
The Air Force Office of Scientific Research
The Office of Naval Research
The U.S. Army Signal Corps

DISTRIBUTORS:
INTERSCIENCE PUBLISHERS • NEW YORK • LONDON

PROCEEDINGS OF THE SYMPOSIUM ON

ELECTROMAGNETICS AND FLUID DYNAMICS OF GASEOUS PLASMA

NEW YORK, N. Y., APRIL 4, 5, 6, 1961

Microwave Research Institute Symposia Series

VOLUME XI

POLYTECHNIC PRESS
OF THE
POLYTECHNIC INSTITUTE OF BROOKLYN, BROOKLYN, N. Y.

[1962]

Edited by
Jerome Fox

Associate Editor
Martha Crowell

Library of Congress Catalog Card Number 62-13174

TABLE OF CONTENTS

FOREWORD

WELCOMING ADDRESS BY DR. ERNST WEBER
PRESIDENT, POLYTECHNIC INSTITUTE OF BROOKLYN

Colleagues, Fellows of professional societies, and guests, I am very happy to welcome you to this, the eleventh symposium in our series, which has actually extended over exactly ten years.

This is the tenth year that we have conducted these annual meetings. In a way it is a sign of maturity that we have been able to furnish challenging symposia year after year and have had remarkable attendance for some rather erudite themes. The first one, in 1952, covered "Modern Network Synthesis--from Audio to Microwaves." Since that time we have broadened the topic, staying fairly close to the word "networks." We have covered linear networks, nonlinear, passive and active networks, and at one time covered solid-state phenomena and their utilization for circuit design.

This time we have a topic which is quite different, though it has a very obvious relation to the broad aspects of network circuit theory; that is, "Electromagnetics and Fluid Dynamics of Gaseous Plasma." As in all other instances, the symposium will present certain tutorial material to bring us up to date, as well as research results at the frontier of activities in laboratories and universities.

This symposium is significant in several ways: We have, as in all previous cases, the co-sponsorship of the three military services, but, for the first time, two of the departments in the Institute, the Microwave Research Institute and the Department of Aerospace Engineering have cooperated in organizing the symposium. This indicates the interdepartmental character of the topic that we are to discuss. I might stress that today all new research -- frontier research -- has become interdisciplinary, interdepartmental; therefore there is a tendency at the universities to attempt to diffuse departmental lines as far as possible. This is not always easy; the more efficient way is to establish cooperation as we have done.

The second new aspect of this symposium is a remarkable blending of physics and engineering, a new tendency in engineering education that extends back for a number of years but has only recently come to full bloom: namely, the need for scientific engineering. It is no longer possible for engineers to use what they learned ten or twenty years ago; they have to keep up with the most rapid progress of science and utilize it even before all research results that scientists can furnish are available. This symposium illustrates just that type of problem.

We have, also for the first time, the co-sponsorship of two professional organizations -- the Institute of Radio Engineers and the Institute of the Aerospace Sciences -- very significant professional interdisciplinary cooperation. Our symposia have always been of an international nature. We have had lectures by authors from all over the world. This time we will find that the largest number of papers have been contributed by the United States contingent and by a sizeable Soviet delegation, which is rather interesting. Perhaps significant is the fact that space research is so costly that very few nations can afford it and, interestingly, those that can are nations of rather different political philosophies.

This meeting is personally gratifying to me because of its interdisciplinary aspect, which we have tried to implement in our own Institute to as large a degree as is feasible. I would like to thank particularly, Professor Nathan Marcuvitz who was director of our Microwave Research Institute until his recent appointment to the vice-presidency for research at Polytechnic Institute of Brooklyn, and Professor Antonio Ferri, head of our Department of Aerospace Engineering and Applied Mechanics.

Though I have mentioned the two department heads, you all realize that the real work is really done by others, and so I would like to acknowledge the real contributions by Professor Martin Bloom of the Aerodynamics Laboratory and Professor Enrico Levi of the Microwave Research Institute who, as co-chairmen, organized the details for this symposium.

I should like to call attention to the fact that we do have quite a number of foreign representatives in the audience. We have a delegation of seven members from the Union of Soviet Socialist Republics; we have contingents from France, Canada, Japan, Imperial College of London and RCA Laboratories in Quebec.

I now take great pleasure in introducing the representative of Naval Research, which is the senior partner in sponsored research in support of basic research in the military services. I take great pleasure in introducing Rear Admiral Coates.

GREETINGS FROM THE CO-SPONSORING AGENCIES

REAR ADMIRAL L. D. COATES, USN
OFFICE OF NAVAL RESEARCH

I am delighted to be here at the eleventh international symposium of the Polytechnic Institute of Brooklyn. The Institute has become world famous for these symposia. This one, I am sure, will further enhance its reputation for international critical symposia of the highest scientific content.

This symposium is truly international because of the countries represented, and also because of the world-wide interest in the electromagnetics and fluid dynamics of gaseous plasma. The organization of this symposium by the Polytechnic's Department of Aerospace Engineering and the Microwave Research Institute, in cooperation with three professional groups of the Institute of Radio Engineers - those of Electron Devices, Microwave Theory and Techniques, and Nuclear Science -- together with the Institute of Aerospace Sciences - indicates not only the great technical importance but also the scientific frontier aspects of this area.

Shortly before the war many physicists and engineers believed that the last word had been said about ionization and conduction in gases. However, a few loyal scientists, such as Leonard Loeb and Irving Langmuir kept the subject to the forefront. For instance, we have fluorescent lighting now because fundamental knowledge of the control of gaseous plasma in mercury vapor tubes allowed us to exploit the newly developed fluorescent powders.

During World War II, again, this field of gaseous conduction was especially fruitful because radar became practical with the development of the transmit-receive tube. This tube, as you know, is dependent upon our fundamental knowledge of gaseous conduction.

Now, of course, the study of gaseous plasma has moved great distances in many directions. For one thing, it enables us to make progress in the most advanced aerodynamics. And it is my hope that eventually it will furnish for us and the world a source of unlimited power.

Another unique feature of this symposium is the support extended by the cooperation of the Army, through the Office of Scientific Research, and the Navy, through the Office of Naval Research.

I wish you Godspeed in your presentations, deliberations, and discussions.

DR. PAUL A. SIPLE
ARMY RESEARCH OFFICE

I consider it both a privilege and a pleasure to have been given the opportunity to make a few brief remarks on behalf of the U. S. Army Research Office to so distinguished a gathering. I would like to comment first on the most profitable relationship that has existed between the Army and Polytechnic Institute of Brooklyn over the years, and particularly, I would commend the staff of your Microwave Research Institute for its outstanding contributions in connection with a Joint Service Contract, which, although funded rather modestly, has proved a constant source of new and very worthwhile ideas.

The basic research in electronics and the electronic sciences supported by this contract has lead to the development of revolutionary new devices and systems having important military significance.

The high power microwave and plasma research performed by Dr. Marcuvitz and his associates is but one example of Brooklyn Poly's unique basic research capability. In fact, it was the recognition of this capability, which you share with a number of other institutions, that prompted the three services to initiate the program for supporting university "centers" of research. As a result of this farsighted program, pools of outstanding scientists are now available to serve as a core or nucleus should the need ever arise for the rapid creation of national defense research type laboratories.

Participants in the Army's research program include not only most of the nation's leading universities, but also the many Army Technical Service laboratories, industrial research laboratories, nonprofit organizations, off-shore research activities, and others. Responsibility for the over-all planning, direction, management, and coordination of this very sizable effort is vested in the Director of Army Research, Major General William J. Ely, who reports in turn to the Chief of Army Research and Development, Lieutenant General Arthur G. Trudeau. The staff agencies and field activities which directly monitor the Army's research program include the Army Research Office at Arlington Hall, Virginia, the European Research Office in Frankfurt, Germany; the Far East Research Office in Tokyo, Japan; and the recently created Army Research Office at Duke University, Durham, North Carolina. This latter activity was formerly known as the Office of Ordnance Research, and has the primary mission of handling all basic research in the physical sciences contract grants for the Army. ARO Durham will have as one of its major functions the awarding of grants to outstanding university researchers.

The Army's research program is extensive and encompasses all of the major scientific disciplines. It includes more than 2600 research tasks, and is currently funded at about $170, 000, 000 annually, approximately $40, 000, 000 of which is for basic research. Our research program is carried out about forty per cent in-house and sixty per cent by outside agencies. It is conducted at sixty Army installations, in coordination and cooperation with twenty-four other government agencies, by nearly 300 profit-making and more than 110 nonprofit firms or institutions, and by well over 200 colleges and schools.

Overseas we are pursuing research on a contract basis in fourteen nations through our European Research Office. In the Far East we have a growing program, little more than a year old, that presently is limited to Japan and the biological sciences field. We are currently making plans for extending our program in Central and South America.

The Army Research Office guides rather than directs this research program. Our highly trained scientists and engineers review, evaluate, and aim to integrate research proposals in the formulation of the over-all Army program. We seek to minimize duplication of research tasks, to eliminate unprofitable activities, to get the maximum for the Army's research expenditures. Control is exercised principally through budgetary power and exception to proposals made by the Technical Services or other activities under our direct supervision.

Considering the theme of this symposium, it might be of interest to summarize the more significant internal and external work in plasmas that the Army is doing. Most of the internal effort in this area is performed at the U. S. Army Signal Research and Development Laboratory at Fort Monmouth, New Jersey. In studying the properties of hot and dense plasmas generated at the 100, 000 joule plasma facility, Signal Corps investigators developed a new and efficient technique that uses the reflections and transmissions of 4. 3 mm microwave beams to study the dependence of the dielectric properties of the plasmas on their time and space variation. The measurements obtained provide a diagnostic tool for determining the plasma density and temperature as a function of time, and allow the determination of other relevant physical parameters, such as the ambipolar diffusion coefficient of the plasma.

A parallel theoretical study resulted in a mathematical theory of the dielectric properties of dense, hot plasmas that was compared with the experimental data.

A long-range goal of this work is the eventual understanding of plasma properties under extreme conditions of temperature and density to enable the use of these laboratory plasmas in simulating larger scale ionospheric electromagnetic wave propagation phenomena under known and reproducible conditions.

Additional experimental studies in plasmas resulted in the design of a plasma-gun vacuum switch capable of switching high currents rapidly and reliably. Further results included interesting new findings concerning instabilities of pinch discharges at very high current values. The experiments also confirmed prior research of several European plasma groups on the importance of extreme purity of the gases used.

The Army also supports plasma research at a number of universities, either by contributing to the Joint Service Contract Program, as we do at the Microwave Research Institute, or by contracting separately. Excellent examples are the contract on "Plasma Acceleration" with Stevens Institute of Technology which has resulted in the design of a plasma machine (Megatron) for creating 1000 ampere beams of 150-Mev electrons; the Joint Service Contract with the Research Lab of Electronics at MIT where work is being done on the hollow cathode discharge, high-power pulsed microwave gas discharge, and the effect of collisions on plasma waveguide propagation; and the contract with the Stanford Electronics Lab where studies are being made on the diffusion of microplasmas in silicon.

I would like to close on the note that the Army depends heavily on the nation's universities, for generating the fundamental knowledge necessary to nourish and sustain the Army's ever expanding science and technology.

DR. KNOX MILLSAPS
AIR FORCE OFFICE OF SCIENTIFIC RESEARCH

I bring you greetings from the Air Force Office of Scientific Research, and since this is my first opportunity as Head of AFOSR to address this specialized group of scientists and engineers, I want to tell you how highly pleased and honored I feel to speak these words of welcome from my office and from the Air Force. Although I have a reputation for liking to talk, I shall leave the talking to the experts assembled here. But in this connection I am reminded of the first meeting with my staff at AFOSR. I told each director to prepare a little orientation talk. One director quickly asked "What shall I talk about?" I quickly answered, "About five minutes." This was considered funny by the assembled group but whether funny or not I shall try to abide by my own suggestion in my talk here.

Now as to plasmas. Although known from the days of Irving Langmuir and before, plasmas continue their stubborn resistance to giving up the secrets of their highly unorthodox and unpredictable behavior. I suppose this is one reason why President Weber and his associates chose this particular plasma culprit for closer examination and attack by means of this annual symposium. There have, of course, been many plasma conferences and there will be many more. But if I can judge by past performance at the Polytechnic, this symposium will add some new and interesting ingredients; it will shed new light and resolve at least some of the confusion which surrounds the plasma problem. More than that, it will serve as a fine review of the state of the art for those of us who may be getting initiated into its mysteries, and I class myself with these. However, as Executive Director of AFOSR, I am supposed to be knowledgeable about everything, so I will venture at least one of my own observations about plasmas.

It seems to me that there is too much loose talk about "plasmas" without some precision in defining the type or kind of plasma in question. Perhaps it is because of my mathematical training that I am especially sensitive to this lack of precision. But isn't it true that the term "plasma" may characterize anything from an ordinary gas discharge to the incredibly energetic processes associated with thermonuclear reactions and helium burning in stars? Yet, the plasma properties at these two extremes differ as night does from day and the energy release is many, many orders of magnitude apart. I under stand that a plasma having an electron density below about 10^{12} electrons per cubic centimeter is a relatively well behaved one and can be treated by good, everyday statistics, since its behavior is substantially linear. Not so, however, for a really "hot" plasma. This one is so turbulent and unruly as to challenge to this very day the best efforts of our mathematical physicists and hydrodynamicists.

Why do we in the Air Force feel that plasmas are important? Let us forget for the moment the obvious applications in plasma and ion propulsion. There are many more reasons, as you well know. Some plasmas are important because of their nuisance value, as in problems of space charge and multipactor effect, or in the sheath that surrounds a missile in flight and interferes with good communication and control. Then there are the wonderful plasma phenomena as exhibited in lightning, in aurorae, the ionosphere, in the radiation belts and in the sun and stars! Some of these can crucially affect communication and space travel. On the other hand, some of these streams of ionized particles make the "whistler" mode of EM signal propagation possible and some provide for amplification of the "whistler" signal through a "traveling-wave-tube" effect in space, thus causing faint signals to become strong. Also, beyond the earth laboratory, a problem of great interest is the formation and development of solar flares which spew plasma material for millions of miles beyond the sun's disk and from which streams of particles travel to the earth and beyond. Hopefully, laboratory research on the interactions between plasmas and magnetic fields aided by high resolution solar radio astronomy may soon provide answers to this great riddle.

These are only some of the more startling aspects of plasmas which concern us in the Air Force today. There are many more, but I think I have mentioned enough to justify our great interest in plasma research and wholehearted support for this symposium.

Since you will be hearing about these things out of the mouths of experts, I will merely repeat that we in AFOSR continue to be intrigued by this unpredictable yet scientifically promising state of matter. So much so that we have contracts amounting to some millions of dollars with universities and industry in this field. The results of some of this Air Force supported research will be reported here. You will notice that this research covers the spectrum from a laboratory gas discharge to astrophysics except for the region pre-empted by the "Sherwood" thermonuclear fusion program.

In closing, let me again express my pleasure and that of my office in the opportunities these important annual symposia provide for Air Force participation and for advancement of research in a vital area of physics and electronics. May your symposium be a very successful one indeed.

C. TILGNER, JR.
INSTITUTE OF THE AEROSPACE SCIENCES

It is my great pleasure to bring you greetings on behalf of the officers and council of the Institute of the Aerospace Sciences. It is always gratifying to cooperate in a symposium where new, valuable information is going to be discussed. Research in many fields is uncovering much knowledge which reaches its full value only when it has been disclosed to those who can use it. There are never "too many meetings" when these tenets are observed.

Through the Grumman Company's participation in the activities of the Microwave Research Institute and the Aerodynamics Laboratory of the Brooklyn Polytechnic Institute, I have become familiar with their work and it is impossible in mere words to describe the outstanding quality of their research. The success of this symposium is assured even before it begins.

DR. L. I. SEDOV
ACADEMY OF SCIENCES, U. S. S. R.

Mr. President, Gentlemen:

I would like to convey greetings and wishes of success in these proceedings on behalf of the Academy of Sciences of the U. S. S. R. and the Lomonossov State University of Moscow.

I sincerely believe that the proceedings of this symposium are a very valuable addition to the family of measures directed toward the development of international cooperation among scientists, to better the over-all situation, and direct research to the benefit of all nations.

At the present time we are witnessing the fusion of mechanics and electrodynamics. Doubtlessly, in the near future, the methods and research in the field of magnetohydrodynamics -- that is, the two merged disciplines, mechanics and electro-dynamics -- will be the main method of learning about nature on terrestrial and cosmic scales. I am also certain that the technology of the near future, terrestrial as well as cosmic, will be closely connected with magnetohydrodynamic research.

We are presenting two papers at this meeting, one on microwave amplification by plasma by Chernov, and one on MHD waves in ionized gas by Sagdeev.

I would like also to mention some highlights of some of the theoretical work done at the Moscow University. We have conducted some research on the subject of circum-flow of a conducting medium around magnetized bodies. We made detailed studies of the structure of shock waves, upon which depends the radiation of electromagnetic waves. We have also investigated the formations connected with motion and electrodynamic effects. Perhaps this work can lead toward the explanation of the phenomenon of "fireball."

I would also like to mention the recently completed work on disintegration of any discontinuity and the problem of the piston in MHD. These problems have been solved by means of analysis of three basic cases; in MHD, however, there are 648 such basic cases which must be studied and classified. The context of these works is available to the interested.

Again, I wish you success and the best friendly relations at this conference.

UNITED STATES RESEARCH IN NUCLEAR TEST DETECTION*

J. P. Ruina
Director, Advanced Research Projects Agency
Department of Defense, Washington, D. C.

The Advanced Research Projects Agency (ARPA) has the responsibility for the national program of research to improve techniques for the detection of underground and high-altitude nuclear detonations. The program is codenamed VELA, and provides the scientific support for the current international negotiations on banning nuclear tests. Dr. Ruina discusses in general terms some of the major technical problem areas involved.

I would like to talk briefly and in general terms about what we do and do not know about detection and identification of nuclear blasts and what we are doing to improve our capabilities. I am sure you will appreciate the brevity of my remarks but I also hope that the content will be of interest to you. You know, of course, why the interest in detection of nuclear blasts. This is an especially timely subject now -- in fact perhaps somewhat uncomfortably timely for me.

The code name the government gives to the research program for improving our capability in the detection of nuclear detonations is Project VELA. The administrative and technical responsibility for Project VELA has been given to the Advanced Research Projects Agency. It is in that way that I personally fit into the picture. I am the Director of ARPA and a rather newly appointed one at that. My personal involvement with Project VELA dates from my coming to ARPA last January.

I will talk primarily about the technical aspects of Project VELA but will also include some historical and administrative aspects: I do not want to talk about the political and policy questions which relate to nuclear test detection. This program had its origin with what is called the Conference of Experts which took place in the summer of 1958 in Geneva with scientific representatives from the United States, United Kingdom, Canada and France on one side and the Soviet Union, Poland, Czechoslovakia and Rumania on the other. The Conference of Experts had as its purpose to assess the technical capability of the detection of nuclear detonations and to recommend a system which could be used by an international control agency for the detection of nuclear detonations. In general the conference concluded

*Address given by Dr. Ruina at the banquet following the opening of the Symposium on Electromagnetics and Fluid Dynamics of Gaseous Plasma, April 4, 1961.

that the capability for detecting tests in the atmosphere was satisfactory. Because of the many detonations that have taken place in the atmosphere, we have a firm base of experience on which to assess such a capability; however, at this conference it was concluded that the same capability did not exist with respect to testing above the atmosphere and underground. The conference proposed a system of 160 to 170 land-based control posts and ten ships to monitor nuclear tests. Each land control post would include equipment to detect seismic, acoustic and electromagnetic waves. There was also general agreement on the types and approximate performance characteristics of the detectors to be used at each control post. The conference reached three critical conclusions concerning the seismic capability of the proposed system which are worth repeating:

1. The network would have " good probability of recording seismic signals from deep underground nuclear explosions in continents equivalent to one kiloton and above. "

2. Within the state of existing knowledge, the network could not distinguish between the signals from underground explosions and those of " some earthquakes, " but it could identify " as being of natural origin about ninety per cent of the continental earthquakes, whose signals are equivalent to five kiloton, and a small percentage of continental earthquakes equivalent to one kiloton. "

3. In some special cases -- for example, shallow underground explosions, detonations on islands in seismic regions and concealed explosions -- the capability of the system would be reduced.

After the Conference of Experts, both the United States and the Soviet Union continued nuclear testing and the United States conducted five underground explosions - in the so-called " Hardtack" series in October 1958 -- which clearly indicated that the Conference of Experts had been optimistic about the capability to detect and identify underground explosions. This extensive new data plus certain important theoretical work on decoupling developed by Dr. Albert Latter of the RAND Corporation, convinced the United States that there were indeed difficulties in the detection and identification of nuclear tests which the Conference of Experts had not envisaged. Most significant, the new American data showed that the Expert's statement on the detectability of five kiloton underground explosions was more applicable to explosions on the order of twenty kilotons.

Dr. Latter's work concerned decoupling or the ability to muffle the seismic signal generated by an underground explosion by detonating in a large cavity. The extent of the muffling achieved depends on a number of variable factors such as the exact geometry of the area and the particular material) for example, salt or granite or volcanic tuff) in which the explosion takes place. The theoretical predictions concerning decoupling have been reasonably well confirmed by the

" Cowboy" series of small chemical explosions. Of course, there still is no experimental evidence available to demonstrate the actual degree of decoupling possible with nuclear explosions.

In early 1959, the Special Assistant to the President for Science and Technology appointed a Panel on Seismic Improvement under the chairmanship of Dr. Lloyd V. Berkner to study the whole question of seismic detection and identification. The panel produced a comprehensive report which included possible detection station configurations to improve the capability to detect and identify seismic events. The panel recommended the use of arrays of the instruments designed to reduce the signal-to-noise ratio for added sensitivity and also to improve the location capability or angle of arrival of the propagated wave.

Of primary interest, however, the Berkner panel recommended a strong research and development effort in this country which would have as its aim: 1) to find out the exact level of seismic activity on the earth; 2) to improve our knowledge of the propagation of seismic signals; 3) to enhance our ability to recognize, by means of the nature of the seismic signal, whether a given event was indeed a natural event or a chemical or nuclear explosion; and 4) to improve our instrument sensitivity and hence the capability of future detection systems. It is these recommendations which sort of set the pattern for what is now the Project VELA-UNIFORM program. In addition to seismic signals, it has also been suggested that it may be possible to identify an underground nuclear blast by means of an electrical signal which seems to be generated by the detonation. The practicability of this technique remains to be determined by experimentation.

It might be worth mentioning here that one of the more important and interesting phenomena under investigation to improve identification capabilities is the first motion criteria. It has been thought that the first motion of the seismic signal is that of a compressional wave. The first motion in the case of a compressional wave from an explosion is that of condensation in all directions around the explosion, whereas, in a natural event it has been postulated that the pressure effect might be positive in some directions and negative in others. First of all, there is serious question as to the extent to which this is true. Secondly, the first motion is a rather weak signal compared to the later wave forms on the seismogram and is not always clearly detected. In some instances, given the normal background noise, even if it is detected it is very difficult to determine that it was truly the first motion. Consequently, you can see that the questions of identification and sensitivity or detection capability are very much interconnected.

Following the Berkner panel activity and the formation of another panel under Dr. Panofsky to study the problem of detecting nuclear explosions at high altitude, international discussions involving the United States, the United Kingdom and the Soviet Union were resumed in Geneva. This will suffice for historical narrative and I shall try now to outline what the present United States technical program contains.

We have divided Project VELA into three parts. The first is called VELA-UNIFORM and encompasses the seismic research portion of the project. It in turn, is subdivided into various tasks. With the advice of the National Academy of Science and the cooperation of the U. S. Coast and Geodetic Survey, establishment of a world-wide network of standardized seismographic stations is being initiated in order to enable seismologists around the world the measure earthquakes on like sets of instruments. One of the great aids to progress in any scientific endeavor is the comparability of data collected by specialists in the field and the standardized stations will provide such an opportunity for scientific collaboration on an international basis. Researchers will be able to exchange their data freely.

An important program in basic seismic research has been launched to obtain an improved understanding of the generation and propagation of seismic waves. We want to learn more about the characteristics of all types of seismic and hydroacoustic waves. Crustal studies are under way to enlighten us on the media through which seismic waves must pass. The earth's crust is layered and the media have different signal travel times; furthermore, as the seismic wave travels from one medium to another, it may be reflected, refracted and attentuated by the various layers. And of fundamental importance, studies of the seismicity of the earth are being undertaken in order to acquire understanding of the natural background against which nuclear explosions will be compared.

VELA-UNIFORM includes work on systems development and systems concepts concerned with the detection and identification of underground explosions. A prototype Geneva-model seismic detection station, based on specifications agreed on by the Conference of Experts, was opened in Oklahoma last October and is in daily operation recording natural seismic events. About fifteen earthquakes per day are being recorded there. ARPA also plans to construct a station with improved instrumentation, as recommended by the Berkner panel. A key problem in systems development work is the development of sufficiently sensitive instrumentation, particularly equipment to detect and identify decoupled explosions in the presence of natural background noise. Allied to this problem, even if an explosion is detected and identified, methods of location are required in order to determine precisely where it took place.

The ultimate test to verify that a suspected event occurred is of course on-site inspection. Experience to date indicates that much more than simply a quick survey with radiation detectors will be required. Consequently, a variety of inspection techniques are under study including evidence of permanent displacement, discoloration of vegetation, evidence of unusual human activity in the area, drilling for samples, and increased local seismic noise.

It is clear that in order to fully test theories, instruments, detection techniques, detection station configurations and on-site inspection methods, it will be necessary to conduct a program involving nuclear explosions. Chemical explosions can, of course, provide important information and will be utilized. They will not, however, provide those signal characteristics which are unique to nuclear explosions. Plans have been formulated for the detonation of chemical and nuclear explosions of varying yields at different depths, locations and cavity sizes. As you well know, there will be no nuclear detonations without first receiving Presidential approval, so this portion of the program is presently not authorized.

The second and third major portions of VELA are both concerned with the detection of nuclear tests at high altitude. VELA-SIERRA denotes detection by means of instrumentation located on the surface of the earth; VELA HOTEL is concerned with satellite-based detection. In the ground-based detection work we are studying a variety of optical and electromagnetic techniques, for example; detection of light emitted from the explosion, detection of atmospheric changes induced by radiation or debris, and detection of electromagnetic waves generated by the detonations. It is possible too that natural phenomena such as cloud cover, lightning, meteors, and aurora will degrade equipment performance and this must be accounted for in systems analyses.

In the area of space-based detection of high altitude nuclear tests, a large number of factors must be studied. One must consider the natural radiation background and the general environment in which the detection system will operate. Natural signals, for example, solar flares, gamma and x-rays must be distinguished from signals emanating from test detonation. The actual amount of radiation emitted from a nuclear explosion, the distance between the detonation and the detection system, and the sensitivity of the detection system sensors and associated electronic instrumentation are obviously critical variables in the detection problem. Experimental payloads and satellites are planned to obtain needed experimental data.

This outline of the major elements of Project VELA and the brief historical discussion which preceded it will, I hope, give you an introduction to the technical and scientific dimensions of the nuclear test detection question. Technically, the challenges are stimulating indeed. I need only remind you that prior to 1960, the field of low-frequency seismology was supported nationally in this country at the level of less than one million dollars a year. The commitment of millions of dollars to work in this field should bring a great flow of new data of value to researchers everywhere as well as contributing to the immediate problem of test detection. Project VELA-UNIFORM is now the largest single terrestrial science effort presently under way within the United States. By bringing to bear the best scientific and managerial talent available in the universities, industry and the government, within a single national research and development program, it is hoped that a meaningful improvement in our capability to detect nuclear explosions underground and at high altitudes will be forthcoming.

SYMPOSIUM ON

ELECTROMAGNETICS AND FLUID DYNAMICS OF GASEOUS PLASMA

April 4, 5, 6, 1961

Tuesday, April 4, 1961

Morning Session

WELCOMING ADDRESS
Dr. Ernst Weber, *President, Polytechnic Institute of Brooklyn*
OPENING REMARKS
Rear Admiral L.D. Coates, *Chief of Naval Research*
Dr. Paul A. Siple, *Scientific Advisor, Army Research Office*
Dr. Knox Millsaps, *Chief Scientist, Air Force Research Division*
Dr. Ernst Weber, *Chairman, Professional Groups Committee, IRE*
C. Tilgner, *Eastern Regional Vice President, Institute of the Aerospace Sciences*
Dr. L.I. Sedov, *Vice President, U.S.S.R. Academy of Sciences*

OPENING SESSION

Chairman: A. Ferri
Polytechnic Institute of Brooklyn

IS AERODYNAMICS BREAKING AN IONIC BARRIER?
A. Busemann, *NASA, Langley Research Laboratory*
LINEAR WAVE PROPAGATION IN PLASMAS
I.B. Bernstein, *Princeton University*
AMPLIFICATION OF MICROWAVES BY MEANS OF PLASMA
Z.S. Chernov and G.A. Bernashevski, *Academy of Sciences, U.S.S.R.*

Afternoon Session

MICROSCOPIC AND MACROSCOPIC THEORY

Chairman: R.K.M. Landshoff
Lockheed Missile Space Division, Burbank, California

MICROSCOPIC AND MACROSCOPIC MODELS IN PLASMA PHYSICS
H. Grad, *New York University*
CONCERNING A CONTINUUM THEORY OF THE ELECTRODYNAMICS AND DYNAMICS OF MOVING MEDIA
S. Goldstein, *Harvard University*
ON THE APPLICATION OF TWO-PARTICLE DISTRIBUTION FUNCTIONS
J.M. Burgers, *University of Maryland*
STABILITY ANALYSIS OF PLASMAS BY A MODIFIED HYDROMAGNETIC THEORY
O. Buneman, *Stanford University*
THE EFFECT OF COLLISIONS ON TWO-STREAM INSTABILITIES IN A PLASMA
D.A. Tidman and G. Weiss, *University of Maryland*

Tuesday Evening, April 4, 1961 -- Symposium Banquet

UNITED STATES RESEARCH IN NUCLEAR TEST DETECTION

Guest Speaker: J.P. Ruina
Director, Advanced Research Projects Agency
Department of Defense, Washington, D.C.

Wednesday, April 5, 1961

Morning Session

WAVE PHENOMENA
Chairman: W.P. Allis
Massachusetts Institute of Technology

INTERACTION OF MICROWAVES IN GASEOUS PLASMAS IMMERSED IN MAGNETIC FIELDS
L. Goldstein, *University of Illinois*
RADIATION FROM ELECTRIC CHARGES AND CURRENTS IN COMPRESSIBLE PLASMAS:
PART I - UNIFORMLY MOVING CHARGE;
PART II - OSCILLATING DIPOLE
M. Abele, A. Hessel and J. Shmoys, *Polytechnic Institute of Brooklyn*
ON A VARIATIONAL PRINCIPLE FOR PLASMAS
S. Gartenhaus, *Purdue University*
POWER AND ENERGY RELATIONS IN BI-DIRECTIONAL WAVEGUIDES
P. Chorney, *Massachusetts Institute of Technology*

Afternoon Session

COMPARISON OF THEORY AND EXPERIMENT
Chairman: A.C. Kolb
U.S. Naval Research Laboratory

INTERACTION BETWEEN MAGNETIC FIELDS AND MOVING PLASMAS
W.H. Bostick, *Stevens Institute of Technology*
THEORY AND EXPERIMENT ON THE CONTRIBUTION OF SPACE CHARGE TO THE ACCELERATION OF PLASMAS
R.V. Hess, J. Burlock and J.R. Sevier, *NASA, Langley Research Laboratory*
PRELIMINARY EXPERIMENTS ON MHD CHANNEL FLOW IN SLIGHTLY IONIZED GASES
G.W. Sutton and F. Robben, *General Electric Company*
PLASMA STUDIES IN A SHOCK TUBE
J.W. Daiber and H.S. Glick, *Cornell Aeronautical Lab., Inc.*
MAGNETICALLY-DRIVEN SHOCK WAVES
J.D. Cole and C. Greifinger, *The Rand Corporation*

Thursday, April 6, 1961

Morning Session

SHOCKS AND FLOWS - I

Chairman: A. Kantrowitz
AVCO Research Laboratory, Everett, Mass.

SOME PARADOXES OF SUB-ALFVENIC FLOW OF A COMPRESSIBLE CONDUCTING FLUID
W. Sears, *Cornell University*
IONIZATION IN CROSSED ELECTRIC AND MAGNETIC FIELDS
S.A. Colgate, *University of California*
OBLIQUE SHOCK WAVES IN STEADY TWO-DIMENSIONAL HYDROMAGNETIC FLOW
J. Bazer, *New York University* and W.B. Ericson, *Grumman Aircraft Corp.*
ELECTROMAGNETIC DIFFUSION INTO A CYLINDRICAL PLASMA COLUMN
J. Neuringer, L. Kraus and H. Malamud, *Republic Aviation Corp.*

Afternoon Session

SHOCKS AND FLOWS - II

Chairman: A. Kantrowitz
AVCO Research Laboratory, Everett, Mass.

PROBLEMS IN MFD TURBULENCE
L. Napolitano, *University of Naples, Italy*
MHD SHOCK WAVES IN LOW DENSITY IONIZED GAS
R.Z. Sagdeev, *Kurchatov Institute, U.S.S.R.*

PANEL DISCUSSION

Moderator: N. Marcuvitz
Polytechnic Institute of Brooklyn

I.B. Bernstein, *Princeton University*
O. Buneman, *Stanford University*
A. Busemann, *NASA, Langley Research Laboratory*
A. Ferri, *Polytechnic Institute of Brooklyn*
A. Kantrowitz, *AVCO Research Laboratory*
A.C. Kolb, *U.S. Naval Research Laboratory*
R.K.M. Landshoff, *Lockheed Missile Space Division*
L. Sedov, *Academy of Sciences, U.S.S.R.*

The editors wish to express their appreciation to Mrs. Susan De Blat and Mrs. Shirley Fleischer for the typing of the final manuscripts; to Mrs. Edith Tagliavia for the preparation of the illustrations; and to Miss Hermine Rutman for her editorial assistance.

IS AERODYNAMICS BREAKING AN IONIC BARRIER?

Adolf Busemann
NASA Langley Research Center
Langley Field, Virginia

Since it is the task of external aerodynamics to find the optimum configurations of aircraft, aerodynamicists in recent years had to learn quite a number of new tricks when, first, the sound barrier and, then, the heat barrier were broken by the ever increasing speeds of flight. The change of flow behavior at the speed of sound and the melting of materials by heat are both distinct and crucial effects, whereas the ionization of the air resembles, to a certain extent, dissociation and other changes of the air molecule and should not change the mechanical flow reactions themselves in any special way. Radio communication can, however, become impossible when an aircraft surrounds itself with a Faraday cage composed of ionized air, and communication is generally accepted as a vital accessory to high-speed flight. Fear of ionization as a first reaction would, therefore, once again establish a barrier for the development of flight. Magnetofluiddynamics, on the other hand, reveals marvelous new methods to direct ionized gases. In this regard, the aerodynamicists of today begin to wonder whether there are offered enough real benefits to counteract the mounting difficulties - old ones encountered since the breaking of the sound and heat barriers and new ones created by ionization itself. For the benefit of progress it is worth while to analyze this situation in the light of present knowledge and to leave to an afterthought estimates of the practical importance of an extended flight within the specific speed and altitude regime for ionization.

I. INTRODUCTION

It is not easy, in modern technology, to evaluate the present state of the art with respect to progress just around the corner. But, even thirty years ago, a well-informed aeronauticist seriously asked me, "I know your work and I appreciate it, but do you really think that the compressibility of the air will be of practical importance within our lifetime?" Realizing that this was not a question for a "yes" or "no" answer, I replied, "Compressibility is here right now, when within the high-velocity zone of a wing a protuberance creates another excess velocity and a rivet head adds its own excess velocity to it." Even I did not then imagine that, within thirty years, our children with their babies would fly commercially at air speeds in the compressibility range.

I would not like to make his mistake today in underestimating progress; neither would I like to give my adapted answer, that the ionic barrier has already been broken. The reason is that we have a more

---

Presented at the Symposium on Electromagnetics and Fluid Dynamics of Gaseous Plasma, Polytechnic Institute of Brooklyn, April 4, 5, 6, 1961

delicate situation in which progress may bypass higher aerodynamic speeds and may concentrate on high-speed travel in space. The atmosphere is no longer of unlimited altitude and negligible curvature. At a satellite speed of about Mach 26, or twenty-six times the speed of sound, aerodynamic lift is no longer needed. Even drag can be avoided by going to higher altitudes where there is no need for air-breathing engines, since the aircraft is merely coasting. There will always be starting and landing, but aerodynamic flight on earth is limited unless someone insists on reaching any place on earth in less than forty minutes. It is within this limited range of future flying speeds that the conventional aerodynamicist feels his responsibility for optimum shape of aircraft at steady-state flight. With respect to this, his very own territory, the aerodynamicist may ask, "Does the zigzag course of aerodynamic progress, starting with the birth of rational aerodynamics early this century and leading across the sound barrier and further, across the heat barrier, make another turn with another re-evaluation of all experiences when the ionization barrier of the air is broken? Or can we finish our job on earth without change?"

II. BENEFITS OF IONIZATION

Considering that air behind a front shock of an aircraft does not become sufficiently ionized below a Mach number of 18, or even with additives of alkaline metals not earlier than a Mach number of 12, the importance of the last-minute change to magnetofluidynamics can easily be minimized. On the other hand, there are at least two great expectations for magnetofluidynamics: (1) Since magnetofluidynamics is being developed for handling hot matter -- plasmas, with temperatures aimed at millions of degrees--it should be the very tool to help protect the aircraft against its own mantle of hot air, which is still a major problem after breaking the heat barrier by ablation. (2) Electric switching is obviously superior and, with the use of servomotors, is even more direct than any mechanical device to change the aircraft shape for variable conditions. Therefore, the safety engineer should be on our side when variable sweep, spoilers, and flaps can be replaced by magnetic reactions between the aircraft and the electrically conductive air around it.

III. TROUBLES CAUSED BY IONIZATION

There is an immediate reason which makes consideration of the ionization of the air necessary, as an added obligation to the external aerodynamicist who cares about the optimum shape of any aircraft within the demands of the customer, whenever he needs a cutout in the wing for vision or a machine gun; whenever he needs a plastic bubble on the canopy for orientation; or when he wants an antenna shaped like a Christmas tree in front of all the metal. As soon as the mantle of ionized air surrounds the aircraft at a Mach number above 15 or

18, the aircraft puts itself in a Faraday cage and its radio communication blacks out. In many cases the life of the passenger depends on communication at all times. Thus, we are, by the very nature of air at high speeds, at another crossroad: either to fear the ionized state of the air and to stay away from it, or to conquer it by breaking the ionic barrier. In the latter case we take part in all the benefits offered by magnetofluidynamics for the electrically conductive air.

There are mainly three central ideas for breaking the ionic barrier:

1) Re-establishment of communication in order to obtain the benefits of magnetofluidynamics free of penalties.

2) Help in curing the headaches left after breaking the sound and heat barrier: heat shielding, supersonic boom, and boundary-layer control.

3) New concepts of lift and drag creation, power generation, thrust, control, etc.

IV. RE-ESTABLISHMENT OF COMMUNICATION

The re-establishment of radio communication when the aircraft has surrounded itself with ionized air is mandatory for many unmanned and manned reentry applications. It is not surprising that the proposals for achieving this goal range from application of brute force to rather ingenious methods. Since the high-speed motion causes the trouble in an originally un-ionized air, the aerodynamicist may be called upon first to cure it.

A flat bottom behind a sharp leading edge would provide an opening toward the earth for radio communication. However, it is not very promising that edges persist (let us say by a combination of different ablating materials similar to the achievement of the edge on non-dripping wax candles) since even the best ablation material available forms blunt noses at these high Mach numbers. Another method is to maintain an ablating antenna ahead of the nose by pushing it continuously forward like the welding rod in a blow-torch.

A more sophisticated method is the ejection of halogens or electronegative compounds. Negative ions, being heavier, have a much reduced mobility compared with free electrons. However, this process, if at all possible, would re-establish the communication only by spoiling the chances of magnetofluidynamics. Magnetofluidynamics prefers the opposite effect accomplished by ejections of alkaline metals or electropositive compounds. It may, of course, be possible to use the aircraft body or wing as a separator between ejections of halogens toward the earth for better communication, and ejections of alkaline metals toward the sky for better lifting. However, this dual ejection appears far-fetched.

A more ingenious method is the proposed application of magnetic windows. The magnetic field is able to do for the two directions perpendicular to the field lines what added mass is supposed to accomplish in all three directions, namely, reduce the mobility of the free electrons. If none of these proposals opens a window for the customary wavelengths of communications, a change of the wavelength must be added.

V. THE HEAT SHIELDING PROBLEM OF RE-ENTRY

Magnetofluidynamics has become popular as a tool for harnessing atomic energy by creating controlled fusion at a temperature of several millions of degrees. If there is any hope for this type of development, it would seem that the heat problem caused by re-entering vehicles coming from outer space and which has the equivalent of only several ten thousands of degrees is child's play in comparison. There are, however, substantial differences in the two flow regimes: while the conductivity is high in the atomic case, the conductivity is extremely low at re-entry. It almost seems that nature is not quite fair to the aeronautical problem in causing communication troubles at lower conductivity than is required for participating in the benefits. Such a complaint is usually an outgrowth of a temporary situation rather than the statement of a permanent fact. Comparing this transient region with the transonic speed range of accumulated difficulties gives great hope that the gap will narrow or even disappear as technology is improved.

When complete shielding by magnetic deflection of the air ahead of the body appears impossible at the given low conductivity of the air, ablation of the body nose may still be the last resort. Nevertheless the ablation rate could be influenced by application of magnetic drag added to the mechanical drag. (The optimum solution of a greater class of permissible variations cannot be worse than the optimum solution of the restricted class completely inside the other.) In general, the magnetic drag has the same over-all tendency as has the drag by viscosity, namely, to return the friction heat to the same element of the fluid which has experienced the drag losses. This is certainly accomplishing the energy conservation with the minimum of bookkeeping, and the total enthalpy, or in less exact terms, the total temperature of all streamlines, stays constant in such an arrangement. While there is a second law of thermodynamics which predicts equalization of the actual temperatures if there is no compensation, there is no similar law for the total temperature. Moreover, there is plenty of compensation wherever drag is created, if such were needed. It is, therefore, necessary to investigate more closely the existing exceptions and to develop methods for enlarging them.

Generally, when the designing engineer needs familiarity with the smaller details of a phemomenon which, in its bulk, is not in his favor, the problem arises of adapting intricate information to the engineering language. Cumbersome relations have to be presented in the most helpful coordinates. In this connection I am always reminded of the work of R. Mollier who created two engineering diagrams, one for the compressible flow, his enthalpy-entropy diagram,[1] and the other one for binary mixtures, his enthalpy-composition diagram.[2] In contrast to other diagrams, his graphical representations automatically suggest the right answers. Therefore these "thinking" diagrams played an important role in clearing the air, the first in breaking the sound barrier, the second in breaking the heat barrier by ablation. There should be more "thinking" diagrams when we attempt to break the ionic barrier.

VI. MAGNETIC FORCES IN PLASMAS OF LOW CONDUCTIVITY

A. Misalignments by Velocity Dependent Forces

The primary task of creating large forces in plasmas of very low degrees of ionization has been studied in the last couple of years and has led to many puzzling results. The characteristics of electric and magnetic fields usually have a familiar ring to the aerodynamicist, but there are a few phenomena that do not enjoy the benefit of such a precedent. One of these phenomena is the pseudo-individuality of magnetic lines. While it appears almost possible to treat a magnetic line as being a substance that can be grasped and held, the creation of an electric field can allow it to slip away and to be replaced by another magnetic line. This effect is really the Einstein relativity of magnetic fields, replacing velocity by electric field components. It is a major science in the art to bottle and duct plasmas. The troubles and their cure by the creation of classes of magnetic lines essentially different from their neighbors is more at home in plasmas of high conductivity than in plasmas of low conductivities.

Electric conductivity, or more specifically, its reciprocal value, electric resistivity, has a very close relation to the viscosity of fluids. It even enters the so-called magnetic Reynolds number in exactly the same position that is held by viscosity in the flow Reynolds number. Both are responsible for the dissipation of energy. Nevertheless, the two properties seem these days to diverge in the light of the generalized Ohm's Law. At least with all the generalizations of viscosity applied for many purposes, there has never been a reason to generalize viscosity in such a manner that the principal axes of shear stress and shear strain in isotropic liquids and gases are not aligned. The corresponding misalignment between electric field and electric current is due to the velocity-dependent forces of magnetic fields on charged particles. There certainly are velocity-dependent forces known in mechanics. The well-known Coriolis force in rotating coordinate systems is in such a close relation to the magnetic force on charges that it is standard procedure to mention them together. It may be, therefore, that aerodynamicists have to learn these new features of electric conductivity only because they have not done their own homework when it was time for it.

The standard example used in explaining fluid viscosity for gases is the Couette flow of Fig. 1(a). There is no speed limitation

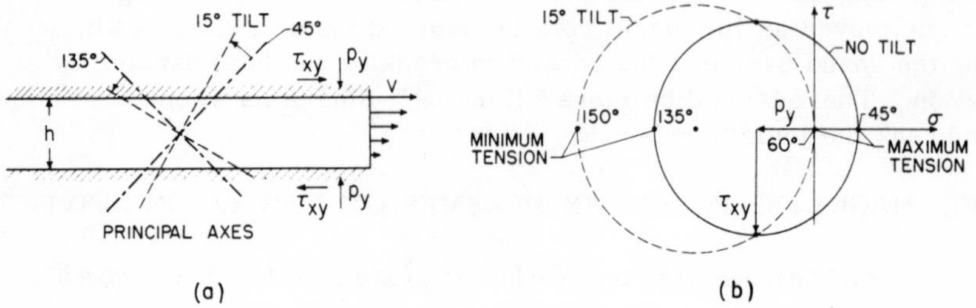

Fig. 1 Tilt of principal axes: (a) Couette flow; (b) σ - τ Mohr's Diagram

in the customary derivation of shear stress by regarding the exchange of particles in neighboring layers under the random motion according to their temperatures. Changing to the principal axes, however, large shear stresses τ_{xy} at limited gas pressure p_y from wall to wall can make the lowest principal pressure change from pressure to tension, for which there is no place in gases at all. Collisions can push, not pull. This so-called "cavitation danger" or "cavitation paradox" in the Couette flow is a result of the complete alignment of the principal axes for stress and strain, although there is a rotation of all fluid elements with the angular velocity $\omega = V/2h$ (V = velocity difference of the parallel motion of the walls; h = wall distance). Figure 1 shows that a misalignment of about 15° of the principal axes would eliminate the negative pressure according to Mohr's tension diagram, as indicated in Fig. 1(b).

B. Electron Motion

Coming back to the electrical problem, it is possible to represent the influence of the magnetic field on the electric current in gases by a simple transformation of the case without the magnetic field (Fig. 2). Since the side forces caused by the magnetic field are linearly dependent upon the velocity of the charged particles, the problem of interaction can best be presented in velocity coordinates (hodograph). Inasmuch as figures preferably demonstrate two-dimensional relations, the velocity plane may be chosen perpendicular to the magnetic field pointing into the plane. In other words, the magnetic field has only a negative z component while the velocity plane is parallel to the x, y plane of an x, y, z space. It is the result of the presence

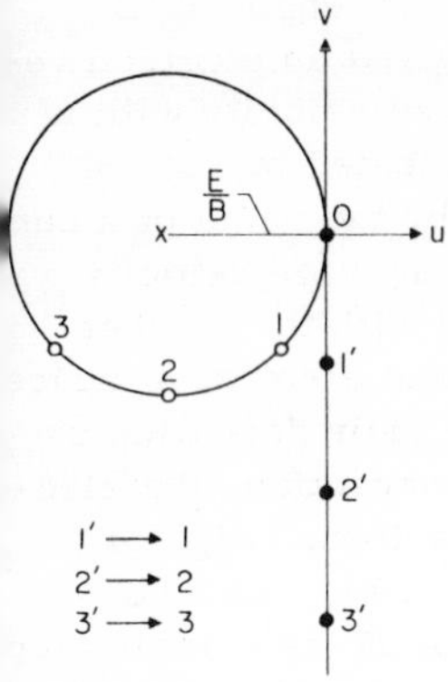

Fig. 2 Direct transformation

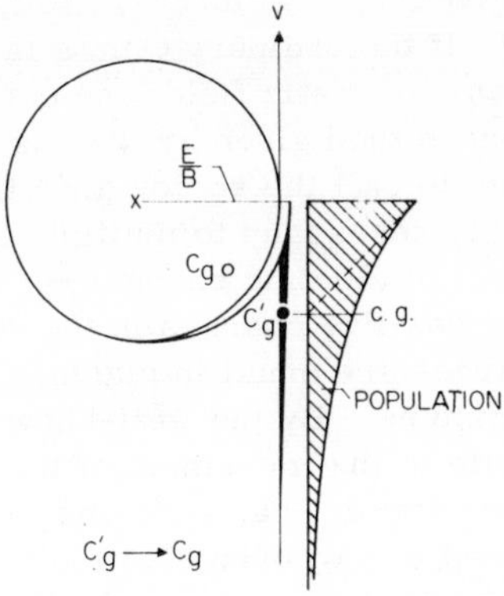

Fig. 3 Statistical transformation

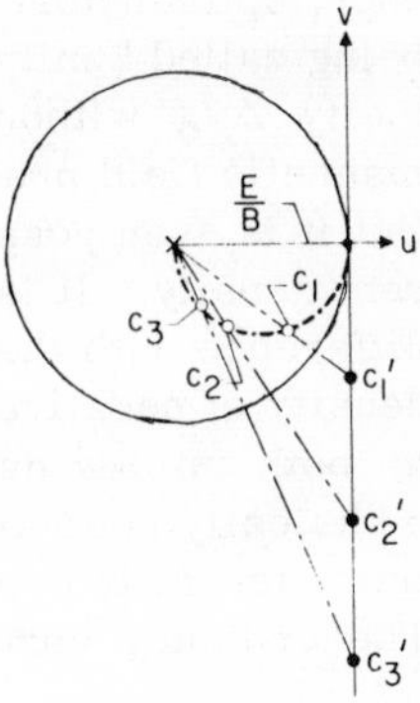

Fig. 4 Locus of population centers

of the magnetic field B that velocities achieved under acceleration by an electric field start bending around and finally complete a circle in the velocity coordinates whose center is the actual or apparent drift speed of the magnetic field, E/B. It is understandable that, according to the frustrating advance on a circle instead of on a straight line, the resulting velocity is vastly reduced. The total deviation from the beginning is restricted to $2E/B$. To introduce statistical averages, the conventional simplification of using one typical collision is not recommended. It is more correct for small disturbance velocities (including the case of large magnetic fields) to use a collision probability in relation to time independent of the velocity disturbance - don't hit us, we hit you. This probability assumption leads to an exponential distribution of the population over the different states according to Fig. 3. It has the rare advantage, besides being correct for small disturbance velocities, that its population center is identical with its collision center. (The assumption of constant life puts the collision center at full life span, the population center at half life span, and requires more attention to put the factor 1/2 on the proper places.) If, now, under the action of the electric field alone, the straight acceleration is wrapped around the circle representing the change introduced by the presence of the magnetic field, the population center is not a point on the circumference of the circle but a point inside the circle. The exact position is easily integrable with the help of complex numbers. The result is given in Fig. 4 for a variety of population centers assumed on the straight line. The locus inside the circle is the semicircle over the initial radius; old and new positions are on the same ray from the point marked by a cross representing the drift velocity of the magnetic lines, E/B. The transformation from the point c_g' without magnetic interference to the point c_g with magnetic interference is, therefore, given by "reciprocal radii," the length E/B being called "unity." If the ordinary Ohm's law gives an electron velocity Δv_0 without any magnetic field, the expected velocity with a magnetic field present is then given by Δv as indicated in Fig. 5. But it is even possible to call the vector directly by the name of a current density. It is only necessary to multiply the average velocity difference with the unit of electric charge $\mp e$ and with the number density of negative or positive charges in the volume element of space n; both number densities are equal in plasmas by their definition as a basically neutral mixture. By the well-known convention, the electric current is opposite to the movement of the electrons (Fig. 6). The ordinary conductivity σ_0, at zero magnetic field, can be used to plot even electric fields E as velocity vectors in the same coordinates, as equal to the current density j or its velocity value when divided by the charge density en. The two scaling factors en and σ_0, are the only quantities required to assemble all information in the same coordinates. This graphical representation is, of course, equivalent to Eqs. (1) or abbreviated (2) of the analytic treatment indicated in the Appendix, part A.

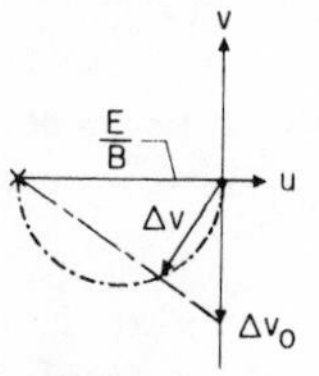

Fig. 5 Resulting velocity

Figure 6 indicates a visible reduction in the actual current density as compared with the expected one without any magnetic interference. Since large forces are the aim of aerodynamics, such a difference is disturbing. Induced electric fields E result from motions in magnetic fields and are not excessive. Currents j create the forces $f = j \times B$ per unit volume and are required to be as large as possible. The apparent ineffectiveness of electric fields in the presence of magnetic fields is, therefore, a major cause of concern. The fact that the component of the electric field parallel to the created electric current is still the same one required by Ohm's law shows that there is no excess creation of ohmic heat for given currents. On the other hand, if the electric field E is the proper reference, Eq. (4), in the case of B and E perpendicular and no B_E component in the direction of E, indicates a greatly reduced conductivity.

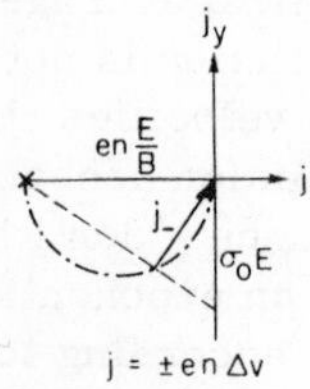

Fig. 6 Electric current plane

C. Lift by Hall Effect

The classical procedure for finding out whether the proper reference for the aerodynamic forces is the current or the electric field has been originated by N. H. Kemp and H. E. Petschek[3] and is represented in Figs. 7, 8 and 9. Figure 7 shows the exciting result that lift can be created when all conditions are kept symmetrical. Anyone

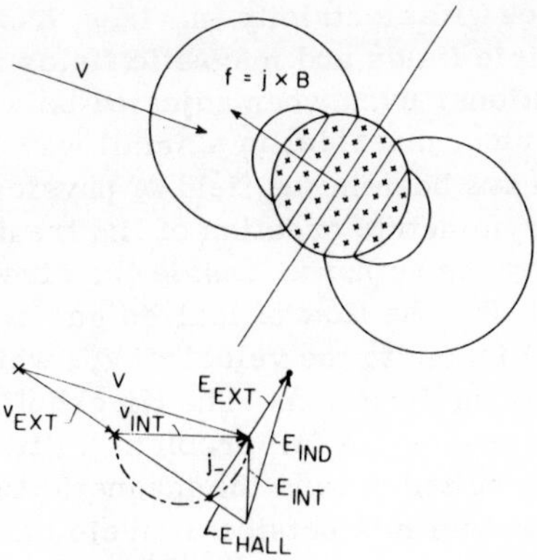

Fig. 7 Lift by Hall effect

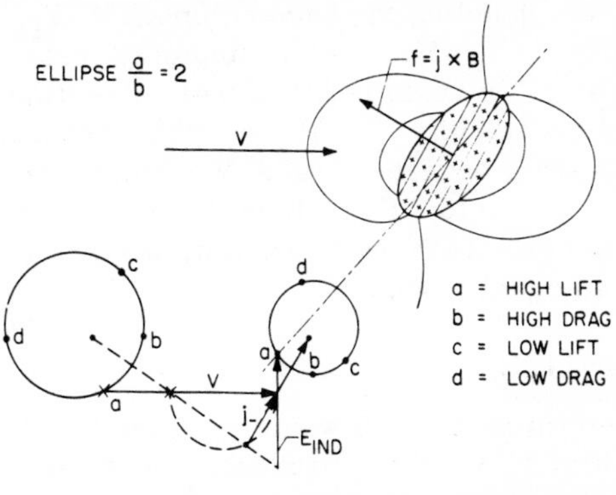

Fig. 8 More lift by shape and Hall effect

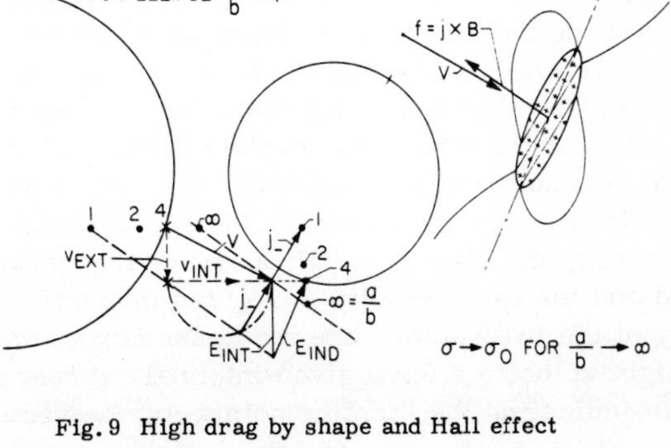

Fig. 9 High drag by shape and Hall effect

who, from experience with electricity in wires, has acquired the habit of thinking that electric fields and magnetic fields have an arbitrary sign fixed by conventions, even when adjusted between the two fields by some right-hand rules, must feel in a small way the sensation which loss of parity must have been in the field of physics, when he sees for the first time this asymmetric creation of lift treated theoretically and experimentally by the authors. Inside the circular cross section of the magnetic field B, the flow of ionized gas creates an induced electric field perpendicular to the velocity V, which tries to promote currents j in an oblique direction. The Kirchhoff condition that currents must be closed makes the full problem a little more difficult than the one short-circuited around the magnetic field. The two-dimensional problem of currents outside a circle has the simplified result that the external region is the equivalent of the internal region. Thus the closing outside without any magnetic interference affords only the Ohm portion of the electric field inside. The total induced electric field is, therefore, achieved by accepting a single Hall component E_{HALL} but doubling the Ohm component E_{Ω} parallel to j. The volume forces, $f = j \times B$, are created only inside the magnetic field and have a smaller angle between their direction and the direction of the final flow velocity V. By applying stronger magnetic fields, any acute angle between f and V can, however, be achieved. The drag component has to furnish both the internal and the external creation of ohmic heat; both parts consist, according to the quoted equivalence, of an equal amount.

D. Lift by Hall Effect and Shape:

No engineer worth his salt would ever leave this problem in this state. It hurts him to create unnecessary heat, especially for lift, which has no minimum cost whatsoever. He likes to show his talent by giving the magnetic portion of the arrangement a more adequate shape. There is no doubt that curiosity is mainly aroused by the circular shape of Fig. 7, but engineering starts with variation of the shape. Figure 8 represents the case of an elliptical cross section of the magnetic field with an axis ratio $a/b = 2:1$. The necessary external field for closing the currents is known by conformal mapping. The outside losses are only half the inside losses if the current is parallel to the large axis, but they are twice the internal losses if the current is turned parallel to the small axis of the ellipse. If the ellipse is turned around, the locus of all necessary external field requirements leads to a circle with the known points, half and double the internal value, terminating one diameter. Proportionality between the induced electric field and the flow velocity at a given magnetic field and the orthogonality of the two vectors are the reasons why the locus for all necessary flight velocities for a given internal current density is again a circle indicating the starting points for the vectors V. The practical problem of finding forces for given velocities is, of course, the reciprocal relation to the plotted case of unknown velocities for given forces. This reversal influences to a certain degree the proper choice of the true points for: (a) high lift, (b) high drag, (c) low lift, and (d) low drag. But reciprocal relations on circles for a pencil of rays are elementary geometry. It is, therefore, not hard to find the four points a, b, c, and d on both of the circles.

E. Drag by Hall Effect and Shape

The example of high drag for re-entry applications is represented in Fig. 9 on another ellipse with the axis ratio $a/b = 4:1$. Added to the actual example in this figure are the high drag points on both the induced electric field circle and the flight velocity circle for all axis ratios 1, 2, 4, and ∞. At the assumed magnetic field intensity (and the resulting tilt between internal electric field and current) even the axis ratio 4:1 never underbids the internal field strength E_{INT}. Thus, it almost underlines the experience on untilted field-to-current relations that the external closing is an additional burden. The case of infinite axis ratio demonstrates that here are different conditions. The necessary induced field is only the component parallel to the current vector j. The Hall component is saved. Similar, but not quite so complete, savings can be made by high finite axis ratios or larger original angles between electric field and current. The result is that a certain outside field is quite welcome. Even the actually depicted case with the ellipse 4:1 pays very little for the external closing of the currents.

F. Electrically Isolated versus Conductive Nose Section

The practical implications of the lessons learned by investigating elliptical shapes for the magnetic region are demonstrated by comparing a nose section with a conductive skin in Fig. 10 and a nose section with isolated skin in Fig. 11. The returning currents in Fig. 10 through the skin are for convenience not charged with Ohm's losses inside the skin of a sufficient depth. In Fig. 10 the primary induction field E_{IND} perpendicular to the oncoming flow velocity V has no difficulty in closing its correlated current j, since both the return through the skin and the natural closing after one turn around the body are free of any external burden. Thus the internal electric field consumes just the induced field and its correlated current becomes reality. The volume forces $f = j \times B$ are oblique, giving a reduced component for drag, using the other component for a torque. Both components have to be compensated for by ohmic heat out of the product: drag times velocity.

In Fig. 11 the return path of the current is blocked. The original current, with its longitudinal component, creates a space charge

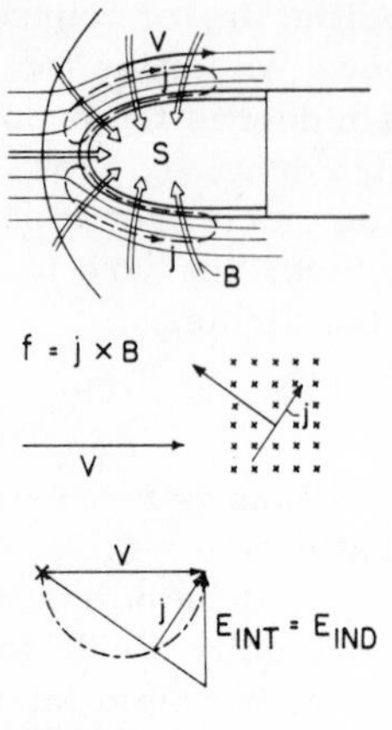

Fig. 10 Conductive nose

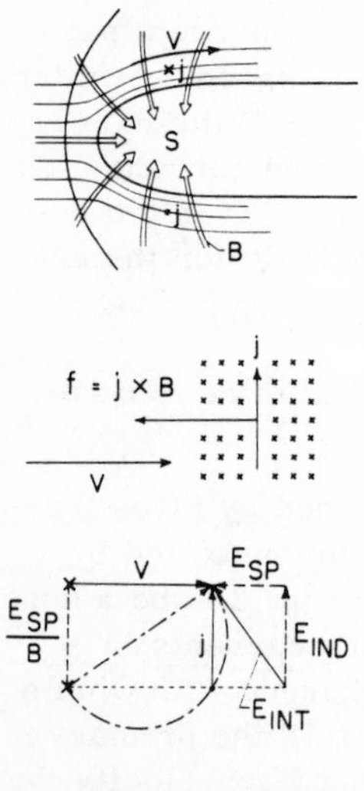

Fig. 11 Isolated nose

because of this blockage, until the resulting electric field is satisfied with a current in circumferential direction only. The electric field of the space charge E_{SP} and the originally induced field E_{IND} add to a total field, to which a strictly circumferential current is now the correlated current. No external currents remain. It is perfectly reasonable to ask about the apparent velocity of the plasma with respect to the magnetic lines, which would create the total field E_{IND} plus E_{SP}. The answer is the velocity V with a certain circumferential component, E_{SP}/B, added. Since the flow cannot spiral in this manner, the magnetic lines could do the circumferential part by spinning like a left-handed propeller. Comparing the two extremes of high conductivity and zero conductivity of the nose skin, as pictured in Figs. 10 and 11, and adding some finite conductivities to change from one to the other gradually, realization that the magnetic lines have a tendency to spin is unavoidable. The torque on the lines is either countered at its maximum by the backstraps of the electric currents with their force $I \times B$ in the magnetic field, or the magnetic lines themselves begin to spin while under reduced load generating electricity inside the nose. Only the extreme case of no backstraps brings the magnetic lines to the idling propeller condition of no load shown in Fig. 11. The south pole S inside the nose is not affected by the twisting of its tuft of magnetic lines. The spinning of the magnetic lines is a proper application of the magnetic relativity. The reality of this movement is not discussed by the theory of relativity and we are fortunate that the ionized layer is of finite thickness so that further concern need not be felt.

G. Ion Slip

Up to now, electrons have been considered the only group of particles not moving with the rest. Stronger electric and magnetic fields can also separate the positive ions from the neutral particles between collisions. Qualitatively, everything is similar to the former case of electron movement. The charge is, of course, reversed, and the mass is about 55, 000 times heavier (take NO^+ as the most probable constituent for positive ions in air). The result for ions in a gas of low conductivity puts the upper semicircle in Fig. 12 in operation for the positive current j_+, while the current of electrons j_- in the lower semicircle is probably close to the end of its journey. The conductivity has to be subdivided into the parts σ_+ and σ_-, with a ratio not quite as high as 1:55, 000, but instead nearer the square root of this value, 1:240, as an order of magnitude reminder. The analytical treatment of Eq. (1) and in symbolic notation in Eq. (2) can be generalized symbolically in Eq. (5) and spelled out in Eq. (6). (See the Appendix, part B.)

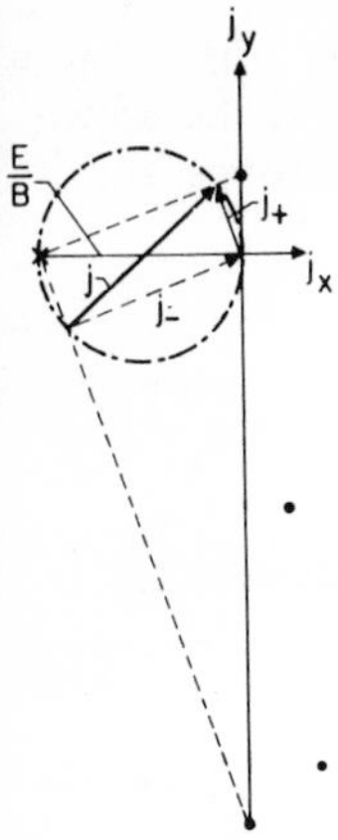

Fig. 12 Effect of ion movement

In the process of giving the engineer not only the puzzling features of magnetic interference but reliable representations, I have to ask for poetic license with respect to the superposition of the negative and the positive charge movements. The first separation from the crowd creates a binary mixture, and the second separation a ternary mixture, no matter which separates first. In a binary mixture one friction coefficient governs all relative motions, but in the ternary mixture not two, but three friction coefficients are needed. Only the case of one dominant group with two very small additional ones degenerates to having no more than two important friction coefficients. Even in this case of very low mixture ratios there is the danger of confusing the mass ratio of the two ingredients 1:55, 000 with the friction ratio 1:240, the common population center and the common collision center, etc. My apology for neglecting the philosophy of ternary mixtures for the sake of simplicity in this paper may be born out of my own work in mixtures. The simplified and widely used representation of Fig. 12 is, of course, also sufficient to restore parity automatically in case of positive and negative ions of equal mass and equal cross section.

Whereas the electron movement by itself did not cost more ohmic heat for the actual current, the adding of ion movement or ion slip is costly. The parallel component of the electric field with respect to the current is too large. The extra heat in the second term of Eq. (7) is positive and equals the force $f = j \times B$ multiplied by the velocity distance of the "friction center" of the total current j from the origin (the friction center cuts the vector in the ratio σ_+/σ_-) and these two vectors are parallel and indicate the friction loss to carry along the bulk of neutrals. The maximum value of the conductivity, which is available if the Hall component is treated in the best possible way, is reduced with respect to σ_o by a term containing the square of the magnetic field normal to the current, B_n^2.

H. The DC Accelerator:

To demonstrate the value of a representation containing not only the resulting current j but also its parts j_- and j_+, the example of the j×B or dc accelerator is given in Fig. 13. All relations are in an oblique fashion and the designing engineer has to find his way through them, having only the exact value of the magnetic field strength as an additional variable not visible in Fig. 13. Rotating Fig. 12 to a favorable position can give only one of several choices. If the application of two long electrodes is the choice, the resulting force and

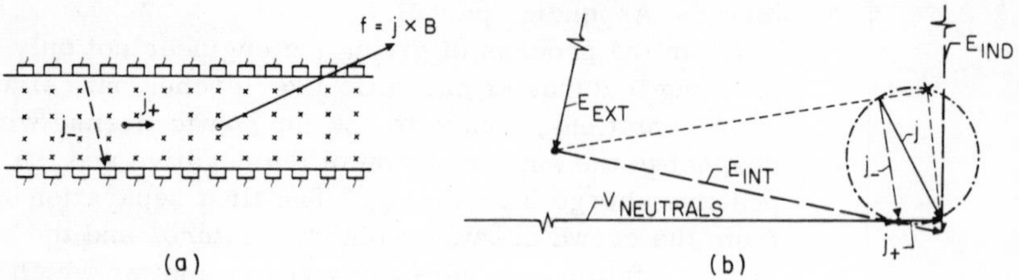

Fig. 13 Acceleration without "electrolysis" : (a) dc j × B accelerator; (b) Electric current diagram

the currents are tilted. If the electron current is closed through the wires on the outside applying multiple sets of electrodes, the side movement of the positive ions can be avoided as in the presented case of no " electrolysis. " The acceleration force is still tilted, but the bulk of the neutrals can develop a small pressure differential between both walls to compensate for that. The conservation of the positive ions over a long accelerator length could indeed be the most important point of view, if the ions are made by a slowly adjusting equilibrium or by seeding with foreign additives. The purpose of the diagram is to leave the decision to the completely informed designer.

VII. CONCLUSION

In conclusion I wish to come back to the basic question of aerodynamic applications: what are the chances that magnetofluidynamics can provide adequate forces between the aircraft and the surrounding mantle of ionized air? While in re-entry, drag and heat have to be weighed against each other, there is a desire for a certain minimum force. Since the flight speed V is given, the other factors are conductivity σ_0 and the square of the magnetic field B^2. These three factors determine the drag per unit volume, while the aerodynamic forces are per unit of area and consist of the dynamic pressure, V^2 times the air density ρ or one-half of it, to be conventional. While in the aerodynamical case every single factor counts, the magnetofluidynamical case is quite exceptional. A practically infinite conductivity would not solve the problem, nor would a practically infinite magnetic field. (See Appendix, part C.)

If the conductivity is large, the induced currents add their own magnetic field to the given magnetic field; they do this, according to Lenz's rule of induction, by diminishing the effect. Hall, as is demonstrated in Section VI-G including the ion slip, does not give the magnetic field an unlimited influence. The useful, generalized conductivity σ_{max} of Eq. (9) in the Appendix finally diminishes inversely as B^2, thus stopping the growth of the force by its explicit factor B^2. Both Lenz and Hall have to be observed and show that the most successful increase is in the smaller of two terms in the denominator of Eq. (18) or (19). If the conductivity is superior, the Lenz limit of the magnetic field strength becomes dominant. If the magnetic field is superior, the Hall limit makes itself felt. On the latter limit, the charged particles are almost stopped by the magnetic field. The drag forces correspond to the "filter friction" on all neutrals by passing the filter of all arrested charged particles.

Practically, we are only at one-tenth of the conductivity and one-tenth of the magnetic field strength where these effects come into play. There is still ample slack for future improvement. If both variables gain by a factor of ten, the magnetic forces are a hundred times larger than the aerodynamical forces in similar dimensions. The main point that I like to convey is the fact that the possibilities depend to a great extent on skill for finding new twists and tricks in these misaligned relations. The worst enemy of rigid mathematical proofs is the designer, who accomplishes the "impossible" by simply violating the assumptions of the proof. For him I have high hopes in breaking the ionic barrier.

REFERENCES

1. R. Mollier, "Neue Diagramme zur technischen Waermelehre," *Z.d.Ver.d. Ing.*, Vol. 48, p. 271 (Berlin 1904).

2. R. Mollier, "Ein neues Diagramm fuer Dampf-luft-gemische," *Z.d.Ver.d.Ing.*, Vol.67 p. 869 (Berlin 1923).

3. N. H. Kemp and H. E. Petschek, "Two-Dimensional Incompressible Magnetohydronamic Flow Across an Elliptical Solenoid," AVCO Research Laboratory Report 26 (April 1958).

APPENDIX

A. Electron Movement Alone

Misalignment of current and field relation (Fig. 6):

$$j + j \times B \frac{\sigma_o}{en} = \sigma_o E \tag{1}$$

or with a symbolical factor

$$j \left[1 + \times B \frac{\sigma_o}{en} \right] = \sigma_o E . \tag{2}$$

Ohmic heat expressed in j^2

$$Q_\Omega = E \cdot j = \frac{j \left[1 + \times B \frac{\sigma_o}{en} \right] \cdot j}{\sigma_o} = \frac{1}{\sigma_o} j^2 . \tag{3}$$

Ohmic heat expressed in E^2

$$Q_\Omega = E \cdot j = \sigma_o \frac{1 + \left[\frac{\sigma_o}{en} \right]^2 B_E^2}{1 + \left[\frac{\sigma_o}{en} \right]^2 B^2} E^2 = \sigma_1 E^2 . \tag{4}$$

B. Electrons and Ions Moving ($\sigma_- / \sigma_+ \approx 240$):

Generalization of Eq. (2):

$$j \left[1 + \times B \frac{\sigma_-}{en} \right] \cdot \left[1 - \times B \frac{\sigma_+}{en} \right] = (\sigma_+ + \sigma_-) E \quad , \tag{5}$$

SYMBOLS USED	
B = magnetic induction B_E = component of B in E-direction B_n = component of B normal to E $\mp e$ = charge of electron, ion E = electric field F_m = magnetic force F_a = aerodynamic force j = electric current density n = number density of electrons, ions ($n_+ = n_-$)	R_m = magnetic Reynolds number V = velocity Q_Ω = ohmic heat per unit of time and volume σ_o = electric conductivity (at zero magnetic field) σ_+ , σ_- = electric conductivity subdivided in electron and ion responsibility

or without using symbolical factors:

$$j + j \times B \frac{\sigma_- - \sigma_+}{en} - (j \times B) \times B \frac{\sigma_-\sigma_+}{e^2 n^2} = (\sigma_+ + \sigma_-)E . \qquad (6)$$

Now the Ohmic heat comparing to Eq. (3) reads:

$$Q_\Omega = E \cdot j = \frac{j^2 - \frac{\sigma_-\sigma_+}{e^2 n^2}\left[(j \times B) \times B\right] \cdot j}{\sigma_+ + \sigma_-} , \qquad (7)$$

$$= \frac{1 + \frac{\sigma_-\sigma_+}{e^2 n^2} B_n^2}{\sigma_+ + \sigma_-} j^2 . \qquad (8)$$

The former maximum conductivity σ_0 is now reduced:

$$\sigma_0 \equiv \sigma_+ + \sigma_- \rightarrow \frac{\sigma_0}{1 + \frac{\sigma_-\sigma_+}{e^2 n^2} B_n^2} = \sigma_{max} , \qquad (9)$$

by the ion slip.

C. Magnetic Forces Compared to Aerodynamic Forces:

$$F_m = \sigma(V \times B) \times B \text{ volume} , \qquad (10)$$

$$F_a = \frac{1}{2} \rho V^2 \text{ area} . \qquad (11)$$

The ratio of magnetic to aerodynamic forces becomes:

$$\frac{F_m}{F_a} = \frac{\sigma V B^2 L}{\rho V^2} = (\mu_0 \sigma V L) \frac{\frac{1}{2\mu_0} B^2}{\frac{1}{2} \rho V^2} . \qquad (12)$$

The second form contains the magnetic Reynolds number

$$R_m = \mu_0 \sigma V L , \qquad (13)$$

the magnetic pressure

$$P_m = \frac{1}{2\mu_0} B^2 , \qquad (14)$$

and the aerodynamic pressure

$$P_a = \frac{1}{2} \rho V^2 . \qquad (15)$$

For high magnetic Reynolds number, the Lenz induction rule makes the following denominator necessary in Eq. (12):

$$\frac{F_m}{F_a} = \frac{R_m}{1 + R_m} \frac{P_m}{P_a} . \tag{16}$$

For high magnetic fields the Hall correction is required:

$$\frac{F_m}{F_a} = \frac{R_{mo}}{1 + \frac{\sigma_+\sigma_-}{e^2 n^2} B^2} \frac{P_m}{P_a} . \tag{17}$$

If both corrections are necessary at the same time, Eq. (12) changes into

$$\frac{F_m}{F_a} = \frac{\mu_0\sigma_0 VL}{1 + \frac{\sigma_+\sigma_-}{e^2 n^2} B^2 + \mu_0\sigma_0 VL} \frac{\frac{1}{2\mu_0} B^2}{\frac{1}{2}\rho V^2} \rightarrow \frac{P_m}{P_a} , \tag{18}$$

with the Lenz limitation P_m/P_a for large σ_0, or with the Hall limitation

$$\frac{F_m}{F_R} = \frac{\frac{\sigma_+\sigma_-}{e^2 n^2} B^2}{1 + \mu_0\sigma_0 VL + \frac{\sigma_+\sigma_-}{e^2 n^2} B^2} \frac{\frac{e^2 n^2 \sigma_0}{2\sigma_+\sigma_-} VL}{\frac{1}{2} \rho V^2} \rightarrow \frac{L}{\lambda_+} \frac{nm_+}{\rho} \tag{19}$$

if the magnetic field is predominantly strong.

The electron conductivity σ_- and ion conductivity σ_+ have the following relations to more conventional expressions as free path λ_-, λ_+ and random velocity c_-, c_+ combining to the collision interval τ_-, τ_+ further the Larmor frequencies, ω_-, ω_+:

$$\sigma_- = \frac{e^2 n}{m_-} \frac{\lambda_-}{C_-} , \tag{20}$$

$$\sigma_+ = \frac{e^2 n}{m_+} \frac{\lambda_+}{C_+} , \tag{21}$$

or

$$\frac{\sigma_- B}{en} = \frac{eB}{m_-} \frac{\lambda_-}{C_-} = \omega_-\tau_- , \tag{22}$$

$$\frac{\sigma_+ B}{en} = \frac{eB}{m_+} \frac{\lambda_+}{C_+} = \omega_+\tau_+ . \tag{23}$$

These expressions are more commonly used in the generalized Ohm's law.

LINEAR WAVE PHENOMENA IN COLLISION-FREE PLASMAS

Ira B. Bernstein
Princeton Plasma Physics Laboratory
Princeton University, Princeton, N. J.

A survey of the present state of the theory of the propagation of small amplitude waves in plasmas is presented. The structure and significance of those models which have been most successfully analyzed are discussed, and certain classes of particularly interesting waves are described. The direction of present investigation is indicated.

In this paper, certain aspects of the theory of small-amplitude waves in plasmas are briefly presented. The topics have been chosen so as to display certain features familiar in microwave electronics and ordinary fluid mechanics and other features which are novel.

A plasma is defined as a substantially ionized gas of effectively zero total charge. For simplicity, we will confine our attention to a proton-electron plasma in which collisions are negligible. The most refined description of this situation (which has already received extensive attention) involves the joint solution of Maxwell's equations governing the electric field $\underline{E}(\underline{r}, \underline{t})$ and the magnetic field $\underline{B}(\underline{r}, \underline{t})$:

$$c \nabla \times \underline{E} = -\partial \underline{B}/\partial t, \tag{1}$$

$$c \nabla \times \underline{B} = 4\pi \underline{J} + \partial \underline{E}/\partial t, \tag{2}$$

$$\nabla \cdot \underline{E} = 4\pi\sigma, \tag{3}$$

$$\nabla \cdot \underline{B} = 0, \tag{4}$$

with, for each species of charged particle, a collisionless Boltzmann equation[1]

$$\partial f/\partial t + \underline{v} \cdot \nabla f + (q/m)(\underline{E} + \underline{v} \times \underline{B}/c) \cdot \nabla_v f = 0. \tag{5}$$

In Eq. (5), $f(\underline{r}, \underline{v}, t)$ is the joint distribution function in position $\underline{r}$ and velocity $\underline{v}$ at time t of one of the species present, a particle,

---

Presented at the Symposium on Electromagnetics and Fluid Dynamics of Gaseous Plasma, Polytechnic Institute of Brooklyn, April 4, 5, 6, 1961

mass of which is m, and charge q. For electrons, $q = -e$, for protons, $q = e$. The symbol ∇ represents the usual gradient with respect to position $\underline{r}$, the symbol ∇_v the gradient with respect to velocity $\underline{v}$. The associated particle density $N(\underline{r}, t)$, mean velocity $\underline{u}(\underline{r}, t)$, stress tensor $\underline{P}(\underline{r}, t)$, and heat flow tensor $\underline{Q}(\underline{r}, t)$ are defined in terms of f via*

$$N = \int d^3v f , \tag{6}$$

$$N \underline{u} = \int d^3v \, \underline{v} f , \tag{7}$$

$$\underline{P} = m \int d^3v \, (\underline{v} - \underline{u})(\underline{v} - \underline{u}) f , \tag{8}$$

$$\underline{Q} = m \int d^3v \, (\underline{v} - \underline{u})(\underline{v} - \underline{u})(\underline{v} - \underline{u}) f . \tag{9}$$

The current density $\underline{J}$ and charge density σ which occur in the Maxwell equations are then given by

$$\sigma = \sum qN , \tag{10}$$

$$\underline{J} = \sum N q \underline{u} \tag{11}$$

where the indicated sum is to be taken over electrons and protons.

The joint solution of Eqs. (1) through (5) is, in general, a formidable task, and one is led to seek less refined descriptions of greater tractability. The most familiar of these is obtained from Eq. (5) on multiplying severally by 1, $m(\underline{v}-\underline{u})$, and $m(\underline{v}-\underline{u})(\underline{v}-\underline{u}) \cdot (\underline{v}-\underline{u})$, and integrating over $\underline{v}$. There result the moment equations

$$\partial N/\partial t + \nabla \cdot (N\underline{u}) = 0 , \tag{12}$$

*In the notation employed here, the symmetric dyadic

$$\underline{P} = \sum_{i,j=1}^{3} P_{ij} \, \underline{e}_i \, \underline{e}_j ,$$

while

$$\underline{Q} = \sum_{i,j,k=1}^{3} Q_{ijk} \, \underline{e}_i \, \underline{e}_j \, \underline{e}_k .$$

For the case of a collision-dominated plasma it is more useful to refer the moments to the center of mass velocity $\underline{u}_o = \sum Nm\,\underline{u} / \sum Nm$. (See, for instance, Ref. 2.)

$$mN\left[\partial \underline{u}/\partial t + \underline{u}\cdot\nabla\,\underline{u}\right] = -\nabla\cdot\underline{P} + Nq\left[\underline{E} + \underline{u}\times\underline{B}/c\right], \tag{13}$$

$$\partial\underline{P}/\partial t + \nabla\cdot\left[\underline{Q} + \underline{u}\,\underline{P}\right] + \underline{P}\cdot\nabla\,\underline{u} + (\underline{P}\cdot\nabla\,\underline{u})^T + (q/mc)\left[\underline{B}\times\underline{P} - \underline{P}\times\underline{B}\right] = 0\ . \tag{14}$$

Note that Eq. (12) is coupled to Eq. (13) via $\underline{u}$, Eq. (13) is coupled to Eq. (14) via $\underline{P}$, and Eq. (14) is coupled to the next equation in the hierarchy (which we have not written) via $\underline{Q}$, etc. In order for this set of equations to be more useful than the equivalent collisionless Boltzmann Eq. (5), it is necessary to truncate them by some device. One circumstance in which this is possible is the case of low effective temperature.* That is, if we define an effective frequency ω and wavenumber k via

$$\omega = |\partial\, \ell n\, X/\partial t|\ , \tag{15}$$

$$k = |\nabla \ell n\, X|\ ,$$

where X is a representative macroscopic scalar, and define the thermal speed v_{th} and effective temperature T via

$$v_{th}^2 \equiv 3KT/m \equiv N^{-1}\int d^3v(\underline{v}-\underline{u})^2 f\ , \tag{16}$$

then it is clear from Eqs. (19), (9), (15), and (16), that in terms of order of magnitude,

$$|\nabla\cdot\underline{Q}|\,/\,|\partial P/\partial t| \sim v_{th}/(\omega/k)\ . \tag{17}$$

Hence, if the effective "phase velocity" $\omega/k \gg v_{th}$, it is plausible that one can neglect $\nabla\cdot\underline{Q}$ in Eq. (14). This serves to truncate the infinite set of moment equations. The same sort of inequality, however, serves equally well to suppress $\nabla\cdot\underline{P}$ in Eq. (13), on comparing it with the right-hand side of that equation. The thermal corrections can then be readily computed by treating $\nabla\cdot\underline{P}$ as a small perturbation, and computing $\underline{P}$ from Eq. (14) with $\nabla\cdot Q$ suppressed, and $\underline{u}$ and $\underline{B}$ expressed in terms of the solution of Eq. (13) with

*The observation of the nature of the low-temperature approximation and its comparison with the results of distribution function theory is due to C. R. Oberman.[3]

$\nabla \cdot \underline{P}$ suppressed.

As an example, consider the high-frequency oscillations of a plasma, such that it is legitimate to neglect the ion motions. The system is assumed to permit a static equilibrium characterized by the conditions, distinguished by a subscript zero,

$$\begin{aligned} \underline{u}_o &= 0\,, \\ \underline{P}_o &= p\underline{I}\,, \\ \underline{B}_o &= 0\,, \\ \nabla p &= -N_o\, e\underline{E}_o\,, \end{aligned} \tag{18}$$

where $\underline{I}$ is the unit dyadic ($\underline{I} = \underline{e}_x\underline{e}_x + \underline{e}_y\underline{e}_y + \underline{e}_z\underline{e}_z$). Designate first-order quantities by a subscript one and write

$$\underline{u}_1 = \partial \underline{\xi} / \partial t\,, \tag{19}$$

where $\underline{\xi}$ is the small displacement of an element of the electron fluid from its equilibrium position, and seek normal mode solutions which vary in time like $e^{-i\omega t}$. Then Eqs. (1), (2), (11), (12), (13), and (14) yield, on linearization and combination,

$$\underline{B}_1 = -i\,(c/\omega)\ \nabla \times \underline{E}_1\,, \tag{20}$$

$$N_1 = -\ \nabla \cdot (N_o \underline{\xi})\,, \tag{21}$$

$$\underline{P}_1 = -\underline{I}\ \nabla \cdot (p\underline{\xi}) + p\left[(\nabla\, \underline{\xi}) + (\nabla\, \underline{\xi})^T\right], \tag{22}$$

$$\omega^2 N_o m \underline{\xi} - N_o e \underline{E}_1 = (\nabla p/N_o)\ \nabla \cdot (N_o \underline{\xi}) + \nabla \cdot \underline{P}_1\,, \tag{23}$$

$$\omega^2 \underline{E}_1 - c^2\ \nabla \times\ \nabla \times \underline{E}_1 = \omega^2\ 4\pi N_o e \underline{\xi}\,. \tag{24}$$

Note that both terms on the right-hand side of Eq. (23) are of the same order of magnitude and are to be viewed as small perturbations. Thus, to lowest order one can write

$$\underline{\xi} = e\underline{E}_1/m\omega^2 \tag{25}$$

and use Eq. (25) to eliminate $\underline{\xi}$ in terms $\underline{E}_1$, on the right-hand side of Eqs. (22) and (23). When the resultant Eq. (23) is combined with Eq. (24), there results

$$(\omega^2 - \omega p^2)\underline{E}_1 - c^2 \nabla \times \nabla \times \underline{E}_1$$

$$= \frac{4\pi e^2}{m^2\omega^2}\left\{ p \nabla \left[\frac{\nabla \cdot (p\underline{E}_1)}{p} \right] + \frac{\nabla p}{p} \underline{E}_1 \cdot \nabla p \right.$$

$$\left. - \frac{p'}{N_0} (\nabla N_0)(\underline{E}_1 \cdot \nabla N_0) + \nabla \cdot \left[p(\nabla \underline{E}_1) + p(\nabla \underline{E}_1)^T \right] \right\}. \tag{26}$$

The right-hand side of Eq. (26) is to be viewed as a small perturbation. It has been written, in a manifestly self-adjoint form, using the consequence of Eq. (18), that since $\nabla \times \underline{E}_0 = 0$, p must be a function of N_0 alone. The derivative of p with respect to N_0 we denote by a prime.

Observe first that if we neglect the right-hand side above, and distinguish the resultant equation and its solutions by a superscript zero, then

$$(\omega^{(0)2} - \omega_p^2)\underline{E}_1^{(0)} - c^2 \nabla \times \nabla \times \underline{E}_1^{(0)} = 0 , \tag{27}$$

which, of course, must be subject to appropriate boundary conditions. If the system in question is isolated in an infinite vacuum, one must prescribe a radiation boundary condition, and, in general, the eigenvalues ω will be complex.[2] If, however, the system is enclosed by rigid, perfectly conducting walls (an ideal cavity) then the appropriate boundary condition is

$$\underline{n} \times \underline{E}_1 = 0 , \tag{28}$$

where $\underline{n}$ is the unit normal to the wall. When this is so, there exists a variational (energy) principle, viz,

$$\omega^2 = \int d\tau \left[c^2 (\nabla \times \underline{E}_1^{(0)})^2 + \omega p^2 \underline{E}_1^{(0)2} \right] \bigg/ \int d\tau \underline{E}_1^{(0)2} ,$$

$$\delta \omega^2 = 0 , \tag{29}$$

equivalent to Eq. (27), with boundary condition (28). It is immediately apparent then, that the eigenvalues $\omega^{(0)2}$ are real. †

Suppose now that the solutions of Eq. (27) are known, subject to boundary condition (28). Then one can immediately compute from perturbation theory the shifts in the resonant frequencies, namely

$$\delta \omega^2 \int d\tau \left| \underline{E}_1^{(0)} \right|^2 = - \frac{4\pi e^2}{m^2 \omega^{(0)2}} \int d\tau \left\{ \frac{\left| \nabla \cdot (p \underline{E}_1^{(0)}) \right|^2}{p} + \frac{\left| \underline{E}_1^{(0)} \cdot \nabla p \right|^2}{p} \right.$$

$$- \frac{p'}{N_o} \left| \underline{E}_1^{(0)} \cdot \nabla N_o \right|^2$$

$$\left. + p (\nabla \underline{E}_1^{(0)})^* : \left[(\nabla \underline{E}_1^{(0)}) + (\nabla \underline{E}_1^{(0)})^T \right] \right\}^{\ddagger} . \tag{30}$$

Consider an infinite homogeneous plasma where the pressure $p = N_o m v_{th}^2$ = const, and N_o = const. We can then seek solutions which vary in space like $e^{i \underline{k} \cdot \underline{r}}$. Equation (27) then splits into the independent equations

$$(\omega^2 - \omega p^2) \underline{k} \cdot \underline{E}_1^{(0)} = 0 , \tag{31}$$

$$(\omega^2 - \omega p^2 - c^2 k^2) \underline{k} \times \underline{E}_1^{(0)} = 0 . \tag{32}$$

Clearly there are modes for which $\underline{k} \times \underline{E}_1^{(0)} = 0$, $\underline{k} \cdot \underline{E}_1^{(0)} = 0$, $\omega^2 = \omega p^2$ (longitudinal modes), and those for which $\underline{k} \times \underline{E}_1^{(0)} = 0$, $\underline{k} \cdot \underline{E}_1^{(0)} = 0$, $\omega^2 = c^2 k^2 + \omega_p^2$ (transverse modes). The former are usually termed plasma oscillations, and the latter are, of course, electromagnetic waves. On applying Eq. (30) with appropriate periodic boundary con-

† The considerations presented here are similar to those discussed by J. C. Slater in Reference 4.

‡ The notation $A{:}B = \sum_{j,i=1}^{3} A_{ij} B_{ji}$.

ditions, there results, for the associated frequencies*,

$$\omega^2 = \omega_p^2 + 3\, k^2 v_{th}^2 \,, \tag{33}$$

$$\omega^2 = c^2 k^2 + \omega_p^2 + k^2 v_{th}^2\, \omega_p^2\, (\omega_p^2 + c^2 k^2)^{-1} \,. \tag{34}$$

We shall see later that these are the same results to first order in $k^2 v_{th}^2 / \omega_p^2$ as those yielded by the Boltzmann equation. One result of the more refined treatment that is not recovered, however, is the phenomenon of Landau damping of the longitudinal waves.

Note that the decomposition into longitudinal $(\nabla \times \underline{E}_1 = 0)$ waves and transverse $(\nabla \cdot \underline{E}_1 = 0)$ waves does not persist when there is a density gradient, as can be readily seen by taking the divergence and curl of Eq. (26).

Clearly, this method can be extended to the case where there is a magnetic field, motions, and an anisotropic material stress tensor in the equilibrium. It provides a framework, within which, hopefully, a wide variety of interesting problems can be successfully treated which are at present intractable from the point of view of Boltzmann's equation.

Let us now consider matters directly from the collisionless Boltzmann equation (5). For simplicity, we restrict our attention to small departures from static equilibrium of an infinite homogeneous proton-electron plasma and to small departures from a static equilibrium in which there is no magnetic field. We write

$$f(\underline{r}, \underline{v}, t) = f_o(\underline{v}) + f_1(\underline{v})\, e^{i(\underline{k} \cdot \underline{r} - \omega t)} \tag{35}$$

with the understanding that $s = -i\omega$ is to be viewed as the argument of the Laplace transform of $f_1(\underline{r}, \underline{v}, t)$ with respect to the time. This is necessary for the unique definition of certain characteristic integrals which occur in the theory. [5] That is to say, we assume that all such expressions are defined with ω possessing a sufficiently large positive imaginary part, and the appropriate analytic continuation determined.

The linearized version of Eq. (5) is then

$$i(\underline{k} \cdot \underline{v} - \omega) f_1 + (q/m) \left[\underline{E}_1 + \underline{v} \times \underline{B}_1 / c\right] \cdot \nabla_v f_o = 0 \,, \tag{36}$$

and those of Eqs. (1) and (2) are

* Note that unless $\omega_p^2 \gg c^2 k^2$, the relativistic corrections, which we have not treated, will be of the same order as the thermal corrections in Eq. (34).

$$\underline{B}_1 = (c/\omega)\, \underline{k} \times \underline{E}_1 , \tag{37}$$

and

$$c^2 \underline{k} \times (\underline{k} \times \underline{E}_1) + \omega^2 \underline{E}_1 = -4\pi i \omega \underline{J}_1 . \tag{38}$$

In deriving Eqs. (37) and (38), we have assumed a space-time variation $e^{i(\underline{k} \cdot \underline{r} - \omega t)}$. The current density $\underline{J}_1$, following Eqs. (7), (11), (36), and (37) can be written

$$\underline{J}_1 = -\underline{Q} \cdot \underline{E}_1 / 4\pi i \omega , \tag{39}$$

where the dyadic $\underline{Q}$ is defined via

$$\underline{Q} = \sum \frac{4\pi q^2 \omega}{m} \int \frac{d^3 v\, \underline{v}}{\underline{k} \cdot \underline{v} - \omega} \left[\nabla_v f_0 + \frac{1}{\omega} \underline{k} \times (\underline{v} \times \nabla_v f_0) \right] . \tag{40}$$

It is instructive to consider a wave packet in $\underline{k}$ which is prescribed at time zero. If we interpret $-\underline{Q}/4\pi i \omega$ as the Fourier-Laplace transform of a conductivity tensor $\underline{\sigma}(\underline{r}, t)$, it then follows from Eq. (40), on application of the Fourier and Laplace inversion and convolution theorems, that

$$\underline{J}_1(\underline{r}, t) = \underline{J}_1(\underline{r}, 0) + \int d^3 r' \int_0^t dt' \, \underline{\sigma}(\underline{r} - \underline{r}', t - t') \cdot \underline{E}_1(\underline{r}', t') . \tag{41}$$

Thus, whereas in a collision-dominated plasma the current density at a point $\underline{r}$ at time t is proportional to the electric field at that same point (the phenomenon is local), the appropriate extension of the notion of conductivity to the collisionless case requires that the conductivity be represented by an integral operator. Physically, the cause is that the charges are not localized in space, but rather convect their past histories by their thermal motions. When these thermal motions are small, however, the situation becomes approximately local, as shown by the macroscopic theory previously presented.

If Eq. (39) is inserted into Eq. (38), a system of homogeneous equations results. The condition that the determinant of the coefficients vanish yields

$$\left| (\omega^2 - c^2 k^2)\, \underline{I} + c^2 \underline{k}\,\underline{k} - \underline{Q} \right| = 0 . \tag{42}$$

The roots ω of Eq. (41) give the asymptotic time dependence of the field quantities. In particular, if there is any root for which $\text{Im}\, \omega > 0$, there is an instability.

Consider the special case where f_o is isotropic (depends only on the magnitude of $\underline{v}$), and let us examine high frequency waves such that the ion motions can be neglected. Then Eq. (40) reduces to

$$\underline{Q} = \frac{4\pi e^2 \omega}{m} \int \frac{d^3 v\, \underline{v}\,\underline{v}}{\underline{k}\cdot\underline{v}-\omega}\, 2\, \frac{\partial f_o(v)}{\partial v^2} . \tag{43}$$

Introduce a cylindrical coordinate system with its pole along $\underline{k} = k\underline{e}_3$, viz,

$$\underline{v} = \underline{e}_3\, u + \underline{e}_2\, w \sin\phi + \underline{e}_1\, w \cos\phi . \tag{44}$$

Then Eq. (43) can be written

$$\underline{Q} = \frac{4\pi e^2 \omega}{m} \int_{-\infty}^{\infty} du \int_0^{\infty} dww \int_0^{2\pi} d\phi\, \frac{\underline{v}\,\underline{v}}{ku-\omega}\, \frac{1}{w}\, \frac{\partial f_o\left[(u^2+w^2)^{1/2}\right]}{\partial w}$$

$$= \frac{4\pi e^2 \omega}{m}\, 2\pi \int_{-\infty}^{\infty} du \int_0^{\infty} dw\, \frac{\underline{e}_3\underline{e}_3 u^2 + \frac{1}{2}(\underline{e}_1\underline{e}_1 + \underline{e}_2\underline{e}_2) w^2}{ku-\omega}\, \frac{\partial f_o\left[(u^2+w^2)^{1/2}\right]}{\partial w}$$

$$= -\frac{4\pi e^2 \omega}{m}\, 2\pi \left\{ \underline{e}_3\,\underline{e}_3 \int_{-\infty}^{\infty} \frac{du\, u^2 f_o(u)}{ku-\omega} \right.$$

$$\left. + (I - \underline{e}_3\underline{e}_3) \int_{-\infty}^{\infty} du \int_0^{\infty} dww\, \frac{f_o\left[(u^2+w^2)^{1/2}\right]}{ku-\omega} \right\} . \tag{45}$$

Clearly, the determinant of Eq. (43) is diagonal in this representation. The condition that the 1-1 and 2-2 elements vanish is the same, namely,

$$\omega^2 = c^2 k^2 + \frac{4\pi e^2}{m} \int \frac{d^3 v\, f_o(v)}{1 - \underline{k}\cdot\underline{v}/\omega} . \tag{46}$$

This corresponds to transverse waves, $\underline{k} \times \underline{E}_1 = 0$. When, on the average, $|\underline{k}\cdot\underline{v}/\omega| \ll 1$ (low temperature) one can expand the denominator in the integral and obtain

$$\omega^2 = c^2k^2 + \frac{4\pi e^2}{m} \int d^3v f_o(v) \left[1 + \frac{\underline{k} \cdot \underline{v}}{\omega} + \left(\frac{\underline{k} \cdot \underline{v}}{\omega}\right)^2 + \cdots \right]$$

$$= c^2k^2 + \frac{4\pi N e^2}{m} \left[1 + \frac{k^2 v_{th}^2}{\omega^2} + \cdots \right]$$

$$\sim c^2k^2 + \omega_p^2 + k^2 v_{th}^2 \, \omega_p^2 \, (\omega_p^2 + c^2k^2)^{-1} \quad . \tag{47}$$

This result agrees with Eq. (34), which rested on the "low temperature" approximation.

The condition that the 3-3 element of the determinant in Eq. (42) vanish, reads

$$\omega^2 = \frac{4\pi e^2}{m} \, 2\pi \int_{-\infty}^{\infty} \frac{du \, f_o(u) \, u^2}{1 - ku/\omega} \quad . \tag{48}$$

If, on the average, $|ku/\omega| \ll 1$, we can approximate Eq. (48) by

$$\omega^2 = \frac{4\pi e^2}{m} \, 2\pi \int_{-\infty}^{\infty} du \, u^2 f_o(u) \left[1 + \frac{ku}{\omega} + \frac{k^2 u^2}{\omega^2} + \cdots \right]$$

$$= \frac{4\pi N e^2}{m} \left[1 + \frac{3k^2 v_{th}^2}{\omega^2} + \cdots \right]$$

$$\sim \omega_p^2 + 3k^2 v_{th}^2 \quad . \tag{49}$$

In arriving at the second line of Eq. (49), we have noted that the average velocity is zero, and in writing the last line we have replaced ω^2 by ω_p^2 in the thermal correction.

In writing Eq. (49) we have made a formal expansion which is not strictly legitimate. Rather, if the root ω which we are seeking has a zero or very small imaginary part, we must write Eq. (48) as

$$\omega^2 = - \frac{4\pi e^2 \omega}{mk} \, 2\pi \int_{\smile} \frac{du \, u^2 f_o(u)}{u - \omega/k} \quad , \tag{50}$$

where the contour is no longer merely along the real u axis, but must be hooked under the pole at $u = \omega/k$. Thus, more precisely, Eq. (50) can be approximated by

$$\omega^2 = -\frac{4\pi e^2 \omega_o}{mk} 2\pi \left\{ P \int_{-\infty}^{\infty} \frac{du\, u^2 f_o(u)}{u - \omega_o/k} + \pi i \left[\frac{\omega_o}{k}\right]^2 f_o\left[\frac{\omega_o}{k}\right]\right\}, \tag{51}$$

where ω_o is effectively given by Eq. (49). Since by assumption, the imaginary part on the right-hand side of Eq. (51) is small, one can write to good approximation

$$\omega^2 = \omega_o^2 \left[1 - \pi i \frac{\omega_o^3}{k^3} \frac{1}{N} f_o\left[\frac{\omega_o}{k}\right]\right], \tag{52}$$

$$\omega = \pm |\omega_o| - \frac{\pi i}{2N} \frac{\omega_o^4}{k^3} f_o\left[\frac{\omega_o}{k}\right]. \tag{53}$$

Clearly, $\operatorname{Im} \omega < 0$ and, since the time dependence is $e^{-i\omega t}$, this corresponds to damping, known as Landau damping. Equation (52) differs from the low temperature result (Eq. (33)) for longitudinal waves in that ω is now complex, with a very small imaginary part arising from the action of the tail of the distribution function. This defect of the fluid low-temperature approximation, where we retain only a few of the lowest moments of the distribution function, is associated with the necessity of giving all the moments in order to describe the exponentially small tail.

As a final example, let us consider a class of wave motions so slow that we must take into account the ion motion.[6] For simplicity, we again assume that the distribution functions are isotropic about zero velocity. Again the determinantal equation will have a root corresponding to longitudinal waves given by

$$\omega^2 = -\sum \frac{4\pi e^2}{m} \frac{\omega}{k} 2\pi \int_{\smile} \frac{du\, u^2 f_o(u)}{u - \omega/k}. \tag{54}$$

If we assume that the ions are cold $(f_{o\,\mathrm{ion}} = N\delta(u)/4\pi u^2)$ and that $|\omega^2/k^2| \ll v_{th\,\mathrm{electron}}^2$, Eq. (54) can be approximated by

$$\frac{\omega^2}{\omega_p^2} \sim \frac{m}{M} - \frac{\omega}{k}\frac{2\pi}{N}\int_{-\infty}^{\infty} du f_o(u)\left[u + \frac{\omega}{k} + \cdots\right]$$

$$\sim \frac{m}{M} - \frac{\omega^2}{k^2}\frac{1}{W^2}, \tag{55}$$

where m is the electron mass, M the ion mass, ω_p is the electron plasma frequency, and the speed W is defined by

$$\frac{1}{W^2} = \frac{4\pi}{N}\int_0^{\infty} du f_o(u) . \tag{56}$$

Note that if f_o is Maxwellian, $W^2 = KT/m$.

Equation (55) can be solved to read

$$\omega/k = \pm (m/M)^{1/2} W \left[1 + k^2W^2/\omega_p^2\right]^{-1/2} \tag{57}$$

and one can often neglect k^2W^2/ω_p^2 compared with one. Thus when this situation exists, and f_o is Maxwellian, Eq. (57) yields

$$\omega/k = \pm (KT/M)^{1/2} .$$

That is, the wave has a phase velocity equal to that of an ion at the electron temperature. It is to be noted however, that this "ion wave" differs from a sound wave where the organization is provided by collisions, in that here it is provided by electrical forces.

REFERENCES

1. A. A. Vlasov, *J. Phys. U.S.S.R.*, Vol. 9, p. 25 (1945).
2. I. B. Bernstein and S. K. Trehan, *Nuclear Fusion*, Vol. 1, p. 3 (1960).
3. C. R. Oberman, *Bull. Amer. Phys. Soc.*, Series II, Vol. 5, p. 364 (1960).
4. J. C. Slater, *Microwave Electronics* (New York: D. Van Nostrand,1950).
5. L. D. Landeau, *J. Exptl. Theoret. Phys.* (U.S.S.R.) Vol. 7, p. 574 (1946).
6. I. B. Bernstein and R. M. Kulsrud, *Phys. Fluids*, Vol. 3, p. 937 (1960).

AMPLIFICATION OF MICROWAVES BY MEANS OF PLASMA

Z.S. Chernov, G.A. Bernashevski
Institute of Radioelectricity and Electronics
Academy of Sciences, U.S.S.R.

At present various types of studies are being carried out to determine the radiophysical properties of plasma. One of the stimuli for such research is that plasma seems to be a very promising medium for amplifying and generating microwaves. Plasma is attractive because it possesses undulating and waveguiding properties, and, in contradistinction to metal structures, electron streams can penetrate into it.

Several theoretical studies[1, 2, 3] have analyzed processes of the interaction between an electron stream and plasma, and the possibility of obtaining large amplification for microwaves has been predicted. This prediction has been subsequently verified experimentally.[4, 5, 6] Although the various investigators started out from different idealizations and accounted for different effects which are to be expected in the real plasma of a gaseous discharge, the main result they all obtained was the discovery that high concentrations of plasma (ω_p/ω close to unity) are necessary for securing the amplification of high frequency signals. The appropriate concentration of electrons in plasma can be obtained by means of a discharge in gases and metal vapors at pressures of 10^{-1} to 10^{-3} mm Hg with the use of special magnetic or electrostatic traps.

It is timely to consider the question of the validity of the idealizations adopted in the theoretical models of plasma and the conclusions drawn from them in view of experimental results obtained using real plasma in discharges.

In our experimental setups (Fig. 1) we used a diode discharge gap with a heated oxide cathode as well as a Phillip's type discharge gap with a heated cathode. The discharge takes place in mercury gas or a residual gas at pressures of 10^{-1} to 10^{-3} mm Hg. The discharge current could be varied from zero to several amperes. The discharge was produced in a longitudinal magnetic field. Thus, we succeeded in obtaining plasma having a high concentration and were also able to study the plasma-electron stream system over a large frequency range.

Modulation and demodulation of the electron stream was used to inject and detect the signal.

Presented at the Symposium on Electromagnetics and Fluid Dynamics of Gaseous Plasma, Polytechnic Institute of Brooklyn, April 4, 5, 6, 1961

The main characteristic of such a system is the amplification of the signal per unit of length. In previous studies[5] it was shown that when the space-charge waves in the electron stream are to be amplified due to the reaction of plasma without introducing the requirement of slow-wave propagation in the plasma itself, the total gain of the system is given by the formula

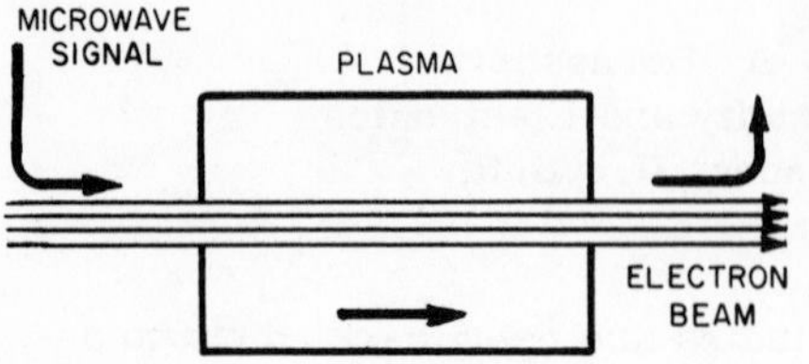

Figure 1

$$G = 8.69\, \gamma_{pe}\, q\ell$$

where q is determined by two parameters: $\gamma_e a$ (of the stream) and ω_p/ω ; the quantity γ_{pe} is equal to

$$\frac{e}{m\epsilon_o}\left[\frac{je}{v_e^3}\right]^{1/2} \sim \left[\frac{je}{V_o^{3/2}}\right]^{1/2},$$

that is, it is directly proportional to the square root of the perveance of the electron stream; ℓ is the length of the system.

Thus we see that when transverse similarity is satisfied in the system, its amplification per unit of length does not depend on the operating wavelength.

When we consider the amplification of a traveling plasma wave interacting with a synchronous electron stream, the amplification of the system is proportional to CN, where C is the transverse coupling impedance for plasma, and N is the number of slow waves which lie within the length of the system. Therefore, in this case we should expect that the amplification per unit of length is directly proportional to the frequency.

In order to determine how the amplification depends on the ratio ℓ/λ (where ℓ is the length of the system, and λ is the operating wavelength) experiments were made on four different models. Here, the quantity $\gamma_e a$ and the perveance of the electron stream were kept as equal as possible for the three cases. The maximum amplification in these systems were measured by varying ω_p in order to obtain the optimum ratio ω_p/ω . This experiment showed that when the signal frequency is varied by almost 20 times (from 2,000 to 38,000 megacycles), the system gain remains constant at the level of 10 decibels per cm length of the system.

As is known, maximum amplification in the system should be observed at a signal frequency near the frequency of the plasma determined by its concentration. In turn, the concentration is determined by the equilibrium between the charges entering the plasma due to ionization and the charges leaving the plasma due to diffusion and recombination. In the plasma concentration range from 10^{11} to 10^{13} electrons/cm^3 and pressures from 10^{-2} to 10^{-3} mm Hg (3×10^{14} to 3×10^{13} molecules per cm^3), the main role is played by the diffusion of charges from the plasma; the process of recombination in the volume can be neglected. The number of ionizations is directly proportional to the discharge current for a constant voltage and pressure.

Figure 2 shows the frequency corresponding to maximum amplification as a function of the current density in the Phillip's-type discharge gap for three different units over a wide frequency range. It is seen that here the resonant frequency of plasma is about proportional to the current density raised to the one-half power.

Figure 3 gives the dependence of the maximum amplification frequency in the plasma-electron beam system on the discharge current

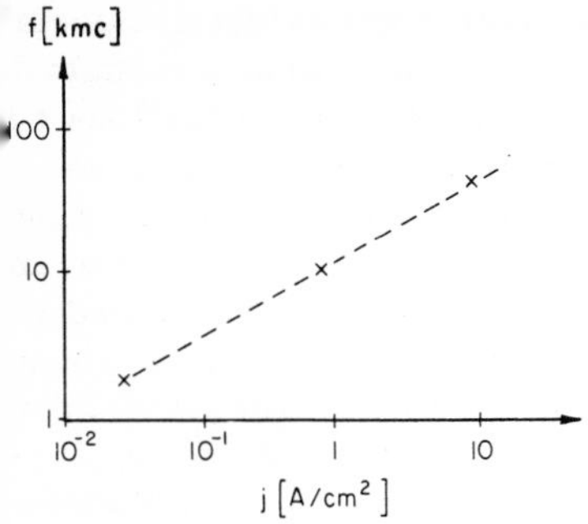

Figure 2

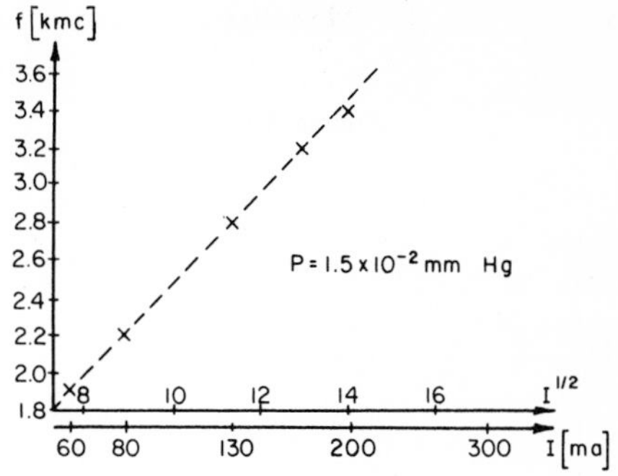

Figure 3

for a constant pressure (using a discharge gap of the diode type). This curve shows that the frequency is very nearly proportional to the current raised to the one-half power. When the gas pressure in the system is raised, a smaller discharge current is needed to obtain maximum amplification at a constant frequency. However, the product PI increases (as is seen from Fig. 4). This indicates that diffusion is increased at a poorer vacuum.

It was of interest to determine to what extent the idealization associated with uniform concentration and no drift of the electron component relative to the ion component of plasma corresponds to real conditions in the discharge gap of the diode type, for example. In this case part of the electrons of the plasma move in a directed manner. In order to check this effect, the amplification was measured in the experimental setup with the discharge gap overturned. The amplification did not noticeably change. Moreover, the diode discharge gap and the Phillip's-type discharge gap of equal length gave a maximum amplification of the same order of 30 to 40 decibels (λ = 10 cm).

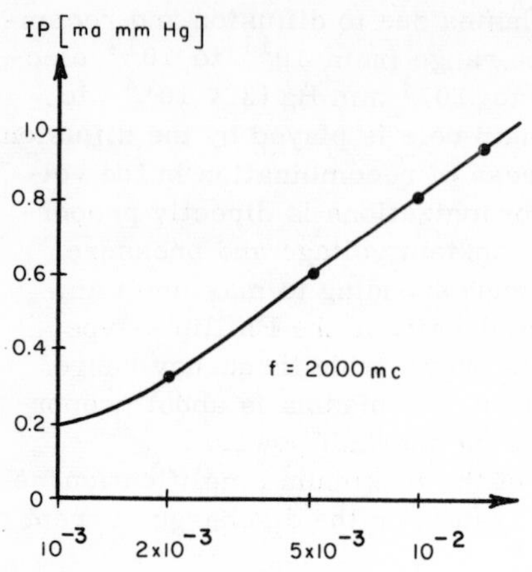

Figure 4

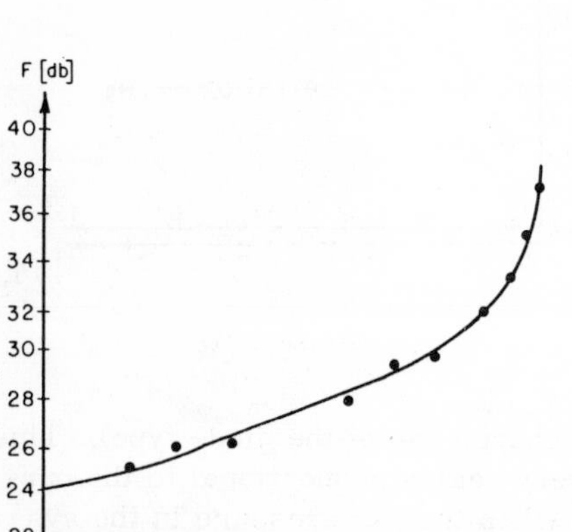

Figure 5

However, in the Phillip's-type discharge gap, the required concentration was obtained with a discharge current about three times smaller than in the diode discharge gap.

Finally, we wanted to get some idea of the noise properties of the system. Although it is quite a common opinion that plasma is a source of intense noise, and, in practice, discharge tubes are employed as noise generators, the conclusion that the plasma-electron stream system has a large noise level is not evident. Special study is required to ascertain to what extent plasma fluctuations can be transformed into noise waves of the electron stream interacting with the plasma. In the 10 cm and 3 cm bands, which were studied at electron stream currents of about 1 ma and cathode currents of about 4 ma with a gain of 30 to 40 decibels, we obtained a noise factor of 40 to 50 decibels. Substantial changes in discharge current hardly influenced the noise factor for the system. These results were compared with the experimental curve for the noise factor of a traveling-wave tube, (see Fig. 5), in which the magnetic field, the pressure and the electron stream current were the same as in the plasma system. From this comparison we see that the noise in the plasma system was determined in this case by noise in the fast electron stream ionizing the medium in the presence of a magnetic field, and the addition of noise from plasma of high concentration was not noticed on this background.

Thus, we come to the conclusion that the development of theoretical concepts at the present time regarding the amplifying properties of plasma do not contradict in the broad sense the experimental results obtained over a wide band of radio frequencies.

REFERENCES

1. A. I. Akhiezer and J. B. Feinberg, *Soviet Physics, JETP*, Vol. 21, p. 1262 (1951).

2. M. A. Lampert, *J. Appl. Phys.*, Vol. 27, p. 5 (1956).

3. S. Sumi, *J. Phys. Soc. Jap.*, Vol. 14, p. 1093 (1959).

4. G. D. Boyd, L. U. Field and R. W. Gould, *Phys. Rev.*, Vol. 109, p. 1393 (1958).

5. E. V. Bogdanov, V. J. Kislov and Z. S. Chernov, *Radiotechnica i electronica* (in Russian), Vol. 5, No. 1, p. 229 (1960).

6. V. J. Kislov, E. V. Bogdanov, *Radiotechnica i electronica*, Vol. 5, No. 12, p. 1974 (1960).

MICROSCOPIC AND MACROSCOPIC MODELS IN PLASMA PHYSICS*

Harold Grad
Institute of Mathematical Sciences
New York University

In choosing a model to describe the behavior of a plasma, a balance must be maintained between the simplicity of a macroscopic description and the detail in a microscopic description. In an ordinary gas, the criterion for behavior as a continuum is that the mean-free-path be small. In a plasma there is a similar criterion; other lengths (Debye, Larmor) may complicate the macroscopic equations but will not destroy their validity. An entirely different criterion (in a collisionless plasma) is that the Larmor radius be small. A consistent treatment of only the lowest-order guiding-center particle motion is sufficient to yield, with a minimum of computation, both a microscopic theory (guiding-center gas) and a macroscopic continuum theory (guiding-center fluid). A comparison shows why certain types of arguments which are conventionally phrased in complicated microscopic terms are exactly equivalent to a potentially less exact macroscopic analysis.

I. INTRODUCTION

One is frequently presented with the alternative of studying a physical problem with a detailed and difficult microscopic model or with a less cluttered and simpler, but not so clearly applicable, macroscopic model. The microscopic detail can be not only burdensome but, on occasion, even irrelevant; we recall from statistical mechanics the existence of macroscopic laws that are almost independent of particular molecular properties or motions. For classical fluids, we have recourse to experiment and to the (quite difficult and easily misinterpreted) theoretical derivation of macroscopic laws. For a plasma, unfortunately, experimental knowledge is not yet comprehensive enough to provide any significant degree of synthesis. Thus, at present, theoretical derivation of macroscopic laws (at least as difficult and as risky as for an ordinary gas) is our only alternative.

The model that one selects to describe a given physical situation is to some extent a matter of choice and may frequently be motivated by one's prejudices or early training. Nevertheless, there do exist objective criteria which should govern the choice between available

*The work presented in this paper is supported by the U. S. Atomic Energy Commission under Contract No. AT(30-1)-1480.

Presented at the Symposium on Electromagnetics and Fluid Dynamics of Gaseous Plasma, Polytechnic Institute of Brooklyn, April 4, 5, 6, 1961

macroscopic and microscopic descriptions. One may ask why the macroscopic path is ever followed since, in principle, the microscopic is more accurate. Sometimes the justification is that a rough answer is sufficient. At other times, the choice lies between obtaining an answer and none at all; there are many problems which are completely inaccesible except to macroscopic techniques. Quite generally, the mathematical tools appropriate to a continuum model are more powerful and more highly developed. Finally, there are cases in which the macroscopic analysis becomes exact in an appropriate limit.

In most problems, macroscopic or microscopic, it is necessary to introduce simplifying assumptions. Since the two mathematical frameworks are so different, the appropriate simplifications are usually different in the two formulations, and the results are frequently non-comparable. In problems where the models are comparable, the microscopic solution can be termed "exact", and the relative validity of the macroscopic model determined; such examples will be discussed. However, we also find, in the literature, important examples where the simplifications made in the microscopic model are precisely what is needed to validate an exactly equivalent macroscopic continuum model, even though the comparison may be hidden by a different choice of variables in the two models. In such cases, we shall usually find that the macroscopic treatment is not only easier but more intuitive; investigation of the particle orbits in detail offers only a psychological feeling of greater knowledge. The guiding-center gas offers such examples. In this case, the comparison of microscopic and macroscopic models is facilitated by proper use of only the lowest-order guiding-center motion; there is no need to consider "first-order" drifts.

Proper choice of a model should, when possible, avoid both the misapplication of an oversimplified continuum treatment and the unnecessary pursuit of the complex paths taken by individual particles. As two extreme examples in ordinary gas dynamics, we mention the slow steady flow past a sphere and the flow between two rotating cylinders. In the first example, a macroscopic treatment (viz., the Navier-Stokes equations with a slip boundary condition) yields the whimsical result of a finite drag in a vacuum. In the second problem, there does not seem to be the slightest hope of even a qualitative explanation via kinetic theory of the occurrence of instability within a kinetic theory framework. Similar situations are easily found in plasma physics.

In the body of this paper, we present a brief survey of the parameter ranges within which one can expect to rely on a macroscopic description, followed by a more detailed study of one such regime, viz., the guiding center limit. Because of the mathematically singular nature of this limit, the full-dress particle description is itself partly macroscopic. Also, the conventional current and charge source relations which couple Maxwell's equations with the particle motion are, in this limit, replaced by certain equations of constraint. Some nevident limitations of this theory occur in strongly anisotropic sit-tions, the inability to deal with plasma oscillations, and the surpris-gly restricted ability to predict long plasma containment with pre-nt theory.

II. MACROSCOPIC CRITERIA AND REGIMES

By a macroscopic model we mean one which uses variables sim-ar to those in a thermodynamic or classical fluid description of a tate rather than a molecular distribution function. This distinction annot be made precise since one can bridge the gap with a sequence f more detailed macroscopic descriptions.[25]

In an ordinary gas, the criterion for a macroscopic theory to be alid is that the mean free path be small compared with any natural ength over which the gas properties change significantly. Heuristic-lly, molecular collisions will prevent a molecule from straying very ar from its neighbors and thus provide a finite fluid element with an dentity in terms of the specific molecules it contains. More quanti-atively, collisions produce a distribution function which is approxi-nately locally Maxwellian and can therefore be described in terms of he local thermodynamic state.

For a plasma, it is necessary to strengthen this criterion some-what and require that both the mean free path and the mean collision ime be short compared with relevant variations in the fluid. In an ordinary gas, slow variation in space implies slow variation in time (with the possible exception of a brief transient period). This dis-tinction can be seen most easily in the dispersion relation for small-amplitude plane waves. In an ordinary gas, large wavelength implies low frequency in any propagating mode, but a plasma can also main-tain modes (e. g., plasma oscillations) in which there is a finite lim-iting frequency in the limit of large wavelength.

The situation is further complicated by the existence of several widely disparate collision times. In a fully ionized plasma, it is suf-ficient to have the ion-ion collision time small. This implies that both the electron and ion distributions are approximately locally Max-wellian although possibly at different speeds and temperatures. Thus the macroscopic description may require several equations for en-ergy conservation (the ion-electron energy relaxation can be macro-scopically slow) but only a single combined momentum equation (the velocity slip or electric current approximates a quasi-equilibrium which can be described by a form of Ohm's law).

The size of a Larmor radius relative to the mean free path does not affect the possibility of a macroscopic description but only its form. For example, Ohm's law will contain a Hall term unless the electron Larmor frequency is low compared with the mean electron collision time. Similarly, a Debye length which is comparable to the

Larmor radius (the Debye length is always small compared with the mean free path) may change the values of the transport coefficients but not the form of the equations. Thus, although there are many forms that the equations can take, and the equations can be quite complex, there are no serious difficulties in obtaining macroscopic equations and no serious doubts as to their range of validity when the mean free path and mean collision time are small.

Appropriate values of transport coefficients can be obtained from either the Boltzmann or the Fokker-Planck equations. For a sufficiently rarefied or hot plasma, the two computations are the same (to "dominant" logarithmic order); thus the traditional Boltzmann values can be used. For a somewhat denser or cooler plasma (with the logarithmic term no longer dominant), neither can be trusted, and satisfactory values have yet to be obtained.

The magneto-ionic theory provides a macroscopic description in an entirely different regime, viz., when there is slow spatial variation but very rapid variation (either transient or oscillatory) in time. In the simplest version, the system consists of Maxwell's equations together with a form of Ohm's law, viz.,

$$\tau \frac{\partial J}{\partial t} + J = \sigma E . \tag{1}$$

The fluid appears only as a carrier of current and is represented by the relaxation time τ and conductivity σ as state variables (density and temperature appear in σ and τ and their ratio is the plasma frequency, $\Omega^2 = \sigma/\kappa_0 \tau$, where κ_0 = permittivity of space). This type of macroscopic description can be obtained by approximating moment equations in a low temperature limit [2] or dispersion relations in a high frequency, long wavelength limit;[26] the range of validity is not yet fully understood.

Finally, we mention a third regime in which macroscopic theories are applicable, viz., when fluid variations are slow compared with the Larmor radius and Larmor frequency. The most striking feature of this situation is the strong degree of anisotropy. Particles are rather tightly bound with regard to motion perpendicular to magnetic lines. Thus there is a tendency to maintain the macroscopic identity of a fluid element, but only with regard to motion in the plane transverse to the magnetic field. We shall find this theory to be quite subtle, largely because of the mathematically singular nature of the relevant guiding-center approximation to the exact orbits. As a consequence, even a fully microscopic theory in terms of a distribution function takes on certain macroscopic features. This is the reason for the otherwise surprising degree of success of the macroscopic theory in certain special cases.

III. GUIDING-CENTER THEORY

The motion of a charged particle can be described relatively mply when there is no significant change in the electromagnetic field en by the particle during one Larmor period, m/eB, and when the ergy of the particle does not change appreciably during this same riod. This implies a limitation on the rate of time variation of $\underset{\sim}{E}$ d $\underset{\sim}{B}$, a limitation on the speed of the particle, and a limitation on e magnitude of $\underset{\sim}{E}$; (to meet the speed limitation, the component of $\underset{\sim}{E}$ rpendicular to B must not exceed the order of $\mathcal{V}B$, and to meet e energy condition, the parallel component must be *small* compared th the order of $\mathcal{V}B$, where $\mathcal{V}$ is the maximum allowable speed). e guiding-center motion is obtained as a formal expansion[3, 4] in e small parameter

$$\delta = m/e \; ; \tag{2}$$

e obtains a series which represents the actual motion asymptoti- lly.[5] Consistent with the remarks made above, we must assume at the component of $\underset{\sim}{E}$ parallel to $\underset{\sim}{B}$ is small of order δ; (the lidity of this condition in an actual plasma will be discussed in Sec- on VII).

Entirely different types of behavior are found for the motion of e guiding center and for the rapid oscillation around it; another es- ntial separation occurs between the components of guiding-center otion parallel and perpendicular to $\underset{\sim}{B}$. Briefly, the parallel motion governed by a second-order equation (acceleration given), the per- ndicular guiding-center motion by a first order-system (velocity ven), and the oscillatory motion is completely integrated. To low- st order, the "drift" velocity perpendicular to $\underset{\sim}{B}$ is given by

$$\underset{\sim}{U} = \underset{\sim}{E} \times \underset{\sim}{B}/B^2 \, . \tag{3}$$

lso to lowest order, the oscillatory motion is described by the state- ent that the magnetic moment (per mass)

$$\mu = \frac{1}{2} v_\perp^2/B \tag{4}$$

constant; ($v_\perp$ is the oscillating perpendicular velocity component ft after removing $\underset{\sim}{U}$). Writing $\underset{\sim}{v}$ for the total guiding-center vel- ity and $\underset{\sim}{V}$ for its parallel component,

$$\underset{\sim}{v} = \underset{\sim}{U} + \underset{\sim}{V} \, , \qquad \underset{\sim}{V} \times \underset{\sim}{B} = 0 \, , \tag{5}$$

e complete the lowest-order description with the equation for the arallel motion

$$\frac{dV}{dt} = \frac{1}{\delta}(\underset{\sim}{\beta}\cdot\underset{\sim}{E}) - \mu\underset{\sim}{\beta}\cdot \nabla B + \underset{\sim}{U}\cdot(\frac{\partial \underset{\sim}{\beta}}{\partial t} + \underset{\sim}{U}\cdot\nabla\underset{\sim}{\beta} + \underset{\sim}{V}\cdot\nabla\underset{\sim}{\beta})$$

$$= \frac{1}{\delta}(\underset{\sim}{\beta}\cdot\underset{\sim}{E}) + \underset{\sim}{\beta}\cdot\nabla(\frac{1}{2}U^2 - \mu B) + V(\underset{\sim}{U}\cdot\underset{\sim}{\kappa}) \qquad (6$$

Here $\underset{\sim}{\beta}$ is the unit tangent vector and $\underset{\sim}{\kappa}$ the curvature of the mag-netic line,

$$\underset{\sim}{\beta} = \underset{\sim}{B}/B, \quad \underset{\sim}{\kappa} = (\underset{\sim}{\beta}\cdot\nabla)\underset{\sim}{\beta}. \qquad (7$$

Note that the parallel component of $\underset{\sim}{E}$ exerts a finite effect on the motion even though it is a higher-order quantity.

Since $\underset{\sim}{\beta}\cdot\underset{\sim}{E}$ is small, $\underset{\sim}{U}$ satisfies the relation

$$\underset{\sim}{E} + \underset{\sim}{U}\times\underset{\sim}{B} = 0 \qquad (8$$

to lowest order. From Maxwell's equation, we get the familiar flux equation,

$$\frac{\partial \underset{\sim}{B}}{\partial t} + \text{curl}\,(\underset{\sim}{B}\times\underset{\sim}{U}) = 0. \qquad (9$$

This equation has the well-known property of carrying magnetic lines into magnetic lines. It is therefore possible to assign an identity to magnetic line and follow its motion in time. Furthermore, one can interpret a guiding center as being constrained to move along a spec-ified magnetic line which is itself in motion at the velocity $\underset{\sim}{U}$ (this has sometimes been questioned[6]). Introducing the line as a constrai with σ as a parameter along the line (σ is constant for a point mov ing with velocity $\underset{\sim}{U}$), we find the motion along the line to be describ-able by the Lagrangian and Hamiltonian

$$\left.\begin{aligned} L &= \frac{1}{2}\dot{\sigma}^2/\zeta^2 + \frac{1}{2}U^2 - \mu B - \phi^*/\delta\,, \\ H &= \frac{1}{2}\zeta^2 p^2 - \frac{1}{2}U^2 + \mu B + \phi^*/\delta\,; \\ \zeta &= \frac{\partial\sigma}{\partial s}, \quad \dot{\sigma} = \zeta V = \zeta^2 p\,. \end{aligned}\right\} \qquad (10$$

Here ϕ^* is the potential of the parallel component of $\underset{\sim}{E}$,† and s is arcleng

The lowest-order theory described above is by itself sufficient

† This potential may be defined in an arbitrary time-varying field, e.g., by taking $\underset{\sim}{B} = \nabla\alpha\times\nabla\gamma$ = curl $\underset{\sim}{A}$ and $\underset{\sim}{A} = \alpha\nabla\gamma$ from which $\underset{\sim}{E} = -\partial\underset{\sim}{A}/\partial t - \nabla\phi = \underset{\sim}{E}^* - \nabla\phi^*$ where $\underset{\sim}{E}^* = (\partial\gamma/\partial t)\nabla\alpha - (\partial\alpha/\partial t)\nabla\gamma$ $(\underset{\sim}{E}^*\cdot\underset{\sim}{B}) = 0$ and $\phi^* = \phi + \alpha\,\partial\gamma/\partial t$.

allow the derivation of a complete macroscopic or microscopic the-ry of a guiding-center plasma. However, for purposes of later dis-ussion, we shall find it illuminating to list the perpendicular "drift" elocity to the next order, viz.†

$$\begin{aligned} \underset{\sim}{U}_1 &= \underset{\sim}{U} + \frac{\delta}{B^2} \underset{\sim}{B} \times \left[\frac{d\underset{\sim}{v}}{dt} + \mu \nabla B \right] \\ &= \underset{\sim}{U} + \frac{\delta}{B^2} \left[\frac{d\underset{\sim}{E}}{dt} + \underset{\sim}{v} \times \frac{d\underset{\sim}{B}}{dt} + \mu \underset{\sim}{B} \times \nabla B \right] ; \end{aligned} \tag{11}$$

ere the time derivative is taken following the lowest-order guiding-enter motion,

$$\frac{d}{dt} = \frac{\partial}{\partial t} + \underset{\sim}{v} \cdot \nabla = \frac{\partial}{\partial t} + \underset{\sim}{V} \cdot \nabla + \underset{\sim}{U} \cdot \nabla . \tag{12}$$

Ve shall see in examples below that the first-order drifts add very ittle to the information that is already contained in the lowest-order escription.

IV. EXAMPLES

Consider a unidirectional steady magnetic field in the z-direc-ion with its magnitude, B, a function of x. There is a first-order rift velocity in the y-direction (cf. (11)) of magnitude

$$v_d = \delta\mu \frac{d}{dx} (\log B) . \tag{13}$$

f there is a uniform electric field in the y-direction, there is an ad-itional zero-order drift in the x-direction of magnitude $U = E/B$. 'he energy of a particle is not constant in the presence of an electric ield. From the lowest-order guiding-center motion, only the "in-ernal" energy μB changes in virtue of the drift $\underset{\sim}{U}$ which carries he particle to a region of different B. From the exact (not guiding-enter) equations of motion, one would compute the energy change as $\underset{\sim}{E} \cdot \underset{\sim}{v}$. Inserting the guiding-center approximation into this formula, 'ields an energy change $e\underset{\sim}{E} \cdot \underset{\sim}{v}_d$. The two energy computations, of ourse, yield the same result,

$$U \frac{d}{dx} (m\mu B) = ev_d E = \frac{1}{2} mv_\perp^2 E \frac{d}{dx} (\log B) . \tag{14}$$

Iowever, the interpretations are worlds apart. The lowest-order uiding-center theory, which expressly ignores the existence of the

† See Reference 9. Many published expressions for this drift (and even for the owest order parallel motion (6)) are either incomplete or incorrect.

(higher-order) drift in the direction of $\underset{\sim}{E}$, yields the correct energy balance as a change in "internal" energy due to the lowest-order drift into a region of different B. One must not supplement this with an *additional* energy increment due to the first-order drift into a region of different electric potential. This examination of higher-order terms only gives insight into the mechanism by which the zero-order guiding-center theory keeps its bookkeeping straight.

We have tacitly assumed above (just for simplicity) that U is small (neglecting the guiding-center energy component $((1/2)\,U^2)$. The complete argument involves a guiding-center energy change in $\mu B + (1/2)\,U^2$ and the complete drift from (11) which has a term involving $d\underset{\sim}{U}/dt = (\underset{\sim}{U} \cdot \nabla)\underset{\sim}{U}$ as well as a gradient of B.

We can invert the argument given above and compute the correct first-order drift velocity using only the zero-order theory and the conservation of energy. One can even use this argument in complete generality, using the zero-order motion (6) together with the drift $\underset{\sim}{E} \times \underset{\sim}{B}/B^2$ and constancy of the magnetic moment, to obtain the first-order drift (11) as a consequence of energy conservation (the computation is intricate, but not difficult). There is one gap, viz., an undetermined drift of *first-order* parallel to $\underset{\sim}{U}$. It is possible that a systematic treatment of higher-order energy balances would eliminate this gap. However, to the order computed, we can only say that the first-order drifts are compatible with energy conservation and are almost a direct consequence of the lowest order theory along.

As another example, take the field surrounding a straight wire carrying a constant current. Since $B \sim 1/r$, there is a field gradient which produces the axial first-order guiding-center drift

$$v_d' = \delta\mu/r = \frac{1}{2}\,v_\perp^2\,(\delta/rB)\,. \tag{15}$$

But there is also a guiding-center acceleration of magnitude $|d\underset{\sim}{v}/dt| = V^2/r$ due to the circular motion which causes an additional axial drift of magnitude (cf. (11)),

$$v_d'' = V^2(\delta/rB)\,. \tag{16}$$

The two drifts are additive,

$$v_d = (V^2 + \frac{1}{2}\,v_\perp^2)(\delta/rB)\,. \tag{17}$$

Now let us apply a constant small axial electric field. This superposes a radial drift U, but it also modifies the parallel motion according to (6),

$$\frac{dV}{dt} = V(\underset{\sim}{U} \cdot \underset{\sim}{\kappa}) = V\;U/r\;; \tag{18}$$

his expresses the conservation of angular momentum for a particle nstrained to move on a circle of variable radius). The lowest-or- er guiding-center energy of the particle is $(1/2)V^2 + \mu B$ (neglect- g $(1/2)U^2$). Exactly as in the first example, the change in μB re- ılting from the radial U drift is equal to the change in electric po- ential produced by the axial "gradient" drift v_d'. Similarly, the nange in $(1/2)V^2$ computed from (18) is equal to the change in elec- ic potential produced by the axial drift v_d''.

The principal conclusion to be drawn from these examples is at the lowest-order guiding-center motion is completely self-con- ined, even though the mechanism by which this is accomplished nay be unfamiliar and is hidden in first-order terms which are ex- ressly excluded. There is also a caution that one should not mis- pply to an approximate theory familiar conceptions which are ap- ropriate only to the exact equations of motion.

V. THE GUIDING-CENTER FLUID[7-9]

We consider a plasma in which we believe that most of the par- cles follow orbits which can be described by the guiding-center the- ry. We shall give a very simple heuristic derivation of a macro- copic fluid theory using only the most elementary properties of the notion of the individual particles.

We have seen that every particle, independent of its mass, harge or energy, has the same perpendicular velocity component $\mathbf{U}$. hus the fluid velocity, $\mathbf{u}$, no matter how it may be defined, can only iffer from $\mathbf{U}$ by a component parallel to $\mathbf{B}$, and the fluid is there- ore perfectly conducting,

$$\mathbf{E} + \mathbf{u} \times \mathbf{B} = 0, \tag{19}$$

nd flux preserving,

$$\frac{\partial \mathbf{B}}{\partial t} + \operatorname{curl}(\mathbf{B} \times \mathbf{u}) = 0. \tag{20}$$

We now write the macroscopic laws of conservation of mass, nomentum (with the usual magnetic Lorentz term as befits a good onductor), and internal energy (heuristically ignoring the heat flow):

$$\left.\begin{aligned} &\frac{d\rho}{dt} + \rho \operatorname{div} \mathbf{u} = 0 \\ &\rho \frac{d\mathbf{u}}{dt} + \operatorname{div} \mathbb{P} = \mathbf{J} \times \mathbf{B} \\ &\rho \frac{d\epsilon}{dt} + P_{ij} \frac{\partial u_i}{\partial x_j} = 0, \end{aligned}\right\} \tag{21}$$

$$\frac{d}{dt} = \frac{\partial}{\partial t} + \underset{\sim}{u} \cdot \nabla \quad . \tag{22}$$

Here $\mathbb{P}$ or P_{ij} is the full stress tensor, and ϵ is the internal energy.

Now, the rapid spiraling about a guiding center implies isotro of the stress tensor in the plane perpendicular to $\underset{\sim}{B}$. In a coordinate system with axes parallel and perpendicular to $\underset{\sim}{B}$,

$$\mathbb{P} = \begin{bmatrix} p_1 & 0 & 0 \\ 0 & p_2 & 0 \\ 0 & 0 & p_2 \end{bmatrix} \quad . \tag{23}$$

Expressed invariantly,

$$P_{ij} = p_2(\delta_{ij} - \beta_i\beta_j) + p_1\beta_i\beta_j \; . \tag{24}$$

We may define temperatures by

$$p_1 = \rho RT_1 \; , \qquad p_2 = \rho RT_2 \; . \tag{25}$$

The internal energy per unit mass ϵ (which would be $(3/2)RT$ in a conventional gas) is obviously given by

$$\epsilon = \frac{1}{2} RT_1 + RT_2' = p_1/2\rho + p_2/\rho \tag{26}$$

since there is one parallel degree-of-freedom and two perpendicular.

Our macroscopic system is now (21) with $\mathbb{P}$ and ϵ replaced in terms of p_1, p_2, and $\underset{\sim}{\beta}$. Setting $\underset{\sim}{J} = (1/\mu_0)\,\mathrm{curl}\,\underset{\sim}{B}$, we have a system of equations in the variables, ρ, p_1, p_2, $\underset{\sim}{u}$, $\underset{\sim}{B}$ which seem to be very similar in appearance to those of conventional magnetoflui dynamics, except for the occurrence of two pressures. To complete the system, one more equation is needed. We use the microscopic fact that the magnetic moment of an individual particle is constant. Macroscopically, we state that the rate of change of total magnetic moment in a fluid element is given by the net rate of flow of magnetic moments carried through the surface. The mean magnetic moment (per mass) is

$$\langle \mu \rangle = RT_2/B = p_2/\rho B \; . \tag{27}$$

Thus we have

$$\frac{d}{dt}(p_2/\rho B) = 0 \; , \tag{28}$$

n neglecting the "heat" flow of magnetic moment relative to the mean ow, $\underset{\sim}{u}$.

By counting, the system of equations is now complete. An easy ıanipulation shows (just as in ordinary gas dynamics) that the energy quation can be replaced by an entropy equation, viz.,

$$\frac{d}{dt}\left(p_1 p_2{}^2/\rho^5\right) = 0 . \tag{29}$$

his is to be compared with p^3/ρ^5 which is ordinarily constant on a article path. Our system of equations, finally, consists of the mass, ıomentum, and flux equations, together with two-particle-path inariants which can be chosen for convenience as any two of the folowing

$$p_2/\rho B, \quad p_1 B^2/\rho^3, \quad p_1 p_2{}^2/\rho^5, \quad p_2{}^3/p_1 B^5 . \tag{30}$$

One can discuss the validity of this system of equations in two istinct contexts: one is by comparison with a presumably better thery; the other is an intrinsic question of the mathematical suitability the system, per se. The second is more urgent, since it is perctly possible to arrive at a mathematically incompatible or otherise unsuitable system by plausible physical reasoning. The equations emselves cannot justify their own validity, but they can specify sitations in which they are definitely invalid. Specifically, unless certain inualities are satisfied, the initial value problem is not well posed. he forbidden regions (non-overlapping) are given by*

$$p_2 + B^2/\mu_o < p_1 \tag{31a}$$

$$3p_1 B^2/\mu_o < p_2(p_2 - 6p_1) . \tag{31b}$$

oughly speaking, one cannot have p_1 too large (31a) or p_2 too rge (31b). These relations were originally found by a linearized lane-wave analysis and interpreted as conditions for instability.[10] lthough this is not a logical deduction, it may be heuristically sound; iz., a complete breakdown of otherwise plausible equations may be dicative of violent behavior in fact. It is worth remarking that the equalities (31) describe a breakdown of the equations in complete enerality; the reversed inequalities must be satisfied at every point a general, nonsteady, nonlinear flow.

*This is obtained by computing the characteristics of the system of differential uations.

Provided that the inequalities (31) are violated, this system of equations is similar in mathematical structure to the conventional perfectly conducting isotropic fluid system. It should be observed that the constraint $p_1 = p_2$ does not reduce the guiding-center system to the conventional one. Although the momentum and energy equations are the same, there is an extra particle path invariant, viz., ${p_2}^3/p_1B^5 \sim p^2/B^5$, and this will not be invariant, in general, for a solution of the conventional equations. In other words, a guiding-center problem which is provided with boundary conditions and initial conditions which are compatible with isotropy of the stress tensor will not in general have an isotropic solution.

There is a special type of flow which does reduce to conventional magneto-fluid flow precisely, viz., a transverse flow in which the magnetic field is unidirectional and the flow lies in the plane perpendicular to $\underset{\sim}{B}$. The pressure p_2 is isotropic in the relevant plane and p_1 does not enter. Furthermore, there is an exact mathematical analog in this geometry between ordinary compressible fluid flow (non-magnetic) and magneto-fluid flow;[11] this analog therefore extends to the guiding-center flow. Finally, since the mechanism which we expect to validate any macroscopic theory, (viz., the coherence of the molecules within a given fluid element) is satisfied in this geometry, we expect the macroscopic theory to approximate closely the exact microscopic theory, provided only that the conditions for the validity of the guiding-center approximation are satisfied. This will be verified in the next section.

The conditions for the validity of the guiding-center fluid equations in general three-dimensional problems are quite subtle. For example, one might think that in an *approximately* transverse flow with only slow variation along the magnetic field direction, the equations would be approximately valid.* This is not so; the reason is the non local behavior of the particle motion along the field lines. The velocity distribution at a certain point may be determined by the maximum value of B along the line (mirror ratio), even though this maximum may be attained at a great distance with correspondingly small field gradients. A simple example in which the macroscopic theory can be compared with the "exact" particle theory is in a nozzle with slowly varying area. One finds the speed at the throat to be $(3RT_1)^{1/2}$ for the fluid and $\left[(2/\pi)RT_0\right]^{1/2}$ for the particle model (T_0 is the entering temperature).

VI. THE GUIDING-CENTER GAS

We again consider a gas in which most of the particle orbits satisfy the conditions for the validity of the guiding-center theory. But instead of a macroscopic theory, we now wish to derive a microscopic theory in terms of an appropriate molecular distribution func-

*For example, see Reference 9

on. Our attitude will be that the lowest-order guiding-center approx-mation defines the exact motion of an artificial guiding-center par-icle. This gas can be described microscopically in terms of a guid-ng-center distribution function. It is this interpretation, (viz., that ne constructs an exact equation for a distribution function which rep-esents a gas of artificial particles,[7]) which offers the simplification f allowing the use of the lowest order guiding-center theory alone, s distinguished from roughly equivalent theories in which a similar xpansion in the parameter δ is introduced into the exact Liouville quation in which the orders of expansion in δ are inextricably nixed.[12-14]

The most direct interpretation is to consider a guiding-center article as a molecule located at its guiding center with the oscilla-on about the guiding center representing internal energy, magnetic noment, and angular momentum of the molecule. With this interpre-ation, we are dealing with a magnetic material, and also with a one-imensional gas which has thermal motion only along the field lines, nd a pressure tensor with only a single non-vanishing component, $_{ij} = p_1\beta_i\beta_j$. All macroscopic consequences will be equivalent to ose in the more conventional interpretation as a three-dimensional as, but a dictionary of equivalents is required (e.g., to translate ternal energy into p_2, etc.). Although we have a choice of inter-retations macroscopically, the only natural microscopic choice is the less familiar one-dimensional gas because of the very singular ature of the laws of motion of a guiding-center particle.

The conventional microscopic treatment of a fully ionized col-sionless plasma is to introduce a distribution function $f(\underset{\sim}{\xi}, \underset{\sim}{x}, t)$ ormalized as a number density) which satisfies the Liouville equa-on

$$\frac{\partial f}{\partial t} + \underset{\sim}{\xi} \cdot \frac{\partial f}{\partial \underset{\sim}{x}} + \frac{e}{m}(\underset{\sim}{E} + \underset{\sim}{\xi} \times \underset{\sim}{B}) \cdot \frac{\partial f}{\partial \underset{\sim}{\xi}} = 0 . \tag{32}$$

ere are two such equations for $f_\pm$ with parameters $m_\pm$ and $e_\pm$ gned). To complete the system, we take Maxwell's equations where source terms are given by

$$\left.\begin{aligned} \underset{\sim}{J} &= e_+ \int \underset{\sim}{\xi} f_+ d\underset{\sim}{\xi} + e_- \int \underset{\sim}{\xi} f_- d\underset{\sim}{\xi} \\ q &= e_+ \int f_+ d\underset{\sim}{\xi} + e_- \int f_- d\underset{\sim}{\xi} . \end{aligned}\right\} \tag{33}$$

e equations of conservation of mass, momentum, and energy (with l stress tensor and heat flow) are rigorous consequences of this stem.

To describe a guiding-center gas, we introduce a distribution function $\hat{f}(V, \mu, \underset{\sim}{x}, t)$ as a number density. We compute the Jacobi[an] of the transformation from $(\underset{\sim}{\xi})$ to (V, μ),

$$d\underset{\sim}{\xi} = d\xi_1 \, d\xi_2 \, d\xi_3 = dV \, dv_\perp^1 \, dv_\perp^2 = \pi \, dV \, d(v_\perp^2) = 2\pi \, B \, dV \, d\mu \tag{34}$$

and from the approximate identification $f d\underset{\sim}{\xi} \sim \hat{f} \, dV \, d\mu$, we conclude that

$$\hat{f} \sim 2\pi B f . \tag{35}$$

This lowest-order identification can be used to compute density, and also pressure (with care), but current not at all (as will be shown). We shall make no use of this connection and shall employ $\hat{f}$ only.

Taking the lowest-order guiding-center motion, we write the Liouville equation for $\hat{f}$,*

$$\frac{\partial \hat{f}}{\partial t} + \frac{\partial}{\partial \underset{\sim}{x}} \cdot \left[(\underset{\sim}{U} + \underset{\sim}{V})\hat{f}\right] + \frac{\partial}{\partial V}\left\{\left[\frac{1}{\delta}(\underset{\sim}{\beta} \cdot \underset{\sim}{E}) + \underset{\sim}{\beta} \cdot \nabla \left(\frac{1}{2} U^2 - \mu B\right) + V(\underset{\sim}{U} \cdot \underset{\sim}{\kappa})\right] \hat{f}\right\} = 0. \tag{36}$$

Note that in these variables $\hat{f}$ is not constant on a particle path. Th[e] independent variables should be kept in mind; e. g., $\underset{\sim}{U}$ is a function of $\underset{\sim}{x}$ and t, $\underset{\sim}{V} = V\underset{\sim}{\beta}$ is a function of V and of $\underset{\sim}{x}$ and t (through $\underset{\sim}{\beta}$), etc.

It is also possible to introduce intrinsic coordinates attached t[o] a moving magnetic line. We can write

$$\underset{\sim}{B} = \nabla\alpha \times \nabla\gamma \tag{37}$$

where α and γ are constant on a given moving magnetic line, and we also introduce a parameter σ along each line in such a way that σ is constant at a point moving with velocity $\underset{\sim}{U}$ (α, γ, and σ are fixed Lagrangian coordinates relative to the motion $\underset{\sim}{U}$). The Jacobia[n] of the transformation from $(\underset{\sim}{x})$ to (α, γ, σ) is obtained from $\underset{\sim}{B} \cdot d\underset{\sim}{S} = d\alpha \, d\gamma =$ flux, and Eq. (10):

*For a distribution function $f(x_1 \ldots x_n)$ in an arbitrary phase space in which th[e] equations of motion are $dx_r/dt = X_r$, the Liouville equation is

$$\frac{\partial f}{\partial t} + \sum \frac{\partial}{\partial x_r}(X_r f) = 0.$$

If div $\underset{\sim}{X} = 0$ (e. g., in a Hamiltonian system) then,

$$\frac{\partial f}{\partial t} + \sum X_r \frac{\partial f}{\partial x_r} = 0$$

which states that f is constant on a particle path.

$$d\underset{\sim}{x} = dx_1 dx_2 dx_3 = \frac{1}{B}\, d\alpha\, d\gamma\, ds = \frac{1}{B\zeta}\, d\alpha\, d\gamma\, d\sigma. \tag{38}$$

ntroducing the number density $\tilde{f}(p, \mu, \alpha, \gamma, \sigma, t)$, where p is the nomentum conjugate to σ, Eq. (10), we have the approximate identifi-ation

$$\tilde{f} \sim \hat{f}/B \sim 2\pi f \tag{39}$$

nd the Liouville equation (here $\tilde{f}$ is a constant on a particle path)

$$\frac{\partial\tilde{f}}{\partial t} + p\zeta^2 \frac{\partial\tilde{f}}{\partial\sigma} + \frac{\partial}{\partial\sigma}\left[\frac{1}{2}U^2 - \mu B - \phi^*/\delta - \frac{1}{2}p^2\zeta^2\right]\frac{\partial\tilde{f}}{\partial p} = 0. \tag{40}$$

 is tempting to replace σ by the arclength s and set $\zeta = 1$, $p = V$. his can be done at any given instant, but we must remember that $\partial\tilde{f}/\partial t$ is the rate of change of $\tilde{f}$ with σ fixed, which is not the same s with s fixed if, e.g., the magnetic line is stretching.

The most striking feature of all of these guiding-center Liouville quations is that they are incomplete. From the distribution function, ne can compute a parallel component of velocity $\langle V \rangle = \underset{\sim}{\beta} \cdot \underset{\sim}{u}$, and rom the Liouville equation an equation for the parallel component of nomentum, i.e., an equation, for $d\langle V \rangle/dt$. However, the tem-oral evolution of the perpendicular component, $\underset{\sim}{U}$, is not obtainable. he Liouville equation only describes the motion of particles which re constrained to lie on a magnetic line, assuming that the motion of he line is given. The system must be supplemented by an equation escribing $d\underset{\sim}{U}/dt$.

Let us tentatively introduce, as the equation determining the ransverse motion, the perpendicular component of the macroscopic nomentum equation in (21),

$$\rho\underset{\sim}{B} \times \frac{d\underset{\sim}{u}}{dt} + \underset{\sim}{B} \times \operatorname{div} \mathbb{P} = \frac{1}{\mu_o}\underset{\sim}{B} \times \operatorname{curl} \underset{\sim}{B} \times \underset{\sim}{B}. \tag{41}$$

t is easy to see that this does specify $d\underset{\sim}{U}/dt$. The omitted component, $\beta \cdot d\underset{\sim}{U}/dt$ is equal to $-\underset{\sim}{U} \cdot d\underset{\sim}{B}/dt$, and $d\underset{\sim}{B}/dt$ is already given by the lux equation. Also, the term $\underset{\sim}{B} \times d\langle \underset{\sim}{V} \rangle/dt$ which is contained in 41) is obtainable from (and is compatible with) the Liouville equation.

The conventional description of a plasma consists of equations escribing the particle motion (32), Maxwell's equations, and the con-ecting source relations (33). In our case, the source relations are ery singular. In passing from macroscopic mass flow, $\rho\underset{\sim}{u} = mn\underset{\sim}{u}$, o macroscopic current flow, $\underset{\sim}{J} = en\underset{\sim}{u}$, it is necessary to multiply by he large quantity $e/m = 1/\delta$, thereby changing the order of the erm. The parallel component of current, $\beta \cdot \underset{\sim}{J}$, which can be com-uted directly as a difference of moments of the two distribution functions, $\hat{f}_{\pm}$, would seem to be very large, of order $1/\delta$, thereby nullifyin the entire theory. To avoid this disaster, we must impose the constraint that $\langle V \rangle_+ = \langle V \rangle_-$ and hope that this can be done compatibly within the framework of our theory. Fortunately there is the small electric field component, $\beta \cdot E$, which should not appear in the theory but does. Tentatively, we can try to adjust the value of $\beta \cdot E$ so as to validate the constraint. Specifically, we take the two moment equations for $d \langle V \rangle_+ / dt$ and $d \langle V \rangle_- / dt$ and set them equal. We obtain the result (familiar as a form of Ohm's law)

$$(1/\delta_+ + 1/\delta_-)(\beta \cdot E) = \beta \cdot \text{div}\, \mathbb{P}_+ / \rho_+ - \beta \cdot \text{div}\, \mathbb{P}_- / \rho_- . \qquad (42)$$

In principle, this expression for $\beta \cdot E$ should be used in computing individual guiding-center orbits, (6), as well as in a plasma theory.

At this stage, the current component $\beta \cdot J$ has completely disappeared; it is zero to order $1/\delta$, and it is not computable to finite order within the theory. A glance shows that the perpendicular component of current has the same status. To order $1/\delta$, there is no current since the drift U is the same for ions and electrons. (The result given above, $\langle V \rangle_+ = \langle V \rangle_-$, also implies that $u_+ = u_-$, which is compatible with charge neutrality to lowest order.) While it is true that a zero-order drift current, J_d, can be computed from the first-order drifts (11), this is technically not contained within our theory. To be complete, we would also add the polarization current, $J_m = \text{curl}\, M$, which is produced by the mean magnetic moment per volume,

$$M = -\beta \left\langle \frac{1}{2} m n v_\perp^2 / B \right\rangle = -\beta\, p_2 / B = -B\, p_2 / B^2 . \qquad (43)$$

Fortunately, it is not at all necessary to compute currents from the particle motions; we can simply use the relation $J = (\text{curl}\, B)/\mu_0$ (which has already been introduced in (41)). In summary, a compatible determinate system describing the lowest-order guiding-center gas is given by a pair of Liouville equations (36) in which the value (42) for $\beta \cdot E$ is inserted, together with the constraint equation (41) for the perpendicular motion, and the flux equation (20). The higher-order drifts and electric fields which we ignore will presumably adjust themselves appropriately to yield the proper lowest-order constraints, (41) and (42); this will be examined in the next section.

A procedure which appears to be more accurate than the one just described is one in which we take a full Lorentz force term, $qE + J \times B$, and include the displacement current. The net effect is to include additional Maxwell stress and electromagnetic momentum terms in (41), E being replaced by $B \times u$. The additional terms have the order A^2/c^2 (A = Alfven speed, see (58)). Our tacit asumption has been that the plasma density is high enough so that this actor is small (this parameter is entirely distinct from the small arameter δ). Inclusion of these extra terms may possibly improve he results for very low-density plasmas, but the situation is not clear. Whereas the charge-neutral formulation is consistently Galilean-in-ariant, the alternative system has no invariance properties at all and hows rather awkward behavior in ordinary magneto fluid dynamics.[16] The only proper way to cover the entire range of densities is by a ompletely relativistic treatment, but this has not yet been done.

The guiding-center treatment of the plasma is seen to be essen-ially macroscopic with regard to the motion of the magnetic field ines, but it is microscopic with regard to the particle motion along he lines. This is consistent with our original heuristic argument re-uiring the preservation of the identity of a fluid element. The value hosen for $\underset{\sim}{\beta} \cdot \underset{\sim}{E}$, viz., (42), is such as to guarantee $\underset{\sim}{u}_+ = \underset{\sim}{u}_-$ pro-ided that this holds initially; in other words there is a single mac-oscopic fluid velocity. From the constraint equation (41) and the noment equation for $d \langle V \rangle / dt$, one obtains exactly the same mo-nentum equation as in the fluid theory (21). The mass equation is lso the same, but the energy equation differs in the presence of a eat flow component which is parallel to $\underset{\sim}{B}$. Apparently, the only ad-antage of the microscopic theory is that it more correctly takes into ccount heat flow and magnetic moment flow. The "only" is mislead-ng, however: the superiority of the classical Boltzmann equation ver fluid dynamics also lies "only" in the treatment of the stresses nd heat flow.

It is a simple matter to verify that the behavior is entirely mac-oscopic in a transverse flow, i.e., one in which the magnetic field s unidirectional, and the spatial variation and flow are perpendicular o the field. One only needs to observe that there is neither heat flow or magnetic moment flow in the transverse plane. In this geometry, ne can obtain higher-order guiding-center equations (as an expan-ion in δ)[17] just as one obtains the Navier-Stokes and other equa-ions as an expansion in mean free path in the Chapman-Enskog the-ry of an ordinary gas.

VII. RECONCILIATION

The lowest-order guiding-center theory in terms of the distri-ution function $\hat{f}$ is quite dissimilar to the exact theory in terms of , especially with regard to the coupling with Maxwell's equations. The simplicity of the preceding analysis lay in choosing constraint quations for $\beta \cdot \underset{\sim}{E}$ and $d\underset{\sim}{U}/dt$ instead of current source relations to omplete the system. It is not difficult to verify that if one computes rift currents using (11), adds the polarization current, and sums ver both fluids, one obtains exactly the constraint equation (41). But simpler procedure is to work with the *exact* momentum equations for the ions and electrons individually as obtained from the full (not guiding-center) Liouville equation (32), viz.,

$$\frac{d\bar{u}}{dt} + \frac{1}{\rho} \operatorname{div} \bar{\mathbb{P}} = \frac{1}{\delta} (E + \bar{u} \times B) . \tag{44}$$

We distinguish the exact velocity $\bar{u}$ from the zero-order guiding-center velocity u; indices ($\pm$) are omitted. Consistent with the guiding center ordering in δ, we obtain $E + u \times B = 0$ to lowest order, and obtain the next order on the right side of (44) by substituting the lowest-order expressions on the left. In terms of

$$J = \rho(\bar{u}-u)/\delta \tag{45}$$

(correct for the perpendicular component only), we get

$$B \times \left[\rho \frac{du}{dt} + \operatorname{div} \mathbb{P}\right] = B \times J \times B . \tag{46}$$

We have obtained approximately the same equation for ions and electrons individually as was previously postulated for the entire fluid (41); the crucial distinction is that J in (46) is J_+ or J_- and cannot be set equal to curl B/μ_0. But we can reverse the argument and solve (46) for J_+ and J_- in terms of zero-order guiding-center quantities. Subtracting curl M, we would find exactly the same expression for J_d as was obtained from the drift calculation. The constraint equation (41) is obtained from the sum of the two equations (46), replacing the total J by (curl $B)/\mu_0$.

In other words, computation of J from the first-order drifts (not in the theory) and curl M is exactly compatible with the constraint equation (41) which was postulated. If the individual currents J_d^+ and J_d^- are desired for any purpose, they can be obtained from the individual momentum equations which, otherwise, contribute nothing new.

Now we examine the *parallel* component of the exact momentum equation (44). Proceeding as before, we would find $B \cdot E = 0$ to lowest order and evaluate $B \cdot E$ to first order in terms of a zero-order left side of the equation. However, if we choose not to impose the constraint that $\beta \cdot u_+ = \beta \cdot u_-$ to lowest order (temporarily violating the expansion in δ) we find (approximating slightly)

$$\beta \cdot \frac{\partial J}{\partial t} + \frac{1}{\delta_-} \beta \cdot \operatorname{div} \mathbb{P}_- = \Omega^2 \kappa_o \beta \cdot E . \tag{47}$$

This should be compared with (42) and also with

$$-\kappa_0 \frac{\partial E}{\partial t} + \frac{1}{\mu_0} \operatorname{curl} B = J . \tag{48}$$

The two equations (47) and (48) describe plasma oscillations (presumably very fast) about an equilibrium given by (42) for $\underset{\sim}{\beta} \cdot \underset{\sim}{E}$ and curl $\underset{\sim}{B}/\mu_0$ for $\underset{\sim}{J}$. A large-amplitude plasma oscillation would interfere with our basic requirements for guiding-center motion. But, for slowly varying "source" terms div $\mathbb{P}$ and curl $\underset{\sim}{B}$, the generated plasma oscillations will be small in amplitude, and the quasi-equilibrium for both $\underset{\sim}{\beta} \cdot \underset{\sim}{E}$ and $\underset{\sim}{\beta} \cdot \underset{\sim}{J}$ will be set up after a short transient comparable to a plasma period.[18]

The situation is more complicated if one includes displacement current and considers problems in which the plasma frequency is not high compared to the Larmor frequency. In such a case one must impose as an additional requirement for the validity of the guiding-center theory that all natural motions be slow compared to the plasma frequency as well as the Larmor frequency. Otherwise, variations in the "source" terms div $\mathbb{P}$ and curl $\underset{\sim}{B}$, will produce inappropriately large values of $\underset{\sim}{\beta} \cdot \underset{\sim}{J}$ and $\underset{\sim}{\beta} \cdot \underset{\sim}{E}$. Thus plasma oscillations must be expressly excluded from any guiding-center theory.*

VIII. EXAMPLES

In this section we give a number of representative examples to show the complex interplay between microscopic and macroscopic interpretations and, specifically, the confusion that can arise in the ordering with respect to δ.

To start, we generalize the first example of Section IV and consider a unidirectional z-field, $\underset{\sim}{B}$, which is a function of both x and y. The drift velocity (12) produces a macroscopic current

$$\underset{\sim}{J}_d = \frac{p_2}{B^2} \underset{\sim}{\beta} \times \nabla B \quad . \tag{49}$$

To this we must add a current $\underset{\sim}{J}_m$ = curl $\underset{\sim}{M}$ from (43), viz.,

$$\underset{\sim}{J}_m = \underset{\sim}{\beta} \times \nabla (p_2/B) \quad . \tag{50}$$

There is a "drift" component in the direction of the contour of constant B and a "polarization" component along the contour of constant p_2/B. The total current, $\underset{\sim}{J} = \underset{\sim}{J}_m + \underset{\sim}{J}_d$, is easily seen to be in the direction of the contour p_2 = constant; quantitatively,

$$\underset{\sim}{J} = \frac{1}{B} \underset{\sim}{\beta} \times \nabla p_2 \tag{51}$$

*The parallel component of $\underset{\sim}{E}$ is frequently mishandled; both by omission, (e.g., see Refs. 7 and 13) and by excess (including plasma oscillations e.g., see Ref. 14).

or

$$\underset{\sim}{J} \times \underset{\sim}{B} = \nabla p_2 \ . \tag{52}$$

The macroscopic pressure balance is verified precisely. The striking feature is that this macroscopic relation, which is contained in the guiding-center fluid theory, is obtained microscopically by combining two current components, neither of which has any recognizable connection with the guiding-center fluid derivation in Section V.

Returning to the specialization of this problem with x-dependence only but with a uniform electric field in the y-direction (cf. Section IV), we easily compute the energy interchange between particles and field as

$$\left.\begin{aligned} \underset{\sim}{E} \cdot \underset{\sim}{J}_m &= B\, \underset{\sim}{U} \cdot \nabla (p_2/B) \\ \underset{\sim}{E} \cdot \underset{\sim}{J}_d &= p_2\, \underset{\sim}{U} \cdot \nabla (\log B) \\ \underset{\sim}{E} \cdot \underset{\sim}{J} &= \underset{\sim}{U} \cdot \nabla p_2 \ . \end{aligned}\right\} \tag{53}$$

This is quite uninformative, except possibly for the last line which agrees with the corresponding guiding-center fluid result.

For the next example, we take the field derived from a straight line current as in Section IV, but we superpose a uniform Maxwellian plasma filling all space. There is no current flow in the plasma, and the exact orbits must be compatible with the given vacuum magnetic field. But the guiding-center orbits are quite complex. Corresponding to the first-order axial drift (17), there is the finite axial current

$$J_d = ne\langle v_d\rangle = \langle V^2 + \frac{1}{2} v_\perp^2\rangle(\rho/rB) \ . \tag{54}$$

But there is also a polarization current

$$\underset{\sim}{J}_m = \text{curl}\, \underset{\sim}{M} = p_2\, \underset{\sim}{B} \times \nabla(1/B^2) \ . \tag{55}$$

The sum, $\underset{\sim}{J}_d + \underset{\sim}{J}_m$, must, of course, cancel. But we are presented with a problem in which a macroscopically trivial result is masked by rather complex microscopic considerations.

For the next example, we take a uniform magnetic field in the z-direction together with a uniform but time-varying electric field in the y-direction. The lowest-order guiding-center motion is simply a motion in the x-direction, $\underset{\sim}{U}(t) = \underset{\sim}{E}(t) \times \underset{\sim}{B}/B^2$. To next order we have a y-component; from Eq. (11),

$$\underset{\sim}{U}_1 = \frac{1}{B^2}\left[\underset{\sim}{E} \times \underset{\sim}{B} + \delta\, \frac{d\underset{\sim}{E}}{dt}\right] \ . \tag{56}$$

If $\underset{\sim}{E}(t)$ is oscillatory, the path of a guiding center is an ellipse with small eccentricity (viz., the ratio of the frequency of oscillation of $\underset{\sim}{E}$

compared to the Larmor frequency); see Fig. 1(a). If E changes by the definite amount ΔE, the guiding-center changes its speed in the

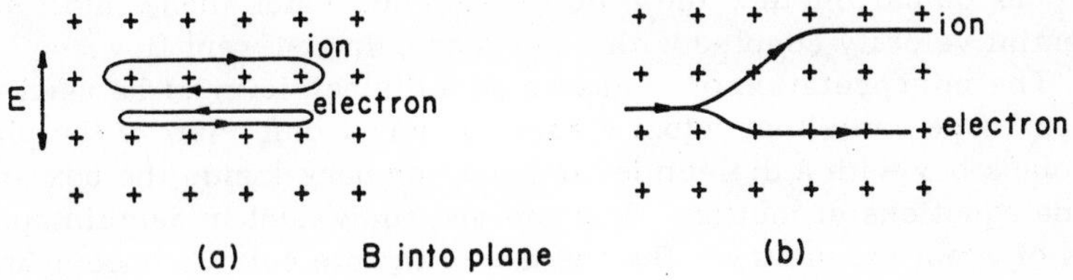

Fig. 1 Ion and electron orbits

x-direction and is displaced in the y-direction by an amount $\delta(\Delta E)/B^2$ (Fig. 1(b)) Assuming a neutral plasma, the current flow from (56) is

$$\underset{\sim}{J} = \frac{\rho}{B^2}\frac{d\underset{\sim}{E}}{dt} . \tag{57}$$

If we wish, we can interpret this as a polarization current. In the absence of $\underset{\sim}{E}$, a given ion and electron attached to the same magnetic line can be considered to form a molecule; with a specified value of $\underset{\sim}{E}$, they are displaced by a definite amount. From

$$\underset{\sim}{J}_p = d\underset{\sim}{D}/dt - \kappa_o\, d\underset{\sim}{E}/dt \qquad \text{and} \qquad \underset{\sim}{D} = K\kappa_o \underset{\sim}{E} ,$$

we compute an equivalent dielectric constant

$$\left.\begin{aligned} K &= 1 + \rho/\kappa_o B^2 = 1 + c^2/A^2 \\ A^2 &= B^2/\mu_o \rho \ ; \end{aligned}\right\} \tag{58}$$

where A is the Alfven speed.

Now we turn to a macroscopic guiding-center fluid description of the problem. To be precise, let us consider a perfectly conducting homogeneous fluid placed between two parallel (or concentric cylinder) condenser plates. Any transverse electric field $\underset{\sim}{E}(t)$ in the fluid must be accompanied by a macroscopic fluid velocity $\underset{\sim}{u} = (\underset{\sim}{E} \times \underset{\sim}{B})/B^2$. By symmetry, there are no pressure gradients; thus, the fluid acceleration is balanced by the Lorentz force,

$$\rho \frac{d\underset{\sim}{u}}{dt} = \underset{\sim}{J} \times \underset{\sim}{B} . \tag{59}$$

From

$$\frac{d\underset{\sim}{u}}{dt} = \left(\frac{d\underset{\sim}{E}}{dt} \times \underset{\sim}{B}\right)/B^2 , \tag{60}$$

we obtain exactly the same result as before, Eq. (57).

Both analyses are so simple that there is nothing to be gained from one over the other. But it is worth remarking that, while the particle picture describes a drift velocity to two different orders in an expansion parameter, the fluid version separates these into a single tangential velocity coupled with a perpendicular current flow.

The interpretation of a plasma as a dielectric must be used with caution. One can either adopt a super-macroscopic view of the plasma as a black box with a dielectric constant, or peek inside the box and use the equations of motion. The two are equivalent in certain special cases of great symmetry. But the use of the dielectric concept in non-steady and inhomogeneous situations as a replacement for one drift term among many* is decidedly improper for even a heuristic argument. For example, from the value of the dielectric constant, one might deduce that the signal speed has the value A (for $c^2 \gg A^2$). However, the correct transverse signal speed is $(A^2 + 2RT_2)^{1/2}$. In other words, a dielectric constant which is evaluated in a simple situation in which there are no pressure gradients cannot be correctly used under more general circumstances.

Next, we return to the magnetic field surrounding a line current but this time we study a more realistic problem in which the plasma is of finite extent and is contained within a certain toroidal flux tube. We now present the classical orbit argument which is given to show that such a configuration (viz., a toroidal Stellerator) cannot be used for containment. To simplify matters, we assume that the plasma is tenuous and hardly perturbs the vacuum magnetic field. The field gradient and curvature set up an axial drift, v_d, as before. But the plasma is of finite extent, so a separation of charge and subsequent axial electric field is produced, after which the plasma as a whole moves outward radially with some velocity $\underset{\sim}{U} = \underset{\sim}{E} \times \underset{\sim}{B}/B^2$. Since only guiding-center motion has been referred to, and no mention has been made of heat flow along the magnetic lines, there must be an equivalent macroscopic argument, even though this is not a geometry in which the macroscopic and microscopic theories are identical. Indeed, there is an elementary argument. following from either the isotropic magneto fluid or guiding-center fluid equations, which shows that there exists no equilibrium configuration with the given symmetry unless p (or $p_1 + p_2$) is constant on a cylinder of given radius. In particular, there is no equilibrium which is finite in extent. If one postulates the existence of a macroscopic plasma of finite extent as an initial condition, an outward acceleration can be easily computed by balancing the excess of the external over the internal magnetic pressure against the total mass of the plasma.

The transient problem, looked at microscopically, is more subtle. One must first postulate an undetermined value for the radial acceleration. This acceleration modifies the drifts according to (11).

*For example, see Reference 6.

One either computes that value of the acceleration which produces zero mean drift (quasi-neutral approximation) or computes the revised drift current and from it a value for $d\underset{\sim}{E}/dt$, thus $d\underset{\sim}{U}/dt$, which latter should be set equal to the assumed acceleration.

There is one point at which the microscopic and macroscopic analyses may differ. The electric field produced by the charge separation is essentially a displacement current effect. The macroscopic procedure mimics the quasi-neutral microscopic analysis. There is a reversal of "cause" and "effect". In the first argument, an electric field is created which is then said to induce a motion of the plasma. In the second argument, an unbalanced force results in motion of the plasma with a concomitant electric field (and charge separation which can be computed afterwards). The second argument ignores a rapid transient on the order of the plasma frequency. This is rarely of quantitative importance. Its significance lies only in masking the essential equivalence of a macroscopic investigation of the existence of an equilibrium with a qualitative microscopic description of a transient phenomenon. In all but the simplest geometries, the microscopic argument becomes hopelessly involved, but the investigation of the equilibria is feasible.

Such dual arguments are common, e. g., in some stability analyses which are deeply involved with the behavior of electric fields but which are substantially equivalent to macroscopic arguments in which the electric field does not even make an appearance.

IX. CRITIQUE OF THE GUIDING-CENTER THEORY IN STATIC EQUILIBRIUM

The requirements of a theory of equilibrium or steady flow are frequently more stringent than those of a general dynamic theory since the solutions are expected to be valid over a relatively long time. For example, a dynamic theory of the pinch might have to be accurate for a few microseconds, but for containment of a plasma, one would hope to find an equilibrium theory that is valid for seconds.

If one wishes to be very cautious in assessing the reliability of a guiding-center theory result, then, from the fact that the solution may be in error by $O(\delta)$, one can only conclude a containment time which is $O(1/\delta)$ before the solution breaks down. One might be very optimistic, on the other hand, and hope that there exists a neighboring exact solution which the zero-order guiding-center solution approximates. The existence of such an exact self-consistent solution implies infinitely long containment for the particles following their exact orbits (ignoring collisions, of course). Such exact solutions have only been obtained in very special cases, and, from ergodic considerations, one should be doubtful of their existence in any generality. An intermediate possibility is the existence of equilibria to some higher order than $O(\delta)$ in the guiding-center theory. This is greatly to be desired, since a containment time of order $0(1/\delta)$ is much too short to be practicall useful. This is not to say that we cannot hope for much better contain ment of plasmas; we only point out that present theory is unable to predict more.

Some further progress can be made by splitting the problem into two parts: first, the analysis of orbits in a given field; and second, the requirement that the field be self-consistent with the orbits. The first problem is much simpler and can shed some light on the second. For example, the existence of an exact equilibrium requires, as a pre requisite, the existence of fields which can contain orbits indefinitely.

From the lowest-order theory, which ignores drifts $0(\delta)$, one cannot preclude the possibility of particles moving to the wall in a time $0(1/\delta)$. If the drifts are tangential to some surface which avoids the walls, we can do better. For example, in an axially-symmetric field, the first-order drifts are azimuthal and cannot lead out of the system. As a matter of fact, the orbits are absolutely contained in the radial direction and can only emerge axially. Since the adiabatic invariant (magnetic moment to lowest order) is constant to an arbitrarily high order in δ (provided that the field is sufficiently smooth),[4,19] the individual particle containment is valid to arbitrarily high order in $1/\delta$.

Moreover, even in a somewhat asymmetric mirror field, it can be shown that guiding centers are constrained to lie on certain surfaces (approximately flux tubes) to arbitrarily high order in δ. This follows from the existence of a so-called second adiabatic invariant.* Thus, although self-consistent equilibria have been only shown to exist to lowest order,** the orbit theory at least does not rule out the possibility of much better results.

One might ask: if it has been proved that particles are contained for a long time in quite general fields, why worry about self-consistency? The answer is that the proof of containment depends on time-independence or, at most, slow time variation of the field. Lack of self-consistency could vitiate this assumption.

For a toroidal configuration (e. g., a Stellerator) similar results can be proved, viz., the existence of guiding-center surfaces to arbitrarily high order.† We are content here to quote the weaker result that, although the drifts are not tangential to a flux tube, the *average value* of the normal drift component on a pressure surface is zero (see Appendix). This is sufficient to guarantee a particle containment which is large compared to $1/\delta$.

The error made in self-consistency, viz., $0(\delta)$, can be improved if we restrict ourselves to low-pressure plasmas. A vacuum field is,

*The idea of such an invariant is attributed to M. Rosenbluth; its existence was proved by C. S. Gardner,[19] and by T. G. Northrup and E. Teller.[20]

**For example, see Reference 21.

† Unpublished

of course, exactly self-consistent. In a low-pressure plasma in which $J = 0(\delta)$, the error in self-consistency of the lowest-order solution becomes $0(\delta^2)$. If one wished to make use of more accurate orbit results, say $0(\delta^r)$, in a consistent way, one might sacrifice the plasma pressure to be $0(\delta^{r-1})$. In other words, the plasma pressure is inversely proportional to the required containment time, using the best available theory. This is not to say that low pressure plasmas are better contained; they are more amenable to mathematical analysis.

The self-consistency problem becomes very difficult when carried to higher order. One reason is that the surfaces on which the particles are constrained no longer fill the space simply; there is a different, mutually intersecting family of surfaces for each value of the energy and magnetic moment.

Our general philosophy is not to cast doubt on the possibility of containing plasmas, but to delimit the predictions which can be made with current theory. These limitations are independent of any stability considerations. A self-consistent equilibrium may be valid to very high order and be unstable; or it may not exist to second order even though the first-order solution is found to be stable.

REFERENCES

1. H. Grad, "Theory of Rarefied Gases," Sect. 23 presented at First International Conf. on Rarefied Gases, 1958; published in *Rarefied Gas Dynamics*, (New York: Pergamon Press, 1960).

2. I. B. Bernstein, "Linear Wave Propagation in Plasmas," *Proc. Symp. on Electromagnetics and Fluid Dynamics of Gaseous Plasma* (New York: Polytechnic Press, 1961).

3. G. Hellwig, *Z. Naturforschung*, Vol. 1, p. 508 (1955).

4. M. D. Kruskal, "The Gyration of a Charged Particle," Project Matterhorn Report PM-S-33, NYO-7903, March 1958.

5. J. Berkowitz and C. S. Gardner, *Comm. Pure and Appl. Math.*, Vol. 12, p. 501 (1959).

6. M. N. Rosenbluth and C. L. Longmire, *Ann. Physics*, Vol. 1, p. 120 (1957).

7. H. Grad, "A Guiding Center Fluid," AEC Report TID-7503, February 1956, p. 495.

8. M. Goldberger, "One Fluid Hydrodynamics and the Boltzmann Equation," AEC Report TID-7503, February 1956, p. 260.

9. G. Chew, M. Goldberger and F. Low, *Proc. Royal Soc.* (London), Vol. A236, p. 112 (1956)

10. R. Lust, "On the Stability of a Homogeneous Plasma with Non-isotropic Pressure," AEC Report TID-7582, November 1959.

11. H. Grad, *Revs. Modern Phys.*, Vol. 32, p. 830 (1960).

12. K. M. Watson, *Phys. Rev.*, Vol. 102, p. 12 (1956).

13. K. A. Brueckner and K. M. Watson, *Phys. Rev.*, Vol. 102, p. 19 (1956).

14. S. Chandrasekhar, A. N. Kaufman and K. M. Watson, *Ann. Phys.*, Vol. 2, p. 435, (1957).

15. M. N. Rosenbluth and N. Rostoker, *Phys. Fluids*, Vol. 2, p. 23 (1959).

16. A. A. Blank and H. Grad, "Fluid Magnetic Equations," NYU Inst. of Math. Sciences Report NYO-6486-VI, July 1958.

17. Marion H. Rose, "On Plasma Magnetic Shocks," NYU Inst. of Math. Sciences Report NYO-2883, March 1960.

18. H. Grad, "Ohm's Law," NYU Inst. of Math. Sciences Report NYO-6486-IV, August 1956.

19. C. S. Gardner, *Phys. Rev.*, Vol. 115, p. 791 (1959).

20. T. G. Northrup and E. Teller, *Phys. Rev.*, Vol. 117, p. 215 (1960).

21. A. Oppenheim, "Equilibrium Configuration of a Plasma in a Guiding Center Limit," NYU Inst. of Math. Sciences Report NYO-9353, September 1960.

22. H. Grad and H. Rubin, *Proc. 2nd International Conf. on the Peaceful Uses of Atomic Energy*, Geneva 1958, Vol. 31, p. 190.

23. M. D. Kruskal and R. M. Kulsrud, *Proc. 2nd Int. Conf. on the Peaceful Uses of Atomic Energy*, Geneva 1958, Vol. 31, p. 213.

24. R. M. Kulsrud, *Phys. Fluids*, Vol. 4, p. 302 (1961).

25. H. Grad, *Comm. Pure & Appl. Math.*, Vol. 2, p. 331 (1949).

26. R. Liboff, "Long Wavelength Disturbances in a Plasma," NYU, Inst. of Math. Sci. Report NYO-9762, October 1961.

APPENDIX

AVERAGE DRIFTS ON A TOROIDAL SURFACE

We suppose that there is given a toroidal solution of $\nabla p = \text{curl}\, \underset{\sim}{B} \times \underset{\sim}{B}/\mu_0$;* i. e., a solution with nested toroidal pressure surfaces which are also flux tubes (Refs. 22, 23). The drift velocity in the absence of an electric field is

$$\underset{\sim}{v}_d = \frac{\delta}{B^2} \underset{\sim}{B} \times \left[(\underset{\sim}{V} \cdot \nabla) \underset{\sim}{V} + \mu \nabla B \right] \quad . \tag{A-1}$$

Using the identity

$$\nabla p \cdot \underset{\sim}{B} \times (\underset{\sim}{B} \cdot \nabla) \underset{\sim}{B} = \nabla p \cdot \underset{\sim}{B} \times \nabla (\tfrac{1}{2} B^2) \;, \tag{A-2}$$

we can write the rate of change of p following the particle as

$$\frac{dp}{dt} = \underset{\sim}{v}_d \cdot \nabla p = \frac{\delta}{B^3} (V^2 + \tfrac{1}{2} v_\perp^2)(\nabla p \cdot \underset{\sim}{B} \times \nabla B)$$

$$= \frac{\delta}{B^3} (W^2 - \mu B)(\nabla p \times \underset{\sim}{B} \cdot \nabla B) \tag{A-3}$$

where

$$W^2 = V^2 + v_\perp^2 \tag{A-4}$$

is a constant of the motion, as is μ. It is convenient to introduce new variables (p, ω, ϕ) for (x) where

$$\underset{\sim}{B} = \nabla p \times \nabla \omega = \nabla \phi - \underset{\sim}{n}(\underset{\sim}{n} \cdot \nabla \phi) \;; ^{**} \tag{A-5}$$

and $\underset{\sim}{n}$ is the unit normal, $\nabla p / |\nabla p|$, and the element of flux is given by $\underset{\sim}{B} \cdot d\underset{\sim}{S} = dp\, d\omega$. Part of the transformation of base vectors is

$$B^2 \frac{\partial \underset{\sim}{x}}{\partial \omega} = \nabla \phi \times \nabla p = \underset{\sim}{B} \times \nabla p \tag{A-6}$$

from which we obtain

$$\frac{dp}{dt} = -\delta (W^2 - \mu B) \frac{\partial}{\partial \omega} \log B \;. \tag{A-7}$$

The mean change in p after a long interval of time

$$\left[p(t) - p(0) \right] / t = \langle dp/dt \rangle = \frac{1}{t} \int_0^t \left(\frac{dp}{dt}\right) dt \tag{A-8}$$

can be replaced by an ergodic average with respect to the invariant measure which, in three dimensions, is

$$dm = (\underset{\sim}{B} \cdot d\underset{\sim}{S})\, dt \tag{A-9}$$

where dt is the time interval along an orbit. From $dt = ds/V = d\underset{\sim}{\phi}/BV$, we conclude that

$$\langle dp/dt \rangle = \int \frac{\partial Q}{\partial \omega}\, dp\, d\omega\, d\phi \tag{A-10}$$

where

$$Q(B) = -\delta \int_{B_0}^{B} \frac{W^2 - \mu B}{(W^2 - 2\mu B)^{1/2}} \frac{dB}{B^2} \;. \tag{A-11}$$

The integration in (A.10) extends over the volume between two p-surfaces. For the

*It is easily shown that an appropriate guiding-center distribution function can be found which corresponds to any given macroscopic, scalar-pressure, toroidal equilibrium.

**See Reference 22.

correct ergodic average on a p-surface, we need only integrate with respect to ω and ϕ. From the form of the integrand (despite the fact that ω and ϕ are not single-valued on a torus) we easily conclude that $\langle dp/dt \rangle = 0$.

The above argument indicates that the eventual rate at which a particle moves away from a pressure surface is small compared to δ. One would expect to obtain a stronger and more precise result, viz., that the drift is $0(\delta^2)$, by use of an appropriate adiabatic invariant. This analysis can be done but is much more subtle and requires more refined estimates about higher-order guiding-center motion; (e. g., in the non-toroidal case, see Refs. 21 & 22). A toroidal adiabatic invariant has been introduced by Kulsrud,[24] but it is inadequate for such a purpose since it is shown to be invariant for only the lowest-order guiding-center motion. As a result of this restriction it is easily shown that this invariant supplies no information at all about containment in a strictly time-independent field and, in a time-dependent problem, only if the time variation, while slow, is fast compared to the spatial variation (say $0(\delta^{1/2})$). Such results can be shown to follow from the existence of an exact constant of the lowest-order motion which is closely related to Kulsrud's adiabatic invariant and is obtained as follows.

A concentric nest of toroidal flux surfaces is postulated. According to the lowest-order (flux-preserving) motion, this topological property is preserved with time even if the motion is not slow. Further, it is easily seen that the property of a particular surface being covered ergodically by its magnetic lines is an invariant property of the surface.

From the conventional analysis, one is led to consider an integral of the form (cf. (10))

$$\int V\, ds = \int p\, d\sigma$$

(hereafter, p will denote momentum, not pressure), where the integral is taken along a magnetic line, but the limits are rather imprecise on a torus. We can write

$$\int p\, d\sigma = \int p\, (d\sigma/dt)\, dt = \int \zeta^2 p^2\, dt$$

and, tentatively, replace the time integral by a volume integral with respect to the invariant measure. We write

$$\underset{\sim}{B} = \nabla \alpha \times \nabla \gamma$$

where α is constant on a flux tube (the pressure is not constant on a flux tube in a general equilibrium), and observe that

$$dm = d\alpha\, d\gamma\, d\sigma / \zeta^2 p\ ,$$

which leads us to the definition

$$I = \int p\, d\alpha\, d\gamma\, d\sigma = \int V B\, d\underset{\sim}{x}\ .$$

The variables γ and σ are integrated over the complete surface of a torus, and α is integrated between two fixed but arbitrary values. Or, the α integration can be omitted. For an arbitrary time variation of the electromagnetic field, taking the initial momentum p as an arbitrarily given function of (α, γ, σ), we follow each of these initial values in time as a solution of the guiding-center equations. Thus I becomes a function of time. Since (α, γ, σ) are Lagrangian (fixed) coordinates with respect to the motion, we may differentiate under the integral sign, obtaining

$$\frac{dI}{dt} = \int \frac{dp}{dt}\, d\alpha\, d\gamma\, d\sigma$$

$$= -\int \frac{\partial H}{\partial \sigma}\, d\alpha\, d\gamma\, d\sigma$$

which clearly vanishes. Thus I is an exact constant of the lowest-order motion.

CONCERNING A CONTINUUM THEORY OF THE ELECTRODYNAMICS AND DYNAMICS OF MOVING MEDIA

Sydney Goldstein
Division of Engineering and Applied Physics, Harvard University

A re-discussion of Minkowski's theory of the electrodynamics of moving media. Remarks on the Maxwell and mechanical stress tensors, electromagnetic momentum and angular momentum. Magnetohydrodynamic consequences; simple examples; the Eichenwald and Wilson experiments.

I. INTRODUCTION

The subject matter of this paper is a continuum theory in the strictest sense. Developments of Minkowski's theory of the electrodynamics of moving media,* are considered. In particular, for a medium in motion whose refractive index is not unity, the constitutive relations between the electric field strength $\underset{\sim}{E}$ and displacement or excitation $\underset{\sim}{D}$, and the magnetic field strength $\underset{\sim}{H}$ and induction $\underset{\sim}{B}$ (or excitation $\underset{\sim}{H}$ and field strength $\underset{\sim}{B}$ as Sommerfeld, more correctly, prefers to call them) involve terms (of order v/c, not v^2/c^2, where v is the velocity of the medium and c the velocity of light) not usually taken into account in magnetohydrodynamics.

The first question considered is that of the influence of these terms on the usually accepted equations of momentum and energy. (The influence on the momentum equation involves the question of an electromagnetic effect on the mechanical stress tensor.) An attempt is made to answer, correctly to order v/c, the questions that arise, and to do so as simply as possible. The extra terms found are usually quite negligible; it appears that they could become detectable only for a medium with a refractive index sensibly different from unity and subject to large crossed electric and magnetic fields. (Since quantities of order v^2/c^2 are not retained, v is, of course, assumed much less than c; relativistic mechanics and thermodynamics are not introduced.)

The same questions have been considered with the full formalism of the theory of relativity by Pham Mau Quan,[2] but it appears that the underlying physical assumptions are different from those made here, so the answers are not the same. It should also be mentioned

*Reference 1, Part IV

Presented at the Symposium on Electromagnetics and Fluid Dynamics of Gaseous Plasma, Polytechnic Institute of Brooklyn, April 4, 5, 6, 1961

that a theory different from Minkowski's has been offered by L. J. Chu[3]. No crucial experiment which could be performed and which would distinguish between the theories appears yet to have been devised.

Two examples on Minkowski's theory are considered, whose solutions depend on the electromagnetic equations, but not on the equations of momentum and energy. The solutions do not depend, therefore, on the physical guesses introduced in the first part, but only on Minkowski's theory itself.

Sommerfeld* points out that, according to the theory, an electric space charge appears in a rotating solid body in the presence of a magnetic field parallel to the axis of rotation. He regards this as an indication that Minkowski's theory is " not directly applicable to problems involving rotation. " If this is indeed so, then the theory would not be directly applicable to any problem of magnetohydrodynamics involving fluid vorticity, as most of them do. It is shown that in any conducting medium (no matter how small the conductivity), there is a space-charge density wherever there is vorticity and a magnetic field with a component along the axis of the vorticity. The result does not depend qualitatively on the additional terms in the constitutive relations, but the quantitative answer does. The opportunity is taken to write and discuss the equation for the charge density with these additional terms included. The numerical value of the charge density in any terrestrial experiment would be very small, and the question of its existence or non-existence could probably not be experimentally settled. However, it is certainly difficult to find a simple theory that would not lead to such a charge density. Moreover, as we shall see, it is difficult to see why Minkowski's theory should not apply in the presence of vorticity in the medium.

In contradistinction to the question of charge density, the answer to the last question considered does (a) depend qualitatively on the additional terms in the constitutive relations; and (b) produce an effect which is measurable. The question is that of an explanation and generalization of the result of Eichenwald's experiment on the Roentgen current. ** A thin dielectric disk is rotated between the charged plates of a parallel plate condenser, the axis of rotation being perpendicular to the plates and to the disk. A magnetic field was observed, which was of the same strength as if the "bound" charge on the faces of the disk were " true" charge and the magnetic field were associated with the currents produced by its motion.

In the explanation given by Sommerfeld and by Cullwick† the motion of any element of the disk is replaced by a uniform rectilinear velocity. The theory then leads to the existence of a radial magnetic induction B_r in the material of the disk. This induction is continuous

*Reference 1, page 363.

**Reference 1, page 284

†Reference 4, page 37.

across the edge of the disk, and there will be a radial magnetic field just outside the edge. However, it appears from the illustrations in Eichenwald's paper that what was measured was a magnetic field perpendicular to the plates, and that the measurement was outside, and not between, the plates.

The problem then is to explain, on Minkowski's theory, the appearance of a magnetic field parallel to the axis of rotation when a dielectric disk is spun in the presence of an electric field in that direction. The explanation is found to depend crucially on the fact that the disk was rotating; a uniform rectilinear motion will not give the effect. In fact, the result comes directly from applying Minkowski's theory to a medium moving with vorticity (and applying rather similar calculations to those that led above to a charge density).

The general result shows that if there is vorticity in a dielectric medium whose refractive index is not unity, then if there is an applied electric field along the axis of vorticity a magnetic field must appear, and if there is an applied magnetic field along that axis then an electric field must appear. Moreover, for a solid-body rotation, as in Eichenwald's experiment, the magnetic field that appears is of the same strength as that produced by a true surface charge equal to the "bound" charge on the faces of the disk, and rotating with the disk. In general, however, with a dielectric fluid in shearing rotational motion, this would not be the case; for example, a dielectric fluid between counter-rotating disks should give a measureably different effect, and this could be experimentally tested if satisfactory precautions can be taken to remove ions from the fluid for a sufficient time, to keep the fluid motion laminar and nearly in circles about the axis, and so on.

Since the theory predicts the appearance of an electric field when there is an applied magnetic field along the axis of vorticity, it may also be used in connection with Wilson's experiment.* The arrangement here may be thought of as a dielectric in the form of a hollow cylinder between the plates of an uncharged cylindrical condenser, with a uniform magnetic field applied parallel to the axis of the cylinders. When the dielectric is rotated, a radial electric field is now produced, and the condenser is charged. However, not only the roles of the electric and magnetic fields, but also the geometry, are now quite different from those in the previous case. The result is that the main effect is usually associated with the motion of the surfaces of the dielectric, and, therefore, the theory here suggested results only in a small refinement of the theory usually presented. The best chance for a discriminating experiment seems to be with a thick annulus of dielectric ferrite.

The examples here discussed all depend on an interaction of a magnetic or electric field with vorticity (rotation), and suggest experiments which may help towards deciding the question of the validity of

*Reference 1, page 285 and Reference 4, page 166.

Minkowski's theory in such situations.

II. THE ELECTROMAGNETIC EQUATIONS FOR A CONTINUUM

MKSQ units are used.[1] The dielectric constant ϵ, the magnetic permeability μ, and the electric conductivity σ will all be taken as constant scalars. Thus striction is not considered, nor anisotropy, nor Hall currents, nor dispersion of electromagnetic waves, etc.

Maxwell's equations are

$$\text{curl}\,\underset{\sim}{E} = -\partial \underset{\sim}{B}/\partial t, \quad \text{curl}\,\underset{\sim}{H} = \partial \underset{\sim}{D}/\partial t + \underset{\sim}{J}, \quad \underset{\sim}{\nabla}\cdot\underset{\sim}{D} = \rho_e, \quad \underset{\sim}{\nabla}\cdot\underset{\sim}{B} = 0, \tag{1}$$

and correct to order v/c (v^2/c^2 neglected), the constitutive relations are

$$\underset{\sim}{D} = \epsilon \underset{\sim}{E} + \lambda (\underset{\sim}{v} \times \underset{\sim}{H}), \quad \underset{\sim}{B} = \mu \underset{\sim}{H} - \lambda (\underset{\sim}{v} \times \underset{\sim}{E}), \tag{2}$$

where

$$\lambda = \epsilon\mu - \epsilon_o \mu_o = (n^2 - 1)/c^2, \tag{3}$$

and

$$\underset{\sim}{J} - \rho_e \underset{\sim}{v} = \sigma (\underset{\sim}{E} + \underset{\sim}{v} \times \underset{\sim}{B}). \tag{4}$$

(See Ref. 1, Section 34; Ref. 5, Chapter 3). $\underset{\sim}{E}$, $\underset{\sim}{D}$, $\underset{\sim}{H}$, $\underset{\sim}{B}$ have been previously defined; $\underset{\sim}{J}$ is the electric current density, and ρ_e the electric charge density; ϵ_o, μ_o are the values of ϵ and μ in vacuo (MKSQ units), and c the velocity of light in vacuo, so $c^2 = (\epsilon_o \mu_o)^{-1}$; n is the refractive index of the medium. $\underset{\sim}{v}$ is the velocity of the medium at the point P considered and at the time t considered, relative to the "laboratory" frame of reference in which we write the equations. (The mechanical equations, written in the same frame, will (with v^2/c^2 omitted) be taken to be Newtonian, so the "laboratory" frame is assumed to be an inertial frame.)

The equations may be obtained by using an orthogonal Lorentz transformation of space-time to a local frame at (P, t), in which the constitutive relations are taken to be $\underset{\sim}{D}' = \epsilon \underset{\sim}{E}'$, $\underset{\sim}{B}' = \mu \underset{\sim}{H}'$, $\underset{\sim}{J}' = \sigma \underset{\sim}{E}'$, and then using an inverse Lorentz transformation back to the laboratory frame.[1, 5]

A somewhat more convincing procedure is as follows. The whole trouble is with the constitutive relations. Maxwell's equations are in any case acceptable. In the moving medium in the laboratory frame, the constitutive relations are a priori unknown. Use a transformation which will, as far as possible, bring an element of the continuum in the space-time neighborhood of (P, t) to rest. The velocity and acceleration, elemental rotation (vorticity), and rate-of-strain may be annulled, correct to the second order in the dimensions of the element in space-time. Assume this transformation (not orthogonal) used on the whole field. In this frame of reference, take the element as completely at rest, neglect the influence of the neighbors, and take the constitutive relations as the relativistic equivalent of

$$\underset{\sim}{D}' = \epsilon \underset{\sim}{E}', \quad \underset{\sim}{B}' = \mu \underset{\sim}{H}', \quad \underset{\sim}{J}' = \sigma \underset{\sim}{E}'$$

for accelerating frames. (See, for example, Ref. 6.) Then transform back to the laboratory frame. (Maxwell's equations will transform back into Maxwell's equations.) Constitutive relations are obtained in the laboratory frame which become (2) and (4) when v^2/c^2 is omitted.

It is now clear that these relations are not correct (even with v^2/c^2 retained.) However, the error is seen to arise not from the rotation, but from the neglected influence of apparent gravity (acceleration) on the constitutive relations in the new frame. (In microscopic terms, the error arises from the neglect of the inertia of the electrons, both free and bound.) For very, very large accelerations this effect might be important.*

The boundary conditions at a *moving* surface of separation between two different media are not strictly relevant here, but the following remarks may be interpolated. The boundary conditions may be obtained from the limit of the integral forms of Maxwell's equations for a sharp but continuous transition, and so long as the time-derivatives which occur are finite in the limit, they will have the same form as for a stationary surface. In a transformation from one frame of reference to another, the transformation of time-derivatives involves space derivatives. For these considerations, it is sufficient to consider a local Lorentz transformation at any point of the surface of separation. Space-derivatives tangential to the surface are finite in the limit, but the normal derivatives of the tangential components of $\underset{\sim}{B}$ and $\underset{\sim}{D}$ (and of the normal component of $\underset{\sim}{D}$ also, if there is surface charge) become infinite. The usual boundary conditions, in the same form as for a stationary surface, may therefore be applied either in the local frame of any point on the surface or in any frame with a relative velocity tangential to the surface. This includes the laboratory frame if the surface is moving tangentially to itself in that frame. Thus surface slip causes no trouble in the application of boundary conditions. However, if the relevant time-derivatives are finite in one frame they will be infinite at the surface in any other frame having a velocity relative to the first which has a component normal to the surface. There can, therefore, be only one such frame in which the time-derivatives are finite. Since there is only one, this must be a frame having the normal velocity of that point on the surface

*This last remark, and a detailed consideration of the transformation, were made by Mr. R. C. Costen, a research student of mine at Harvard.

which is under consideration. In such a frame, the boundary conditions take the usual form. They may now, if required, be transformed to the laboratory frame. Note that the normal velocity must (for a continuum) be continuous across the surface, so again no difficulty arises. (In electromagnetic fields, what is called "cavitation" in hydrodynamics introduces another "medium",)

III. MINKOWSKI'S STRESS-ENERGY TENSOR

Expressions for the components of Minkowski's stress-energy tensor are written below. The notation is the same as in Chapter 3 of Reference 5, W, $\underset{\sim}{N}$, and $\underset{\sim}{G}$ denote the electromagnetic energy per unit volume, the Poynting vector, and the electromagnetic momentum, respectively, with

$$W = \frac{1}{2}(\underset{\sim}{E} \cdot \underset{\sim}{D} + \underset{\sim}{H} \cdot \underset{\sim}{B}), \quad \underset{\sim}{N} = \underset{\sim}{E} \times \underset{\sim}{H}, \text{ and } \underset{\sim}{G} = \underset{\sim}{D} \times \underset{\sim}{B} \tag{5}$$

T_{ij} are the components of the stress-energy tensor (and with i, j = 1, 2, 3 they are the components of the Maxwell stress tensor) with

$$T_{ij} = D_i E_j + B_i H_j - W\delta_{ij}, \quad \text{for } i, j = 1, 2, 3 ; \tag{6a}$$

$$T_{4j} = -icG_j, \quad T_{j4} = -iN_j/c, \quad T_{44} = W, \tag{6b}$$

where $\delta_{ij} = 1$ if $i = j$, and $= 0$ if $i \neq j$. In a vacuum, or for a medium at rest, the tensor thus defined is symmetrical. It is also symmetrical in the laboratory frame in the case of a moving medium if the λ-terms in Eq. (2) are neglected. If that is done, then to the order of accuracy retained, everything turns out satisfactorily, and acceptable equations of momentum and energy of any fluid medium may be obtained in the forms

$$\begin{aligned} \rho(f_i - F_i) &= \partial p_{ji}/\partial x_j + \partial T_{ji}/\partial x_j - \partial G_i/\partial t \\ &= \partial p_{ji}/\partial x_j + \rho_e E_i + (\underset{\sim}{J} \times \underset{\sim}{B})_i \end{aligned} \tag{7}$$

and

$$\begin{aligned} \rho \frac{D}{Dt}\left[\mathcal{E} + p/\rho + \frac{1}{2}\underset{\sim}{v}^2 + \Omega\right] = \rho\frac{\partial\Omega}{\partial t} + \frac{\partial p}{\partial t} + \rho R + \frac{\partial}{\partial x_j}(v_i \pi_{ji}) \\ + \frac{\partial q_j}{\partial x_j} + \underset{\sim}{E} \cdot \underset{\sim}{J} \end{aligned} \tag{8}$$

ee Ref. 5, Chapter 3.) Here ρ is the density of the medium, $\underset{\sim}{f}$ the :celeration of an element, $\underset{\sim}{F}$ the body force per unit mass, p_{ij} the echanical stress tensor, and ρ_e the density of electric charge. Fur- er, in the energy equation, p_{ij} has been put equal $- p\delta_{ij} + \pi_{ij}$, here p is the thermodynamic pressure and π_{ij} the viscous stress; is the internal energy per unit mass, and (with the forces $\underset{\sim}{F}$ assumed onservative) Ω is the potential energy per unit mass; $\underset{\sim}{q}$ is the eat-flux vector by conduction, and R the rate of heat addition per unit ass by radiation or any other process not specifically allowed for.

Note that in a continuum theory the electric and magnetic forces any part of a medium are to be thought of as surface forces, arising om stresses - tensions along the lines of force and pressure across em - in the manner of Faraday and Maxwell, and not as body forces. particular, the work done by the electromagnetic forces on an ele- ent when it is deformed must be included in the equation of energy, d this is done simply, correctly, and without artificiality by com- iting the work done by surface stresses T_{ij}. (In a microscopic theory, e forces are, of course, to be thought of as body forces, in the anner of Lorentz. Presumably, a complete and correct statistical vestigation would show the connection of the two theories, but such correct investigation for polarized matter, involving non-central rces between molecules, seems never to have been made, and to be ery difficult.)

It might also be mentioned that in considering the energy balance r the volume inside a moving surface, the Poynting vector must be ken, not in the laboratory frame, but in the local frame at each oint of the surface at the right time.[5]

In accordance with the theory, the forces on any portion of a olarized medium (fluid or solid) arise as surface forces. Striction , however, omitted, as previously mentioned.

Thus, with the λ-terms in Eq. (2) omitted, the theory seems atisfactory, as far as it goes. The inclusion of these terms will ter Eqs. (7) and (8). The question now is, in what circumstances, if y, are these alterations significant?

The expressions in (5) and (6) are independent of (2), and will ere be retained. The expression for $\underset{\sim}{G}$ and T_{ij}, however, are not iquely determined for a moving medium. The great advantage of) and (6) is that this gives the simplest form (invariant under a orentz transformation and giving the desired results for a vacuum a medium at rest) which has been suggested. However, the tensor no longer symmetrical (except in each local frame); and other ymmetrical) forms of the stress-energy-momentum tensor have een suggested, especially by M. Abraham.[7] It is, however, not ear why, in a continuum theory, T_{ij} should be symmetrical in a olarized medium; clearly it never occurs except in conjunction with j, nor is it at all clear that a correct statistical theory starting rom a microscopic model must lead to a symmetrical electromagnetic stress tensor. So the expressions in (5) and (6) are here retained.

IV. THE EQUATIONS OF MOMENTUM AND ENERGY. ELECTROMAGNETIC EFFECT ON THE MECHANICAL STRESS TENSOR

Consider first the electromagnetic momentum in free space. This is to be considered fixed in space. Let an element dS of a clos surface be moving with velocity $\underset{\sim}{v}$. If there were no flux of electromagnetic momentum across this moving surface, we should have

$$\int T_{\nu i}\, dS = \frac{D}{Dt}\int G_i\, d\tau = \int \frac{\partial G_i}{\partial t}\, d\tau + \int G_i v_\nu\, dS$$

(where the subscript ν refers to the direction normal to the surfac $\underset{\sim}{\nu}$ is unit vector in that direction, and $d\tau$ is an element of volume). However, in free space, where there is no charge and no current,

$$\partial T_{ji}/\partial x_j = \partial G_i/\partial t\,,$$

and

$$\int T_{\nu i}\, dS = \int \nu_j T_{ji}\, dS = \int \frac{\partial T_{ji}}{\partial x_j}\, d\tau = \int \frac{\partial G_i}{\partial t}\, d\tau\,,$$

so there is a flux of momentum across the moving surface which jus cuts out the term $\int G_i v_\nu\, dS$ where $G = \epsilon_0\mu_0 \underset{\sim}{N}$ (with $\underset{\sim}{N} = \underset{\sim}{E} \times \underset{\sim}{H}$). This is because momentum $\epsilon_0\mu_0 \underset{\sim}{N}$ is "fixed" in free space and doe not move with the surface, and the surface "sees" this influx of momentum.

In a dielectric or magnetized medium, however, the momentum, $\underset{\sim}{D} \times \underset{\sim}{B}$, depends on the polarization. All the momentum in a dielectri for example, cannot be fixed in space; some must move with the dielectric. The presence of the polarized medium has itself changed the fields; and the most nearly correct assumption as to the amount of each is by no means obvious. Here I make what seems to be the simplest assumption: that momentum $\epsilon_0\mu_0 \underset{\sim}{N}$ is fixed and that $\underset{\sim}{D} \times \underset{\sim}{B} - \epsilon_0\mu_0 \underset{\sim}{N} \approx \lambda \underset{\sim}{N}$ moves with the dielectric.

For the region inside a closed surface moving with the mediu the equation of momentum then becomes

$$\int (p_{\nu i} + T_{\nu i})\, dS + \int \rho F_i\, d\tau = \frac{D}{Dt}\int \rho v_i\, d\tau + \int \frac{\partial G_i}{\partial t}\, d\tau + \lambda \int N_i v_\nu\, dS \qquad (9$$

hence

$$\frac{\partial}{\partial x_j}(p_{ji} + T_{ji}) + \rho F_i = \rho f_i + \frac{\partial G_i}{\partial t} + \lambda \frac{\partial}{\partial x_j}(N_i v_j) \qquad (10)$$

t every point of mathematical continuity, since

$$\frac{D}{Dt}\int \rho v_i \, d\tau = \int \rho f_i \, d\tau .$$

The last term on the right in (10) is the divergence of a term hat is not symmetrical, and here again (since the effects are very mall and could hardly be measured) some assumption is forced on us. have assumed for the present that the flux of electromagnetic momenum will not cause rotation in a uniformly moving dielectric in a ariable field, that the asymmetry in the flux of electromagnetic momntum is balanced by a flux of angular momentum, and that the sum $_{ji} + T_{ji}$ must still be symmetrical.

Then $T_{ji} - T_{ij} = p_{ij} - p_{ji}$, and from (6a) and (2) a small calcuation shows that

$$T_{ji} - T_{ij} = p_{ij} - p_{ji} = \lambda (v_i N_j - v_j N_i) . \qquad (11)$$

enote by T_{ij}^* and p_{ij}^* the symmetrical parts of T_{ij} and p_{ij}. Then

$$p_{ji} + T_{ji} = p_{ji}^* + T_{ji}^* . \qquad (12)$$

lso, after some calculation, it is found from (6a), (1) and (2) that

$$\frac{\partial T_{ji}}{\partial x_j} = \rho_e E_i + (\underset{\sim}{J} \times \underset{\sim}{B})_i + \frac{\partial G_i}{\partial t} + \lambda N_j \frac{\partial v_j}{\partial x_i} , \qquad (13)$$

nd

$$\frac{\partial T_{ji}^*}{\partial x_j} = \frac{\partial T_{ji}}{\partial x_j} - \frac{1}{2}\frac{\partial}{\partial x_j}(T_{ji} - T_{ij})$$

$$= \frac{\partial T_{ji}}{\partial x_j} - \frac{\lambda}{2}\frac{\partial}{\partial x_j}(v_i N_j - v_j N_i) . \qquad (14)$$

ence the equation of momentum (10) becomes

$$\rho\,(f_i - F_i) - \rho_e E_i - (\underset{\sim}{J} \times \underset{\sim}{B})_i = \frac{\partial}{\partial x_j}\left[\overset{*}{p}_{ji} - \frac{\lambda}{2}(v_i N_j + v_j N_i)\right] + \lambda\, N_j \frac{\partial v_j}{\partial x_i} \qquad (15$$

For a uniform dielectric in uniform motion,

$$\rho_e = 0, \quad \underset{\sim}{J} = 0, \quad f_i = 0, \quad \partial v_j/\partial x_i = 0,$$

there are no viscous stresses and the body forces F_i (if any) are balanced by pressure gradients. No body forces arise from the polarization (only surface forces). However, N_i may be variable in x_j. These considerations lead us to try putting

$$p_{ij} = \overset{+}{p}_{ij} + \lambda\, v_i N_j, \qquad (16$$

where $\overset{+}{p}_{ij}$ is symmetrical. We shall, in fact, take $\overset{+}{p}_{ij}$ for a fluid to be the sum of the pressure and the viscous stress, as usually definec in the absence of electric and magnetic fields. Then

$$\overset{*}{p}_{ij} = \overset{+}{p}_{ij} + \frac{1}{2}\lambda\,(v_i N_j + v_j N_i)$$

and also

$$p_{ij} - p_{ji} = \lambda\,(v_i N_j - v_j N_i),$$

in agreement with (11). The equation of momentum becomes

$$\rho\,(f_i - F_i) = \rho_e E_i + (\underset{\sim}{J} \times \underset{\sim}{B})_i + \frac{\partial \overset{+}{p}_{ji}}{\partial x_j} + \lambda\, N_j \frac{\partial v_j}{\partial x_i}\,. \qquad (17$$

This can also be written in the form

$$\frac{\partial}{\partial x_j}(\overset{+}{p}_{ji} + T_{ji}) + \rho\, F_i = \rho\, f_i + \frac{\partial G_i}{\partial t}\,, \qquad (18$$

which clearly brings out the asymmetry, and the need for a flux of angular momentum.

The term $\lambda\, v_i N_j$ in (16) represents an electromagnetic effect on the mechanical stress tensor, which on a molecular model arises rom a transport of momentum. Very crudely, some support for a erm such as $\lambda\, v_i\, N_j$ may be obtained from a molecular model, but his is of no great value at present because of the difficulty of a proper tatistical investigation.

The extra term, $\lambda\, N_j\, \partial v_j / \partial x_i$, in (17) is certainly insensible xcept with very large crossed fields. Even then, it will be very mall in terrestrial experiments. It may then be of the same order s $\rho_e \underset{\sim}{E}$, where ρ_e is produced by the interaction of vorticity and a nagnetic field (as we shall see).

The momentum equation obtained by Pham Mau Quan[2] differs rom Eq. (17), and is considerably more complicated. It is, however, nteresting to observe, as Professor Ludford has pointed out to me, hat the difference is entirely due to making the tensor terms that ccur symmetrical. Without that, the results, though arrived at uite differently, would be the same.

A similar consideration of the equation of energy necessarily nvolves v^2/c^2, and would therefore have to be both more detailed and nore complex, with relativistic mechanics and thermodynamics in- luded. This I have not done. It is possible to proceed some way in rather simple fashion, and then assume that a fuller treatment vould make the result correct for free space (as it must), and so to nake plausible the result that the equation of energy becomes

$$\rho \frac{D}{Dt}\left[\mathcal{E} + p/\rho + \frac{1}{2}\underset{\sim}{v}^2 + \Omega\right] = \rho\frac{\partial \Omega}{\partial t} + \frac{\partial p}{\partial t} + \rho R + \frac{\partial}{\partial x_j}(v_i \pi_{ji}) + \frac{\partial q_j}{\partial x_j} + \underset{\sim}{E}\cdot\underset{\sim}{J} - \lambda \underset{\sim}{N}_j \frac{\partial v_j}{\partial t} \tag{19}$$

. e., that we have simply to subtract $\lambda\, N_j\, \partial v_j/\partial t$ from the right-hand side of (8).

Now, however, the thermodynamics usually used requires rein- estigation in the light of the term $\lambda\, v_i\, N_j$ in p_{ij}.

V. THE EQUATION FOR THE CHARGE DENSITY

The opportunity is first taken to write the equation for the charge ensity both with the λ-terms included in (2), and in the form suitable or the present discussion.

From Eqs. (1)-(4) it follows that

$$0 = \text{div curl}\ \underset{\sim}{H} = \frac{\partial}{\partial t}\ \text{div}\ \underset{\sim}{D} + \text{div}\ (\rho_e \underset{\sim}{v}) + \sigma\ \text{div}\ (\underset{\sim}{E} + \underset{\sim}{v} \times \underset{\sim}{B}),$$

hat is,

$$\frac{\partial \rho_e}{\partial t} + \operatorname{div}(\rho_e \underset{\sim}{v}) + \sigma \operatorname{div}\left[\frac{\underset{\sim}{D}}{\epsilon} - \frac{\lambda}{\epsilon}\underset{\sim}{v} \times \underset{\sim}{H} + \underset{\sim}{v} \times \underset{\sim}{B}\right] = 0,$$

that is,

$$\frac{\partial \rho_e}{\partial t} + \operatorname{div}(\rho_e \underset{\sim}{v}) + \frac{\sigma}{\epsilon}\rho_e = \sigma\left(1 - \frac{\lambda}{\epsilon\mu}\right)\operatorname{div}(\underset{\sim}{B} \times \underset{\sim}{v})$$

(with v^2/c^2 neglected). Since

$$1 - \lambda/(\epsilon\mu) = (\epsilon_o \mu_o)/(\epsilon\mu) = 1/n^2,$$

and

$$\operatorname{div}(\underset{\sim}{B} \times \underset{\sim}{v}) = \underset{\sim}{v} \cdot \operatorname{curl} \underset{\sim}{B} - \underset{\sim}{B} \cdot \operatorname{curl} \underset{\sim}{v}$$

$$= \mu \underset{\sim}{v} \cdot \underset{\sim}{J} + \mu \underset{\sim}{v} \cdot \dot{\underset{\sim}{D}} - \underset{\sim}{B} \cdot \underset{\sim}{\omega}$$

(v^2/c^2 neglected), where $\underset{\sim}{\omega}$ is the vorticity, it follows that

$$\epsilon\left[\frac{\partial \rho_e}{\partial t} + \operatorname{div} \rho_e \underset{\sim}{v}\right] + \sigma \rho_e = \frac{\sigma}{n^2}\left[\epsilon\mu \underset{\sim}{v} \cdot \underset{\sim}{J} + \epsilon\mu \underset{\sim}{v} \cdot \dot{\underset{\sim}{D}} - \epsilon \underset{\sim}{B} \cdot \underset{\sim}{\omega}\right. \tag{20}$$

If $\partial \rho_e/\partial t + \operatorname{div} \rho_e \underset{\sim}{v} = 0$ (as it is in some simple examples), and σ is not zero,

$$\rho_e = \frac{1}{c^2}(\underset{\sim}{v} \cdot \underset{\sim}{J} + \underset{\sim}{v} \cdot \dot{\underset{\sim}{D}}) - \frac{\epsilon}{n^2}\underset{\sim}{B} \cdot \underset{\sim}{\omega}. \tag{21}$$

The charge density in a local frame is

$$\rho_e' = \rho_e - \underset{\sim}{v} \cdot \underset{\sim}{J}/c^2$$

(again with v^2/c^2 neglected), and for a steady field ($\dot{\underset{\sim}{D}} = 0$), is

$$\rho_e' = -\frac{\epsilon}{n^2}\underset{\sim}{B} \cdot \underset{\sim}{\omega} \approx -\frac{1}{c^2}\underset{\sim}{H} \cdot \underset{\sim}{\omega} \tag{22}$$

All this holds accurately to order v/c if

$$\partial \rho_e/\partial t + \operatorname{div} \rho_e \underset{\sim}{v} = 0.$$

It still holds approximately otherwise unless the magnetic Reynolds number, $R_M = \mu\sigma UL$ (where U and L are a typical macroscopic velocit nd length of the system, respectively), is very small. For the ratio of he third term on the left in (20) to the second term is of order R_M/n^2) (c^2/U^2); its ratio to the first term on the left is of the same rder for " hydrodynamic" phenomena, where a typical time is L/U, nd of order (R_M/n) (c/U) for electromagnetic wave phenomena.

Thus, if a conducting medium is moving with vorticity, and here is a (large) magnetic field along the axis of the vorticity at any oint, then there is a space-charge density at that point, even when bserved in a local frame moving with the point. The charge density s numerically very small in any conceivable terrestrial experiment, ut its existence is a definite result of our equations. Many simple xamples of this general result may be shown.

VI. EICHENWALD'S EXPERIMENT AND THE ROENTGEN CURRENT

Consider a thin dielectric disk rotating between the charged lates of a parallel plate condenser, with its faces parallel to the lates and the axis of rotation perpendicular to the plates.*

The dielectric disk is in an applied electric field, and any point f the disk not on the axis of rotation has a velocity at right angles to he applied electric field. From the second of Eqs. (2) it therefore ollows that there is, in the dielectric, a magnetic induction $\underset{\sim}{B}$ at ight angles both to the velocity and the electric field, and therefore n a radial direction. The magnetic induction in this direction is ontinuous across the edge of the disk, so there is also a radial mag- etic induction B_r, and therefore also a radial magnetic field H_r, ust outside the edge of the disk.

As explained in the introduction, however, our problem is to xplain the existence of a magnetic field parallel to the electric field, nd measured not just outside the edge of the disk, but at a point not etween the plates of the condenser.

The theory presented is rather general, but depends essentially, n the case of Eichenwald's experiment, on the *rotation* of the disk, r expressed more generally, it depends essentially on the existence f vorticity in the motion of the dielectric medium when the geometry s that of Eichenwald's experiment. Only a brief introduction to the heory will be given here.

For steady fields in a dielectric ($\sigma = 0$, $\rho_e = 0$, $\underset{\sim}{J} = 0$), Eqs. (1) nd (2) become

*This is the experiment with which we shall be concerned here. We shall not e concerned with the magnetic effect of the motion of charged metal plates, i. e., the Rowland effect. The point is that the motion of "true" charge, on metal plates, does roduce a convection current which has a magnetic effect on the theory here consid- red; the motion of the "bound" charge on the surface of a dielectric does not, and f a magnetic effect is observed in the latter case, some other explanation must be ought.

$$\text{curl}\,\mathbf{E} = 0, \quad \text{curl}\,\mathbf{H} = 0, \quad \text{div}\,\mathbf{B} = 0, \quad \text{div}\,\mathbf{D} = 0, \tag{23}$$

$$\mathbf{D} = \epsilon\,\mathbf{E} + \lambda\,(\mathbf{v} \times \mathbf{H}), \qquad \mathbf{B} = \mu\,\mathbf{H} - \lambda\,(\mathbf{v} \times \mathbf{E})\,. \tag{24}$$

But, if $\boldsymbol{\omega}$ is the vorticity, equal to curl $\mathbf{v}$,

$$\text{div}\,(\mathbf{v} \times \mathbf{H}) = \mathbf{H}\cdot\text{curl}\,\mathbf{v} - \mathbf{v}\cdot\,\text{curl}\,\mathbf{H} = \mathbf{H}\cdot\boldsymbol{\omega},$$

and similarly

$$\text{div}\,(\mathbf{v} \times \mathbf{E}) = \mathbf{E}\cdot\boldsymbol{\omega}\,.$$

Hence

$$\epsilon\;\text{div}\,\mathbf{E} + \lambda\,\mathbf{H}\cdot\boldsymbol{\omega} = 0 \tag{25}$$

$$\mu\;\text{div}\,\mathbf{H} - \lambda\,\mathbf{E}\cdot\boldsymbol{\omega} = 0 \tag{26}$$

These equations, together with curl $\mathbf{E} = 0$, curl $\mathbf{H} = 0$, are equations for $\mathbf{E}$ and $\mathbf{H}$. From (25) and (26) it is immediately clear that if there is an applied magnetic field in the direction of the axis of the vorticity, then there must be an electric field, and if there is an applied electric field in that direction, then there must be a magnetic field.

Further, a vacuum is to be considered as at rest, and if a dielectric is moving in a vacuum, then its surface is to be considered a surface of slip, or vortex sheet. If there is a magnetic (or electric) field applied in the direction of the vorticity in that sheet, then this too will produce an electric (or magnetic) field. Of course, the same will be true of any vortex sheet in an inviscid fluid, or at the surface of a solid body in an inviscid fluid.

Consider now a dielectric disk rotating about its axis in an electric field parallel to the axis. Take the axis of z along the axis of rotation. For a solid-body rotation with angular velocity Ω, $\boldsymbol{\omega}$ is along the z-axis and its value is 2Ω.

For this geometry, the " surface vorticity" is radial, and is at right angles to the electric field. Therefore it does not contribute to the effect being studied.

For simplicity, all that is done here is to consider (25) and (26) when edge effect is completely neglected, the fields being purely axial and depending only on z. Then (25) and (26) lead to

$$\epsilon\,\frac{dE_z}{dz} + 2\Omega\lambda\,H_z = 0, \qquad \mu\,\frac{dH_z}{dz} - 2\Omega\lambda E_z = 0 \tag{27}$$

The boundary conditions to be applied are the continuity of D_z at each face of the disk. Since B_z is continuous at each face of the disk, H_z may be found outside. The result is easily seen to be

$$H_z = \pm \epsilon_o \frac{\mu}{\mu_o} \Omega \ell E_1 \left(1 - \frac{1}{n^2}\right), \tag{28}$$

where ℓ is the thickness of the slab of dielectric and E_1 is the electric field between the plates of the condenser outside the dielectric.

For non-magnetic material ($\mu = \mu_o$) the result is equal to the magnetic field produced by current sheets when a true charge, equal to the bound charge, on the faces of the dielectric disk rotates with the disk.

The calculation set out above contains the physics of the problem, but is mathematically unsatisfactory in several respects. In place of the crude manner of neglecting edge effect employed above, an expansion of the solution, with appropriate dimensionless variables, may be sought in powers of the ratio of the thickness to the radius of the disk. Moreover, since H is of order $E_1 \Omega \ell / c$, care should be taken to show that the inclusion of terms of order v^2/c^2 will not alter the result to the order required, and is unnecessary.

These calculations have been carried out by Mr. Peter H. Stone at Harvard. He has also proved mathematically that, with edge effects included, the equations above will, for non-magnetic material and a solid-body rotation, lead to the same magnetic field as the current sheets previously mentioned. This last step is certainly necessary, since it was one of the main results obtained by Eichenwald, and he measured the axial magnetic field near the level of the edge of the disk.

However, this last result holds only for non-magnetic matter and for a solid-body rotation. Hence, as mentioned in the introduction, an experimental test can be carried out by using a dielectric fluid between two disks rotating with quite different angular velocities, care being taken to keep the fluid motion laminar and nearly in circles round the axis.

It is hoped that a more extended account of this investigation may be published elsewhere.

Finally, as mentioned in the Introduction, since the theory predicts the appearance of an electric field when there is an applied magnetic field along the axis of vorticity, it may also be used in connection with Wilson's experiment. However, consider a dielectric circular or annular cylinder rotating about its axis in the presence of a magnetic field parallel to that axis. The geometry is quite different from that of the rotating disk above. The " surface vorticity" is now parallel to the axis, and therefore to the applied magnetic field, and contributes materially to the effect being studied. It is this contribution which is usually taken into account. For an annular cylinder, what the full theory would do would be to introduce as a correction a contribution due to the thickness of the annulus. Although the predictions are not as striking as those for the fluid between counter-rotating disks with an applied electric field, mentioned above, they may nevertheless be well worth testing, thick annuli of a dielectric ferrite being used.

SUMMARY

1) An electromagnetic effect on the mechanical stress tensor, a flux of electromagnetic angular momentum, and forms of the momentum and energy equations, are suggested for a strictly continuum theory of magnetohydrodynamics when terms usually neglected in the electromagnetic constitutive relations are retained. The effects will usually be very small.

2) If, as has been suggested, Minkowski's theory of the electro dynamics of moving media does not apply to rotating systems, then the equations of magnetohydrodynamics might not apply to motions involving vorticity. Certain consequences of the interaction of vorticity with applied fields according to the theory are displayed. In particular, it is shown why it is thought that such an interaction is necessary to explain Eichenwald's experiment on the Roentgen current. Generalizations, according to the theory given, may be used to test the theory, which also may be used to predict a refinement in the theory of Wilson's experiment.

ACKNOWLEDGMENT

This research was supported by the U. S. Office of Naval Research under contract Nonr - 1866(34).

REFERENCES

1. A. Sommerfeld, *Lectures on Theoretical Physics, Vol. III, Electrodynamics*[(English Translation) New York: Academic Press, 1952].
2. Pham Mau Quan, Étude electromagnétique et thermodynamique d'un fluide relativiste chargé, *J. Rat. Mechs. and Analysis*, Vol. 5, pp. 473-538 (1956).
3. R. M. Fano, L. J. Chu and R. Adler, *Electromagnetic Fields, Energy, and Forces*, [New York: John Wiley and Sons, Inc., 1960].
4. E.G. Cullwick, *Electromagnetism and Relativity*, 2nd. Ed.(London: Longmans, 1959)
5. S. Goldstein, *Lectures on Fluid Mechanics*, (New York: Interscience, 1960).
6. H. Weyl, *Space-Time-Matter* (London: Methuen, 1922) Section 23.
7. W. Pauli, *Encyklopadie der mathematischen Wissensschaften*, B.G. Teubner, Band V 19, Relativitatstheorie, pp. 539–775 (especially 665–7).

ON THE APPLICATION OF TWO-PARTICLE DISTRIBUTION FUNCTIONS

J. M. Burgers
Institute for Fluid Dynamics and Applied Mathematics,
University of Maryland

The dc electrical conductivity of a fully ionized gas is calculated by using a moment equation derived from the Boltzmann equation with a collision term expressed with the aid of a two-particle distribution function. The two-particle distribution function itself is obtained from an equation given by the kinetic theory, in which the three-particle distribution function and two integrals depending upon other two-particle distribution functions are replaced by expressions involving the Debye potential. Further approximations are introduced by the assumption of Maxwellian functions (with unknown flow velocities) for the single-particle distribution functions occurring in this equation.

The integral depending upon the two-particle distribution function occurring in the moment equation derived from Boltzmann's equation can then be worked out. The expression for the electrical conductivity given by this procedure has a main term which, for low flow velocities, agrees with that given by the usual theory of collisions depending upon Coulomb forces, while for high flow velocities this term gives the "runaway" effect. Two correction terms are obtained: one, which may be of some importance, depends upon the increased concentration of particles of opposite charge around a given particle; the other represents a minor effect due to a distortion of the Debye cloud by the exterior electric field.

I. INTRODUCTION

The object of this paper is to derive an expression for the electrical conductivity of a fully ionized gas by making use of the two-particle distribution function. Limitation of time makes it necessary to restrict our discussion to the simplest case, where the gas is subjected to a uniform time-independent electric field and where magnetic fields are absent. The two-particle distribution function is applied in the hope that it will give a good evaluation of the aggregate effect of weak interactions, which in the case of Coulomb forces are more important than the effects of single collisions. The basic equation, therefore, is the Boltzmann equation in which the usual expression for the effect of binary collisions is replaced by an integral depending upon the two-particle distribution function, as follows:

*This research was supported in part by the United States Air Force through the Air Force Office of Scientific Research under Contract AF 49-(638)-401.

Presented at the Symposium on Electromagnetics and Fluid Dynamics of Gaseous Plasma, Polytechnic Institute of Brooklyn, April 4, 5, 6, 1961

$$\frac{\partial F_a}{\partial t} + \xi_{ah}\frac{\partial F_a}{\partial x_{ah}} + \frac{f_{ah}}{m_a}\frac{\partial F_a}{\partial \xi_{ah}} = \frac{1}{m_a}\sum_b \iint dx_b\, d\xi_b \frac{\partial \Phi_{ab}}{\partial x_{ah}}\frac{\partial F_{ab}}{\partial \xi_{ah}} \tag{1}$$

Notation:

The gas is composed of particles of types a, b, . . . ; the mass of a particle of type a is m_a and its electric charge e_a; its coordinates are x_{ah}, its velocity components ξ_{ah}. The subscripts h (and k) refer to the three coordinate directions. When the same coordinate subscript occurs twice in a product, summation must be carried out over all three directions. The f_{ah} stand for the components of exterior forces acting upon the particles, not produced by the charges of the particles themselves; when there is an exterior electric field E_h one has $f_{ah} = E_h e_a$. The function $\Phi_{ab} = e_a e_b \phi_{ab} = e_a e_b / r_{ab}$ is the Coulomb potential for the interaction between particles of types a and b when the distance between these particles is r_{ab}. To avoid certain difficulties that can arise when r_{ab} decreases without limit, we modify the definition of the potential function ϕ_{ab} by assuming:

$$\phi_{ab} = \begin{cases} 1/r_{ab} & \text{if} \quad r_{ab} > R; \\ 1/R & \text{if} \quad r_{ab} < R. \end{cases} \tag{2}$$

Here R is a minimum distance, which may depend upon the dimensions of the two particles. It can be different for each combination a, b, but it is not necessary to indicate this by subscripts.

The function F_a is the ordinary velocity distribution function for a single particle of type a; it is defined in such a way that $F_a d\underset{\sim}{x}_a d\underset{\sim}{\xi}_a$ (with $d\underset{\sim}{x}_a = dx_{a1}dx_{a2}dx_{a3}$; $d\underset{\sim}{\xi}_a = d\xi_{a1}d\xi_{a2}d\xi_{a3}$) gives the number of particles of type a, at a given instant t located within the element of volume $d\underset{\sim}{x}_a$ of the coordinate space and having velocity vectors with their endpoints in the element $d\underset{\sim}{\xi}_a$ of the velocity space. We have

$$\int F_a \, d\underset{\sim}{\xi}_a = N_a ,$$

the integration being extended over the entire velocity space, where N_a is the number density of the particles of type a at the location $\underset{\sim}{x}_a$.

The function F_{ab} is defined in such a way that $F_{ab}\, d\underset{\sim}{x}_a\, d\underset{\sim}{x}_b\, d\underset{\sim}{\xi}_a\, d\underset{\sim}{\xi}_b$ gives the product of the number of particles of type a located within $d\underset{\sim}{x}_a\, d\underset{\sim}{\xi}_a$ at the instant t, into the number of particles of type b located within $d\underset{\sim}{x}_b\, d\underset{\sim}{\xi}_b$ at the same instant. When the distance between $\underset{\sim}{x}_b$ and

$\underset{\sim}{x}_a$ becomes very large, the function F_{ab} becomes equal to the product $F_a F_b$.

The integrations with respect to $d\underset{\sim}{x}_b$ and $d\underset{\sim}{\xi}_b$ in the multiple integral on the right-hand side of (1) must be extended over the entire coordinate space and the entire velocity space available to the particles. The summation with respect to b must be carried out over all types of particles, including type a (in order to account for the interaction of type a with other particles of the same type).

Equation (1) is the first equation of a hierarchy of equations for multi-particle functions of increasing order. Systems of this kind have been introduced by various authors, including Bogoliubov.* Along with Eq. (1) we shall be concerned with the equation for F_{ab}, which has the form:

$$\frac{\partial F_{ab}}{\partial t} + \xi_{ah}\frac{\partial F_{ab}}{\partial x_{ah}} + \xi_{bh}\frac{\partial F_{ab}}{\partial x_{bh}} + \frac{f_{ah}}{m_a}\frac{\partial F_{ab}}{\partial \xi_{ah}} + \frac{f_{bh}}{m_b}\frac{\partial F_{ab}}{\partial \xi_{bh}} =$$

$$= \frac{1}{m_a}\frac{\partial \Phi_{ab}}{\partial x_{ah}}\frac{\partial F_{ab}}{\partial \xi_{ah}} + \frac{1}{m_b}\frac{\partial \Phi_{ab}}{\partial x_{bh}}\frac{\partial F_{ab}}{\partial \xi_{bh}} +$$

$$+ \sum_c \iint d\underset{\sim}{x}_c \, d\underset{\sim}{\xi}_c \left[\frac{1}{m_a}\frac{\partial \Phi_{ac}}{\partial x_{ah}}\frac{\partial F_{abc}}{\partial \xi_{ah}} + \frac{1}{m_b}\frac{\partial \Phi_{bc}}{\partial \xi_{bh}}\frac{\partial F_{abc}}{\partial \xi_{bh}}\right]. \tag{3}$$

As before, the integrations with respect to $d\underset{\sim}{x}_c$ and $d\underset{\sim}{\xi}_c$ must be extended over the entire coordinate space and velocity space, while the summation with respect to c must be extended over all types of particles, including the types a and b.

The equation contains the three-particle function F_{abc}, which is defined analogous to the definition of F_{ab}. The problem is how to deal with this function without running into an endless chain of ever more complicated functions. When this question can be settled by the con-

*N. N. Bogoliubov, in "Problems of a Dynamical Theory in Statistical Physics," (translated from the Russian by E. K. Gora, Geophysics Research Directorate, Air Force Cambridge Research Center), Jan. 1959 (AFCRC-TR-59-235), p. 57, Eq. (6.10) Earlier publication in Journal of Physics (U.S.S.R.) Vol. 10, p. 265, 1946.

Similar equations have been given by M. Born and H. S. Green in Proceedings of the Royal Society (London) Part A, Vol. 188, pp. 10-18, 1946; H. S. Green, in "Molecular Theory of Fluids" (Amsterdam 1952), p. 128, Eq. (2.7) etc.; and J. G. Kirkwood, in Journal of Chemical Physics, Vol. 14, pp. 180-201, 1946, and Vol. 15, pp. 72-76, 1947.

See also C. M. Tchen, "Kinetic Equation for a Plasma with Unsteady Correlations," Physical Review, Vol. 114, pp. 397, Eqs. (9) and (10).

struction of an expression giving F_{abc} in terms of the functions F_a, F_b, F_{ab}, etc., the system of equations is still nonlinear and complicated. This forces us to consider methods for further simplification. The problem of finding a suitable method of attack and constructing an expression for the electric conductivity will be the subject of this communication.

II. REDUCTION TO A CLOSED SYSTEM OF EQUATIONS: INTRODUCTION OF THE DEBYE POTENTIAL.

We write: $F_{ab} = F_a F_b + F'_{ab}$;

$$F_{abc} = F_a F_b F_c + F_a F'_{bc} + F_b F'_{ac} + F_c F'_{ab} + F'_{abc} \tag{4}$$

When these expressions are substituted into Eqs. (1) and (3) they are transformed into:

$$\frac{\partial F_a}{\partial t} + \xi_{ah}\frac{\partial F_a}{\partial x_{ah}} + \frac{f_{ah}}{m_a}\frac{\partial F_a}{\partial \xi_{ah}} = \tag{5}$$

$$= -\frac{e_a E^o_h}{m_a}\frac{\partial F_a}{\partial \xi_{ah}} + \frac{1}{m_a}\sum_b \iint d\underset{\sim}{x}_b\, d\underset{\sim}{\xi}_b \frac{\partial \Phi_{ab}}{\partial x_{ah}}\frac{\partial F'_{ab}}{\partial \xi_{ah}};$$

$$\frac{\partial F'_{ab}}{\partial t} + \xi_{ah}\frac{\partial F'_{ab}}{\partial x_{ah}} + \xi_{bh}\frac{\partial F'_{ab}}{\partial x_{bh}} + \frac{f_{ah}}{m_a}\frac{\partial F'_{ab}}{\partial \xi_{ah}} + \frac{f_{bh}}{m_b}\frac{\partial F'_{ab}}{\partial \xi_{bh}} =$$

$$= \frac{1}{m_a}\frac{\partial F_a}{\partial \xi_{ah}}\left\{\frac{\partial \Phi_{ab}}{\partial x_{ah}}F_b + \sum_c \iint d\underset{\sim}{x}_c\, d\underset{\sim}{\xi}_c \frac{\partial \Phi_{ac}}{\partial x_{ah}}F'_{bc}\right\} +$$

$$+ \frac{1}{m_b}\frac{\partial F_b}{\partial \xi_{bh}}\left\{\frac{\partial \Phi_{ab}}{\partial x_{bh}}F_a + \sum_c \iint d\underset{\sim}{x}_c\, d\underset{\sim}{\xi}_c \frac{\partial \Phi_{bc}}{\partial x_{bh}}F'_{ac}\right\} +$$

$$+ \frac{1}{m_a}\frac{\partial F'_{ab}}{\partial \xi_{ah}}\left[\frac{\partial \Phi_{ab}}{\partial x_{ah}} - e_a E^o_h\right] + \frac{1}{m_b}\frac{\partial F'_{ab}}{\partial \xi_{bh}}\left[\frac{\partial \Phi_{ab}}{\partial x_{bh}} - e_b E^o_h\right]$$

$$+ \sum_c \iint d\underset{\sim}{x}_c\, d\underset{\sim}{\xi}_c \left\{\frac{1}{m_a}\frac{\partial \Phi_{ac}}{\partial x_{ah}}\frac{\partial F'_{abc}}{\partial \xi_{ah}} + \frac{1}{m_b}\frac{\partial \Phi_{bc}}{\partial x_{bh}}\frac{\partial F'_{abc}}{\partial \xi_{bh}}\right\}. \tag{6}$$

These equations are still exact. To abbreviate, we have written E_h^o for the electric field produced by the particle charges, according to the equation:

$$\sum_b \int dx_b\, N_b \frac{\partial \Phi_{ab}}{\partial x_{ah}} = -e_a E_h^o . \tag{7}$$

Although the separate integrals on the left-hand side of (7) may be divergent, it is assumed that the sum can be arranged to yield convergent integrals when the gas on the average is neutral. In the case of a gas of uniform density, where the number densities N_b are independent of the coordinates and where the gas as a whole is uniformly neutral, we have $E_h^o = 0$.

On the right-hand side of Eq. (6), we now introduce the following approximations for the functions F'_{bc}, F'_{ac}, and F'_{abc}, where they occur in the multiple integrals with respect to $dx_c\, d\xi_c$:*

$$\left.\begin{aligned} F'_{ac} &= -F_a F_c \Psi_{ac}/\kappa T ;\\ F'_{bc} &= -F_b F_c \Psi_{bc}/\kappa T ;\\ F'_{abc} &= -F'_{ab} F_c (\Psi_{ac} + \Psi_{bc})/\kappa T. \end{aligned}\right\} \tag{8}$$

The functions Ψ_{ac}, Ψ_{bc} are Debye potentials, and will be defined below. The justification for the first and second lines of (8) is that these expressions will be obtained later as first approximations for F'_{ac}, F'_{bc}, respectively. The third line has been constructed on the image of the other lines, taking account of the symmetrical relation of F'_{abc} to a and b.

The purpose of these substitutions is to obtain an approximate representation of the effect of the third particle, c, on the two-particle function F'_{ab}. The temperature T used in (8) is supposed to be uniform over the whole field, and the same for all particles.

The Debye potential is defined by:

$$\Psi_{ab} = e_a e_b \psi_{ab},$$

*These expressions have already been given in a paper "Some Aspects of Particle Interaction in Gases," Example II (p. 18), published as Technical Note of the Institute for Fluid Dynamics and Applied Mathematics, University of Maryland BN-176 (June 1959); also printed in NOL Aeroballistic Research Facilities Dedication and Decennial, NOLR 1238, (May 1959), p. 69. They owe their origin to a translation into coordinate language of certain results obtained by Tchen from the application of Fourier analysis.

with

$$\psi_{ab} = \begin{cases} \dfrac{\exp(-\lambda r)}{r} \quad \dfrac{\exp(\lambda R)}{1+\lambda R+\frac{1}{3}\lambda^2 R^2} & (\text{if } r > R) \\[2ex] \dfrac{\exp(-\lambda R)}{R} \quad \dfrac{\exp(\lambda R)}{1+\lambda R+\frac{1}{3}\lambda^2 R^2} & (\text{if } r < R) \end{cases} \tag{9}$$

Here λ is the reciprocal of the "Debye screening distance", given by

$$\lambda^2 = \frac{4\pi \sum_a N_a e_a^2}{\kappa T} . \tag{10}$$

Although formally this expression would make λ a function of the coordinates, we shall neglect this detail and assume that constant mea values are used for the number densities N_a in Eq. (10).

Usually the Debye screening distance, $1/\lambda$, is much larger thar the distance R, and λR is a quantity small compared with unity. The fact

$$\exp(\lambda R) \Big/ (1+\lambda R+\tfrac{1}{3}\lambda^2 R^2)$$

consequently differs from unity only in terms of the second and higher orders in λR, and in nearly all calculations it can be replaced by unity. It is needed only for the adjustment of the value of a certain integral.

The Debye potential satisfies the following relation:

$$\phi(r) - \frac{\lambda^2}{4\pi} \int d\underset{\sim}{x}_c\, \phi(r_1)\, \psi(\rho) \cong \psi(r), \tag{11}$$

the relative difference between the left-hand side and the right-hand side being of the second order in λR in all cases*. The integration refers to a situation in which the points $\underset{\sim}{x}_a$ and $\underset{\sim}{x}_b$ are fixed, their distance being the fixed vector $\underset{\sim}{r}$; while the point $\underset{\sim}{x}_c$ moves over the entire coordinate space. The distances of $\underset{\sim}{x}_c$ from $\underset{\sim}{x}_a$ and $\underset{\sim}{x}_b$, respectively, are $\underset{\sim}{r}_1$ and $\underset{\sim}{\rho}$, with $\underset{\sim}{\rho} = \underset{\sim}{r}_1 - \underset{\sim}{r}$.

*When the integration is worked out, the following results are obtained for the left-hand side:

For $r > 2R$: $\quad \psi(r) \cdot (1 + \frac{1}{6}\lambda^2 R^2)$

(the introduction of the factor $\exp(\lambda R) / [1 + \lambda R + 1/3, \lambda^2 R^2]$ in Eq. (9) was necessary in order to get rid of a term $\lambda^2 R^2 / 6r$ which would otherwise remain in the result):

For $R < r < 2R$: $\quad \psi(r) \cdot \left\{ 1 - \frac{\lambda^2 r^2}{2} + \frac{2\lambda^2 r R}{3} - \frac{\lambda^2 R^2}{6} + \frac{\lambda^2 r^3}{6R} - \frac{\lambda^2 r^4}{48R^2} \right\}$;

For $r < R$: $\quad \psi(r) \cdot \left\{ 1 + (\lambda^2 r^2/6) - (\lambda^2 r^3/48R) \right\}$.

It follows from this relation that, when the second line of (8) is substituted into the first multiple integral on the right-hand side of (6), the following result is obtained:

$$\sum_c \iint d\underset{\sim}{x}_c \; d\underset{\sim}{\xi}_c \; \frac{\partial \Phi_{ac}}{\partial x_{ah}} \; F'_{bc} = - F_b \left\{ \frac{\partial}{\partial x_{ah}} (\Phi_{ab} - \Psi_{ab}) \right\}. \qquad (12)$$

The addition of this result to the term just preceding the multiple integral results in the Coulomb potential in that term being replaced by the Debye potential.

We apply a similar transformation to all multiple integrals on the right hand side of (6). After some calculation, it is found that this equation reduces to

$$\frac{\partial F'_{ab}}{\partial t} + \xi_{ah} \frac{\partial F'_{ab}}{\partial x_{ah}} + \xi_{bh} \frac{\partial F'_{ab}}{\partial x_{bh}} + \frac{f_{ah}}{m_a} \frac{\partial F'_{ab}}{\partial \xi_{ah}} + \frac{f_{bh}}{m_b} \frac{\partial F'_{ab}}{\partial \xi_{bh}} =$$

$$= \frac{F_b}{m_a} \frac{\partial F_a}{\partial \xi_{ah}} \frac{\partial \Psi_{ab}}{\partial x_{ah}} + \frac{F_a}{m_b} \frac{\partial F_b}{\partial \xi_{bh}} \frac{\partial \Psi_{ab}}{\partial x_{bh}} +$$

$$+ \frac{1}{m_a} \frac{\partial F'_{ab}}{\partial \xi_{ah}} \left[\frac{\partial \Psi_{ab}}{\partial x_{ah}} - e_a E^o_h \right] + \frac{1}{m_b} \frac{\partial F'_{ab}}{\partial \xi_{bh}} \left[\frac{\partial \Psi_{ab}}{\partial x_{bh}} - e_b E^o_h \right]. \qquad (13)$$

The system of equations formed by (5) and (13), written out for as many types of particles and as many types of pairs of particles as are present in the gas, forms a complete system of partial differential equations for the functions F_a, F'_{ab}, etc. This system is linear in functions F'_{ab}, but nonlinear in F_a, etc. We shall follow a method of treatment which obviates the difficulty connected with the nonlinearity.

III. ADAPTATION TO THE CASE OF A UNIFORM (HOMOGENEOUS) AND TIME-INDEPENDENT FIELD. INTRODUCTION OF MAXWELLIAN EXPRESSIONS FOR F_a, F_b.

We consider the motion of ions and electrons under the influence of a uniform and steady exterior electric field E_h. The state of the gas will be uniform and time-independent; hence we can assume that the gas is everywhere neutral and have $E^o_h = 0$.

Equation (5) reduces to:

$$\frac{e_a E_h}{m_a} \frac{\partial F_a}{\partial \xi_{ah}} = \frac{1}{m_a} \sum_b \iint d\underset{\sim}{x}_b \, d\underset{\sim}{\xi}_b \frac{\partial \Phi_{ab}}{\partial x_{ah}} \frac{\partial F'_{ab}}{\partial \xi_{ah}}, \tag{5*}$$

where we have replaced f_{ah} by e_a E_h. We multiply on both sides with m_a ξ_{ak} and intergrate with respect to $d\underset{\sim}{\xi}_a$ over the entire velocity space. After omission of the factor δ_{hk} on both sides this gives:

$$N_a e_a E_h = \sum_b \iiint d\underset{\sim}{\xi}_a \, d\underset{\sim}{\xi}_b \, d\underset{\sim}{x}_b \frac{\partial \Phi_{ab}}{\partial x_{ah}} F'_{ab}. \tag{14}$$

Equation (14) is exact and does not itself involve any approximation. If desired, similar equations can be obtained by calculating higher moments of Eq. (5*), that is, by multiplying Eq. (5*) on both sides with some power of ξ_{ak} or with a product of such factors, and integrating again over the entire velocity space.

Equation (13) will be written in the following form:

$$\left.\begin{aligned} &\frac{\partial F'_{ab}}{\partial t} + \xi_{ah} \frac{\partial F'_{ab}}{\partial x_{ah}} + \xi_{bh} \frac{\partial F'_{ab}}{\partial x_{bh}} = \\ &\quad = \frac{F_b}{m_a} \frac{\partial F_a}{\partial \xi_{ak}} \frac{\partial \Psi_{ab}}{\partial x_{ak}} + \frac{F_a}{m_b} \frac{\partial F_b}{\partial \xi_{bk}} \frac{\partial \Psi_{ab}}{\partial x_{bk}} + \\ &\quad + \frac{1}{m_a} \frac{\partial F'_{ab}}{\partial \xi_{ak}} \frac{\partial \Psi_{ab}}{\partial x_{ak}} + \frac{1}{m_b} \frac{\partial F'_{ab}}{\partial \xi_{bk}} \frac{\partial \Psi_{ab}}{\partial x_{bk}} - \\ &\quad - \frac{e_a E_k}{m_a} \frac{\partial F'_{ab}}{\partial \xi_{ak}} - \frac{e_b E_k}{m_b} \frac{\partial F'_{ab}}{\partial \xi_{bk}}. \end{aligned}\right\} \tag{15}$$

There are three lines on the right-hand side, to be distinguished as (I), (II), (III). The contribution derived from (I) is the most important one and gives the main effect. The contribution derived from (II) can be considered as a correction connected with the effects of close encounters. The contribution derived from (III) represents an effect produced by the distortion of the Debye screening cloud caused by the electric field E_h.

The following approximations will now be introduced into Eq. (15)

In the first line on the right-hand side we use Maxwellian ex- ›ressions for F_a, F_b, with the same temperature T (constant hroughout the field), but with different and unknown mean flow veloci- ies $\underset{\sim}{u}_a$, $\underset{\sim}{u}_b$, respectively. Equation (14), written out for each type of ›article, will give the means for the determination of the differences ›f the mean flow velocities. In principle it is possible to introduce modified Maxwellian expressions (or other expressions) for F_a, F_b, :ontaining a finite number of unknown parameters. We must then de- luce a set of moment equations from (5*), in such number that there are as many equations as there are unknown parameters. The solu- ion of such a system will make it possible to obtain a greater accuracy in the results, but requires lengthy calculations. We shall therefore restrict ourselves to Eq. (14) and calculate only the flow velocities.

In the second and third lines of Eq. (15) we substitute an approxi- mation for F'_{ab}, obtained from line (I).

When the Maxwellian expressions:

$$\left.\begin{aligned} F_a &= N_a \left[\frac{m_a}{2\pi\kappa T}\right]^{3/2} \exp \frac{-m_a\left[\xi_{ah} - u_{ah}\right]^2}{2\kappa T} \\ F_b &= N_b \left[\frac{m_b}{2\pi\kappa T}\right]^{3/2} \exp \frac{-m_b\left[\xi_{bh} - u_{bh}\right]^2}{2\kappa T} \end{aligned}\right\} \qquad (16)$$

are introduced into line (I) of Eq. (15), this line can we written:

$$\frac{(g_k - v_k)\ F_a F_b}{\kappa T} \frac{\partial \Psi_{ab}}{\partial x_{ak}},$$

where

$$g_k = \xi_{bk} - \xi_{ak}; \qquad v_k = u_{bk} - u_{ak}.$$

The integral of an equation of the type

$$\frac{\partial F'}{\partial t} + \xi_{ah} \frac{\partial F'}{\partial x_{ah}} + \xi_{bh} \frac{\partial F'}{\partial x_{bh}} = q\,(t, x_{ah}, x_{bh})$$

is given by

$$F' = \int_0^\infty d\tau \; q\,(t-\tau,\; x_{ah} - \xi_{ah}\,\tau,\; x_{bh} - \xi_{bh}\,\tau),$$

if we assume that F' has the value zero for $t = -\infty$.

In the case under consideration, the quantity (I) on the right-hand side of (15) does not contain t, while the coordinates x_{ah} and x_{bh} occur only in the function Ψ_{ab}. We write:

$$r_{lh} = x_{bh} - x_{ah}\,; \quad \rho_h = x_{bh} - x_{ah} - (\xi_{bh} - \xi_{ah})\,\tau;$$

Furthermore, we introduce

$$r_h = (\xi_{bh} - \xi_{ah})\,\tau = g_h\tau,$$

so that $\rho_h = r_{lh} - r_h$. The integral of (15), insofar as it depends upon the first line on the right-hand side, can then be written:

$$F'^{(I)}_{ab} = \frac{(g_k - v_k)\,F_a\,F_b}{\kappa T} \int_0^\infty d\tau\, \frac{\partial\,\Phi(\rho)}{\partial x_{ak}}\,. \tag{17}$$

In the case where the relative flow velocity of the particles of types a and b is zero (where the particles are of the same type) and in other cases, where it may sometimes hold approximately, we can omit v_k and make use of the relation

$$g_k \frac{\partial\,\Psi(\rho)}{\partial x_{ak}} = \frac{\partial\Psi}{\partial\tau}\,.$$

The integration with respect to $d\tau$ in (17) can then be carried out at once, and since $\rho_h = r_{lh}$ for $\tau = 0$, we obtain the approximation:

$$F'_{ab} \cong -\frac{F_a\,F_b}{\kappa T}\,\Psi_{ab}\,(r_1). \tag{17*}$$

This approximation has been used in (8). It will also be introduced into lines (II) and (III) of Eq. (15).

IV. APPLICATION OF EQUATION (14) TO THE RESULT GIVEN BY (17).

In view of the length of the required calculations, we start with the contribution from line (I) of Eq. (15), as given in (17). When this expression is introduced on the right-hand side of (14) it is seen that we must evaluate the integral

$$\sum_b \frac{e_a^2 e_b^2}{\kappa T} \iint d\underset{\sim}{\xi}_a \, d\underset{\sim}{\xi}_b \, F_a \, F_b \, (g_k - v_k) \int_0^\infty d\tau \int d\underset{\sim}{x}_b \frac{\partial \phi(r_1)}{\partial x_{ah}} \frac{\partial \psi(\rho)}{\partial x_{ak}} . \qquad (18)$$

The potentials Φ_{ab} and Ψ_{ab} have been expressed by means of $\phi(r_1)$ and $\psi(\rho)$; the order of the integrations has been changed slightly. When use is made of the definitions of $\underset{\sim}{r}_1$ and $\underset{\sim}{r}$ as give above, and when a partial integration is applied, one finds that:

$$\int d\underset{\sim}{x}_b \frac{\partial \phi(r_1)}{\partial x_{ah}} \frac{\partial \psi(\rho)}{\partial x_{ak}} = - \frac{\partial^2}{\partial r_h \, \partial r_k} \int d\underset{\sim}{x}_b \; \phi\,(r_1)\, \psi\,(\rho) .$$

The integral occurring here is of a type similar to the one that occurs in (11). Although the variable point is now written $\underset{\sim}{x}_b$ (instead of $\underset{\sim}{x}_c$) the outcome of the integration again depends exclusively upon the fixed vector $\underset{\sim}{r}$. We shall write:

$$\int d\underset{\sim}{x}_b \; \phi\,(r_1)\, \psi\,(\rho) = \frac{4\pi}{\lambda} \, G\,(r) , \qquad (19)$$

which makes G(r) a dimensionless function. Evaluation of the integral gives;

$$\left.\begin{aligned} G &= \frac{1 - \exp(-\lambda r)}{\lambda r} - \frac{\lambda R^2 \exp(-\lambda r)}{3r} && \text{if } r > 2R ; \\ G &= 1 - \frac{2\lambda R}{3} - \frac{\lambda r^2}{6R} + \frac{\lambda r^3}{48R^3} && \text{if } r < 2R, \end{aligned}\right\} \qquad (19^*)$$

neglecting quantities of the order $\lambda^2 R^2$ in the second expression. As G(r) is a scalar function of $\underset{\sim}{r}$, we have:

$$\frac{\partial^2 G}{\partial r_h \, \partial r_k} = \frac{r_h \, r_k}{r^2} \frac{d^2 G}{dr^2} + \frac{\delta_{hk} - r_h r_k / r^2}{r} \frac{dG}{dr} .$$

With regard to the relation $r_h = g_h \tau$, the integration with respect to $d\tau$ can now be worked out, provided use is made of expressions (19*).

We observe that

$$r_h r_k / r^2 = g_h g_k / g^2,$$

which is a constant when the integration with respect to $d\tau$ is performed. Since $dG/dr = 0$ for $r = 0$ as well as for $r \longrightarrow \infty$, and is continuous at $r = 2R$, the term with d^2G/dr^2 does not give a contribution to the result. The other term gives:

$$\int_0^\infty d\tau \int d\underset{\sim}{x}_b \frac{\partial \phi(r_1)}{\partial x_{ah}} \frac{\partial \psi(\rho)}{\partial x_{ak}} = 2\pi C \frac{\delta_{hk} - g_h g_k / g^2}{g},$$

where C is a numerical factor, defined by

$$C = -\frac{2}{\lambda} \int_0^\infty \frac{dr}{r} \frac{dG}{dr} = -\ell n (2\lambda R) - \gamma + \frac{3}{2} \tag{20}$$

(γ = Euler's constant = 0. 577). This result turns the integral (18) into:

$$2\pi \sum_b \frac{Ce_a^2 e_b^2}{\kappa T} \iint d\underset{\sim}{\xi}_a \, d\underset{\sim}{\xi}_b \, F_a \, F_b \, (g_k - v_k) \frac{\delta_{hk} - g_h g_k / g^2}{g} . \tag{18*}$$

The product of g_k into $(\delta_{hk} - g_h g_k/g^2)$ gives zero; therefore the resulting expression will have $- v_k$ as a factor. This means that a force results only when there is a relative flow velocity between two types of particles. The "static" Debye cloud, which is obtained in the absence of relative flow velocity, does not give a resulting force on the particle at its center.

The multiple integral with respect to $d\underset{\sim}{\xi}_a \, d\underset{\sim}{\xi}_b$ can be worked out most conveniently when $\underset{\sim}{\xi}_a$ and $\underset{\sim}{\xi}_b$ are expressed by means of the velocity of the center of gravity of the two particles,

$$\underset{\sim}{C} = (m_a \underset{\sim}{\xi}_a + m_b \underset{\sim}{\xi}_b) / (m_a + m_b),$$

and the relative velocity, $\underset{\sim}{g} = \underset{\sim}{\xi}_b - \underset{\sim}{\xi}_a$. The integration with respect to $d\underset{\sim}{C}$ can be effected at once; that with respect to $d\underset{\sim}{g}$ requires the application of polar coordinates with the direction of the vector $\underset{\sim}{v}$ as axis. The final result is that Eq. (14) is turned into:

$$N_a e_a E_h = -\sum_b \frac{4\pi C N_a N_b e_a^2 e_b^2}{\mu} \frac{v_h}{v^3} \left[\mathrm{Erf}\, \frac{v}{\alpha} - \frac{2v}{\pi^{1/2}\alpha} \exp\left(\frac{-v^2}{\alpha^2}\right) \right] \tag{21}$$

Here μ has been written for $m_a m_b/(m_a + m_b)$*, and $\alpha = (2\kappa T/\mu)^{1/2}$, which is a measure for the mean relative velocity of the particles of type a with respect to the particles of type b, in consequence of the heat motion.

When the relative mean flow velocity $\underset{\sim}{v}$ of the particles is small compared with α, the velocity-dependent factor on the right-hand side of (21) reduces to $(4/3\pi^{1/2})\, v_h/\alpha^3$, while for very large values of the relative flow velocity it reduces to v_h/v^3. This gives the decrease of electrical resistance occurring with large flow velocities, which is termed the "runaway" phenomenon. **

The system of equations obtained in this way has the same structure as that given by the application of the method of first moments to the ordinary Boltzmann equation. To the present approximation it gives the same result, with the coefficient C in the place of the quantity $\ell n \Lambda$ occurring in other notations. † The simplest case is that where there is only one kind of positive ion and one kind of negative ion (electron). The only term occurring in the sum on the right-hand side of (21) in this case is the term referring to the case where a and b are different.

*The presence of μ in the denominator on the right-hand side of (21) can be interpreted as introducing the factor $(1/m_a + 1/m_b)$. In Tchen's calculations (op. cit.), which lead to a Fokker-Planck equation, this factor is obtained from a combination of the $\underline{A}$ and $\underline{B}$ coefficients, as indicated in Tchen's Eq. (29b) (loc. cit., p. 402).

In a paper by S. Gasiorowicz, M. Neuman and R. J. Riddell, Jr., "Dynamics of Ionized Media" (Physical Review, Vol. 101, pp. 922-934, 1956) the two parts of the result are obtained separately, as "polarization effect" and "statistical effect," by a reasoning which seems to be rather involved.

**See, for instance, F. H. Clauser, "Plasma Dynamics" (Addison-Wesley Publishing Co., 1960, Section 5-15, pp. 155-157). The result is also contained in Tchen's formulas (37a) and (37b) (loc. cit., p. 403).

† Compare Section 5-5, in F. H. Clauser, "Plasma Dynamics" (see footnote above), expressions for the cross sections given in Eqs. (5-20) - (5-22c). The factor $1/(1-\Delta)$, appearing in the refined expression (5-69) (p. 152), is not obtained by the present calculations. For this purpose it would be necessary to use a modified Maxwellian function for F_a, F_b and to determine the extra parameter with the aid of a higher moment equation derived from (5*), as was indicated in the text. The factor $1/(1 - \Delta)$ produces a decrease of the electrical resistance in comparison with the value given by the first approximation. The corrected result corresponds closely to that obtained by Spitzer in a different way (see, for instance, values given on p. 84 of L. Spitzer Jr., "Physics of Fully Ionized Gases," Interscience Publishers, Inc., 1956).

V. CONTRIBUTION OF THE TERMS IN THE SECOND LINE ON THE RIGHT-HAND SIDE OF EQ. (15).

As mentioned before, we substitute the approximation (17*) for F'_{ab} in line (II) of Eq. (15). This line then takes the form:

$$- \frac{(g_k - v_k) F_a F_b}{(\kappa T)^2} \Psi_{ab} \frac{\partial \Psi_{ab}}{\partial x_{ak}} ,$$

which leads to:

$$F'^{(II)}_{ab} = - \frac{(g_k - v_k) F_a F_b}{(\kappa T)^2} \int_0^\infty d\tau \, \Psi(\rho) \frac{\partial \Psi(\rho)}{\partial x_{ak}} . \qquad (22)$$

Much of the scheme of calculation used in the previous section can be retained, with the difference that instead of the function G(r) defined in (19) we must use another function, $G^{II}(r)$, defined by:*

$$\int d\underset{\sim}{x}_b \, \phi(r_1) \left\{ \psi(\rho)^2 \right\} = 4\pi G^{II}(r) . \qquad (23)$$

This leads to the introduction of a new numerical coefficient, C^{II}, which we define as

$$C^{II} = - R \int_0^\infty \frac{dr}{r} \frac{dG^{II}}{dr} . \qquad (24)$$

Numerical integration gives approximately $C^{II} = 0.89$. We then obtain

*The following expressions have been obtained for G^{II}:

$$G^{II} \cong \frac{1}{2\lambda r} \quad \text{if } r >> \frac{1}{\lambda} ;$$

$$G^{II} = \frac{3}{2} - \frac{2R}{3r} - \ell n(2\lambda R) - \gamma - \ell n \frac{r+R}{R} - \frac{(r-R)^2}{4rR} \ell n \frac{r+R}{r-R} \quad \text{if } \frac{1}{\lambda} >> r > 2R;$$

and

$$G^{II} = \frac{7}{12} + \frac{3r}{8R} - \frac{r^2}{12R^2} + \frac{r^3}{48R^3} - \ell n(2\lambda R) - \gamma - \frac{(r+R)^2}{4rR} \ell n \frac{r+R}{R} \quad \text{if } r < 2R.$$

$$\int_0^\infty d\tau \int d\underset{\sim}{x}_b \frac{\partial\phi(r_1)}{\partial x_{ah}} \psi(\rho) \frac{\partial\psi(\rho)}{\partial x_{ak}} = \frac{2\pi C^{II}}{R} \frac{\delta_{hk} - g_h g_k/g^2}{g} .$$

When the integrations are worked out, we find

$$- \sum_b \frac{e_a^3 e_b^3}{(\kappa T)^2} \iint d\underset{\sim}{\xi}_a \, d\underset{\sim}{\xi}_b \, F_a F_b (g_k - v_k) \int_0^\infty d\tau \int dx_b \frac{\partial\phi(r_1)}{\partial x_{ah}} \psi(\rho) \frac{\partial\psi(\rho)}{\partial x_{ak}} =$$

$$= + \sum_b \frac{4\pi C^{II} N_a N_b e_a^3 e_b^3}{\mu R \kappa T} \frac{v_h}{v^3} \left[\operatorname{Erf} \frac{v}{\alpha} - \frac{2v}{\pi^{1/2} \alpha} \exp \frac{-v^2}{a^2} \right] . \tag{25}$$

This result can be compared with that given by (21). Both expressions have the same dependence on the relative flow velocity $\underset{\sim}{v}$. It is easy to combine the right-hand side of (25) with the right-hand side of (21), since all that is needed is to replace the coefficient C in (21) by

$$C - C^{II} \frac{e_a e_b}{R\kappa T} .$$

When the particles of types a and b have charges of the same sign, the new coefficient leads to a decreased resistance coefficient. This can be interpreted as a result of the repulsion between such particles, which makes the density of the b particles in the immediate neighborhood of an a particle somewhat smaller than average and thus introduces a slight decrease of the collision frequency. On the other hand, when the particles have opposite charges, there is an increase in the resistance coefficient. As to order of magnitude, $e_a e_b/\kappa T$ in absolute magnitude represents what is often taken as a measure for the distance of closest approach between particles of a mean temperature T, a distance which usually is several times larger than the diameter of the particles. Since we have assumed that R would be of the order of the ionic diameter, the ratio $e_a e_b/(R\kappa T)$ can be, say of the order of 5 or 10. As $\underset{\sim}{C}$ can be of the same order (perhaps reaches up to 20 or 30), the correction due to C^{II} can be important. *

*When the correction becomes too large to appear admissible (as might be the case with special conditions of density and temperature), it would point to the necessity for using a better method of approximation in the solution of Eq. (15). The application of straight line characteristics may then be too crude.

VI. CONTRIBUTION OBTAINED FROM THE TERMS IN LINE (III) ON THE RIGHT-HAND SIDE OF EQ. (15).

Again we substitute the approximation (17*) for F'_{ab}. Line (III) takes the form:

$$- \frac{E_k w_k F_a F_b}{(\kappa T)^2} \Psi_{ab},$$

where w_k has been used as an abbreviation for

$$w_k = e_a (\xi_{ah} - u_{ak}) + e_b (\xi_{bk} - u_{bk}) =$$

$$= (e_a + e_b) C_k - \frac{e_a m_b - e_b m_a}{m_a + m_b} g_k - (e_a u_{ak} + e_b u_{bk}).$$

We observe that

$$w_k = 2 e_a (C_k - u_{ak})$$

when the particles are of the same type; and that

$$w_k = - e_a (g_k - v_k)$$

when the particles have charges of opposite magnitude (the masses may be arbitrary). The following contribution is obtained for F'_{ab}:

$$F'^{(III)}_{ab} = - \frac{E_k w_k F_a F_b}{(\kappa T)^2} \int_0^\infty d\tau \; \Psi(\rho). \qquad (26)$$

For the calculation of the expression on the right-hand side of (14), we need the integral:

$$\int_0^\infty d\tau \int dx_b \frac{\partial \phi(r_1)}{\partial x_{ah}} \Psi(\rho) = - \frac{4\pi}{\lambda} \int_0^\infty d\tau \frac{\partial G}{\partial r_h} =$$

$$= - \frac{4\pi}{\lambda} \frac{g_h}{g^2} \int_0^\infty dr \frac{dG}{dr} = \frac{4\pi}{\lambda} \frac{g_h}{g^2}.$$

There remains to calculate:

$$- \frac{4\pi E_k}{\lambda} \sum_b \frac{e_a^2 e_b^2}{(\kappa T)^2} \iint d\underset{\sim}{\xi}_a \, d\underset{\sim}{\xi}_b \, F_a F_b w_k \frac{g_h}{g^2} .$$

The calculation is straightforward, but tedious. The integral disappears when the particles are of the same type. Since there is no magnetic field in the case considered here, we can make use of the fact that the relative flow velocities will have the direction of the electric field, so that $v_h/v = E_h/E$. The result of the integration is:

$$- \frac{4\pi E_k}{\lambda} \sum_b \frac{e_a^2 e_b^2}{(\kappa T)^2} \iint d\underset{\sim}{\xi}_a \, d\underset{\sim}{\xi}_b \, F_a \, F_b \, w_k \int_0^\infty d\tau \int d\underset{\sim}{x}_b \frac{\partial \phi(r_1)}{\partial x_{ah}} \psi(\rho) =$$

$$= 4\pi E_h \sum_b \frac{N_a N_b e_a^2 e_b^2}{\lambda (\kappa T)^2} \frac{m_b e_a - m_a e_b}{m_a + m_b} W, \qquad (27)$$

with

$$W = \left[1 + \frac{\alpha^2}{v^2}\right] \exp\left[\frac{-v^2}{\alpha^2}\right] \int_0^1 dz \, \exp \frac{v^2 z^2}{\alpha^2} - \frac{\alpha^2}{v^2} \qquad (27^*)$$

This quantity has the value 1/3 for very small values of v/α, while it goes to zero when v/α increases without limit. The factor

$$(m_b e_a - m_a m_b)/(m_a + m_b)$$

in (27) vanishes when the particles are of the same type, and becomes e_a when they are of opposite charge.

When the gas has only two types of particles, positive ions and electrons, all having unit charges, the final form of the momentum equation can be written as follows:

$$NeE_h \left\{1 - \frac{4\pi Ne^4}{\lambda (\kappa T)^2} W\right\} =$$

$$= -\frac{4\pi N^2 e^4}{\mu}\left[C + C^{II}\frac{e^2}{R\kappa T}\right]\frac{v_h}{v^3}\left[\operatorname{Erf}\frac{v}{\alpha} - \frac{2v}{\pi^{1/2}\alpha}\exp\left(\frac{-v^2}{\alpha^2}\right)\right] \quad (28)$$

With regard to formula (10) defining λ^2, and the circumstance that $e^2/\kappa T$ is perhaps 10 times the value of R, it will be seen that the correction term introduced on the left-hand side to account for the contribution from line (III) is of the order of perhaps 5 to 10 times the value of λR, which has been considered small compared with unity. Thus the effect of line (III) seems to be much smaller than that of line (II).

STABILITY ANALYSIS OF PLASMAS BY A MODIFIED HYDROMAGNETIC THEORY*

O. Buneman
Stanford Electronics Laboratories, Stanford University

Hot plasmas carrying high currents can be confined to dimensions much smaller than the mean-free path. Conventional hydromagnetic theory employing a scalar pressure and a scalar conductivity then becomes dubious.

A two-component theory (separate electron and ion fluids) with two pressure tensors following fully adiabatic laws can, however, be justified by the moment method for supersonically propagating phenomena. Only a damping process is missed by such a theory, which would therefore err on the pessimistic side when used for stability tests.

The one-dimensionally confined plasma current sheet is being subjected to a stability test by this method. Two-stream instabilities, gyromagnetic resonances and familiar hydromagnetic instabilities could occur but it appears that all can be suppressed.

I. INTRODUCTION: MODIFICATIONS OF MAGNETOHYDRODYNAMICS

The aim of the work discussed in this paper is to test a simple non-uniform plasma configuration for stability under conditions where the dimensions of the plasma or the perturbations are small compared with the mean free path. The work is, as yet, incomplete, but some general considerations may be of interest regarding the nature of stable configurations, the physical laws involved and the methods and approximations to be employed in the analysis.

The basic assumption of conventional magnetohydrodynamics (that scales are large compared with the mean free path) breaks down for many plasmas of practical importance; including the plasma surrounding the earth, and the plasma to be bottled for thermo-nuclear power. Transversely to the magnetic field, one can rescue magneto-hydrodynamics[1] whenever a small Larmor radius acts as a localizing agent, instead of a small mean free path. However, quite apart from longitudinal effects not covered, the thicknesses of current sheets are often smaller than the ion Larmor radius, therefore better theories are needed. (A current sheet will be the first plasma model to be studied here.)

*This work has been supported in part by the U.S. Air Force, A. F. Cambridge Research Laboratories under contract AF-19(604)-5480.

Presented at the Symposium on Electromagnetics and Fluid Dynamics of Gaseous Plasma, Polytechnic Institute of Brooklyn, April 4, 5, 6, 1961

Rigorous formulation of the problem from Boltzmann-Liouville theory is possible.[2, 3] It leads to complicated integro-differential equations. In simple geometries (cylindrical and slab) these equations have been written down more or less explicitly. Their solution is unmanageable; typically, even the unperturbed particle orbits are available only in numerical form.

Approximations have been tried: for instance, slow variation of density on some appropriate scale.[4] An approximation to be explored here is closely related to magnetohydrodynamics on the one hand and has, on the other hand, been tested for its ability, or lack of ability, to reproduce strict kinetic-theory results.[5]

The theory is a two-component form of magnetohydrodynamics in which each species, separately, moves according to a strict adiabatic gas law in the combined electromagnetic field of the two species. The pressure tensor is not assumed to be isotropic. Both the presence of a strong electromagnetic field and the rapidity of microwave perturbations cause pressure anisotropies. This means that the adiabatic gas law must be generalized.[5]

The general adiabatic law for anisotropic pressure tensors[5, 6] is obtained by the truncation method. Variations of the third moments of the distribution of peculiar velocities are ignored, but it can be shown that in application to near-equilibrium plasmas, this method is already as good as a more elaborate calculation which postpones the cutoff to fourth moments.

Since electron and ion motion in response to an electric field are calculated separately, the conductivity can be calculated by superposition of the electron and ion currents.

The theory has been compared[5, 7] with strict kinetic theory for uniformity in space and has been found to give correctly the "warm" plasma approximation. It fails to reproduce Landau damping,[8] i. e., dissipation by phase mixing. It is a "supersonic" theory. The localizing effect needed to rescue a hydrodynamical treatment is provided by the inability of particles to cover great distances within one cycle of the perturbation wave.

In general, the omitted phase-mixing effects should have a damping effect on any instabilities (this has been checked carefully for the electrostatic two-stream instability) which our theory may throw up. We, therefore, use it with confidence as a pessimistic theory for stability tests.

After finding the application of the theory to a uniform plasma feasible and moderately successful, we have now set up the mathematical apparatus for applying it to simple configurations of non-uniform confined plasmas. While there are considerable complications arising from non-uniformity, and while the calculations are still far from complete, the problem seems decidedly manageable.

II. THE EQUILIBRIUM STATE: A CURRENT SHEET

It is necessary for the equilibrium state to be compatible with all the dynamical laws employed for the perturbation calculation. This leaves little to the imagination, since the two species are separately tied down in our analysis.

Regarding the remaining freedom of choice, we simply select the most probable distribution of each species in the electromagnetic field provided for it by the other species. This automatically leads to Chapman-Cowling's[9] condition that each species must have a drift distribution as if it were in rigid motion,and a Maxwellian distribution of peculiar velocities. The particle density observed in the frame of the drift is proportional to $\exp(\pm e\phi/\kappa T)$ where ϕ is the electrostatic potential applicable in the frame (with an addition for centrifugal potential when this frame rotates).

Making the charge and current density consistent with the field, one is led to a fairly limited set of equilibriums. Best known among these is the old cylindrical column of Bennet.[10] For mathematical reasons, we find it easier to consider a simple slab geometry, and it is fortunate that in this case the most probable distributions of electrons and ions with mutual drift make up a plausible and realistic model of a current sheet, the very object which it seems most imperative to investigate.

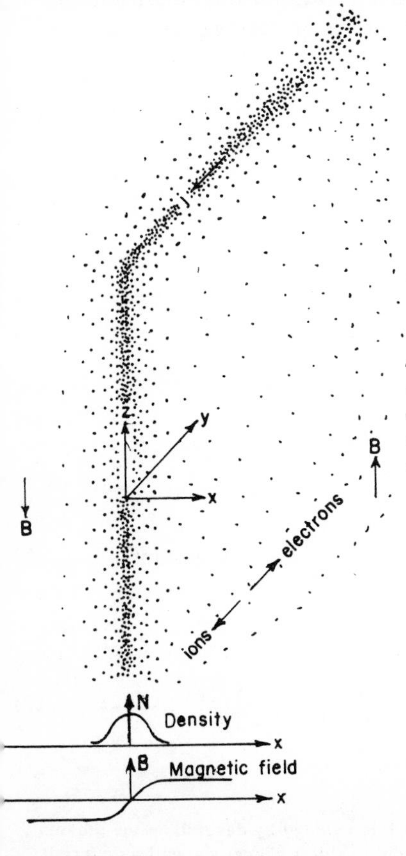

Fig. 1 Current sheet

Such a sheet is illustrated in Fig. 1. The electron and ion drift velocities are in opposite directions and each is uniform across the sheet. The density follows a sech^2 law with distance; the magnetic field follows a tanh law. Each species has its own temperature and isotropic pressure, and obeys the conditions of magnetohydrostatic equilibrium.

To get good confinement with moderate currents per unit width, one would make the drift of the electrons relative to the ions as large as possible. However, stability considerations (see Section III of this paper) limit the drift energy to the thermal energy of the electrons approximately. Assum-

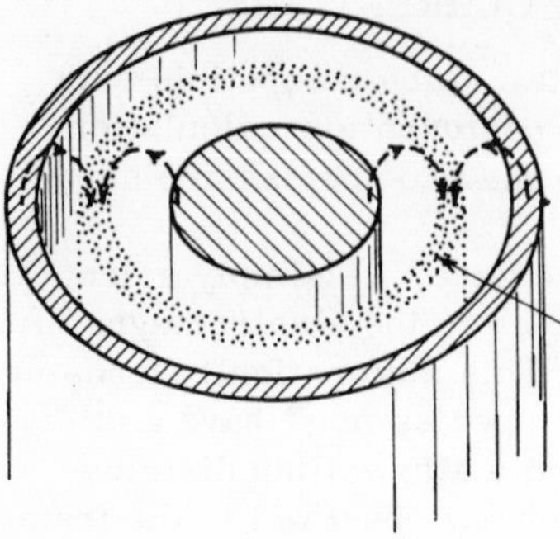

Fig. 2 "Triax" plasma configuration

ing the thermal energy of the electrons to be comparable to that of the ions, one finds an electron Larmor radius comparable to the sheet thickness and a Debye length of the order V/c smaller.

A physical realization of such a current sheet is obtained in the "triax" pinch (see Fig. 2) where current flows in the same direction in both the inner and outer solid conductors of a coaxial arrangement while returning via the plasma. The current sheet that envelops the more common type of pinch has a dense plasma on one side and therefore differs from the model used here.

The details of our model are obtained from the conditions of magnetostatic equilibrium for each species as follows:

$$\nabla p_{e,i} = \underline{j}_{e,i} \wedge \underline{B}/c \quad , \tag{1}$$

$$p_{e,i} = NKT_{e,i} \quad , \tag{2}$$

$$\underline{j}_{e,i} = \pm eN\underline{V}_{e,i} \quad \text{(along y-axis)} \quad , \tag{3}$$

$$\nabla \wedge \underline{B} = 4\pi\,(\underline{j}_e + \underline{j}_i)/c \quad , \tag{4}$$

so that:

$$-\frac{c}{eB(x)}\,\frac{d(\ell n\,N)}{dx} = \frac{|Ve|}{KT_e} = \frac{|Vi|}{KT_i} = \text{constant*} \tag{5}$$

$$\frac{1}{N(x)}\,\frac{d(eB(x)/c)}{dx} = 4\pi e^2\left[|V_e| + |V_i|\right]/c^2 \quad . \tag{6}$$

*The condition $|V_e|/|V_i| = T_e/T_i$ could be avoided by describing the plasma in a different frame of reference in which it would exhibit charge as well as current.

he last pair of equations ((5) and (6)) is solved by

$$N(x) = \frac{K(T_e + T_i)}{4\pi W_e r_o a^2} \operatorname{sech}^2(x/a) , \tag{7}$$

$$eB(x)/c = \frac{K(T_e + T_i)}{|V_e| + |V_i|} \frac{2}{a} \tanh \frac{x}{a} , \tag{8}$$

here

$$r_o = e^2/mc^2 = \text{classical electron radius} = 2.8 \times 10^{-13} \text{cm} , \tag{9}$$

$$W_e = m_e\left[|V_e| + |V_i|\right]^2/2 , \tag{10}$$

W_e is the drift energy of the electrons relative to the ions, and a is length indicating the effective thickness of the sheet. The particle ressure, $NKT_e + NKT_i$, is a fraction, $\operatorname{sech}^2(x/a)$, of the constant otal pressure $NKT_e + NKT_i + B^2/8\pi$, so that

$$\beta = 1/\sinh^2(x/a). \tag{11}$$

he multiplier in (8) determines the sheet current per unit width since his is $(c/4\pi)\left[B(+\infty) - B(-\infty)\right]$.

A uniform field along the current flow direction can be super-mposed without changing the nature of the sheet. The total field then otates across the sheet through a certain angle.

III. STABILITY: GENERAL CONSIDERATIONS

Our model is in equilibrium macroscopically, i. e., to the extent hat the particle structure of the electronic and ionic fluid is ignored. n other words, the model is in accordance with Vlasov's equation, in hich no account is taken of close collisions or of Fokker-Planck erms.

While each species is already in its most probable state and has distribution function immune to collisions, the two species are not n mutual equilibrium.

No confined plasma configuration can be found in which ions and lectrons are in equilibrium both with themselves and with each other. his is readily deduced from the Chapman-Cowling[9] theorem that in a iven field only rigid drift distributions are in equilibrium plus the fact that relative drifts would be destroyed by collisions.

Confinement requires internal currents and hence mutual drift One must deviate in some manner from absolute statistical equilibrium and its uninteresting uniformity; one must interfere with nature.

The speed of return to perfect statistical equilibrium depends upon the avenues available for such a process. Collisions do provid a means of destroying mutual drifts, but at high temperatures and in astronomical plasmas they are very infrequent and an "unnatural" state might maintain itself for a long time. The state must, howeve be in macroscopic, collision-free equilibrium: it must obey Vlasov's equation. This situation[11] has been called "metaequilibrium."

Moreover, the equilibrium must be stable within the framewor of the macroscopic picture. Instabilities due to collective electroma netic interaction tend to be associated with growth-times much short than time intervals between collisions. Typically, two-stream insta bilities have an energy-doubling time of one electron-plasma period. The more familiar types of instabilities deduced from simple, conve tional, single-fluid magnetohydrodynamics also have rapid rates of rise.

We have guarded against some types of instabilities by choosin a state with internal statistical equilibrium of each species. We hav chosen their most probable distribution functions (the logarithms of which depend linearly on the total energy and total momenta, the "summational invariants").

One may go further and invoke an entropy argument such as th given by Newcomb[12] for the uniform plasma. This would show that each species is stable in the field provided for it by the other specie even to electromagnetic field perturbations created by its own internal fluctuations.

It is rather important that the electron distribution should be chosen stable in this sense, since its collective electromagnetic instabilities would rise so rapidly that the ions could not respond.

The choice of a "probable" ion distribution (in the field provide for them by a hypothetically "frozen" electron cloud) cannot be similarly justified. Electrons respond to ion density fluctuations readil and the ions cannot be uncoupled from them. We justify our choice primarily from lack of information. There are also mathematical conveniences associated with a distribution function whose logarithm depends linearly on the invariants. (In close collisions, the ions communicate with each other much better than with the electrons, so tha one may justify a Maxwellian state of the ions as the outcome of occasional collisions, but the drifting Maxwellian state of the electrons as the outcome of rapid collective interaction.)

This discussion shows that instabilities can only be due to inte actions between the two species: they must both participate. For instance, our choice of the electron distribution eliminates crossed-field instabilities or gyroresonances of the electrons such as those r onsible for magnetron phenomena and some forms of enhanced ossed-field diffusion.

A two-stream instability[13] due to electron-ion interaction is kely to show up. The center plane of the sheet is free from mag- tic fields transverse to particle drifts, and in its immediate vicin- y the infinite-medium theory should be applicable. The scale of the owing perturbations would be small compared to the sheet thickness r non-relativistic drifts.

The two-stream instability can be suppressed by keeping the lative drift velocity less than the random velocities of the electrons nis suppression will not manifest itself in our adiabatic theory for it due to phase-mixing). We shall, therefore, restrict our search for rther instabilities to sheet models for which this is the case.

Cooperation between electrons and ions also takes place in typ- al magnetohydrodynamic phenomena, such as Alfven waves, and one ight look for instabilities of this type in our model. Conventional agnetohydrodynamic theory (isotropic pressure, single-fluid) pre- cts stability for infinite conductivity, but instability for finite conduc- vity, according to H. P. Furth.[14] Since we are interested in the llision-free problem, a scalar finite conductivity and scalar pres- re are rather unrepresentative assumptions and the question of sta- lity remains open.

The sheet tears into a set of current threads in these instabil- ies. Each thread pinches itself into a cylindrical column of the ennett type.

Furth* has also found this type of instability using a two-fluid agnetohydrodynamic theory, but with a scalar pressure. His sheet odel is the same as ours. However, pressure anisotropies seem to rather important in the presence of magnetic fields (see Section V) d so, again, one wonders whether there might not be stability after l.

Experimental evidence seems to indicate stability, at least for rations shorter than the collision time (O. Anderson,** Berkeley). eet currents have been maintained over time intervals many powers 10 longer than the appropriate times for collective phenomena lectron/ ion plasma frequencies) or gyro-periods. This observed ability is encouraging and calls for theoretical investigation by more fined methods than those used hitherto.

IV. STABILITY: THE TEST PROCEDURE

The stability test consists of calculating the adiabatic magneto- drodynamical response of each species to a small perturbing elec-

*H. P. Furth, private communication

**O. Anderson, private communication

tromagnetic field, determining the charge-current perturbations, closing the problem by means of Maxwell's equations, and looking fo complex eigenfrequencies.

The unperturbed system is uniform in y, z and t and henc the perturbations may be taken proportional to $\exp(i\omega t - ik_y y - ik_z z)$. The variation with x cannot be anticipated in such a simple form.

The dynamical equations determine the velocity perturbations However, two differentiations with respect to x are involved: one i establishing a connection between velocity and density via the continuity equation, the other in forming the pressure gradient. (For anisotropic pressures, the adiabatic law relates pressure components t velocity derivatives as for isotropic pressures.) It follows that ther are three coupled second-order differential equations for the three velocity components.

Similarly, Maxwell's equations constitute three coupled second-order differential equations for, say, the three components of the perturbing electric field.

Altogether, then, there are nine coupled second-order equations for nine variables (ion velocity components, electron velocity components, electric field components).

The unperturbed magnetic field as well as the unperturbed de sity appears in these equations, which therefore have variable coefficients, and numerical methods of solution are indicated. The coefficients can be made rational by using the magnetic field as a substitute variable for x, but the chances of picking out a ready-made solution in terms of familiar special functions are slender.

Solutions have to be run off for each choice of frequency, wavelength, and direction of propagation parallel to the sheet. The condition that they should remain finite at large distances from the sheet on both sides selects the eigenfrequencies. A Nyquist diagram will be constructed to decide on the existence of complex eigenfreque cies.

There are singularities in the problem. They occur at those distances from the median plane where the local gyrofrequency just coincides with the Doppler-shifted perturbation frequency experience by the electrons or the ions. These gyroresonances have to be bypassed in a manner compatible with causality considerations (Laplac transform theory settles this question). Machine solutions will have to be helped over these resonances by analysis. Gyroresonances as such are not expected to cause instabilities (see Section III). On the whole, the program for exploring the macroscopic stability of a current sheet to all kinds of perturbations seems difficult, but feasible.

V. SOME MATHEMATICAL DETAILS: ADIABATIC EQUATION, POLARIZED COORDINATES

The continuity equation and the equation of motion of a charge ırrent-carrying fluid are well known. The adiabatic equation of state •r an anisotropic pressure tensor is thus:[5, 6]

$$d\underline{\underline{P}}/dt + \underline{\underline{P}}\nabla\cdot\underline{u} = (\underline{\underline{P}}\wedge\underline{\Omega} - \underline{\underline{P}}\cdot\nabla\,\underline{u}) + \text{transpose} \ . \quad (12)$$

ere $\underline{\Omega} = \pm e\underline{H}/mc$, and $\underline{\underline{P}}\wedge\underline{\Omega}$ is the tensor given in components by

$$(\underline{\underline{P}}\wedge\underline{\Omega})_{ik} = P_{ij}\,\epsilon_{j\ell k}\,\Omega_\ell \ . \quad (13)$$

he gyrations of the pressure tensor, and the relation of this adiabatic as law to the double and single adiabatic gas laws have been previ- usly discussed by the author.[5]

It is convenient to relate $\underline{\underline{P}}$ to the peculiar velocities, $\underline{c}$, of ıe particles (velocity deviations from the mean drift $\underline{u}$), as follows:

$$\underline{\underline{P}} = Nm\langle\underline{c}\underline{c}\rangle \quad (14)$$

ɪd to study perturbations $\delta\langle\underline{c}\underline{c}\rangle$ of the tensor $\langle\underline{c}\underline{c}\rangle$ from its diagonal quilibrium form (KT/m times the unit tensor).

In the frame of reference which moves along with the unper- urbed drift velocity $\underline{V}$ of the species under consideration ($\underline{V}$ is long the y axis, positive for electrons, (see Fig. 1)) the frequency f perturbations is Doppler-shifted to:

$$\omega' = \omega - \underline{k}\cdot\underline{V} \ . \quad (15)$$

ʌny residual drift velocity $\underline{u}$ observed in this frame can only be a •erturbation.

One obtains the density perturbation δN from the continuity :quation

$$i\omega'\,\delta N = -\nabla\cdot N\underline{u} = i\underline{k}\cdot N\underline{u} \quad (16)$$

vhere the x component of $\underline{k}$ must be interpreted as an operator:

$$k_x = i\partial/\partial x \ . \quad (17)$$

Гhe pressure perturbations follow from $\underline{u}$ by:

$$i\omega'\,\delta\langle\underline{c}\underline{c}\rangle = (\delta\langle\underline{c}\underline{c}\rangle\wedge\Omega - \frac{KT}{m}\nabla\underline{u}) + \text{transpose} \ . \quad (18)$$

The pressure and density perturbations obtained from (16) and (18) are fed into the equation of motion:

$$i\omega' \underline{u} + \frac{KT}{m} \nabla \frac{\delta N}{N} + \frac{1}{N} \nabla \cdot N\delta \langle \underline{cc} \rangle = \pm \frac{e}{m} \delta \underline{E}' + \underline{u} \wedge \underline{\Omega} \tag{19}$$

where

$$\delta \underline{E}' = \delta \underline{E} + \underline{V} \wedge \delta \underline{H}/c = \delta \underline{E} + \underline{V} \wedge (\underline{k} \wedge \delta \underline{E})/\omega \tag{20}$$

is the perturbing electric field observed in the moving frame. This provides the connection between velocity and field perturbations.

Equations involving $\underline{\Omega}$ simplify in "polarized coordinates" about the z axis (the direction of $\underline{\Omega}$):

$$u_{\pm 1} = (u_x \pm i u_y)/\sqrt{2}, \qquad u_o = u_z \tag{21}$$

$$k_{\pm 1} = (k_x \pm i k_y)/\sqrt{2}, \qquad k_o = k_z \tag{22}$$

and similarly for all other vectors.[5] Scalar and vector products are then given by

$$\underline{u} \cdot \underline{k} = \sum u_{-\nu} k_{\nu} = \sum u_{\nu} k_{-\nu} \qquad (\nu \text{ from } -1 \text{ to } +1) \tag{23}$$

$$(\underline{u} \wedge \underline{\Omega})_{\nu} = -i\nu\Omega u_{\nu} \; .$$

Clearly, this only works if $\underline{\Omega}$ has constant direction; hence, our preference for the planar ("slab") geometry.

The equation connecting $\underline{u}$ with $\delta \underline{E}'$ now becomes:

$$(\omega' + \mu\Omega) u_{\mu} - \frac{KT}{m} \sum_{\nu} \Big[k_{\mu} \frac{1}{N\omega'} k_{-\nu} u_{\nu} + \frac{1}{N} k_{-\nu} \frac{N}{\omega' + \nu\Omega + \mu\Omega} (k_{\nu} u_{\mu} + k_{\mu} u_{\nu}) \Big] = \frac{\pm e}{im} \delta E'_{\mu} \; . \tag{24}$$

The positioning of k_{μ}, k_{ν} relative to N and Ω is important since $k_{\pm 1}$ operate on N and Ω.

There is one such equation for each species, with different Ω, KT/m, $\pm e/m$, and also with different ω', $\delta E'$. Maxwell's equations are written in the lab frame:

$$c^2 (\underline{k} \wedge (\underline{k} \wedge \delta \underline{E}) + \omega^2 \delta \underline{E} = 4\pi i\omega \sum \delta \underline{j} \tag{25}$$

(summation over the two species)

with

$$\delta \underline{j} = \pm e(N\underline{u} + \underline{V}\,\delta N) = \pm e(N\underline{u} + \underline{V}\,\underline{k}\cdot N\underline{u}/\omega')\,. \tag{26}$$

t is assumed in these formulas that the "lab frame" is identified with he frame in which the plasma appeared strictly neutral before per- urbation.

The presence of k_1 and k_{-1} in many places shows that our equations are not algebraic, but differential.

Attention is drawn to the denominator $\omega' + \nu\Omega + \mu\Omega$ in (24). This is associated with the anisotropy of the pressure. It produces resonances (singularities) at $\omega' = \pm 2\Omega$ as well as at $\omega' = \pm\Omega$. Anisotropy therefore changes the character of the problem decisively.

It is to be hoped that the system of nine coupled equations (25), 24 - ions), (24 - electrons) will simplify a little more and that, per- haps, the nine variables fall into separable groups. If not, we shall program the equations more or less as they stand. Simple choices of propagation vectors $\underline{k}$, such as those predicted unstable by Furth, are under immediate investigation.

REFERENCES

1. G. F. Chew, F. E. Low and M. L. Goldberger, *Proc. Roy. Soc.*, Part A, Vol. 236, p. 112 (1956)

2. O. Buneman, "The Bennett Pinch," *Plasma Dynamics*, J. Drummond, Ed. (New York: McGraw Hill, 1960).

3. I. B. Bernstein, Contribution to Lockheed Symposium, December 1960, M. Mitchener, Ed. (Stanford, Calif: Stanford University Press, 1961).

4. E. Frieman and A. Pytte, Gatlinburg Conference, November 1960.

5. O. Buneman, "Gas Law and Conductivity of a Collision-Free Plasma," Stanford SEL Report TR 104-5, (to be published in *Physics of Fluids*).

6. T. M. Burgers, *Revs. Mod. Phys.*, Vol. 32, p. 686 (1960).

7. C. Oberman, AEC Res. & Dev. Rept., Project Matterhorn, Matt-57 (1960).

8. L. J. Landau, *J. Phys. U.S.S.R.*, Vol. 10, p. 25 (1946).

9. S. Chapman and T. G. Cowling, *The Mathematical Theory of Non-uniform Gases*, (London: Cambridge University Press, 1958). Chapters 4.14 and 18.2.

0. W. H. Bennett, *Phys. Rev.*, Vol. 45, p. 890 (1934).

1. M. N. Rosenbluth, "Plasma Physics," *Physics Today*, p. 24 (August 1960).

2. (W. A. Newcomb, reported by) I. B. Bernstein, *Phys. Rev.*, Vol. 109, p. 10 (1958).

3. O. Buneman, *Phys. Rev.*, Vol. 115, p. 503 (1959).

4. H. P. Furth, Gatlinburg Conference (November 1960).

TWO-STREAM INSTABILITIES WITH COLLISIONS*

D. A. Tidman and George Weiss
University of Maryland
College Park, Maryland

This paper investigates the effect of electron scattering on the two-stream instability that occurs in a plasma of contrastreaming electrons and ions. This is done by assuming that the electron-ion collision frequency is small and making a perturbation expansion in this quantity.

I. INTRODUCTION

In this paper, we shall discuss the results of some calculations on the effect of scattering on two-stream instabilities in a plasma. It is well known that in the low-density limit, when a stream of electrons passes at sufficiently high speed through a background of ions, a bunching mechanism [1, 2, 3] leads to the amplification of perturbations in the charge density of either component. This two-stream instability has recently been examined by a number of authors making use of Vlasov equations. [4, 5] The growth of this instability competes with Landau damping. The result is, approximately, that a range of wavenumbers for instability of a perturbation exists only when the relative velocity of the components exceeds the largest thermal velocity of the two streams.

The Boltzmann equation will be applied to calculate the effect of a small amount of two-body scattering on the two-stream instability. This is done by making a perturbation expansion in the electron-ion collision frequency and then calculating the correction to the perturbation electric field of an unstable wave to first order in the collision frequency. One expects to find, of course, that as the streaming kinetic energy of the electron and ions is thermalized, the instability disappears. We find some indication that the most effective result of this thermalization process is the enhancement of Landau damping of unstable perturbations in the plasma. This takes the form of an energy loss of an unstable wave through an interaction between the electric

*This research was partially supported by the United States Air Force through the Air Force Office of Scientific Research under Contract AF 18(600)1315.

Presented at the Symposium on Electromagnetics and Fluid Dynamics of Gaseous Plasma, Polytechnic Institute of Brooklyn, April 4, 5, 6, 1961

field of the wave and scattered electrons.

One of the basic difficulties in this problem is the choice of a tractable, and at the same time physically reasonable, expression for the collision terms that appear in the Boltzmann equation. In making these calculations we naturally first applied the method described above to the simplest scattering law we could, namely a relaxation formula (Eq.(24)) in which the electrons are imagined to be scattered into a local Maxwellian distribution in a time τ. After much tedious algebra this gave the unexpected result of an increased instability of the streams in this two-stream problem; a result which has previously been found by Mitchner.[6] This result leads one to suspect that the more exact Fokker-Planck equation for Coulomb scattering should be used, i. e., that the diffusion nature of the Coulomb thermalization of the electron stream is an essential feature of the problem. This latter calculation has recently been carried out[7] and one can estimate a time over which the streaming instability will proceed before being overcome by collisions. This time is proportional to the square root of the electron thermalization time and the growth period of the instability.

In Section II we shall briefly derive some formulas for the perturbation electric field correct to first order in the collision frequency.

II. BASIC EQUATIONS

Our starting point is the Boltzmann equation for the electron and ion distribution functions, $f(\underline{r}, \underline{v}, t)$ and $F(\underline{r}, \underline{v}, t)$, respectively, together with Poisson's equation,

$$\frac{\partial f}{\partial t} + \underline{v}\frac{\partial f}{\partial \underline{r}} - \frac{e}{m}\underline{E}\cdot\frac{\partial f}{\partial \underline{v}} = \left[\frac{\delta f}{\delta t}\right]_e , \tag{1}$$

$$\frac{\partial f}{\partial t} + \underline{v}\frac{\partial F}{\partial \underline{r}} + \frac{e}{M}\underline{E}\cdot\frac{\partial F}{\partial \underline{v}} = \left[\frac{\delta F}{\delta t}\right]_i , \tag{2}$$

$$\underline{\nabla}\cdot\underline{E} = 4\pi e \int (F-f)\, d\underline{v} , \tag{3}$$

where m and M are the electron and ion masses with charges Fe, and $\underline{E}$ is the electric field. The scattering terms on the right side of (1) and (2) will be discussed later.

Now consider an unperturbed state consisting of an infinite uniform plasma with the electron and ion densities everywhere equal. Further, suppose the electron and ion components are in uniform relative streaming motion which is slowly being destroyed by collisions. These time-dependent distribution functions $f_0(t)$ and $F_0(t)$ are then solutions of

$$\frac{\partial f_o}{\partial t} = \left[\frac{\delta f_o}{\delta t}\right]_e , \tag{4}$$

$$\frac{\partial F_o}{\partial t} = \left[\frac{\delta F_o}{\delta t}\right]_i , \tag{5}$$

and are determined by some initial conditions on $f_o(0)$ and $F_o(0)$ for the streaming. If we next introduce a small perturbation into these streams and write in the usual way, $f = f_o + f_1$, $F = F_o + F_1$ and $\underline{E} = \underline{0} + \underline{E}_1$, then the linearized version of Eqs. (1) to (3) becomes

$$\frac{\partial f_1}{\partial t} + \underline{v} \cdot \frac{\partial f_1}{\partial \underline{r}} - \frac{e}{m} \underline{E}_1 \cdot \frac{\partial f_o(t)}{\partial \underline{v}} = \left[\frac{\delta f}{\delta t}\right]_{e1} , \tag{6}$$

$$\frac{\partial F_1}{\partial t} + \underline{v} \cdot \frac{\partial F_1}{\partial \underline{r}} + \frac{e}{M} \underline{E}_1 \cdot \frac{\partial F_o(t)}{\partial \underline{v}} = \left[\frac{\delta F}{\delta t}\right]_{i1} , \tag{7}$$

$$\underline{\nabla} \cdot \underline{E}_1 = 4\pi e \int (F_1 - f_1)\, d\underline{v} , \tag{8}$$

where, by $(\delta f/\delta t)_e$ we mean simply those scattering terms of first order in f_1 and F_1.

In considering this problem, we shall imagine that we start at t = 0 with electrons streaming through a static ion background, together with a perturbation at t = 0, and examine the subsequent development of the perturbation. In order to make this tractable, we must further simplify Eqs. (4) through (8). To do this, we suppose that one of the larger collision frequencies involved in the scattering terms, namely that for the scattering of electrons by ions, is a small quantity α. Then $(\delta f/\delta t)_e$ is of order α, and $(\delta F/\delta t)_i$ will be somewhat smaller due to the large ratio (M/m). The exact choice of α does not matter since it drops out of the calculation anyway. We next further expand all quantities in α and set

$$f = (f_o^o + \alpha f_o^1 + \ldots) + (f_1^o + \alpha f_1^1 + \ldots) + \ldots , \tag{9}$$

$$F = (F_o^o + \alpha F_o^1 + \ldots) + (F_1^o + \alpha F_1^1 + \ldots) + \ldots , \tag{10}$$

$$\underline{E} = \underline{0} + (\underline{E}_1^o + \alpha \underline{E}_1^1 + \ldots) + \ldots . \tag{11}$$

Subscripts refer to the order of expansion in the amplitude of a perturbation and superscripts to the order in the collision frequency α. The perturbations of zero order in α, namely f_1^o, F_1^o and $\underline{E}_1^o$, then obey the well known Boltzmann-Vlasov equations, which will be omitted for brevity, and the corrections of first order in α are governed by

$$\frac{\partial f_1^1}{\partial t} + \underline{v}\cdot\frac{\partial f_1^1}{\partial \underline{r}} - \frac{e}{m}\underline{E}_1^1\cdot\frac{\partial f_o^o}{\partial \underline{v}} = \frac{1}{\alpha}\cdot\left[\frac{\delta f}{\delta t}\right]_{e1}^o + \frac{e}{m}\underline{E}_1^o\cdot\frac{\partial f_o^1}{\partial \underline{v}} = \Phi_e, \tag{12}$$

$$\frac{\partial F_1^1}{\partial t} + \underline{v}\cdot\frac{\partial F_1^1}{\partial \underline{r}} + \frac{e}{M}\underline{E}_1^1\cdot\frac{\partial F_o^o}{\partial \underline{v}} = \frac{1}{\alpha}\cdot\left[\frac{\delta F}{\delta t}\right]_{i1}^o - \frac{e}{m}\underline{E}_1^o\cdot\frac{\partial F_o^1}{\partial \underline{v}} = \Phi_i, \tag{13}$$

$$\underline{\nabla}\cdot\underline{E}_1^1 = 4\pi e\int (F_1^1 - f_1^1)\,d\underline{v}, \tag{14}$$

where by $(\delta f/\delta t)_{e1}^o$ we mean those scattering terms of first order in f_1^o and F_1^o.

It is interesting to intepret the two terms of, for example, Φ_e The second term,

$$(e/m)\ \underline{E}_1^o\cdot\left[\partial f_o^1/\partial \underline{v}\right], \tag{15}$$

represents the interaction between the electric field of a wave and the scattered electrons. It will be responsible for a loss of energy of the wave to these electrons, and in this sense can be thought of as an enhanced Landau damping. Dawson [8] has recently pointed out that Landau damping can be understood in terms of an energy loss of a wave to particles traveling near the phase velocity of the wave. We also note here that using the initial condition $F_o^1(0) = 0$, the quantity f_o^1 is determined from Eq. (4) by scattering in the zero-order streams,

$$f_o^1 = \frac{t}{\alpha}\left[\frac{\delta f}{\delta t}\right]_{eo}^o \tag{16}$$

The first term of Φ_e is not so interesting and represents the direct effect of scattering on the organized electron motions carrying the wave.

Finally, we shall deal with the linear equations (12) through (16) in the usual way and make use of a Fourier space transform and Laplace time transform defined for any function ϕ by

$$\phi_\omega = \int_{-\infty}^{\infty} d\underline{r} \int_{0}^{\infty} dt\, e^{i(\omega t - \underline{k}\underline{r})} \phi \tag{17}$$

with $\mathrm{Im}(\omega) > 0$. The corresponding inverse is

$$\phi = (2\pi)^{-4} \int_W d\omega \int_{-\infty}^{\infty} d\underline{k}\, e^{-i(\omega t - \underline{k}\underline{r})} \phi_\omega \tag{18}$$

where W goes from $-\infty + ia$ to $+\infty + ia$ above all the singularities of the integrand. A subscript ω will be used on all transformed quantities.

If we now use the initial conditions $f_1^1(0) = F_1^1(0) = F_1^0(0) = 0$ and $E_1^1(0) = 0$, we find for the transforms of the perturbations and the first order correction field $\alpha \underline{E}_{1\omega}^1$

$$\underline{E}_{1\omega}^0 = \frac{4\pi e \underline{k}}{k^2 H_L} \int_{-\infty}^{\infty} \frac{d\underline{v} \int_{-\infty}^{\infty} d\underline{r}\, e^{-i\underline{k}\underline{r}} f_1^o(0)}{(\underline{k}\underline{v} - \omega)} \tag{19}$$

$$f_{1\omega}^0 = \frac{e\underline{E}_{1\omega}^0 \frac{\partial f_0^0}{\partial \underline{v}}}{im(\underline{k}\underline{v} - \omega)} + \frac{\int_{-\infty}^{\infty} d\underline{r}\, e^{-i\underline{k}\underline{r}} f_1^0(0)}{i(\underline{k}\underline{v} - \omega)}, \tag{20}$$

$$\alpha \underline{E}_{1\omega}^1 = \frac{4\pi e \underline{k}}{k^2 H_L} \int_{-\infty}^{\infty} \frac{d\underline{v}}{(\underline{k}\underline{v} - \omega)} \left[\left[\frac{\delta f}{\delta t}\right]_{e1\omega}^0 - \frac{ie}{m} \cdot \frac{\partial \underline{E}_{1\omega}^0}{\partial \omega} \cdot \frac{\partial}{\partial \underline{v}} \left[\frac{\delta f}{\delta t}\right]_{eo}^0 - \left[\frac{\delta F}{\delta t}\right]_{i1\omega}^0 - \frac{ie}{M} \cdot \frac{\partial \underline{E}_{1\omega}^0}{\partial \omega} \cdot \frac{\partial}{\partial \underline{v}} \left[\frac{\delta F}{\delta t}\right]_{io}^0 \right] \tag{21}$$

and

$$\underline{E}_{1\omega} \cong \underline{E}_{1\omega}^0 + \alpha \underline{E}_{1\omega}^1, \tag{22}$$

where the propagation function for the perturbations is

$$H_L = 1 - \frac{4\pi e^2}{M} \int_{-\infty}^{\infty} \frac{d\underline{v}\, F_0^0}{(\underline{k}\underline{v} - \omega)^2} - \frac{4\pi e^2}{m} \int_{-\infty}^{\infty} \frac{d\underline{v}\, f_0^0}{(\underline{k}\underline{v} - \omega)^2} \tag{23}$$

The integrals in (19) through (23) are defined for Im $(\omega) > 0$. Their continuation across the real axis to Im $(\omega) < 0$ is usually a simple matte We note that in the inversion of $\underline{E}_{1\omega}$ to find $\underline{E}_1(t)$, the zeros of H_L con tribute poles of $\underline{E}_{1\omega}$. Under some circumstances these poles in the ω plane have a positive imaginary part corresponding to the well-known two-stream instability.

III. REMARKS ON MODELS FOR THE COLLISION TERMS

In order to calculate the perturbation field $\underline{E}_1(t)$ in the electron-ion streams, we next require an explicit form for the collision terms in Eq. (21). In this section we shall summarize some preliminary results obtained by using two different expressions for the electron scattering.

Most realistic expressions for the electron-ion and electron-electron scattering terms that appear in Eq. (21) [for example, the Fokker-Planck expressions*] are complicated. For this reason we first applied our formulas to a simple model in which the electron scattering is represented by

$$\left[\frac{\delta f}{\delta t}\right]_e = \frac{f_s(\underline{r}, \underline{v}, t) - f(\underline{r}, \underline{v}, t)}{\tau} \tag{24}$$

where the function f_s is taken as a Maxwellian distribution at rest relative to the ions and with a temperature $T(r, t)$ and density $N(r, t)$ which conserve the local energy and numbers of the electron stream, That is,

$$f_s = N\left[\frac{m}{2\pi kT}\right]^{3/2} \exp\left[-\frac{mv^2}{2kT}\right], \tag{25}$$

$$N = \int f\, d\underline{v}, \tag{26}$$

$$T = \frac{m}{3kN} \int v^2 f\, d\underline{v}. \tag{27}$$

The electrons are scattered into the local equilibrium state f_s in a characteristic time τ. Also, the ions are assumed to have no stream velocity initially and to gain none in their interaction with the electrons in the time scales of interest.

We found, after some tedious algebra which will not be repro-

*See, for example, Reference 9.

duced here, that the expression (24) gave the result of an increased instability for the electron streams. This property of the simple relaxation collision term has been previously discussed by Mitchner.[6]

The above result led us to examine the problem using the Fokker-Planck equation for Coulomb scattering given by Rosenbluth, MacDonald and Judd.[9] We considered a plasma in which the initial state consisted of a zero-temperature electron stream passing through a zero-temperature ion background, i. e.,

$$f_o(0) = N_o^o\,\delta(\underline{v} - \underline{U}), \qquad F_o(0) = N_o^o\,\delta(\underline{v})$$

Also, the initial perturbation of the electron stream was taken as

$$f_1^o(0) = n\,\delta(\underline{v}-\underline{U})\,e^{i\underline{k}\cdot\underline{r}}$$

with $n \ll N_o^o$. The zero-order streams are thus in equilibrium with themselves, so that not much error would be involved in accounting only for electron-ion scattering We therefore set

$$\frac{1}{\gamma}\left[\frac{\delta f}{\delta t}\right]_e \cong -\frac{\partial}{\partial v_i}\left[f\frac{\partial}{\partial v_i}\int d\underline{v}_1\,\frac{F_o(\underline{v}_1)}{|\underline{v}-\underline{v}_1|}\right] + \frac{1}{2}\,\frac{\partial^2}{\partial v_i \partial v_j}\left[f\,\frac{\partial^2}{\partial v_i \partial v_j}\int d\underline{v}_1\,F_o\,|\underline{v}-\underline{v}_1|\right]. \tag{28}$$

We also assumed $m/M \cong 0$ in the scattering terms, so that $\delta F/\delta t) = 0$. Further, the Coulomb scattering of electrons by the ions was cut off at an impact parameter of $U/\omega e$ so that,

$$\gamma = \frac{4\pi e^4}{m^2}\,\ell n\left[\frac{mU^3}{2e^2\omega_e}\right] \tag{29}$$

Using the above formulas, one then finds[7] for the perturbation electric field correct to first order in the collision frequency,

$$\underline{E}_1 = -\frac{4\pi\,ei\underline{k}}{K^2}\,e^{i\underline{k}\,\underline{r} - i\omega_1 t}\,(a + bt + ct^2) + (\text{oscillating terms}) + (\text{damped terms}) \tag{30}$$

where,

$$a = \frac{\omega_1 (\underline{K}\cdot\underline{U} - \omega_1)^2}{2\left[(\underline{K}\cdot\underline{U}-\omega_1)^3 - \omega_e^2 K\cdot U\right]}, \tag{31}$$

$$b = \frac{N\gamma\omega_e^2}{4K^2U^5 \left[(\underline{K}\cdot\underline{U}-\omega_1)^3 - \omega_e^2 \underline{K}\cdot\underline{U}\right]^2} \Bigg\{ 3\omega_1^3 (\underline{K}\cdot\underline{U})^3 - 3\omega_1^4 (\underline{K}\cdot\underline{U})^2$$

$$+ \omega_1^4 K^2 U^2 - 7\omega_1^2 K^2 U^2 (\underline{K}\cdot\underline{U})^2 + 6\omega_1^3 K^2 U^2 \underline{K}\cdot\underline{U}$$

$$- 4\omega_1^2 K^4 U^4 + 6K^4 U^4 \omega_1 \underline{K}\cdot\underline{U} - 2\omega_1 K^2 U^2 (\underline{K}\cdot\underline{U})^3 \Bigg\} -$$

$$- \frac{N\gamma\omega_e^2 (\underline{K}\cdot\underline{U} - \omega_1)^2 \omega_1 \left[3K^2U^2 - 2\omega_1 \underline{K}\cdot\underline{U} - (\underline{K}\cdot\underline{U})^2\right]}{8U^3 \left[(\underline{K}\cdot\underline{U}-\omega_1)^3 - \omega_e^2 \underline{K}\cdot\underline{U}\right]^3} \Bigg\{ (\underline{K}\cdot\underline{U}-\omega_1)^2$$

$$- 4\omega_1 (\underline{K}\cdot\underline{U}-\omega_1) - \omega_e^2 + \frac{\omega_e^2\omega_1^2}{(\underline{K}\cdot\underline{U}-\omega_1)^2} \Bigg\} \tag{32}$$

and

$$c = - \frac{N_i \gamma \omega_e^2 \omega_1^2 (\underline{K}\cdot\underline{U}-\omega_1)^2}{8U^3 \left[(\underline{K}\cdot\underline{U}-\omega_1)^3 - \omega_e^2 \underline{K}\cdot\underline{U}\right]^2} \left\{ 2\underline{K}\cdot\underline{U} + \frac{3K^2U^2 - (\underline{K}\cdot\underline{U})^2}{(\underline{K}\cdot\underline{U}-\omega_1)} \right\} \tag{33}$$

The quantity ω_1 is that root of the dispersion relation

$$0 = \omega^2 (\underline{K}\ \underline{U}-\omega)^2 \quad (\frac{m}{M})\, \omega_e^2 (\underline{K}\ \underline{U}-\omega)^2 - \omega_e^2 \omega^2 \tag{34}$$

which has a positive imaginary part. This root corresponds to the usual two-stream instability and so the first term of Eq. (30) for the electric field $\underline{E}_1$ has an exponentially growing factor exp $(-i\omega_1 t)$. The terms in t and t^2, however, subtract from the factor a in the curly bracket, thus representing the growing effect of electron scattering as t increases.

REFERENCES

1. J.R. Pierce, *Proc. I.R.E.*, Vol. 37, p. 980 (1949).
2. A. V. Haeff, *Proc. I.R.E.*, Vol. 37, p. 4 (1949).
3. D. Bohm and E. P. Gross, *Phys. Rev.*, Vol. 75, p. 1864 (1949).
4. A. Vlasov, *J. Phys. U.S.S.R.*, Vol. 9, p. 25 (1945).
5. A. Jackson, *Phys. Fluids*, Vol. 3, p. 786 (1960).
6. M. Mitchner, *Bull. Amer. Phys. Soc.*, Series II, Vol. 5, p. 25 (June 15, 1960).
7. D. A. Tidman, *Phys. Fluids*, Vol. 4, p. 703 (June 1961).
8. J. Dawson, "Landau Damping," Princeton Univ., Project Matterhorn, Matt-54 (1960).
9. M. N. Rosenbluth, W. M. MacDonald and D. L. Judd, *Phys. Rev*, Vol. 107, p. 1 (1957).

INTERACTION OF MICROWAVES IN GASEOUS PLASMAS IMMERSED IN MAGNETIC FIELDS*

L. Goldstein, K. V. Narasinga Rao, and J. T. Verdeyen
University of Illinois, Urbana, Illinois

The phenomenon of radio frequency electromagnetic-wave interaction in gaseous plasmas is reviewed The application of microwave interaction to the study of plasmas immersed in magnetic fields is discussed Attention is focused on the effects produced in such plasmas when one of the simultaneously propagating microwaves is in electron cyclotron resonance It is demonstrated that, for relatively modest amplitudes of the resonating wave, the kinetic energy of the electrons increases considerably, which in turn affects the electron collision frequency and the magnetic field control of the plasma confinement.

I. INTRODUCTION

It is now well known that the phenomenon of wave interaction was first observed (1933) between low frequency radio waves which were propagated in a common region of the ionosphere.[1] Since it was possible to trace the effect to a region of the ionosphere which was strongly irradiated by the powerful waves (150-200 kw) transmitted by the radio station of Luxemburg, the phenomenon became known as the "Luxemburg Effect."

The theory explaining this effect was first proposed (1934) by V. A. Bailey and R. F. Martyn.[2] Later (1937) V. A Bailey[3] extended the theory, taking into account the influence of the earth's magnetic field on the propagation of the ionospheric radio waves involved. The theory predicted, in particular, that when the frequency of one of the interacting waves is in the vicinity of or at the gyrofrequency of the electrons in the ionospheric region of interest, the wave interaction will be enhanced. These predictions have been since borne out by direct experimental observations.[4]

By 1953 the simple phenomenon of radio-wave interaction had been extended[5] to (guided) microwaves propagated in laboratory gaseous plasmas under readily controlled conditions with a consequent generalization and close check of the theory (1955).[6] Using the generalized theory as a basis, it was then possible to develop a method of rather detailed investigations of high radiofrequency electromagnetic (em) wave interaction with gaseous plasmas, which in turn permitted the detailed study of the interaction processes taking place

*This work is sponsored by the Air Force Cambridge Research Center, Geophysics Research Directorate.

Presented at the Symposium on Electromagnetics and Fluid Dynamics of Gaseous Plasma, Polytechnic Institute of Brooklyn, April 4, 5, 6, 1961

among the charged constituents as well as among the charged and neutral constituents of gaseous plasmas. [7,8]

This paper deals with an experimental investigation of the inter action of two or more electromagnetic waves guided through a magneto-plasma medium. The magneto-plasma referred to here is a plasma obtained in the afterglow of a pulsed gas discharge (degree of ionization less than 10^{-4}) which is immersed in an external dc magnetic field, variable from 0 to 0.3 webers/m^2. The gases used are primarily the inert gases in the pressure range 0. 5 to 10. 0 mm Hg. The em waves utilized are in the frequency range 4. 0 to 10 Gc and are guided along the external magnetic field. The general topic of investigation is concerned with the transfer of em energy to the electron gas in the plasma and the effects of this transfer of energy on the plasma parameters and the associated wave propagation characteristics of the plasma. This has been investigated, in particular, when the frequency of one em wave is at or in the vicinity of the cyclotron frequency of the electrons. The body of this paper is divided into six sections: In Section II, a qualitative description of the interaction of em waves of radio frequency is given. Section III deals with a description of the plasma medium and a quantitative treatment of the wave interaction phenomenon in gaseous plasmas. The experimental apparatus used in this investigation is described in Section IV. Section V is devoted to the experimental results and Section VI contains the conclusions and the possible implications of these results.

II. INTERACTION OF ELECTROMAGNETIC WAVES IN A PLASMA

It is known that the propagation of electromagnetic waves in material media is different from their propagation in free space because there is energy exchange between the media and the waves. A plasma, being a material medium, will alter the propagation of electromagnetic waves, and this fact has been used to determine those plasma parameters that influence electromagnetic wave propagation. These techniques have usually been used to study the plasma in any given time-independent energy state. The probing electromagnetic wave used in such a study must be of sufficiently small amplitude so that it does not appreciably disturb the plasma.

If the amplitude of the electromagnetic wave propagating in a plasma does not satisfy this condition, a change in the energy state of the electron gas of the plasma results, and this in turn affects the propagation of any succeeding wave packet. This means that each wave packet propagates in a slightly different plasma than the preceding one. This phenomenon is generally referred to as self-modulation or self-distortion. While the change of the energy state of the electron gas thus affects wave propagation in a plasma, it also affects those processes occurring in the plasma which are dependent upon the energy state of the electron gas, such as recombination, diffusion, production rate, etc.

We have considered above the effect of only one electromagnetic wave on a plasma and the resulting reaction of the plasma on the electromagnetic wave in the two cases: 1) negligible perturbations corresponding to small wave amplitudes; and 2) significant disturbances corresponding to large wave amplitudes. The next step is to combine the two effects by applying two electromagnetic waves to the plasma. One wave will be of sufficiently small amplitude so as to be capable of probing the plasma - hence the name "sensing wave"; the other will be of sufficient amplitude and of different frequency to disturb the plasma - hence the name "disturbing wave". The effect that the disturbing wave causes on the plasma, as detected by the sensing wave, is generally referred to as wave interaction and, when modulation is involved, as cross-modulation.

Let us consider the processes by which energy is transferred from an electromagnetic wave to the electron gas of a plasma. When a high-frequency electromagnetic wave impinges upon a plasma, it causes an ordered oscillatory motion of the electrons which is superimposed onto the existing disordered thermal motion. The ordered electron velocity is 90° in time phase with respect to the driving force of the E field of the wave. The energy associated with this ordered motion, if not interfered with, is taken from the em wave in half a cycle, and returned to the wave in the following half cycle so that the average power transferred to the electron gas is zero. When, however, the electrons collide with other constituents of the plasma, the ordered momentum is scattered; consequently the velocities of the electrons no longer have a definite phase relationship to the driving force. Following such collisions, the previous ordered energy of the electron gas is not returned to the electromagnetic wave and hence represents rf power transferred into the electron gas. However, the electron gas loses a fraction of this energy to the heavy constituents of the plasma.

These momentum transfer collisions between electrons and the heavy particles of a plasma constitute one mechanism by which em energy is transferred into disordered thermal energy of the electrons. There exists, however, under particular conditions, another mechanism of em energy transfer to a plasma, in which the collisions hinder the energy transfer by interrupting the ordered motion of the electrons.

Such conditions occur when resonance prevails between a proper frequency of the plasma electrons, such as their cyclotron frequency and the particular frequency of the em waves. In this case, an initial value problem must be considered, the solution of which indicates that the energy of an electron grows, in between collisions, as $(Et)^2$ where E is the applied electric field and t is the time elapsed since its last collision. In the study reported here we are concerned mainly with the effects of this electromagnetic energy transfer from one of the em waves whose frequency is at or in the vicinity of the cyclotron frequency of electrons.

III. CHARACTERISTICS OF AN AFTERGLOW PLASMA

As mentioned earlier, the plasma considered here is that obtained in the afterglow of a partially ionized rare gas whose degree of ionization is less than 10^{-4}. We shall assume that only three types of constitutent gases are present in the afterglow: the gas of the electrons, that of the positive ions, and that of the neutral molecules. The fundamental parameters of interest are essentially: 1) the number density of the charged particles; 2) the temperature of the constituent gases; 3) the type of neutral molecules in which the plasma is formed.

Upon removal of the external plasma excitation source, the constituent particles undergo mainly elastic collisions among themselves and with the walls of the reservoir, and thereby attain thermodynamic equilibrium at the temperature of the reservoir ($T_e = T_i = T_g = T_r$). This plasma tends, however, towards a neutral gas state by means of various loss mechanisms of the charged particles. These mechanisms are: 1) volume recombination of electrons and ions, 2) diffusion of electrons to boundaries; 3) attachment of electrons to neutral particles. The absence of any electronegative gases in these experiments permits us to neglect the attachment process, and hence the rate of loss of the charged particles is given by

$$dn/dt = -\alpha n_e \cdot n_i + D \nabla^2 n \tag{1}$$

where α is the recombination coefficient of electrons and ions whose densities are respectively, n_e, n_i; and D is the diffusion coefficient.

If we assume that only elastic collisions of electrons with other constitutents of the plasma take place in the afterglow, it is possible to define certain fundamental quantities which describe the interactions of the electrons with other constitutents of the plasma. The probability of electron molecule collision for momentum transfer, P_{e-m}, is related to the effective cross section of molecules, Q_{e-m}, and to the corresponding electron-molecule collision frequency ν_{e-m}; by the equation

$$P_{e-m}(v)p = N_m Q_{e-m}(v) = \nu_{e-m}/v, \tag{2}$$

where N_m = number density of molecules, v = velocity of electrons and p = pressure (at 0°C). Analogous quantities for electron-ion collisions are

$$N_i Q_{e-i} = \nu_{e-i}/v. \tag{3}$$

f Q_{e-m} does not vary appreciably with electron velocity, then the collision frequencies mentioned above may be reduced to the following functional forms:

$$\nu_{e-m} = AT_e^{1/2} , \tag{4}$$

$$\nu_{e-i} = \frac{BN_i}{T_e^{3/2}} \ \ell n \left[CN_i^{-1/2} T_e^{1/2} \right] , \tag{5}$$

where A, B, C are constants and T_e is the electron temperature. In any case, the total effective collision frequency defined by

$$\nu_t = \nu_{e-m} (T_e) + \nu_{e-i} (T_e) \tag{6}$$

is thus dependent upon the number density of the charged particles, pressure of the gas, kind of gas, and electron temperature. To facilitate the interpretation of the experimental results on the interaction of microwaves, a plot of $N_i Q_{e-i}$ and P_{e-m} as a function of electron temperature is shown in Fig. (1) It can be seen from this figure that an enhancement in electron temperature may cause either a decrease or an increase in the total electron collision frequency ν_t depending on whether e-i or e-m collisions are predominant. If we neglect the slow variation of the logarithmic term in Eq. (5), then the total collision frequency will *increase* with electron temperature provided $\nu_{e-m} > 3\nu_{e-i}$ or *decrease* if $\nu_{e-i} > 1/3 \, \nu_{e-m}$. This result is obtained by differentiating Eq. (6) with respect to T_e. In certain gases like Xe, Kr, or Ar, an increase in electron temperature from ~ 300° K causes a decrease in ν_t, even without any Coulomb collisions. The variation of ν_{e-m} in these gases with increasing T_e is similar to the variation of ν_t in a low-pressure, high-density neon plasma as can be inferred from Fig. 1. These aspects of the total collision frequency dependence on electronic energy have been demonstrated in this investigation using the technique of wave interaction, and are discussed in Section V.

We shall now consider briefly the dependence of the electron-loss mechanisms in a non-magnetized decaying rare gas plasma upon the electron temperature. It is known that the volume recombination decreases with increasing electron temperature since α, the recombination coefficient, is inversely proportional to some power (~ 3/2) of T_e.[9] However, if free diffusion of electrons occurs in a plasma, it will be enhanced when T_e increases. In a plasma of high charge densities, interactions among the charges of opposite sign results in the ambipolarity of the diffusion. The ambipolar diffusion coefficient is given by the equation:

$$D_a = D_+ \left[1 + (T_e/T_i)\right] \tag{7}$$

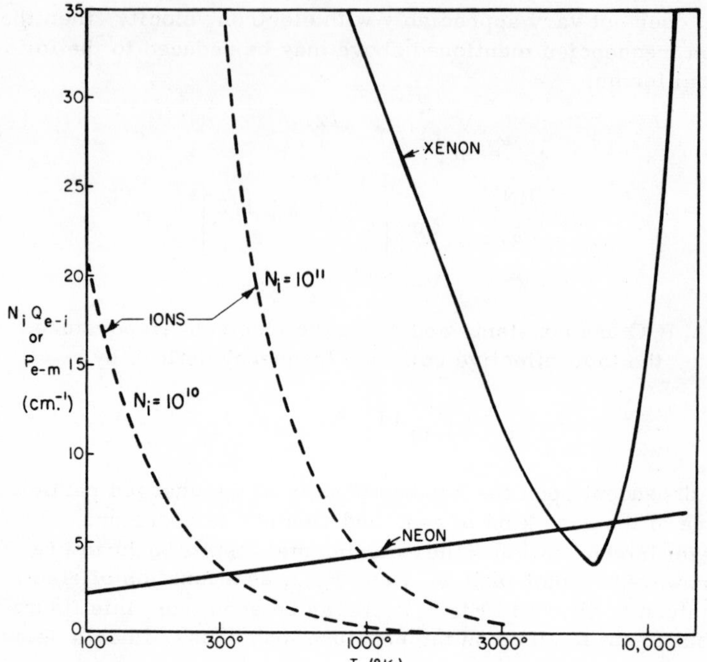

Fig. 1 Probability of electron-molecule collision for momentum transfer P_{em} or N_iQ_{e-i} vs electron temperature (°K). The dashed curves represent N_iQ_{e-i} for two electron densities 10^{11}/cc and 10^{10}/cc. The solid curves represent P_{e-m} in neon and xenon gases. Data for solid curves is obtained from Ref. 20 and dashed curves are plotted using Eq. (5), as given by Ref. 6.

Where D_+ is the diffusion coefficient of the positive ions. It is seen that D_a increases with T_e.

The ambipolar diffusion in a magneto-plasma depends upon the direction of the magnetic field. The diffusion coefficients parallel and perpendicular to the direction of the magnetic field are given[10, 11] in terms of the magnetic field intensity by:

$$D_\perp = \frac{D_\parallel}{1 + \dfrac{\omega_H}{\nu_e} \dfrac{\Omega_H}{\nu_i}} \tag{8a}$$

$$D_\parallel = D_a , \tag{8b}$$

where: ω_H and Ω_H are the cyclotron frequencies of the electrons and ions, respectively, and ν_e, and ν_i are the total electron and ion collision frequencies.

It can be seen for Eqs. (8a) and (8b) that in plasmas where the condition $(\omega_H/\nu_e) \cdot (\Omega_H/\nu_i) >> 1$ is satisfied, the diffusion of charged particles in the transverse direction is negligible compared to that in the parallel direction, i. e., $D_\perp / D_\parallel << 1$. However, the absorption of em waves under electron cyclotron resonance conditions results in a considerable heating of the electron gas only. In the plasma considered here, it is possible to change ν_t appreciably by this process; this results in making the ratio $D_\perp / D_\parallel$ approach unity. The implication of this statement is that the transverse diffusion of the plasma can be considerably enhanced due to the heating of the electron gas. In other words, the external magnetic field, which impedes the transverse diffusion of the cool electrons and thus delays plasma disintegration, loses its control over the diffusion process when the electrons become energetic.

Electromagnetic Description of the Plasma

A mathematical description of the influence of the electromagnetic wave upon a plasma consists of the simultaneous solution of Maxwell's equations and Boltzmann's equation.

$$\nabla \times \vec{H} = \vec{J} + \epsilon_o \frac{\partial \vec{E}}{\partial t}, \tag{9}$$

$$\nabla \times \vec{E} = - \mu_o \frac{\partial \vec{H}}{\partial t} \tag{10}$$

$$\frac{\partial f}{\partial t} + \vec{v} \cdot \nabla_r f + \frac{q}{m}(\vec{E} + \vec{v} \times \vec{B}) \cdot \nabla_v f = \left. \frac{\partial f}{\partial t} \right|_{coll}, \tag{11}$$

$$\vec{J} = - e \iiint \vec{v} f d^3 v . \tag{12}$$

However, a somewhat less rigorous but a more easily solved set of equations is the combination of Maxwell's equations with the Langevin equation:

$$\frac{\partial \vec{v}}{\partial t} + \vec{v} \nu = \frac{q}{m} (\vec{E} + \vec{v} \times \vec{B}) , \tag{13}$$

$$\vec{J} = - n e \vec{v} \tag{14}$$

In Eq. (13), ν is responsible for viscous damping and is related to the average momentum transfer collision frequency of the electrons with the other constituents of the plasma. The restrictions and assumptions, which are inherent in the usage of Eq. (13) rather than (11) have been discussed by several authors[12-14] and will not be considered here. Suffice it to say that the use of Eqs. (13) and (14) leads to an expression for the current density which is reasonably accurate for our case.

Equations (13) and (14) can be solved for the current density in terms of the plasma parameters and the electromagnetic fields.

$$\begin{bmatrix} J_x \\ J_y \\ J_z \end{bmatrix} = \begin{bmatrix} \sigma_{xx} & \sigma_{xy} & 0 \\ -\sigma_{xy} & \sigma_{yy} & 0 \\ 0 & 0 & \sigma_{zz} \end{bmatrix} \begin{bmatrix} E_x \\ E_y \\ E_z \end{bmatrix} \tag{15}$$

where

$$\sigma_{xx} = \sigma_{yy} = \omega_p^2 \, \epsilon_o \left[\frac{\nu + j\omega}{(\nu + j\omega)^2 + \omega_H^2} \right],$$

$$\sigma_{xy} = \omega_p^2 \, \epsilon_o \left[\frac{\omega_H}{(\nu + j\omega)^2 + \omega_H^2} \right],$$

$$\sigma_{zz} = \omega_p^2 \, \epsilon_o \left[\frac{1}{\nu + j\omega} \right],$$

$$\omega_p^2 = \frac{n_e e^2}{m \epsilon_o},$$

$$\omega_H = \frac{eB_o}{m},$$

$$\vec{B} = B_o \hat{a}_z \quad \text{(the external magnetic field).}$$

In principle we could now use Eq. (15) in conjunction with Eqs. (9) and (10) to solve for the propagation constant of the electromagnetic waves in the guiding structures used for this experiment. However, this procedure leads to a transcendental equation which must be solved numerically for the propagation constant,[15] and an interpretation of the experiments, which follows, would be difficult.

In order to facilitate the interpretation of our experiments, we use Poynting's theorem for the average power (per unit of volume) input to the plasma:

$$\langle p \rangle = \frac{1}{2} \operatorname{Re} \sigma_{xx} \left[|E_x|^2 + |E_y|^2 \right] + \frac{j}{2} \operatorname{Im} \sigma_{xy} \left[E_x^* E_y - E_x E_y^* \right] + \frac{1}{2} \operatorname{Re} \sigma_{zz} |E_z|^2 \tag{16}$$

where (*) denotes complex conjugate.

Most of the experiments described in this paper were performed on plasmas located in the center of a rectangular waveguide as shown in Fig. 6(b). We note that when the magnetic field is not present, $\sigma_{xy} = 0$, hence E_y and E_z are zero for the TE_{10} mode of propagation. In addition to this fact, E_y and E_z must go to zero at the x walls even in the presence of the magnetic field. Hence the products $\sigma_{xy} E_y E_x$ and $\sigma_{zz} E_z^2$ are of second order and are neglected. Under these assumptions, Eq. (16) may be written :

$$\langle p \rangle = \frac{1}{2} \operatorname{Re} \sigma_{xx} |E|^2 \tag{16a}$$

It is seen that the absorption is proportional to the real part of

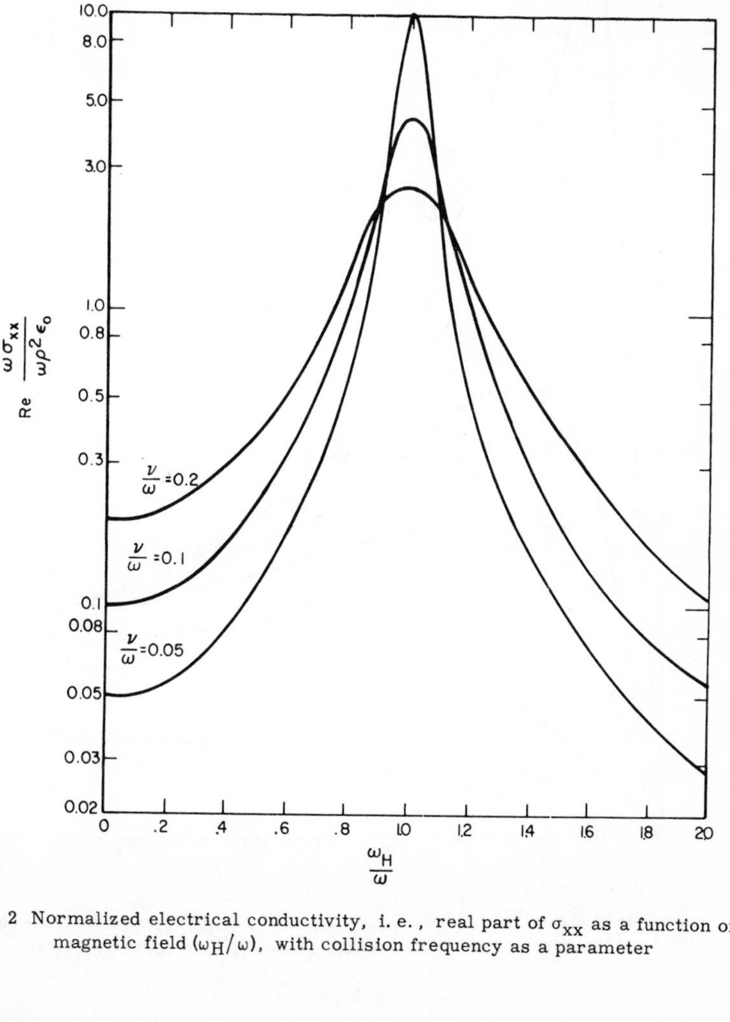

Fig. 2 Normalized electrical conductivity, i. e., real part of σ_{xx} as a function of magnetic field (ω_H/ω), with collision frequency as a parameter

the main diagonal component of the conductivity matrix. This conductivity is plotted as a function of ω_H/ω for various values of ν/ω in Fig. 2. It is interesting to note that the absorption increases with increasing collision frequency for values of the magnetic field variable $(\omega_H/\omega) \neq 1$; whereas at cyclotron resonance, $\omega_H = \omega$, the absorption decreases with increasing collision frequency. This is consistent with our earlier observation that the collisions cause the transfer of energy from an electromagnetic wave to the electron gas of the plasma in the absence of resonance conditions, and impede the energy transfer in the close vicinity of resonance.

Figure 3 illustrates the variation of Re σ_{xx} with ν/ω, where the magnetic field is a fixed parameter. This is the case which cor-

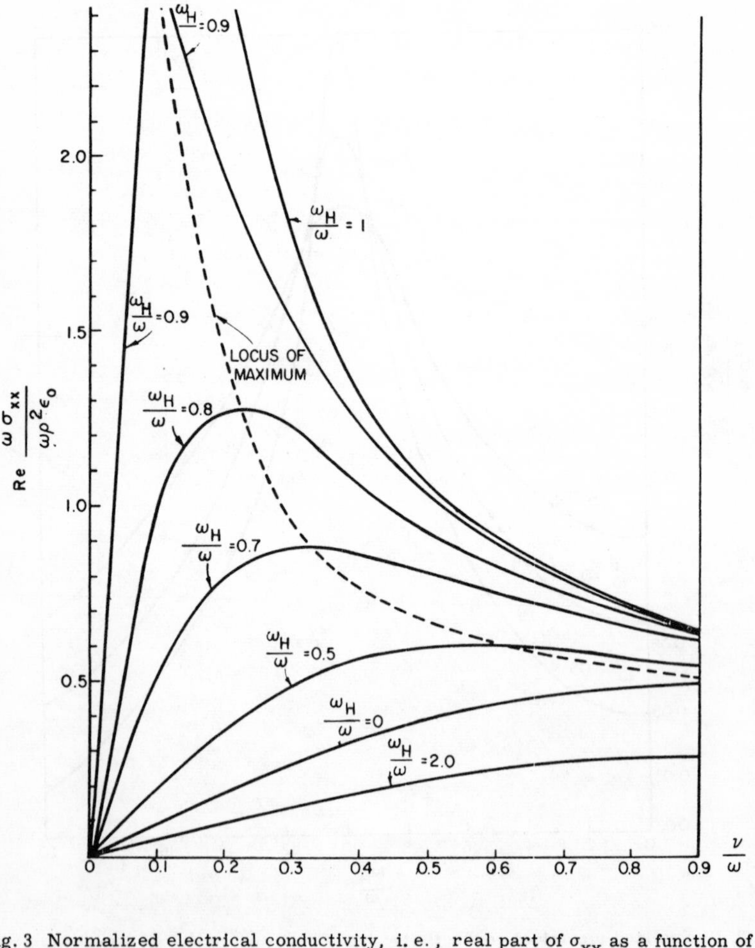

Fig. 3 Normalized electrical conductivity, i. e., real part of σ_{xx} as a function of collision frequency (ν/ω), with magnetic field (ω_H/ω) as a parameter

responds to most of the experiments described here. It is noticed in this figure that for a fixed value of the magnetic field variable $(\omega_H/\omega) \neq 1$, σ_{xx} first increases, reaches a maximum and then decreases as the quantity ν/ω increases. Such behavior on the absorption of an electromagnetic wave will be shown in Section V. If the statement can be made that the E field inside the plasma is related to the applied E field by a function that is weakly dependent upon the collision frequency, then, as the collision frequency is varied, the point at which the absorption reaches a maximum is the point at which σ_{xx} is a maximum. This point was used to measure the effective electron collision frequency in both disturbed and unperturbed plasmas.

So far we have considered only the attenuation of an electromagnetic wave, which is one of the two characteristic quantities in wave propagation. The other measurable quantity is the phase velocity of the electromagnetic wave in the plasma. However, the phase velocity does not lend itself to dynamic measurement as easily as the absorption. For this reason, phase velocity measurements will be presented by static, point-by-point, measurements.

In order to correlate attenuation and phase measurements to the plasma parameters, an analytic expression for the propagation constant, γ, must be obtained. It was mentioned earlier that a rigorous solution of Maxwell's equations in the guiding structures considered here leads to a transcendental equation which must be solved numerically for the propagation constant. However, in many cases, approximate techniques can be fruitfully used to obtain admittedly less rigorous but useful solutions.

One such approximation technique uses an integral equation which expresses the propagation constant in terms of the fields inside the plasma. This is the approach which is used for the study of magnetoplasmas located in a rectangular waveguide as illustrated in Fig. 6(b). It is shown in the Appendix that the propagation constant in this guiding system can be approximated by:

$$\gamma^2 + \beta_o^2 = j\omega\mu_o \sigma_{xx} g \tag{17}$$

where β_o = phase constant in the structure without a plasma, and g = geometrical factor.

Experiments which will be described in Section V have shown that Eq. (17) is qualitatively correct, and appear to justify the assumptions listed in the Appendix.

Another possible approximate method of solving for the propagation constant is to assume that the plasma is unbounded and is subjected to a uniform plane wave. This approach is especially useful in discussing the experiments performed in circular waveguides. For the case when the electromagnetic wave is propagating along the direction of the magnetic field, the propagation constant for circularly polarized waves can be simply expressed by:[16, 17]

$$\gamma_{e,i}^2 = -\frac{\omega^2}{c^2}\left[1 - \frac{\omega_p^2/\omega^2}{\left(1 \pm \frac{\omega_H}{\omega}\right) - j\frac{\nu}{\omega}}\right] \tag{18}$$

where $\gamma = \alpha + j\beta$, α = attenuation constant, and β = phase constant.

In Eq. (18), the minus sign is associated with γ_e, the propagation constant of the extraordinary wave (which rotates in the same sense as the electrons). The positive sign is associated with γ_i, the propagation constant of the ordinary wave (which rotates in the same sense as the positive ions). The decomposition of a linearly polarized wave into two contra-rotating circular waves leads to the well known Faraday rotation of the plane of polarization of the linear wave. The angle of rotation, θ, is proportional to the difference of the phase constants β_i and β_e and the length of the path:

$$\frac{2\theta}{L} = \beta_i - \beta_e. \tag{19}$$

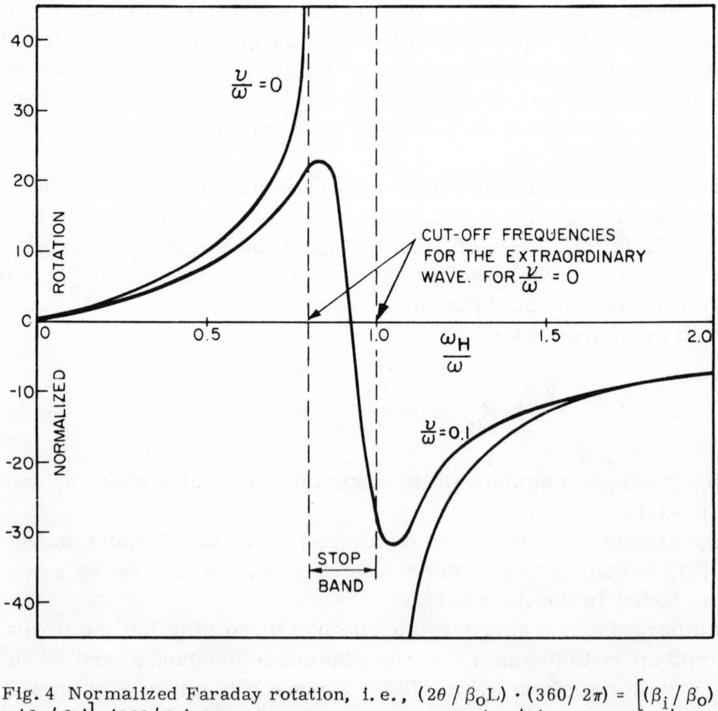

Fig. 4 Normalized Faraday rotation, i.e., $(2\theta / \beta_o L) \cdot (360/2\pi) = \left[(\beta_i/\beta_o) - (\beta_e/\beta_o)\right] \cdot (360/2\pi)$ dependence on magnetic field (ω_H/ω) shown for ν/ω = 0 and ν/ω = 0.1. These curves are plotted for the particular value of the parameter ω_p^2/ω^2 = 0.2.

The waveguide Faraday rotation[18] in a magneto-plasma does not appear to differ, in the first approximation, from that of the unbounded case. The angle of rotation of a linearly polarized wave propagating in an unbounded plasma is plotted in Fig. 4. It is seen that the angle of rotation per unit length is proportional to the number density of the electrons, and is nearly independent of the collision frequency for values of ω_H/ω much different from unity.

For ω_H/ω close to one, the rotation angle is dependent upon both n and ν. The phenomenon of Faraday rotation is used here to study the enhancement of plasma disintegration resulting from a significant rise in the electron temperature following e-m energy transfer at cyclotron resonance to the electron gas of the plasma.

IV. EXPERIMENTAL TECHNIQUES AND APPARATUS

The technique of interaction of guided microwaves in a non-magnetized plasma developed in our laboratory[5] has been extended in this study to investigate the above phenomena in magneto-plasmas. The main problems associated with this technique can be broadly divided into three categories: 1) production of a suitable gyromagnetic plasma; 2) propagation of microwaves of proper characteristics through the magneto-plasma; 3) investigation of the mutual interaction of these waves and the plasma. In addition to the method of probing the plasma by microwave interaction techniques, the visible light intensity emitted by the afterglow was simultaneously observed; this

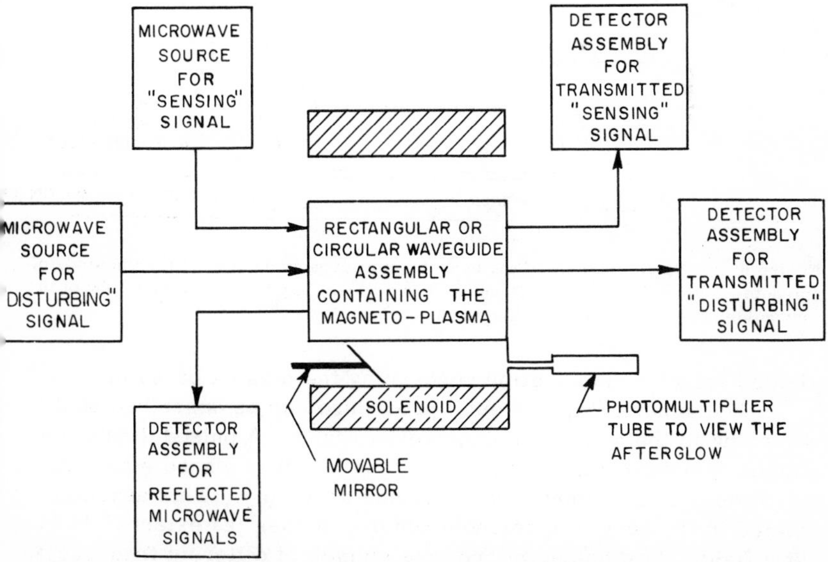

Fig. 5 Schematic diagram illustrating the technique for the study of wave-interaction phenomenon in laboratory magneto-plasmas

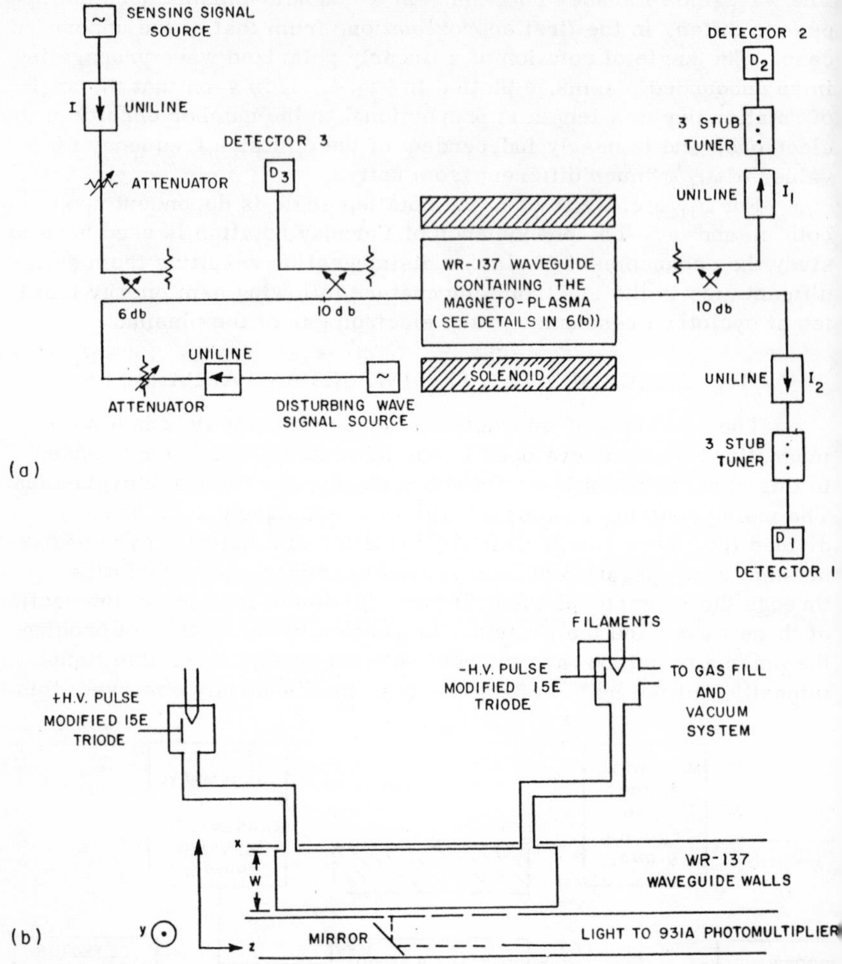

Figure 6 a) Block diagram of the experimental arrangement used for the study of magneto-plasmas located in rectangular waveguides; b) Cross-sectional view of the waveguide assembly containing the discharge tube.

yielded valuable information concerning the plasma behavior.

The general experimental procedure can be described best by referring to the schematic diagram in Fig. 5. A pulsed discharge plasma is obtained in a cylindrical tube which is placed either in a cylindrical or a rectangular waveguide assembly. This assembly is located in the core of a solenoid which provides the external dc magnetic field. Two pulsed microwave signals of different frequencies and amplitudes are propagated nearly simultaneously through the decaying plasma. The transmission and reflection characteristics of hese two waves and their mutual interaction in the plasma is studied ınder varied experimental conditions, which will be described later.

For the investigation of magneto-plasmas located in rectangular vaveguides the experimental arrangement shown in Fig. 6 was used. 'igure 6(b) shows the waveguide assembly containing the magneto-ɪlasma. A 2.5 or 5-cm long pyrex glass tube with an outside diameter ıf 1 cm and a wall thickness of 0.7 mm is used as a discharge tube n which the magneto-plasma is produced. This discharge tube is ocated at the center of a WR 137 rectangular waveguide, such that he E field of the wave is approximately uniform across the discharge ube. The waveguide assembly containing the discharge tube is in a ıearly uniform magnetic field (variation 1%), which can be varied from to 3000 gauss. The plasma is produced in the discharge tube by a ecurrent electrical discharge through the gas.

The microwave apparatus is shown schematically in Fig. 6(a). 'wo klystrons generate microwave power at frequencies f_d and f_s. 'he microwave signal of frequency f_d has a peak power of 100 milli-vatts. This signal is designated as the disturbing signal and is in esonance with the electrons in the magneto-plasma, i. e., $f_d = f_H =$ $B_o/2\pi m$. The second microwave signal, $f_s > f_d$, of sufficiently low mplitude ($\lesssim$ 10 microwatts) and designated as the sensing wave, is etected by D_2; D_1 receives only the "disturbing wave" f_d. The micro-'ave signals reflected by the 3-stub tuners are absorbed in the ferrite

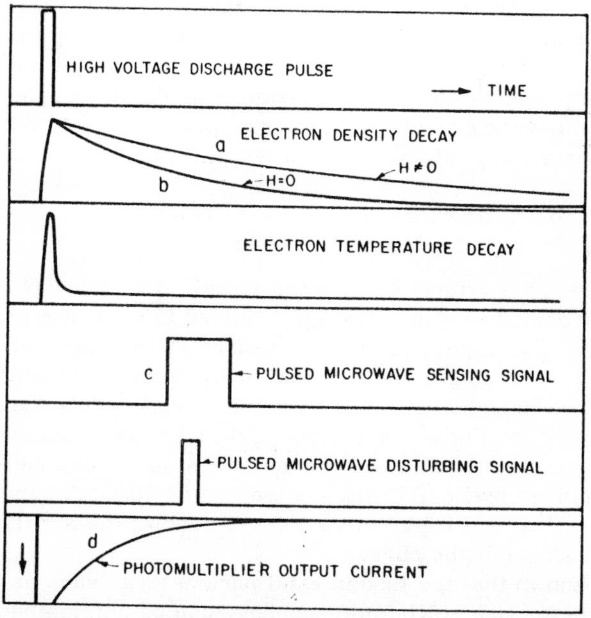

'ig. 7 Timing diagram of the sequence of events in a typical wave-interaction experiment isolators I_1 and I_2, preventing their re-entry into the plasma.

Before presenting the experimental results, the sequence of events occuring in a typical experiment are described in a timing dia gram shown in Fig. 7. A 2-microsecond-wide, 5 kv, dc discharge pulse, repeated at the rate of 100 pps, establishes a plasma which then decays as represented by (a) and (b) of Fig. 7. The pulsed microwav signals of controllable widths are propagated at the desired times durin the afterglow. The visible light intensity emitted by the afterglow a recorded by a photomultiplier is also sketched in trace (d). The envelopes of the transmitted and reflected microwave signals can be displayed on a dual-beam oscilloscope.

V. EXPERIMENTAL RESULTS

In order to show the general validity of the simple theory of wave interaction in gaseous plasmas and to verify the discussions given in Section III, we report here the results of experiments performed in plasmas produced in neon and xenon gases. The gas pres sures are chosen so as to achieve an efficient transfer of electromag netic energy to the electron gas under cyclotron resonance condition hence the quantity ν/ω_d should be much smaller than unity. Xenon was chosen as a typical gas whose collision frequency exhibits the Ramsauer behavior for low energy electrons, as opposed to that of neon. The presence of electron-ion collisions in a neon plasma of appropriate charge densities results in the fact that the total collisic frequency in such a plasma varies with electronic energy in a manne similar to that of ν_{e-m} in xenon (see Fig. 1). In the following paragraphs, the propagation characteristics of an electromagnetic wave in a low-temperature isothermal (300^oK) plasma is studied. This is followed by a similar study in perturbed plasma.

Propagation Characteristic of Sensing Signal Guided Through a Magneto-Plasma

A low-power pulsed microwave signal, f_s = 4. 566 Gc, is guid through a decaying magneto-plasma obtained in neon at a pressure c 1. 6 mm Hg. The experimentally measured attenuation and phase shift undergone by this sensing signal are plotted as a function of magnetic field in Fig. 8(a). The solid curve represents the measure attenuation and the dotted curve, the measured phase constant. The theoretical attenuation and phase constants α and β obtained from the expression given by Eq. (17) are plotted in Fig. 8(b). A comparison of the theoretical and experimental curves shows the similarity in the general shape of the curves.

It is known that the fundamental parameters, such as electro density and effective collision frequency, can be determined from such experimental data. The technique is also applicable to the determination of these parameters in a plasma which is perturbed,

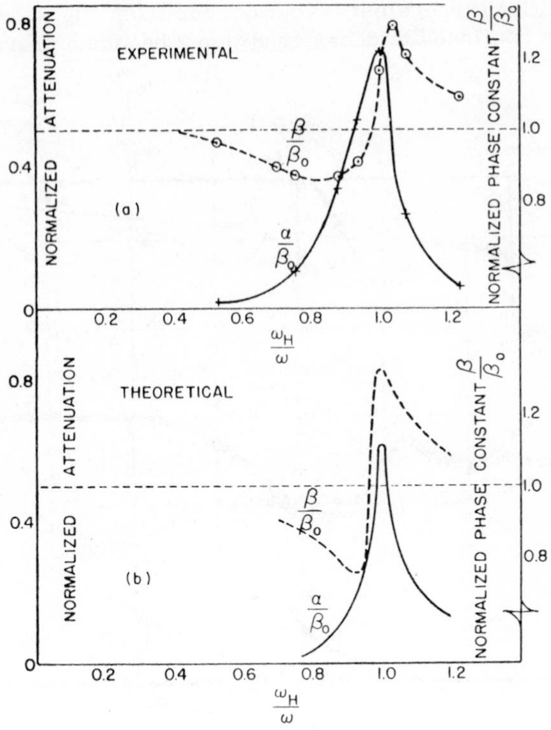

Figure 8 a) Experimental values of the normalized attenuation and phase constants as a function of (ω_H/ω). f_s = 4.96 Gc; peak power 150 microwatts; the pulsed probing signal is transmitted 1.0 millisecond after the termination of a 2μ secs wide, 5 kv discharge pulse through neon gas (1.6 mm Hg). b) Theoretical plot of normalized attenuation and phase constants for $\omega_p{}^2/\omega^2$ = 0.1 and ν/ω = 0.04.

for example, by another electromagnetic wave. If the two em waves are propagated in the time sequence shown in Fig. 7, then this technique provides information on the state of the plasma prior to, during, and in the wake of, the disturbance.

Cross-Modulation in a Neon Afterglow

The experiments described below were performed in a decaying neon plasma under two different conditions: 1) $\nu_{e-i} > (1/3)\,\nu_{e-m}$; and 2) $\nu_{e-m} > 3\,\nu_{e-i}$. These conditions determine whether the total collision frequency decreases with energy of the electrons as in case 1, or increases with the energy of the electrons as in case 2. In the early part of a (1 mm Hg) neon afterglow, the electron density is in the range 10^{12} to 10^{10} electrons (per c. c.) and $T_e \sim 300^oK$. Hence the first condition is prevalent, as can be seen from Fig. 1. Of course, as the plasma continues to decay condition 2 becomes prevalent.

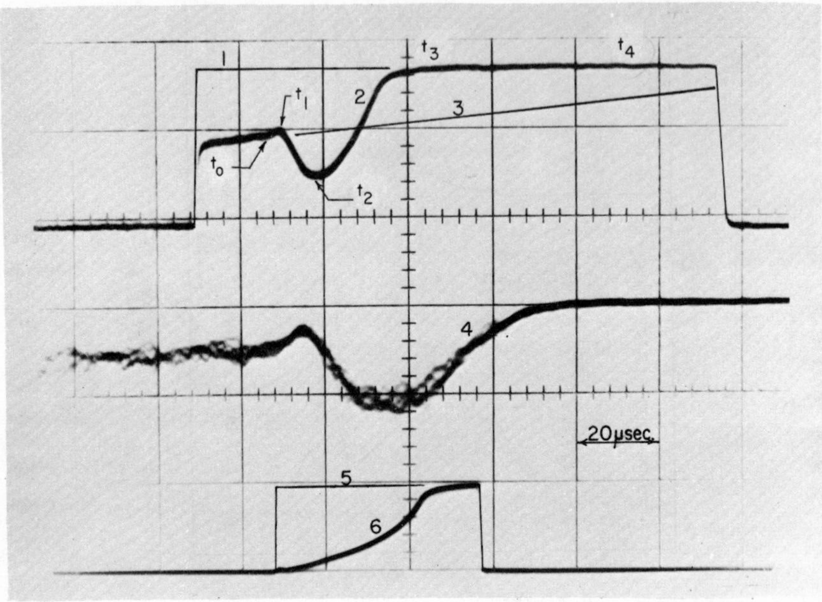

Fig. 9 Wave-interaction in the afterglow of a neon magneto-plasma (pressure 1 mm Hg). $f_H = eB/2\pi m = f_d = 4.80$ Gc; peak power 75 milliwatts; pulsed disturbing signal is propagated 1.0 millisecond after the termination of 2 microsecond wide, 5 kv discharge pulse. $\nu_{ei} > \nu_{em}$ $f_s = 6.2$ Gc; peak power 20 microwatts. Traces 1 and 5 are the rf envelopes of the transmitted sensing and disturbing pulses in the absence of the plasma; trace 3 is the envelope of f_s when f_d is shut off. When f_d is incident on the plasma, traces 2 and 6 are transmitted rf envelopes of f_s and f_d respectively. Trace 4 is the photomultiplier output representing the light intensity emitted in the afterglow. Downward deflection indicates increased light output.

Figure 9 displays the oscilloscope traces of the transmitted microwave signals and the photomultiplier output for a typical experiment in which condition 1 prevails. Notice that the amplitude of the transmitted sensing wave initially increases, reaching a maximum at the point denoted by t_1, even though the electron-energy is increasing from $t = t_0$ to t_1. Since the absorption of the sensing signal is proportional to ν_t for this value of the magnetic field $(\omega_H = \omega_d)$, [i. e., $B = (m/e) \cdot \omega_d$], the increased transparency indicates that the total collision frequency has decreased. At $t = t_1$, the derivative of ν_t with respect to T_e is zero, or $\nu_{e-i} = (1/3)' \nu_{e-m}$. An independent measurement of the number density of the electrons would then yield the temperature, T_e. As the energy of the electron gas is further increased, the electron collisions with the neutrals predominate over those with ions, so that now the absorption of the sensing wave increases.

At the point $t = t_2$, the absorption reaches a maximum despite the continued energy rise of the electron gas. This point corresponds to the maximum value of σ_{xxs} as a function of ν/ω_s, as seen in Fig. 3. This interpretation is correct provided it is assumed that the number density of the electrons does not vary appreciably in the time interval t_2 to t_0.

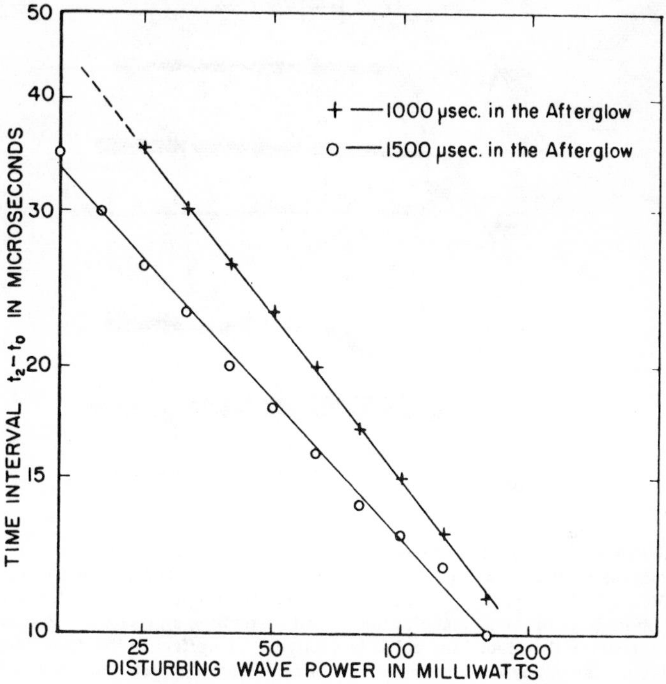

Fig. 10 Time elapsed since the initiation of the disturbing microwave pulse to establish a constant energy state of the electron gas, (i. e., corresponding to $\nu/\omega_s \sim 0.2$ at $t = t_2$) as a function of the amplitude of the disturbing wave. The two curves correspond to two different values of n_e and ν_t. Neon gas 1.0 mm Hg. $f_H = eB/2\pi m = 4.86$ Gc; $f_s = 6.2$ Gc.

If this assumption is correct, the product of the disturbing power P_d and the time interval t_2 to t_0 should be a constant, provided the rate of energy increase of the electron gas is large compared to the rate of energy loss. This is the case, even for relatively modest values of electric field, when the frequency of the disturbing wave is close to cyclotron resonance. Figure 10 is a plot of $\log P_d$ as a function of $\log (t_2 - t_0)$ and verifies that $P_d(t_2 - t_0)$ is a constant whose value depends on the initial value of ν/ω_d. Hence it is reasonable to neglect the variation of n_e in the time interval t_2 to t_0 and assign an energy state to the electron gas such that at $t = t_2$, ν/ω_s has the

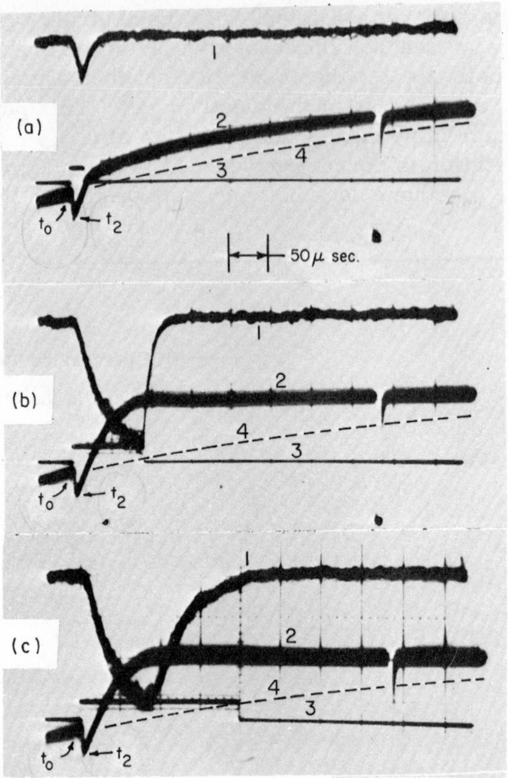

Fig. 11 Wave-interaction phenomena, when the amplitude of disturbing wave is constant but the pulse duration is varied. Neon 0.8 mm Hg. $f_H = eB/2\pi m = 4.97$ Gc; peak power 100 mw; $f_s = 5.86$ Gc. Trace 4 represents the amplitude of the transmitted sensing signal (cw) in the absence of the pulsed disturbing signal; trace 3 shows the duration for which the disturbing pulse is applied. The effect of the disturbing signal on the plasma "seen" by the sensing signal is represented in trace 2; trace 1 is the photomultiplier output.

value which maximizes σ_{xxs}. For the frequencies used here, $\nu/\omega_s \sim 0.2$ This is about a 100-fold rise in collision frequency.

This large rise in the collision frequency is also indicated by the amplitude of the transmitted disturbing wave itself. Since the absorption of the disturbing wave is proportional to $1/\nu_t$, this large increase of ν_t results in a decreased absorption.* This is the pheno- menon referred to earlier as self-modulation.

It is also shown in Fig. 9 that the amplitude of the transmitted sensing wave reaches its unattenuated value at the point $t = t_3$. In view of the preceding discussion, this is possible if the number density of the electrons in the plasma has decayed considerably in the time

*The experiment described here illustrates insertion loss only. However, reflection measurements have shown that the absorption is very closely approximated by the insertion loss.

nterval t_3 to t_2. This will be shown later to be the case. This fact ndicates that the plasma is being rapidly destroyed due to the drastic eating of the electron gas by the resonating disturbing wave. The ariation of the visible light intensity, as seen in Fig. 9, also shows the ffect of the disturbing wave on the plasma. Immediately after the nitiation of the disturbing pulse, the light intensity decreases due to reduction in the electron-ion recombination coefficient. This re-luction in light intensity is known[19, 5] as "quenching of the afterglow." Vith the collision frequency of the electrons decreased, the rate of ransfer of electromagnetic energy to the electrons is thus accelerated. Electrons reach energies high enough to undergo inelastic collisions vith neon atoms in their ground state (~1.85eV) or certainly with neon toms in their metastable states (~2eV). Such collisions result in a net ncrease of light intensity following the termination of the initial quenching. The decrease in photomultiplier current after the removal of the disturb-ng pulse is most likely due to the decreasing number of inelastic collis-ons as well as to the reduction in recombination light intensity (which in he prevailing charge density range is approximately proportional to n^2).

We shall now describe effects produced at constant amplitude vhen the width of the disturbing pulse is varied. Figure 11, shows he oscilloscope traces of the transmitted microwave signals and hotomultiplier current for three different pulse-widths of the dis-urbing wave under the condition $\nu_{e-m} >> 3\nu_{e-i}$. It should be noted hat the sensing microwave signal is operated in this instance as a ontinuous wave pulsed off for a short duration in order to obtain a eference level. In the absence of the disturbing signal, trace 4 in ll three parts of this figure shows that attenuation of the sensing signal decreases as a function of time due to the normal decay of the lectron density. For a narrow pulse of the disturbing wave, only he increasing absorption of the sensing signal and immediate relaxa-ion is seen on trace 2 of Fig. 11(a). However, for wider (width > $t_2 - t_o$) listurbing pulses, it is observed that the amplitude of the trans-nitted sensing signal reaches a value corresponding to its original nattenuated level even before the conclusion of the disturbing pulse trace 2 of Fig. 11(b), (c). This is again attributed to the rapid loss of electrons from the plasma when they are subjected to resonant eating for the time intervals indicated above.

One of the possible reasons for this phenomenon is that it ap-ears necessary to keep the electrons energetic for such a time nterval that they are capable of diffusing to the walls with a very onsiderably enhanced diffusion coefficient. In addition to the enhanced ollisional diffusion, the rapid disintegration of the plasma might lso be due to some instability which can develop when considerable selective heating of the electron gas occurs, which is the case at yclotron resonance. When the cross-modulation experiment was erformed in neon (0.5 mm Hg), as shown in Fig. 12, a low frequency

(143 kc) amplitude modulation was observed on the amplitude of the transmitted sensing signal during the time interval of the disturbing wave pulse.* However, such variations in the transmitted amplitude of the sensing wave were not observed at higher pressures or for lower electron densities.

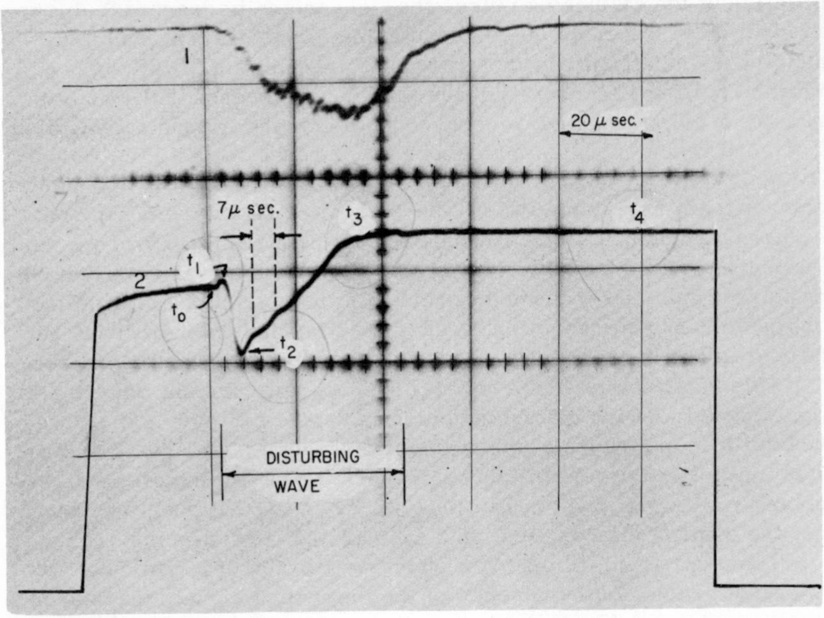

Fig. 12 Low frequency (~140 kc) amplitude modulation which was observed on the transmitted amplitude (trace 2) of the sensing signal, when plasma electrons are accelerated by the resonating disturbing wave. Trace 1 is the photomultiplier output. Neon gas 0.5 mm Hg; $f_H = eB/2\pi m = f_d = 5.1$ Gc; peak power 100 mw; $f_s = 5.86$ Gc.

The phenomena are considerably different at later times in the afterglow (see Fig. 13) but can be readily understood on the basis of the previous experiments. It is seen that the absorption of the sensing wave increases immediately with increasing electron energy. This may be understood on the basis of the expression of the total collision frequency $\nu_t = \nu_{e-i} + \nu_{e-m}$. Since the electron density is much lower at these times in the afterglow, the contribution of ν_{e-i} to the total collision frequency is negligible. Hence, an increase of the energy of the electrons can only increase their collision frequency as contrasted to the initial decrease which was observed in Fig. 9.

It is also seen that the increase in photomultiplier current occurs almost immediately (< 1 μ sec) after the start of the disturbing pulse. This occurs because the electrons are accelerated to high

*It is to be noted that this modulation frequency is very nearly the cyclotron frequency of the Ne^+ ions ($\Omega_i = (eB/m) \sim 139$ kc).

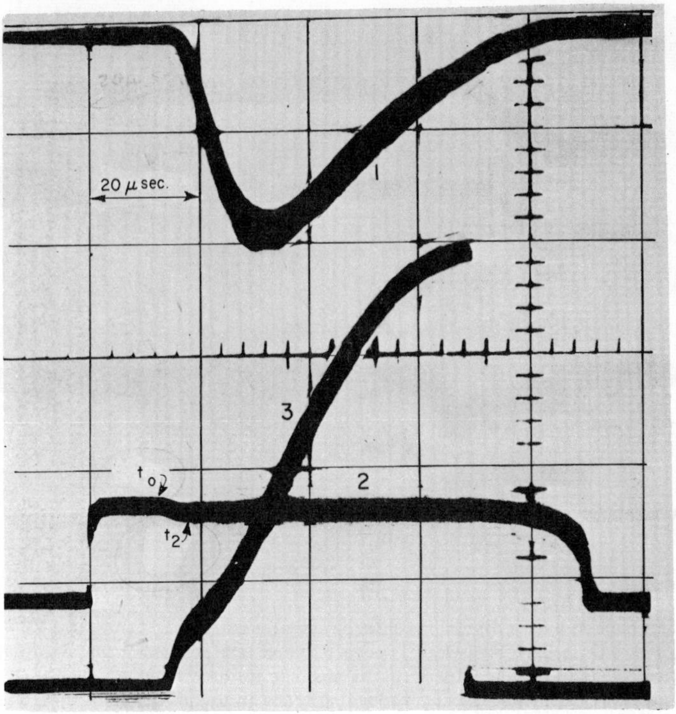

Fig. 13 Wave-interaction in the afterglow of a neon plasma for the condition $\nu_{e-m} >> 3\nu_{e-i}$. Neon 1.0 mm Hg; f_d = 4.78 Gc = f_H; f_s = 6.47 Gc. Trace 1 shows photo-multiplier output; trace 3 represents the amplitude of transmitted disturbing signal and trace 2 represents that of the sensing signal. (Peak power of f_d = 100 mw).

energies (from about 0.04 to at least 2 ev) within very few collision times. This rapid acceleration is attributed to the fact that the power from the disturbing wave is inversely proportional to $1/\nu_t$ for $\omega_H = \omega_d$. The total collision frequency at $t = t_0$ is, of course, smaller than in the experiment described in Fig. 9, since the contribution of ν_{e-i} to the total collision frequency is here insignificant. Hence the energy rise when only ν_{e-m} is present is more rapid than in the case when $\nu_t = \nu_{e-i} + \nu_{e-m}$.

This rapid rise in the electronic energy is also evidenced by the self-modulation of the transmitted disturbing wave. It is seen that the transmitted disturbing wave increases more rapidly in this figure than in Fig. 9. This is consistent with the above discussion.

Additional experiments were performed to verify the fact that the point t_2 of Figs. 9, 11, and 13 is in every case the point where Re σ_{xxs} reaches its maximum. Two sensing frequencies, ω_{s1} and ω_{s2}, are used such that $\omega_{s1} > \omega_{s2} > \omega_d = \omega_H$. Thus, as predicted by Fig. 3, the point of maximum absorption (t_2) as sensed by ω_{s2} is closer to t_0 than the corresponding point sensed by ω_{s1}. (see Fig. 14).

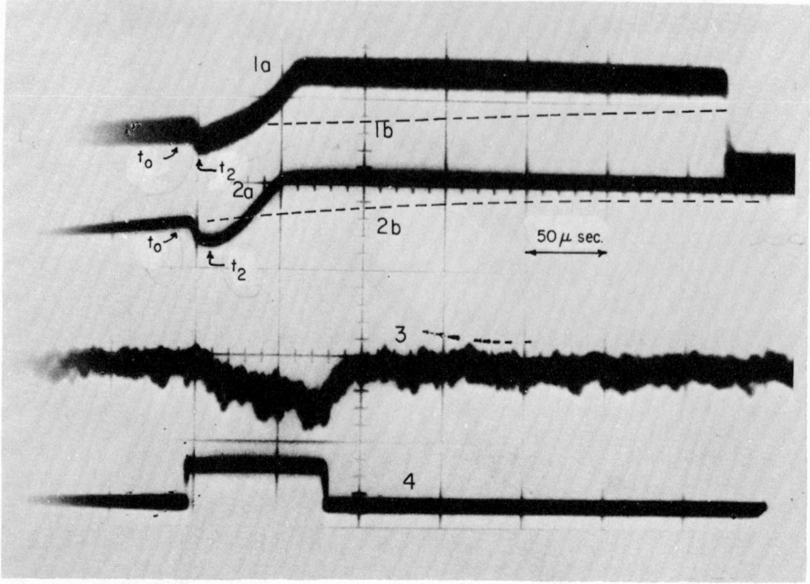

Fig. 14 Effect caused by the disturbing microwave signal (f_d = 5.05) on two sensing signals; f_{s1} = 6.0 Gc.; f_{s2} = 6.7 Gc. Traces 1(b) and 2(b) represent the amplitudes of transmitted f_{s1} and f_{s2} respectively in the absence of the disturbing signal whereas traces 1(a) and 2(a) represent the corresponding trace in the presence of the disturbing signal; trace 4 shows the duration for which the pulsed signal is present; trace 3 represents the photomultiplier output. (Neon gas 0.9 mm Hg.)

Figure 14 also illustrates the enhanced disintegration of the plasma in the time interval t_4 to t_2. All other quantities being equal, the propagation of ω_{s2} is affected by a smaller electron density than that of the higher frequency, ω_{s1}, because ω_{s2} is closer to cyclotron resonance than ω_{s1}. Hence the plasma becomes completely transparent to ω_{s1} at an earlier time than to ω_{s2}.

The enhanced disintegration of the plasma as a result of rapid rise of electron energy has been studied in greater detail by using Faraday rotation[18] of guided electromagnetic waves through plasmas. In this experiment, the plasma (same dimensions as in the rectangular guide experiments) is centrally located in a circular waveguide immersed in a longitudinal magnetic field. By measuring the angle of rotation of a linearly polarized TE_{11} pulsed sensing wave as a function of time in the late afterglow, during and in the wake of a pulsed disturbing wave, ($\omega_d = \omega_H$), information is obtained on the influence of the resonance heating of the electrons on the phase velocities of the extroardinary and ordinary sensing waves.

Figure 15 shows typical results of such an experiment for several amplitudes of the disturbing wave. Notice that at any time $t > t_1$, the angle of rotation does not return to its unperturbed value

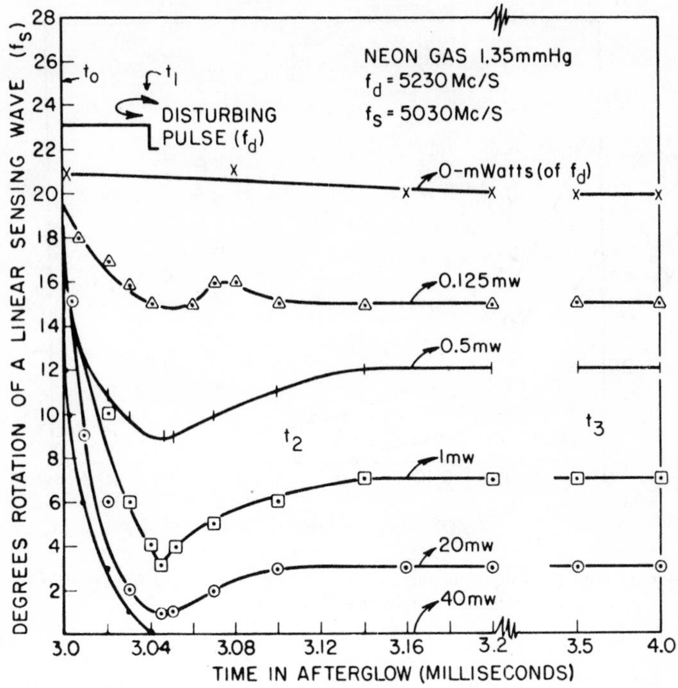

Fig. 15 Faraday rotation of 1 μ sec wide sensing signal (f_S) as a function of time in the afterglow, during and in the wake of the pulsed disturbing signal (f_d). The Faraday rotation is shown for different amplitudes of the disturbing signal.

for large amplitudes of the disturbing wave. However, for smaller amplitudes of the disturbance, the angle tends to relax towards the undisturbed value. Since the rotation angle is directly proportional to the total number of electrons in the magnetized plasma, the difference in angles at $t = t_3$ (after the plasma electron gas has relaxed to its initial temperature) represents the loss of electrons. Notice the correspondence of the experimentally obtained dependence of Faraday rotation upon collision frequency in the interval t_1 to t_o to that predicted theoretically from Eq. 18 and plotted in Fig. 16.

Cross-Modulation in a Ramsauer Gas (Xenon):

In the previous experiments, it was shown that it is possible for the total collision frequency in a neon plasma to decrease with increasing electronic energy, despite the fact that the cross section for momentum transfer between electrons and neon atoms is a slowly increasing function of electron temperature. The decreasing collision frequency with increasing electron energy is due to the Coulomb collisions between the electrons and ions which are dominant when the

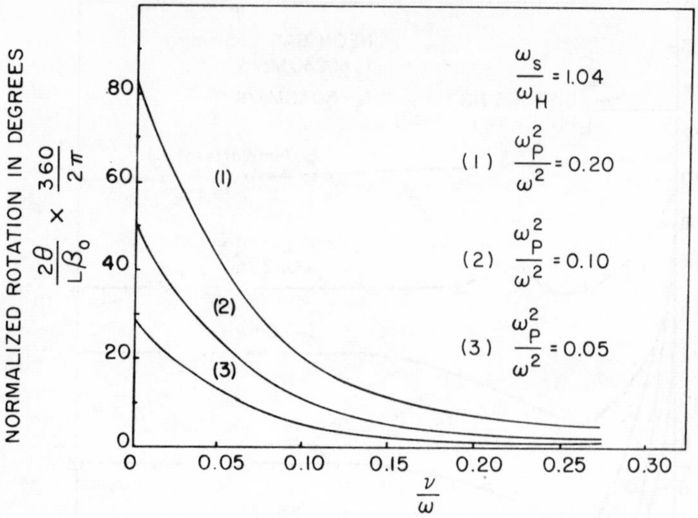

Fig. 16 Normalized Faraday rotation as a function of ν / ω for different values of $\omega_p{}^2/\omega^2$, and constant $\omega_s/\omega_H = 1.04$.

degree of ionization is greater than 10^{-5} and at low electron temperatures ($\leqslant 300^oK$).

As is well known, the cross section for momentum transfer of electrons with xenon atoms decreases very rapidly with increasing T_e from ~ 300^oK reaching a minimum and then increasing as shown in Fig. 1. In view of the large absolute values of xenon cross section for slow (~300^oK) electrons, the electron-ion collision frequency contributes little, if at all, to the total collision frequency at the xenon pressure indicated, even at the maximum electron densities used in these experiments (~10^{11} per cc). At these electron densities however, a neon (1mm Hg, 300^oK) plasma is already completely Coulomb interaction dominated, as just mentioned. Therefore, in view of the falling cross sections with increasing electron energy in both cases, the phenomena of wave interaction will be completely similar.

Figure 17 shows the oscilloscope traces of the amplitudes of the transmitted signals obtained from the experiment performed in a xenon afterglow. These photographs show the effects for three different amplitudes of the disturbing wave ($\omega_d = \omega_H$). It is seen that immediately after the application of the disturbing microwave signal, the absorption of the sensing signal decreases in the time interval t_1 to t_o. This is, of course, due to the decreasing collision frequency with increasing electron energy, as is the case in a coulomb interaction dominated neon plasma. At the instant t_1, the electron energy corresponds to that energy for which Q_{e-m} and therefore ν_{e-m} is a minimum (Ramsauer). In the time interval t_1 to t_2, (Fig. 17(a)) the ab-

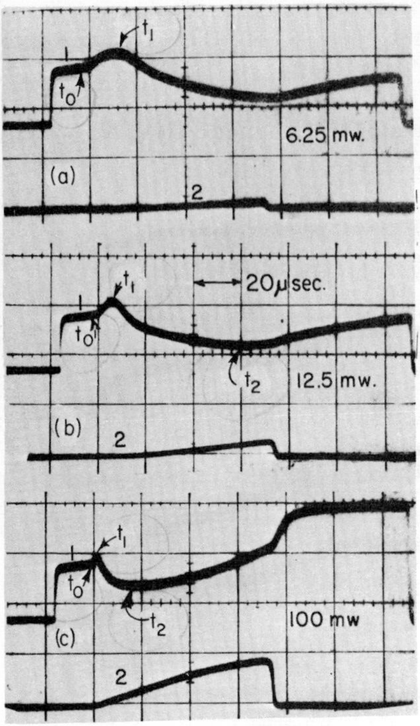

Fig. 17 Wave interaction phenomena in Xenon; pressure 0.4 mm Hg. Trace 1 is the transmitted amplitude of the sensing signal in the presence of a disturbing signal; trace 2 is the transmitted amplitude of the disturbing signal; f_s = 6.1 Gc; $f_H = eB/2\pi m = f_d$ = 5.2 Gc. The three photographs show the effects for three amplitudes of the disturbing pulse.

sorption of the sensing signal increases, reaching a maximum at $t = t_2$ despite the increasing collision frequency. The interpretation of this point is identical with the corresponding point in the neon plasma discussed earlier and shown in Fig. 9. It is also seen in Fig. 17(c), as opposed to (a) and (b), that as a result of the relatively high level (100 mw) of the disturbing wave and immediately following its conclusion, the complete unattenuated amplitude of the sensing wave signal is transmitted. In the case of a passive plasma this could occur only as a result of a drastic loss of electron density in the short time interval observed.

The results of these experiments led to a simple method of determination of electron collision frequencies in a magneto-plasma. This method will now be described.

Cross-Modulation Technique for Determining Collision Frequency

The method is based upon the interpretation of the point $t = t_2$ in Fig. 9. At this point $\partial\sigma_{xxs}/\partial\nu = 0$. If the magnetic field intensity is adjusted to a value such that:

$$\left.\frac{\partial\sigma_{xxs}}{\partial\nu}\right|_{t = t_o} = 0 \tag{20}$$

then the value of ν at $t = t_o$ is a solution to Eq. (20). The condition given by Eq. (20) is obtained experimentally by varying the magnetic field and observing the cross-modulation as shown in Fig. 18. Notice that for both $\omega_H/\omega_s \ll 1$ and $\omega_H/\omega_s \gg 1$, the sensing wave undergoes increased absorption for increasing collision frequency. However, for $\omega_H/\omega = 1$, the absorption decreases. It appears obvious that there are two values of the magnetic field for which the cross-modulation disappears. These fields are solutions of Eq. (20). The value of ν is given to a good approximation by:

$$\nu \doteq \omega_s \left| 1 - \frac{\omega_H}{\omega_s} \right| \tag{21}$$

where ω_H corresponds to these values of the magnetic field for which the cross-modulation disappears.

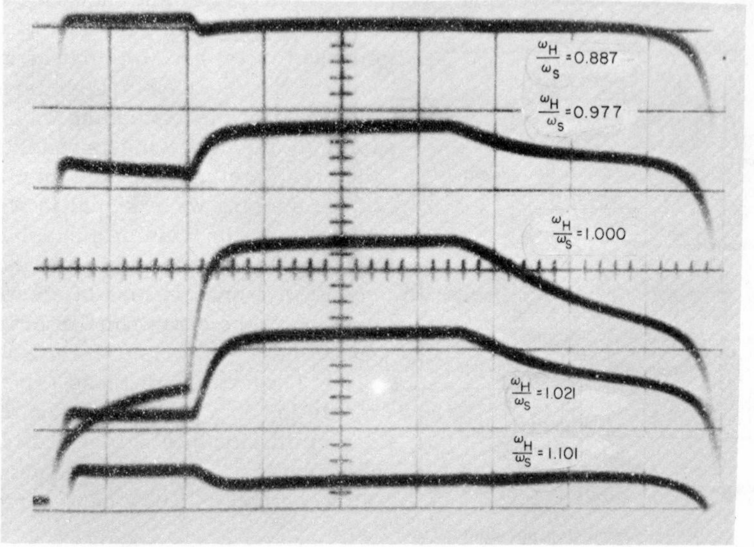

Fig. 18 Variation of the cross-modulation as a function of the magnetic field; Neon gas 12.0 mm Hg; f_H = 4.764 Gc; f_s = 6.72 Gc

The validity of this method is limited by the range of validity of Eq. (16a). Basically, the use of this equation requires that the electron density be small enough so that the electromagnetic fields inside the plasma can be well approximated by the applied fields. It is for this reason that the experiments were performed with very low electron density plasmas ($n_e < 10^8$/cc). Furthermore, experiments have shown that only the value $\omega_H/\omega_s > 1$ can be used in Eq. (21). For $\omega_H/\omega < 1$, both α, the attenuation constant, and β, the phase constant, are dependent upon ν; whereas for $\omega_H/\omega > 1$, β is almost independent of ν. Since attenuation is used for this measurement, the condition $\omega_H/\omega_s > 1$ must be used.

This method yielded collision frequencies in good agreement with published results.

VI. CONCULSION

The typical experimental results reported above adequately illustrate the general phenomenon of radio frequency wave interaction in magneto-plasmas. The theory on which these experimental results are based can be considered as a generalization of Bailey's[3] theory of interaction of radio waves in the ionosphere. It has been shown here that the phenomenon of interaction of microwaves in a magneto-plasma constitutes a useful method for investigating plasma behavior. This method is applied to study some of the detailed aspects of the transfer of electromagnetic energy into kinetic energy of one of the charged constituents of the plasma. Particular emphasis has been placed on the transfer of electromagnetic energy to the electron gas of a plasma under cyclotron resonance condition. The consequent fast rate of kinetic energy increase of the electrons is evidenced by the corresponding change in their collision frequency and also in the magnetic field control of plasma confinement.

APPENDIX: DERIVATION OF EQUATION (17)

In order to derive an approximate expression for the propagation constant for waves propagating as exp $(-\gamma z)$ in an anisotropic medium, let us consider Maxwell's equations with and without the plasma:

$$\nabla_t \times \vec{H}_o - \gamma_o \hat{a}_z \times \vec{H}_o = j\omega\epsilon_o \vec{E}_o \tag{A-1}$$

$$\nabla_t \times \vec{E}_o - \gamma_o \hat{a}_z \times \vec{E}_o = -j\omega\mu_o \vec{H}_o \tag{A-2}$$

$$\nabla_t \times \vec{H} - \gamma \hat{a}_z \times \vec{H} = \vec{J} + j\omega\epsilon_o \vec{E} \tag{A-3}$$

$$\nabla_t \times \vec{E} - \gamma \hat{a}_z \times \vec{E} = -j\omega\mu_o \vec{H} \tag{A-4}$$

where $\vec{E}_o$, $\vec{H}_o$ = electromagnetic fields in the empty structure

$\vec{E}$, $\vec{H}$ = electromagnetic fields in the structure

$\nabla_t = \hat{a}_x \frac{\partial}{\partial_x} + \hat{a}_y \frac{\partial}{\partial_z}$

$\hat{a}$ = unit vector

γ, γ_o = propagation constant of a wave with and without the plasma

$\vec{J}$ = conduction current density as defined by Eq. (15).

The following sum is formed:

$$\vec{E} \cdot \overrightarrow{(A\text{-}1)} + \vec{E}_o \cdot \overrightarrow{(A\text{-}3)} - \vec{H} \cdot \overrightarrow{(A\text{-}2)} - \vec{H}_o \cdot \overrightarrow{(A\text{-}4)} ;$$

and this is integrated over the volume enclosed by the guiding structure. The application of the divergence theorem leads to the following equation:

$$\oint_S\oint (\vec{H}_o \times \vec{E} - \vec{H} \times E_o) . \vec{dS} - (\gamma+\gamma_o) \iiint (\vec{E} . \hat{a}_z \times \vec{H}_o + \vec{E}_o . \hat{a}_z \times H)\, dV =$$

$$= 2j\omega \iiint (\epsilon_o \vec{E} . \vec{E}_o + \mu_o \vec{H} \cdot H_o)\, dV + \iiint \vec{E}_o . \vec{J}\, dV. \tag{A-5}$$

The first integral of Eq. (A-5) is zero because of the boundary conditions on $\vec{E}$ and $\vec{E}_o$. Further simplification is possible if the fields in the absence of the plasma are TE. We can solve Eqs. (A-2) and (A-4) for $\vec{H}$ and $\vec{H}_o$ and substitute this into Eq. (A-5).

$$(\gamma + \gamma_o) = \frac{\iiint \vec{E}_o \cdot \vec{J}\, d V + 2j\omega \iiint (\epsilon_o \vec{E} \cdot \vec{E}_o + \mu_o \vec{H} \cdot \vec{H}_o)\, dV}{\frac{1}{j\omega\mu_o} \iiint (\vec{E}_o \cdot \nabla_t E_z + (\gamma + \gamma_o) \vec{E} \cdot \vec{E}_o)\, dV} \tag{A-6}$$

The fields which were assumed for the plasma partially filling the waveguide as shown in Fig. 6(b) were:

$$\vec{E} = A \sin (\frac{\pi y}{a})\ \hat{a}_x + B \sin (\frac{\pi x}{b})\ \hat{a}_y + C \sin (\frac{\pi x}{a}) \sin (\frac{\pi y}{b})\ \hat{a}_z \tag{A-7}$$

This assumption leads to a solution for the propagation constant given by:

$$(\gamma^2 - \gamma_o^2) = j\omega\mu_o\, \sigma_{xx} \left[\frac{W}{a} + \frac{1}{2\pi} \sin \left[\frac{\pi W}{2a}\right]\right] + \frac{8}{\pi^2} \frac{B}{A}\, \sigma_{xy} \sin \left[\frac{\pi W}{2a}\right] \tag{A-8}$$

The choice of the ratio B/A was made in the following manner. The dominant mode in the waveguide is the TE_{10} mode in the limit of low electron densities. In addition, the amplitude B arises because σ_{xy} is non-zero. Hence the product of σ_{xy} B is considered to be of second order in importance and is neglected.

REFERENCES

1. B. D. H. Tellegan, *Nature*, Vol. 131, p. 840 (1933).
2. V. A. Bailey and D. F. Martyn, *Phil. Mag.*, Vol. 18, p. 369 (1934).
3. V. A. Bailey, *Phil. Mag.*, Vol. 23, p. 774 (1937).
4. V. A. Bailey, et al., *Nature*, Vol. 169, p. 911 (1952).

5. L. Goldstein, J. M. Anderson and G. Clark, *Phy. Rev.*, Vol. 90, p. 151 and p. 486 (1953). L. Goldstein and J. M. Anderson, "Interaction on Microwaves in Gaseous Discharge Plasmas and the Ramsauer Effect," *Rec. 14th Ann. Conf. on Physical Electronics*, Massachusetts Institute of Technology, March 1954.

6. J. M. Anderson and L. Goldstein, *Phy. Rev.*, Vol. 100, p. 1037 (1955).

7. A. A. Dougal and L. Goldstein, *Phy. Rev.*, Vol. 109, p. 615 (1958).

8. L. Goldstein and T. Sekiguchi, *Phy. Rev.*, Vol. 109, p. 625 (1958).

9. C. L. Chen, C. C. Leiby and L. Goldstein, *Phy. Rev.*, Vol. 121, p. 1391 (1960).

10. L. Tonks, *Phy. Rev.*, Vol. 56, p. 360 (1939).

11. W. P. Allis and E. I. Gordon, M.I.T. Research Lab. of Electronics, Quart. Prog. Report, July 15, 1957. (Unpublished)

12. W. P. Allis, *Handbuch der Physik.*, Vol. 21 (Ed., S. Flugge) [Berlin: Springer-Verlag, 1957].

13. P. Molmud, *Phy. Rev.*, Vol. 114, p. 129 (1959).

14. I. P. Shkarofsky, "Values of Transport Coefficients in a Plasma for any Degree of Ionization on a Maxwellian Distribution," Research Report No. 7-801, 9 December 1960, R.C.A. Victor Ltd., Research Labs, Montreal, Canada (Unpublished).

15. H. Suhl and L. R. Walker, *Bell Syst. Tech. J.*, Vol. 33, p. 579 (1954).

16. E. C. Jordan, *Electromagnetic Waves and Radiating Systems* (New York: Prentice Hall, 1950).

17. L. Goldstein, "Electrical Discharge in Gases and Modern Electronics," in *Advances in Electronics and Electron Physics*, Vol. 7 (New York: Academic Press, 1955).

18. L. Goldstein, *I.R.E. Trans. on Microwave Theory and Techniques*, Vol. MTT-6, p. 19 (January 1958).

19. C. Kenty, *Phy. Rev.*, Vol. 32, p. 624 (1928).

20. S. C. Brown, *Basic Data of Plasma Physics* [The Technology Press (New York: John Wiley and Sons, 1959)].

RADIATION IN A PLASMA FROM A UNIFORMLY MOVING DISTRIBUTION OF ELECTRIC CHARGE*

Manlio Abele
Polytechnic Institute of Brooklyn
Aerodynamics Laboratory

Electromagnetic radiation cannot be emitted by a uniformly moving electric charge in a plasma in the absence of external magnetic fields because the phase velocity of an electromagnetic oscillation in a plasma is larger than the velocity of light in a vacuum. Plasma oscillations may be emitted when the velocity of the moving charge is larger than the velocity of sound in the electron gas. In this paper the electron oscillations are analyzed and the spectral distribution of the radiated energy is evaluated, assuming a uniform linear distribution of moving charge.

I. INTRODUCTION

An electric charge moving in a dielectric medium with a uniform rectilinear motion may radiate electromagnetic energy, provided that its velocity is larger than the velocity of light in the medium. The spectral distribution of the radiated energy is limited to the frequencies of the electromagnetic oscillations with a phase velocity smaller than the velocity of the moving charge. This radiation process is the Cerenkov effect, which has been analyzed theoretically in large detail.[1, 2]

Let us assume that the medium is an unbounded and uniform plasma at rest. If no external magnetic field is applied to the plasma, the phase velocity of an electromagnetic oscillation is always larger than the velocity of light in a vacuum. Consequently, no Cerenkov radiation may be expected in the plasma. On the other hand, the electric field associated with the moving charge will produce a local perturbation in the distribution of the ions and electrons in the plasma. Under certain conditions, energy may be radiated by the moving charge in the process of excitation of longitudinal plasma oscillations. If the velocity of the moving charge is sufficiently large, the ion motion may be neglected and only electron oscillations are excited in the plasma.

A detailed analysis of the physical problems related to the interaction process of moving charges in a plasma has been performed by D. Bohm and D. Pines.[3] In this paper, we discuss the electron oscil-

*This paper was prepared under Contract No. AF 30(602)-2045, "Energy Transfer to Surface Through Ionized Shock Waves," Project No. 5561, Task No. 55209, Rome Air Development Center, Air Research and Development Command, United States Air Force.

Presented at the Symposium on Electromagnetics and Fluid Dynamics of Gaseous Plasma, Polytechnic Institute of Brooklyn, April 4, 5, 6, 1961

lations excited by a moving charge located inside and outside a unifor[m] plasma. The analysis is carried out assuming a linear and uniform distribution of moving charge. The damping mechanisms in the plasma are not taken into account and the reaction of the radiation field on the moving charge is not considered. Thus the radiation due to the deceleration of the charge is not included in the scheme discussed here.

II. BASIC EQUATIONS

Let us assume a linear and uniform distribution of electric charge moving with constant velocity u_0 in the positive direction of the x-axis of a fixed system of rectangular coordinates x, y, z. The charge distribution is parallel to the y-axis and moves in the plane z= 0. Let q be the electric charge per unit length.

The medium is a uniform plasma at rest. The electric and magnetic fields associated with the moving charge distribution produce a local perturbation of the ion and electron distributions in the plasma. We assume that the ion mass is so large and the intervals

NOTATION	
$\vec{E}$ = intensity of the electric field	q_0 = electron charge
$\vec{H}$ = intensity of the magnetic field	t = time
$H_0^{(1)}$ = Hankel function	$\vec{u}_e$ = electron velocity
J_0 = Bessel function	u_0 = velocity of the distribution of electric charge
T_{eo} = equilibrium electron temperature	$\bar{\alpha}$ = parameter defined by Eq.(113)
W = Radiated energy per unit time and unit length	γ = ratio of specific heats
a = velocity of sound in the electron gas	$\delta(\ )$ = Dirac function
	$1(\ )$ = unit function
c = velocity of light in a vacuum	ϵ_o = dielectric permeability of a vacuum
ℓ = number of degrees of freedom of the electrons	
i = $\sqrt{-1}$	λ_D = Debye shielding distance
$\vec{j}$ = electric current density	μ_0 = magnetic permeablility of a vacuum
k = Boltzmann constant	
m_e = electron mass	ρ = electric charge density
n_e = electron density	ω = angular frequency
	ω_p = plasma frequency
n_{eo} = equilibrium electron density	ω_0 = cutoff frequency
q = charge per unit length of the distribution of moving charge	ξ = propagation constant

f time involved in the perturbation are so short that the ion velocity ıay be neglected. If the electron-ion collisions are not taken into ccount, the linearized equations governing the electron motion are[4]

$$n_{eo} m_e \frac{\partial \vec{u}_e}{\partial t} = - n_{eo} q_o \vec{E} - \gamma kT_{eo} \nabla n_e, \tag{1}$$

$$\frac{\partial n_e}{\partial t} + n_{eo} \nabla \cdot \vec{u}_e = 0, \tag{2}$$

$$\nabla \times \vec{E} = - \mu_o \frac{\partial \vec{H}}{\partial t}, \tag{3}$$

$$\nabla \times \vec{H} = \epsilon_o \frac{\partial \vec{E}}{\partial t} - n_{eo} q_o \vec{u}_e, \tag{4}$$

/here m_e and q_o are the electron mass and electric charge, respec- ively; T_{eo} is the equilibrium electron temperature, and n_{eo} is the quilibrium value of the electron density n_e; k is the Boltzmann's onstant; and γ is related to the number ℓ of degrees of freedom of he electron adiabatic motion through the equation

$$\gamma = (\ell + 2)/\ell; \tag{5}$$

$_o$, μ_o are the dielectric and magnetic permeabilities of a vacuum, espectively; $\vec{E}$, $\vec{H}$ are the intensities of the electric and magnetic ields; and $\vec{u}_e$ is the electron macroscopic velocity.

From Eq. (4) we have

$$\epsilon_o \frac{\partial}{\partial t} \nabla \cdot \vec{E} - n_{eo} q_o \nabla \cdot \vec{u}_e = 0, \tag{6}$$

ınd by virtue of (2), Eq. (6) yields

$$\epsilon_o \nabla \cdot \vec{E} + q_o (n_e - n_{eo}) = 0, \tag{7}$$

From Eq. (1) we have

$$n_{eo} m_e \frac{\partial}{\partial t} \nabla \cdot \vec{u}_e = - n_{eo} q_o \nabla \cdot \vec{E} - \gamma kT_{eo} \nabla^2 n_e, \tag{8}$$

ınd by virtue of (2) and (7), Eq. (8) becomes

$$\frac{\partial^2 n_e}{\partial t^2} + \omega_p^2 (n_e - n_{eo}) - a^2 \nabla^2 n_e = 0, \tag{9}$$

vhere ω_p is the electron plasma frequency

$$\omega_p = (n_{eo} q_o^2/\epsilon_o m_e)^{1/2} \tag{10}$$

and a is the velocity of sound in the electron gas

$$a = (\gamma kT_{eo}/m_e)^{1/2} , \tag{11}$$

From Eqs. (3) and (4) we have

$$\nabla^2 \vec{H} = \frac{1}{c^2} \frac{\partial^2 \vec{H}}{\partial t^2} + n_{eo} q_o \nabla \times \vec{u}_e , \tag{12}$$

where c is the velocity of light in a vacuum

$$c = (\epsilon_o \mu_o)^{-1/2} . \tag{13}$$

On the other hand, from Eq. (1) we have

$$\frac{\partial}{\partial t} \left[\nabla \times \vec{u}_e - \frac{\mu_o q_o}{m_e} \vec{H} \right] = 0, \tag{14}$$

Thus, Eq. (12) becomes

$$\frac{\partial^2 \vec{H}}{\partial t^2} + \omega_p^2 \vec{H} - c^2 \nabla^2 \vec{H} = 0 \tag{15}$$

Equations (9) and (15) hold for $z \neq 0$. The electric charge density ρ_o associated with the moving linear distribution of electric charge may be written in the form

$$\rho_o = \frac{q}{2\pi u_o} \delta(z) \int_{-\infty}^{+\infty} \exp\left[i\omega \left(\frac{x}{u_o} - t \right) \right] d\omega \tag{16}$$

where $\delta(z)$ is the δ-function satisfying the condition

$$\int_{-\bar{z}}^{+\bar{z}} \delta(z)\, dz, \qquad (\bar{z} \neq 0) . \tag{17}$$

An electric current is created in the plane $z = 0$ by the moving distribution of electric charge. The electric current density $\vec{j}$, associated with the charge density ρ_o, is given by

$$j_y = j_z = 0, \quad j_x = \rho_o u_o = \frac{q}{2\pi} \delta(z) \int_{-\infty}^{+\infty} \exp\left[i\omega \left(\frac{x}{u_o} - t \right) \right] d\omega \tag{18}$$

By virtue of the geometrical distribution of the moving charge density ρ_o, the intensity of the magnetic field reduces to the component H_y and the y-components of both the intensity of the electric field and the electron velocity vanish everywhere.

The solutions of Eqs. (9) and (15) are independent of y and may be written in the form

$$n_e = n_{eo} + \int_{-\infty}^{+\infty} N(z,\omega) \exp\left[i\omega\left(\frac{x}{u_o} - t\right)\right] d\omega \tag{19}$$

and

$$H_y = \int_{-\infty}^{+\infty} H(z,\omega) \exp\left[i\omega\left(\frac{x}{u_o} - t\right)\right] d\omega \tag{20}$$

where N, H satisfy the equations

$$\frac{d^2N}{dz^2} - \frac{1}{a^2}\left[\omega_p^2 - \omega^2\left[1 - \frac{a^2}{u_o^2}\right]\right] N = 0, \tag{21}$$

and

$$\frac{d^2H}{dz^2} - \frac{1}{c^2}\left[\omega_p^2 - \omega^2\left[1 - \frac{c^2}{u_o^2}\right]\right] H = 0. \tag{22}$$

The solutions of (21) and (22) are

$$N = N_1 e^{-\xi_1 z} + N_2 e^{+\xi_1 z}, \tag{23}$$

$$H = H_1 e^{-\xi_2 z} + H_2 e^{+\xi_2 z}, \tag{24}$$

where ξ_1, ξ_2 are given by

$$\xi_1^2 = \frac{1}{a^2}\left[\omega_p^2 - \omega^2\left[1 - \frac{a^2}{u_o^2}\right]\right]. \tag{25}$$

$$\xi_2^2 = \frac{1}{c^2}\left[\omega_p^2 - \omega^2\left[1 - \frac{c^2}{u_o^2}\right]\right] \tag{26}$$

Solution (23) corresponds to the longitudinal electron ocillations excited by the moving electric charge, and solution (24) corresponds to the electromagnetic oscillations in the plasma. Taking into account that u_o is always smaller than the velocity of light c, we observe that ξ_2^2 is always a positive quantity. Hence no electromagnetic wave is radiated from the moving charge. If u_o is smaller than a, then ξ_1^2 is also a positive quantity and no longitudinal oscillation is emitted in the plasma. If u_o is larger than a, then ξ_1^2 becomes a negative quantity for

$$|\omega| > \omega_p \left[1 - \frac{a^2}{u_o^2}\right]^{-1/2} . \qquad (27)$$

Therefore there is a cutoff angular frequency

$$\omega_o = \omega_p \left[1 - \frac{a^2}{u_o}\right]^{-1/2} . \qquad (28)$$

Only the spectrum of frequencies corresponding to $|\omega|$ larger than ω_o may be radiated in the longitudinal oscillations of the plasma.

III. BOUNDARY CONDITIONS

The solutions for the x and z components of $\vec{u}$ and $\vec{E}$ are

$$u_{x,z} = \int_{-\infty}^{+\infty} U_{x,z}(z,\omega) \exp\left[i\omega\left(\frac{x}{u_o} - t\right)\right] d\omega , \qquad (29)$$

$$E_{x,z} = \int_{-\infty}^{+\infty} \overline{E}_{x,z}(z,\omega) \exp\left[i\omega\left(\frac{x}{u_o} - t\right)\right] d\omega ; \qquad (30)$$

where

$$U_x = \frac{1}{\omega^2 - \omega_p^2}\left[\frac{\omega^2 a^2}{n_{eo} u_o} N - \frac{q_o}{\epsilon_o m_e}\frac{dH}{dz}\right] , \qquad (31)$$

$$U_z = -\frac{i\omega}{n_{eo} q_o}\,\frac{1}{\omega^2 - \omega_p^2}\left[a^2 q_o \frac{dN}{dz} - \frac{\omega_p^2}{u_o} H\right] , \qquad (32)$$

$$\overline{E}_x = \frac{i\omega}{\epsilon_o}\,\frac{1}{\omega^2 - \omega_p^2}\left[\frac{a^2 q_o}{u_o} N - \frac{dH}{dz}\right] , \qquad (33)$$

$$\overline{E}_z = \frac{1}{\epsilon_o}\,\frac{1}{\omega^2 - \omega_p^2}\left[a^2 q_o \frac{dN}{dz} - \frac{\omega^2}{u_o} H\right] . \qquad (34)$$

Let us analyze the solutions (23) and (24) in the region $z > 0$. The velocity u_o is smaller than c; thus H converges at $z \longrightarrow \infty$ if

$$H_2 = 0 . \qquad (35)$$

If $u_o < a$, the convergence of N requires

$$N_2 = 0 . \tag{36}$$

If $u_o > a$, condition (36) ensures the convergence of the solution in the range of frequencies

$$|\omega| < \omega_o \tag{37}$$

where ω_o is given by (28). In the range of frequencies (27), the solution N must correspond to an outgoing longitudinal wave. Hence, with $N_2 = 0$, for positive values of ω, Eq. (23) transforms to

$$N = N_1 e^{+i\bar{\xi}_1 z} \tag{38}$$

where

$$\bar{\xi}_1 = \frac{1}{a}\left[\omega^2\left[1 - \frac{a^2}{u_o^2}\right] - \omega_p^2\right]^{1/2} \tag{39}$$

and for negative values of ω, Eq. (23) transforms to

$$N = N_1 e^{-i\bar{\xi}_1 z} . \tag{40}$$

By virtue of (18), the boundary condition for the intensity of the magnetic field at z = 0 is given by

$$(H_y)_{z=+0} = -\frac{q}{4\pi}\int_{-\infty}^{+\infty} \exp\left[i\omega\left(\frac{x}{u_o} - t\right)\right] d\omega . \tag{41}$$

Thus, taking into account Eq. (20), we obtain

$$H_1 = -q/4\pi . \tag{42}$$

By virtue of (16) the boundary condition for the intensity of the electric field at z = 0 is given by

$$(E_z)_{z=+0} = \frac{q}{4\pi\epsilon_o u_o}\int_{-\infty}^{+\infty} \exp\left[i\omega\left(\frac{x}{u_o} - t\right)\right] d\omega , \tag{43}$$

and taking into account Eqs. (30) and (34), we have

$$\frac{1}{\omega^2 - \omega_p^2}\left[a^2 q_o \xi_1 N_1 + \frac{\omega^2}{u_o} H_1\right] = -\frac{q}{4\pi u_o} , \tag{44}$$

Hence, by substituting (42) into (44), we obtain

$$N_1 = \frac{\omega_p^2}{4\pi u_o a^2} \frac{q}{q_o} \frac{1}{\xi_1} . \tag{45}$$

Conditions (35), (36), (42), and (45) determine the solution in the region $z > 0$. In particular, Eq. (32) becomes

$$U_z = \frac{i\omega}{n_{eo} q_o} \frac{q\omega_p^2}{4\pi u_o} \frac{1}{\omega^2 - \omega_p^2} \left[e^{-\xi_1 z} - e^{-\xi_2 z}\right] . \tag{46}$$

At $z = 0$, therefore, U_z satisfies the condition

$$U_z = 0 \tag{47}$$

which means that no flow of electric charges is emitted by the moving perturbation into the plasma.

IV. DISTRIBUTION OF ELECTRON DENSITY AND MAGNETIC FIELD IN THE PLASMA

The electron density n_e is given by Eq. (19), which, by virtue of (23), (36), and (45), becomes

$$n_e = n_{eo} + \frac{\omega_p^2 q}{4\pi a q_o} \frac{1}{\sqrt{a^2 - u_o^2}} \int_{-\infty}^{+\infty} \frac{\exp\left[-z'\sqrt{\alpha^2 + \alpha_1^2}\right]}{\sqrt{\alpha^2 + \alpha_1^2}} e^{i\alpha x'} \, d\alpha \qquad (z' > 0) \tag{48}$$

where

$$z' = z \left[1 - \frac{u_o^2}{a^2}\right]^{1/2} , \quad x' = x - u_o t , \tag{49}$$

and

$$\alpha_1^2 = \omega_p^2/(a^2 - u_o^2) \tag{50}$$

The intensity of the magnetic field H_y is given by Eq. (20), which by virtue of (24), (35), and (42) becomes

$$H_y = -\frac{qu_o}{4\pi} \int_{-\infty}^{+\infty} \exp\left[-z''\sqrt{\alpha^2 + \alpha_2^2} + i\alpha x'\right] d\alpha, \quad (z'' > 0) \tag{51}$$

where

$$z'' = z\left[1 - (u_o^2/c^2)\right]^{1/2} , \tag{52}$$

and

$$\alpha_2^2 = \omega_p^2/(c^2 - u_o^2) . \tag{53}$$

The x- and z- components of the electron velocity and the intensity of the electric field are given by Eqs. (29) and (30) with the aid of Eqs. (31) to (34). Let us assume first

$$u_o < a , \tag{54}$$

that is,

$$\alpha_1^2 > 0 . \tag{55}$$

In Eq. (48) we have

$$\frac{1}{\pi}\int_{-\infty}^{+\infty} \frac{\exp\left[-z'\sqrt{\alpha^2 + \alpha_1^2}\right]}{\sqrt{\alpha^2+\alpha_1^2}} e^{i\alpha x'} d\alpha = iH_o^{(1)}\left[i\alpha_1\sqrt{x'^2 + z'^2}\right] \tag{56}$$

Thus, the electron density becomes

$$n_e = n_{eo} + i\frac{\omega_p^2 q}{4q_o a}\frac{1}{\sqrt{a^2-u_o^2}} H_o^{(1)}\left[i\frac{\omega_p}{\sqrt{a^2-u_o^2}} \times \sqrt{(x-u_o t)^2 + z^2\left[1 - \frac{u_o^2}{a^2}\right]}\right] \tag{57}$$

where $H_o^{(1)}$ is the Hankel' s function. Let us assume now

$$u_o > a \tag{58}$$

Equation (48) may be written again in the form

$$n_e = n_{eo} + \frac{\omega_p^2 q}{4\pi a q_o}\frac{1}{\sqrt{u_o^2-a^2}}\int_{-\infty}^{+\infty} \frac{\exp\left[-\bar{z}'\sqrt{-\alpha^2 + \beta_1^2}\right]}{\sqrt{-\alpha^2 + \beta_1^2}} e^{i\alpha x'} d\alpha, \tag{59}$$

where

$$\bar{z}' = z\left[\frac{u_o^2}{a^2} - 1\right]^{1/2} \tag{60}$$

and

$$\beta_1^2 = \omega_p^2/(u_o^2 - a^2) > 0 \tag{61}$$

According to the boundary conditions at $z \longrightarrow \infty$, we have

$$\frac{1}{2\pi}\int_{-\infty}^{+\infty} \frac{\exp\left[-\bar{z}'\sqrt{-\alpha^2 + \beta_1^2}\right]}{\sqrt{-\alpha^2 + \beta_1^2}} e^{i\alpha x'} d\alpha =$$

$$= J_o\left[\beta_1\sqrt{(x')^2 - (\bar{z}')^2}\right] 1(-x' - \bar{z}') \tag{62}$$

where J_o is the Bessel function of the first kind and $1(-x'-\bar{z}')$ is defined as

$$1(-x'-\bar{z}') = \begin{cases} 1 & (-x'-\bar{z}' > 0), \\ 0 & (-x'-\bar{z}' < 0). \end{cases} \tag{63}$$

By virtue of (62) the electron density is

$$n_e = n_{eo} + \frac{\omega_p^2 q}{2aq_o} \frac{1}{\sqrt{u_o^2 - a^2}} J_o\left[\frac{\omega_p}{\sqrt{u_o^2 - a^2}}\sqrt{(x - u_o t)^2 - z^2\left[\frac{u_o^2}{a^2} - 1\right]}\right]$$

$$\times 1\left[u_o t - x - z\sqrt{\frac{u_o^2}{a^2} - 1}\right]. \tag{64}$$

The perturbation of the electron density created by the moving distribution of electric charge is confined inside the region

$$u_o t - x - z\sqrt{(u_o^2/a^2) - 1} > 0 \qquad (z > 0) \tag{65}$$

Therefore when condition (58) is satisfied, longitudinal electron oscillations are emitted in the plasma. The electron density n_e becomes equal to the equilibrium density n_{eo} at the points of the plasma which satisfy the condition

$$\frac{\omega_p}{\sqrt{u_o^2 - a^2}} \sqrt{(x-u_o t)^2 - z^2 \left[\frac{u_o^2}{a^2} - 1\right]} = \xi_m \tag{66}$$

where ξ_m is the mth root of the equation

$$J_o(\xi) = 0 \tag{67}$$

For large values of the argument of the Bessel function we have

$$J_o(\xi) \sim \sqrt{2/\pi\xi} \cos\left(\xi - \frac{\pi}{4}\right) \tag{68}$$

Thus on the plane z= 0, at a large distance from the moving charge, the spacing between the nodal lines $n_e = n_{eo}$ becomes constant with a period λ given by

$$\lambda = \frac{2\pi}{\omega_p} \sqrt{u_o^2 - a^2} \tag{69}$$

On the other hand

$$a/\omega_p = \sqrt{\gamma} \; \lambda_D \tag{70}$$

where γ_D is the Debye shielding distance

$$\lambda_D = \left[\frac{\epsilon_o kT_e}{n_{eo} q_o^2}\right]^{1/2} . \tag{71}$$

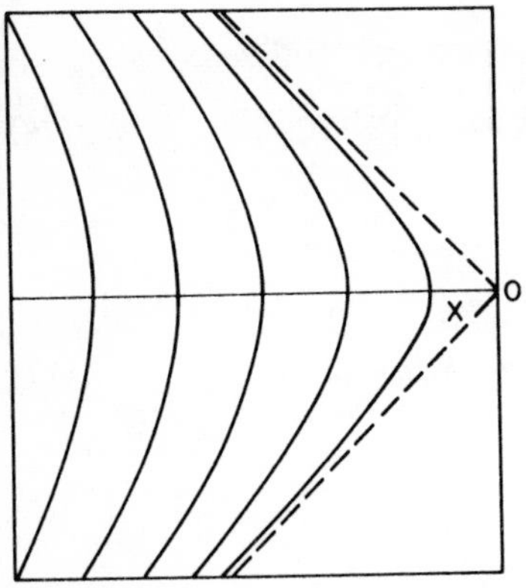

Fig. 1 Electron oscillations in the plasma, the solid lines correspond to $n_e = n_{eo}$, the moving charge is located at point o.

Thus Eq. (69) transforms to

$$\lambda = 2\pi \sqrt{\gamma} \sqrt{(u_o^2/a^2) - 1} \; \lambda_D . \tag{72}$$

We observe that λ becomes large compared to λ_D only if

$$u_o \gg a \tag{73}$$

The distribution of nodal lines $n_e = n_{eo}$ of the electron oscillations emitted in the plasma is shown in Fig. 1.

From Eq. (48) we may calculate the total electric charge induced in the plasma per unit length in the y-direction. The electric charge density is given by

$$\rho = q_o (n_{eo} - n_e) \tag{74}$$

and the total electric charge contained in the region z > 0 per unit length in the y-direction is

$$q_p = \int_{-\infty}^{+\infty} dx \int_0^{\infty} \rho dz . \tag{75}$$

By virtue of (48) and (74), Eq. (75) becomes

$$q_p = \frac{\omega_p^2 q}{4\pi a} \frac{1}{\sqrt{a^2 - u_o^2}} \int_{-\infty}^{+\infty} d\alpha \int_0^{\infty} dz \int_{-\infty}^{+\infty} dx' \times \frac{\exp\left[-z' \sqrt{\alpha^2 + \alpha_1^2}\right]}{\sqrt{\alpha^2 + \alpha_1^2}} e^{i\alpha x'} d\alpha . \tag{76}$$

In (76) we have

$$\frac{1}{2\pi} \int_{-\infty}^{+\infty} e^{i\alpha x'} dx' = \delta(\alpha) . \tag{77}$$

Thus, Eq. (76) yields

$$q_p = \frac{\omega_p q}{2a} \int_0^{\infty} \exp\left[-\frac{\omega_p}{a} z\right] dz = -\frac{1}{2} q . \tag{78}$$

An identical result is obtained in the region z < 0. Consequently, the total system of plasma and moving electric charge remains electrically neutral.

In the calculation of the intensity of the magnetic field given by Eq. (51) we take into account that α_2^2 is always a positive quantity. By virtue of (56) we may write

$$H_y = i \frac{qu_o}{4} \frac{d}{dz''} H_o^{(1)} \left[i\alpha_2 \sqrt{x'^2 + z''^2} \right], \tag{79}$$

which transforms to

$$H_y = \frac{qu_o\omega_p}{4c} \frac{z}{\sqrt{(x-u_o t)^2 + z^2\left[1 - \frac{u_o^2}{c^2}\right]}} H_1^{(1)}\left[\frac{i\omega_p}{\sqrt{c^2-u_o^2}} \times \sqrt{(x-u_o t)^2 + z^2\left[1 - \frac{u_o^2}{c^2}\right]}\right] \tag{80}$$

Therefore, an electromagnetic oscillation cannot be emitted by the uniformly moving electric charge. Within a distance from the moving charge, which is small compared to c/ω_p, the Hankel function in (80) reduces to

$$H_1^{(1)}(\xi) \sim -2i/\pi\xi \ , \tag{81}$$

and H_y becomes

$$H_y \sim -\frac{qu_o}{2\pi} \sqrt{1 - \frac{u_o^2}{c^2}} \frac{z}{(x-u_o t)^2 + z^2\left[1 - \frac{u_o^2}{c^2}\right]} . \tag{82}$$

Hence, at a distance which is small compared to c/ω_p, H_y coincides with the magnetic field created by the linear distribution of electric charge moving in a vacuum.

V. RADIATED ENERGY

The energy radiated into the plasma per unit time and unit length in the y-direction is given by

$$W = 2 \lim_{z \to 0} \int_{-\infty}^{+\infty} E_x H_y \, dx \ . \tag{83}$$

By virtue of (30) and (33) the x-component of the intensity of electric field is given by

$$E_x = i \frac{q}{4\pi\epsilon_o} \int_{-\infty}^{+\infty} \frac{\omega}{\omega^2 - \omega_p^2} \left[\frac{\omega_p^2}{u_o^2 \xi_1} e^{-\xi_1 z} - \xi_2 e^{-\xi_2 z}\right] \exp\left[i\omega\left(\frac{x}{u_o} - t\right)\right] d\omega . \tag{84}$$

Thus the radiated energy W is

$$W = -i \frac{q^2}{8\pi^2 \epsilon_0} \lim_{z \to 0} \int_{-\infty}^{+\infty} d\omega \int_{-\infty}^{+\infty} d\bar{\omega} \int_{-\infty}^{+\infty} dx \, .$$

$$\frac{\omega}{\omega^2 - \omega_p^2} \left[\frac{\omega_p^2}{u_0^2 \xi_1(\omega)} \exp\left[-\xi_1(\omega) z\right] - \xi_2(\omega) \exp\left[-\xi_2(\omega) z\right] \right]$$

$$\times \exp\left[-\xi_2(\bar{\omega}) z + i(\omega + \bar{\omega}) \left[\frac{x}{u_0} - t \right] \right] \qquad (85)$$

In Eq. (85) we have

$$\frac{1}{2\pi u_0} \int_{-\infty}^{+\infty} \exp\left[i (x/u_0)(\omega + \bar{\omega})\right] dx = \delta(\omega + \bar{\omega}) \, . \qquad (86)$$

and (85) becomes

$$W = -i \frac{q^2 u_0}{4\pi \epsilon_0} \lim_{z \to 0} \int_{-\infty}^{+\infty} \frac{\omega}{\omega^2 - \omega_p^2} \left[\frac{\omega_p^2}{u_0^2 \xi_1(\omega)} \exp\left[-\xi_1(\omega) z\right] \right.$$

$$\left. \times -\xi_2(\omega) \exp\left[-\xi_2(\omega) z\right] \right] \exp\left[-\xi_2(-\omega) z\right] d\omega \, . \qquad (87)$$

The function $\xi_2(\omega)$ satisfies the condition

$$\xi_2(\omega) = \xi_2(-\omega) \, . \qquad (88)$$

Thus we have

$$\lim_{z \to 0} \int_{-\infty}^{+\infty} \frac{\omega}{\omega^2 - \omega_p^2} \xi_2(\omega) \exp\left[-2\xi_2(\omega) z\right] d\omega = 0 \qquad (89)$$

and Eq. (87) reduces to

$$W = -i \frac{q^2 \omega_p^2}{4\pi\epsilon_0 u_0} \lim_{z \to 0} \int_{-\infty}^{+\infty} \frac{\omega}{\omega^2 - \omega_p^2} \frac{1}{\xi_1(\omega)} \exp\left[-\xi_1(\omega) z - \xi_2(\omega) z\right] d\omega \tag{90}$$

Let us assume first that u_0 is smaller than the velocity of sound a. In this case in the range of frequencies $-\infty < \omega < +\infty$ we have

$$\xi_1(\omega) = \xi_1(-\omega) \tag{91}$$

and we obtain

$$W = 0 . \tag{92}$$

Let us now assume $u_0 > a$. In the range of frequencies

$$|\omega| < \omega_0 \tag{93}$$

we have

$$\xi_1(\omega) = \xi_1(-\omega) , \tag{94}$$

and in the range of frequencies

$$|\omega| > \omega_0 \tag{95}$$

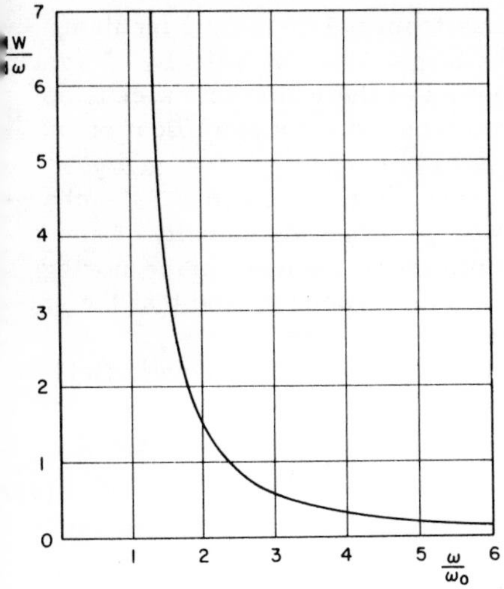

Fig. 2 Spectral distribution of the radiated energy for $u_o = \alpha\sqrt{2}$

we have

$$-\xi_1(-\omega) = \xi_1(\omega) = i\bar{\xi}_1(\omega), \tag{96}$$

where $\bar{\xi}_1$ is given by (39). Consequently Eq. (90) transforms to

$$W = \frac{q^2 \omega_p^2 a}{2\pi\epsilon_0 u_0} \int_{\omega_0}^{\infty} \frac{\omega}{\omega^2 - \omega_p^2} \frac{1}{\sqrt{\omega^2 \left[1 - \frac{a^2}{u_0^2}\right] - \omega_p^2}} d\omega \tag{97}$$

The spectral distribution $dW/d\omega$ given by Eq. (97) is shown in Fig. 2 for the particular case $u_0 = \sqrt{2}$ a. We observe that $dW/d\omega$ is infinite at $\omega = \omega_0$. The singularity in the spectral distribution at $\omega = \omega_0$ is due to the simplifying assumption that the charge moves in a uniform plasma extending up to $z = 0$.

The integral in Eq. (97) converges and the result is

$$W = q^2 \omega_p / 4\epsilon_o \quad . \tag{98}$$

VI. MOVING CHARGE LOCATED OUTSIDE OF THE PLASMA

In the Cerenkov effect radiation also occurs if the electric charge is moving at a finite distance from the dielectric medium, provided that its velocity is always larger than the velocity of light in the medium. A possible application of the radiation process obtained under these conditions is the generation or amplification of electromagnetic waves in the microwave range.[5, 6]

A similar property may be expected in the plasma if the charge moves outside of it with a velocity larger than the velocity of sound in the electron gas. For sake of simplicity we assume that the moving charge is traveling on the plane $z = 0$ in a vacuum, and that the uniform plasma is confined in the regions $z > z_o$ and $z < -z_o$.

In the region $0 < z < +z_o$, the intensity of the magnetic field is given by Eq. (20) with

$$H(z,\omega) = H_o' e^{-\xi_o z} + H_o'' e^{+\xi_o z}, \tag{99}$$

H_o', H_o'' being two new constants and

$$\xi_o = \frac{\omega}{u_o} \sqrt{1 - (u_o^2/c^2)} . \tag{100}$$

The x and z - components of the intensity of electric field are given by Eq. (30) where

$$\bar{E}_x = i \frac{\xi_o}{\omega \epsilon_o} \left[H_o' e^{-\xi_o z} - H_o'' e^{+\xi_o z} \right] \tag{101}$$

and

$$\bar{E}_z = - \frac{1}{u_o \epsilon_o} \left[H_o' e^{-\xi_o z} + H_o'' e^{+\xi_o z} \right] \tag{102}$$

The boundary conditions at $z = z_o$ are given by the continuity of the components of the electromagnetic field. These conditions, together with (42) and the conditions at infinity, lead to

$$H_o' = \frac{q}{8\pi\Delta} e^{\xi_o z_o} \left[\frac{\omega^2}{\xi_o \left[\omega^2 - \omega_p^2\right]} \left[\frac{\omega_p^2}{u_o^2 \xi_1} - \xi_2 \right] - 1 \right] \tag{103}$$

$$H_o'' = -\frac{q}{8\pi\Delta}\, e^{-\xi_o z_o}\left[\frac{\omega^2}{\xi_o\left[\omega^2-\omega_p^2\right]}\left[\frac{\omega_p^2}{u_o^2\,\xi_1}-\xi_2\right]+1\right] \tag{104}$$

here ξ_1, ξ_2 are given by (25), (26) and

$$\Delta = \mathrm{Ch}\xi_o z_o + \frac{\omega^2}{\xi_o\left[\omega^2-\omega_p^2\right]}\left[\xi_2 - \frac{\omega_p^2}{u_o^2\,\xi_1}\right]\mathrm{Sh}\xi_o z_o \tag{105}$$

By virtue of Eq. (83), it is possible to evaluate again the energy ' radiated into the plasma per unit time and unit length in the y-irection. The result is

$$' = \frac{\omega_p^2\, a q^2}{2\pi\epsilon_o u_o}\left[1-\frac{u_o^2}{c^2}\right]\int_{\omega_o}^{\infty}\frac{1}{G(\omega)}\,\frac{\omega}{\omega^2-\omega_p^2}\,\frac{1}{\sqrt{\omega^2\left[1-\frac{a^2}{u_o^2}\right]-\omega_p^2}}\,d\omega \tag{106}$$

here ω_o is given by Eq. (28) and

$$G(\omega) = \left[\sqrt{1-\frac{u_o^2}{c^2}}\,\mathrm{Ch}\xi_o z_o + \frac{u_o}{c}\,\frac{\omega}{\omega^2-\omega_p^2}\sqrt{\omega^2\left[\frac{c^2}{u_o^2}-1\right]+\omega_p^2}\,\mathrm{Sh}\xi_o z_o\right]^2$$

$$+\frac{a^2}{u_o^2}\,\frac{\omega_p^4\,\omega^2}{\left[\omega^2-\omega_p^2\right]^2}\,\frac{1}{\omega^2\left[1-\frac{a^2}{u_o^2}\right]-\omega_p^2}\,\mathrm{Sh}^2\xi_o z_o\,. \tag{107}$$

The spectral distribution of the radiated energy is confined to he values of ω larger than ω_o, as was the case for $z_o = 0$. Comparing q. (106) with the result (97), we observe that $dW/d\omega$ vanishes at $= \omega_o$. Thus, with the moving charge located outside of the plasma, he singularity found in Eq. (97) disappears.

For nonrelativistic velocities, the function $G(\omega)$ reduces to

$$G(\omega) \sim \mathrm{Ch}^2 \xi_o z_o + \frac{2\omega^2}{\omega^2 - \omega_p^2} \mathrm{Ch}\xi_o z_o \mathrm{Sh}\xi_o z_o$$

$$+ \frac{\omega^2}{\omega^2 - \omega_p^2} \frac{\omega^2 \left[1 - \frac{a^2}{u_o^2}\right] - \frac{a^2}{u_o^2} \omega_p^2}{\omega^2 \left[1 - \frac{a^2}{u_o^2}\right] - \omega_p^2} \mathrm{Sh}^2 \xi_o z_o \tag{108}$$

where

$$\xi_o \sim \omega / u_o \; . \tag{109}$$

With the change of variables

$$\theta = \frac{\omega}{\omega_p} \sqrt{1 - \frac{a^2}{u_o^2}} \, , \tag{110}$$

and the condition $u_o \ll c$, Eq. (106) transforms to

$$W \sim \frac{q^2 \omega_p a}{2\pi\epsilon_o u_o} \int_1^\infty \frac{1}{G(\theta)} \frac{\theta}{\theta^2 - (\omega_p^2/\omega_o^2)} \frac{1}{\sqrt{\theta^2 - 1}} \, d\theta \, , \tag{111}$$

where

$$G(\theta) \sim \mathrm{Ch}^2 \bar{\alpha}\theta + 2 \frac{\theta^2}{\theta^2 - \omega_p^2/\omega_o^2} \mathrm{Ch}\bar{\alpha}\theta \, \mathrm{Sh}\bar{\alpha}\theta + \frac{\theta^2}{\theta^2 - \frac{\omega_p^2}{\omega_o^2}} \frac{\theta^2 - \frac{a^2}{u_o^2}}{\theta^2 - 1} \mathrm{Sh}^2 \bar{\alpha}\theta \tag{112}$$

with

$$\bar{\alpha} = \frac{1}{\sqrt{\gamma} \sqrt{(u_o^2/a^2) - 1}} \frac{z_o}{\lambda_D} \; . \tag{113}$$

The exponential terms in the function $G(\theta)$ lead to a sharp decrease of the spectral distribution as θ increases. $dW/d\theta$ exhibits a maximum at a value of θ slightly larger than the cutoff value $\theta = 1$. The maximum value may be large only if

$$\bar{\alpha} \ll 1 \; . \tag{114}$$

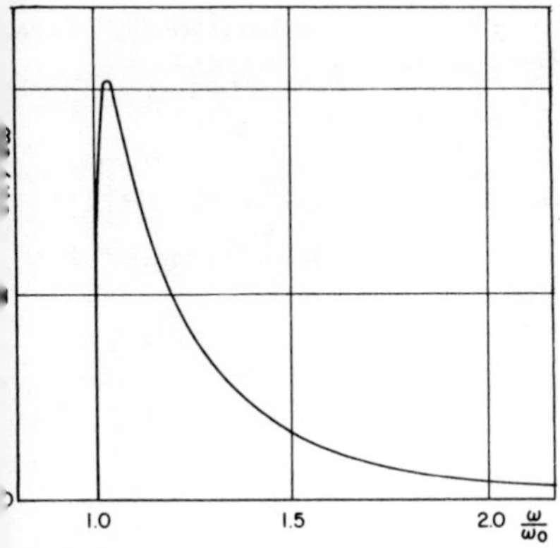

Fig. 3 Spectral distribution of radiated energy with the moving charge at a distance $Z_0 = \lambda_D$ from the plasma, and $u_0 = a\sqrt{2}$

If z_0 is of the same order or larger than λ_D, in order to satisfy condition (114) it is necessary to assume a value of u_0 very large compared to a. Fig. 3 shows the spectral distribution of the radiated energy in the particular case of $z_0 \sim \lambda_D$ and $u_0 = \sqrt{2}$ a.

VII. CONCLUSIONS

The foregoing calculations show that no Cerenkov radiation is emitted by the moving charge. Electron oscillations are excited in the range of frequencies.

$$\omega > \frac{\omega_p}{\sqrt{1 - (a^2/u_0^2)}} \tag{115}$$

if the velocity of the charge is larger than the velocity of sound in the electron gas. If u_0 is large compared to a, the cutoff frequency ω_0 approaches the plasma frequency ω_p.

Along the x-axis, the asymptotic behavior of the electron distribution corresponds to a plane longitudinal oscillation propagating with the same velocity u_0 of the moving charge. The wavelength of the electron distribution becomes large compared to the Debye shielding distance only if u_0 is large compared to a, as shown by Eq. (72).

Energy can also be radiated in the plasma if the charge q is moving outside of the plasma, provided that the distance z_0 is of the same order of λ_D and the velocity u_0 is large compared to a. If the damping mechanisms were taken into account, these results would be modified, due to the fact that short wavelength electron oscillations are strongly absorbed in the plasma. Nevertheless, this does not affect the main property of the radiation phenomenon because, according to the results of Section VI, for $u_0 \gg$ a and $z_0 \sim \lambda_D$, the spectral distribution of the radiated energy is confined to the range of frequencies corresponding to wavelengths large compared to λ_D.

REFERENCES

1. I. Tamm, "Radiation Emitted by Uniformly Moving Electrons," *J. Physics*, Vol. 1, p. 439 (1939).
2. E. Fermi, "Ionization Loss of Energy in Gases and in Condensed Materials," *Phys. Rev.*, Vol. 57, p. 485 (1940).

3. D. Bohm and D. Pines, "A Collective Description of Electron Interactions," *Phys. Rev.*, Vol. 82, p. 625, Part A (1951); Vol. 85, p. 338, Part B (1952).

4. L. Spitzer, *Physics of Fully Ionized Gases* (New York: Interscience, 1956).

5. V. L. Ginsburg, "Utilization de l'éffet Cerenkov pour l'émission de Radio Ondes," *Comptes Rendus de l'Académie des Sciences, URSS*, Vol. 56, p. 253 (1947).

6. M. Abele, "L'effet Cerenkov en optique et dans le domaine des microondes," *Supplemento Nuevo Cimento*, Vol. 9, p. 207 (1952).

EXCITATION OF PLASMA WAVES BY A DIPOLE IN A HOMOGENEOUS ISOTROPIC PLASMA*

A. Hessel and J. Shmoys
Electrophysics Department, Polytechnic Institute of Brooklyn

In this paper the excitation of electromagnetic and acoustic waves by an oscillating point current element in a compressible plasma of infinite extent is investigated. The use of suitable potentials permits the separation of the fields into optical wave contributions and plasma wave contributions. The far field radiation pattern is unaffected by the presence of the plasma. The acoustic wave has maxima of radiation along the axis of the dipole. The ratio of power carried by the acoustic wave to that carried by the optical wave is found to be proportional to the cube of the ratio of velocity of electromagnetic waves in free space to the sound velocity in the electron gas. This large ratio was obtained because Debye shielding of the dipole was not taken into account.

I. INTRODUCTION

The problem we wish to consider is the excitation of electromagnetic and plasma waves by a point current source in a homogeneous electron plasma of infinite extent. For the purpose of this analysis, plasma will be assumed to be an ideal gas coupled to the electromagnetic field by the motion of the electrons. We shall neglect the effect of collisions between electrons and other particles, and assume that the static magnetic field is zero and that the drift velocity of the electrons is zero. Under these assumptions, the equations governing the macroscopic behavior of plasma are as follows:[1]

$$\nabla \times \underset{\sim}{H} = j\omega \epsilon_0 \underset{\sim}{E} - n_0 e \underset{\sim}{v} + \underset{\sim}{J} \tag{1}$$

$$\nabla \times \underset{\sim}{E} = - j\omega \mu_0 \underset{\sim}{H} \tag{2}$$

$$\nabla \cdot \underset{\sim}{v} = - \frac{j\omega}{\gamma p_0} p \tag{3}$$

$$\nabla p = - j\omega m n_0 \underset{\sim}{v} - \underset{\sim}{n}_0 e \underset{\sim}{E} \tag{4}$$

*The work reported here was sponsored by the Rome Air Development Center, Air Force Systems Command, Griffiss Air Force Base, N.Y., under Contract No. AF-30 (602)-2045.

Presented at the Symposium on Electromagnetics and Fluid Dynamics of Gaseous Plasma, Polytechnic Institute of Brooklyn, April 4, 5, 6, 1961

where $\underset{\sim}{E}$ and $\underset{\sim}{H}$ are electric and magnetic fields, $\underset{\sim}{v}$ is the velocity of the electron gas, p_0 is its average pressure and p represents pressure deviation from average; n_0 is the average density of electrons; e and m are the electron charge and mass; γ is the ratio of specific heats of the electron gas; and ϵ_0 and μ_0 are the dielectric constant and permeability of free space. Time variation of the form $\epsilon^{j\omega t}$ has been assumed and suppressed in the above equations. The source current distribution $\underset{\sim}{J}$ appearing in Eq. (1) will be taken to be

$$\underset{\sim}{J} = \mathcal{J}\,\delta(\underset{\sim}{r})\,\underset{\sim}{z}_0 \tag{5}$$

II. POTENTIALS

Equations (1) through (4) simplify if we introduce the following transformation*

$$\hat{\underset{\sim}{E}} = \underset{\sim}{E} - \frac{\omega_p^2}{n_0 e(\omega^2 - \omega_p^2)} \nabla p , \tag{6}$$

$$\hat{\underset{\sim}{H}} = \underset{\sim}{H} , \tag{7}$$

where the plasma frequency ω_p is given by

$$\omega_p^2 = n_0 e^2 / m\epsilon_0 . \tag{8}$$

When we introduce modified electric and magnetic fields, $\hat{\underset{\sim}{E}}$ and $\hat{\underset{\sim}{H}}$ into Maxwell's equations (also making use of the momentum equation (4)), we obtain

$$\nabla \times \hat{\underset{\sim}{H}} = j\omega\epsilon_0(1-\omega_p^2/\omega^2)\,\hat{\underset{\sim}{E}} + \underset{\sim}{J} , \tag{9}$$

$$\nabla \times \hat{\underset{\sim}{E}} = j\omega\mu_0 \hat{\underset{\sim}{H}} \tag{10}$$

Equations (9) and (10) constitute Maxwell's equations for the modified electromagnetic field $\hat{\underset{\sim}{E}}$, $\hat{\underset{\sim}{H}}$, with an effective dielectric constant

$$\epsilon = \epsilon_0(1-\omega_p^2/\omega^2) . \tag{11}$$

Since this is true, we can express these fields in a conventional man-

*This concise procedure was suggested by Dr. H. Kurss.

ner in terms of corresponding scalar and vector potentials. Thus we have

$$\hat{\underset{\sim}{H}} = \frac{1}{\mu_o} \nabla \times \hat{\underset{\sim}{A}} , \tag{12}$$

$$\hat{\underset{\sim}{E}} + j\omega \hat{\underset{\sim}{A}} = - \nabla \hat{\phi} , \tag{13}$$

and, with the gauge condition

$$\nabla \cdot \hat{\underset{\sim}{A}} + j\omega\epsilon\mu_o \hat{\phi} = 0 , \tag{14}$$

we obtain the wave equation

$$\nabla^2 \hat{\underset{\sim}{A}} + k_o^2 \hat{\underset{\sim}{A}} = -\mu_o \underset{\sim}{J} , \tag{15}$$

where the optical wave number k_o is given by

$$k_o^2 = \omega^2 \epsilon \mu_o = \omega^2 \epsilon_o \mu_o (1-\omega_p^2/\omega^2) . \tag{16}$$

The scalar potential must then satisfy the following equation:

$$\nabla^2 \hat{\phi} + k^2 \hat{\phi} = \frac{1}{j\omega\epsilon} \nabla \cdot \underset{\sim}{J} . \tag{17}$$

Equations (15) and (17) yield the modified potentials $\hat{\underset{\sim}{A}}$, $\hat{\phi}$, which, when substituted in Eqs. (12) and (13), give the modified fields $\hat{\underset{\sim}{E}}$ and $\hat{\underset{\sim}{H}}$. Since $\hat{\underset{\sim}{H}}$ and $\underset{\sim}{H}$ are identical, we have already calculated the true magnetic field; in order to calculate the true electric field we must find the pressure distribution. Taking the divergence of Eq. (4) and making use of (3), we have

$$\nabla^2 p = -\frac{\omega^2 m n_o}{\gamma p_o} p - n_o e \nabla \cdot \underset{\sim}{E} . \tag{18}$$

Now, evaluating $\nabla \cdot \underset{\sim}{E}$ by taking the divergence of Eq. (1) and again using (3), we find

$$\nabla^2 p + k_p^2 p = \frac{-n_o e}{j\omega\epsilon_o} \nabla \cdot \underset{\sim}{J} , \tag{19}$$

where the plasma wave number k_p is given by

$$k_p^2 = \frac{\omega^2 mn_o}{\gamma p_o}\left[1-\frac{\omega_p^2}{\omega^2}\right], \tag{20}$$

or, in terms of the acoustic velocity a in the electron gas,

$$a^2 = \frac{\gamma p_o}{mn_o}, \tag{21}$$

$$k_p^2 = \frac{\omega^2 - \omega_p^2}{a^2}. \tag{22}$$

We should note that the equations for $\hat{\underset{\sim}{A}}$, $\hat{\phi}$ and p are coupled only through the inhomogeneous term. The modified electromagnetic potentials are related to each other by the gauge condition, but the pressure is completely independent of the modified electromagnetic field. While Eqs. (15) and (17) appear to couple $\hat{\underset{\sim}{A}}$ and $\hat{\phi}$ only through the inhomogeneous terms, the relation between the inhomogeneous terms is such that the gauge condition (14) is automatically satisfied by the potentials. We observe that we can distinguish between two types of fields: 1) modified electromagnetic, or optical type, which do not involve pressure variation, and 2) acoustic or plasma type, which do not involve magnetic fields. Each of these satisfies, away from the source, a wave equation with a different wavenumber. The two wavenumbers k_o and k_p are given by $\sqrt{\omega^2 - \omega_p^2}/c$ and $\sqrt{\omega^2 - \omega_p^2}/a$, respectively, where c and a are velocities of electromagnetic and acoustic waves in the same gas in the absence of effects due to electronic charge. Such modal decomposition was found by Professor N. Marcuvitz* in the case of plane waves in this medium.

III. RADIATED FIELDS

If we introduce the current distribution (5) into Eqs. (15), (17) and (19), we obtain the following expressions for $\hat{\underset{\sim}{A}}$, $\hat{\phi}$, p:

$$\hat{\underset{\sim}{A}} = \frac{\mu_o \mathcal{I}}{4\pi r}\,\epsilon^{-jk_o r}\,\underset{\sim}{z}_o, \tag{23}$$

*Personal communication.

$$\hat{\phi} = \frac{-\mathcal{I}}{j\omega\epsilon} \frac{\partial}{\partial z}\left[\frac{\epsilon^{-jk_o r}}{4\pi r}\right] = \frac{-\mathcal{I}}{j\omega\epsilon} \frac{d}{dr}\left[\frac{\epsilon^{-jk_o r}}{4\pi r}\right] \cos\theta , \tag{24}$$

$$p = \frac{\mathcal{I} n_o e}{j\omega\epsilon_o} \frac{\partial}{\partial z}\left[\frac{\epsilon^{-jk_p r}}{4\pi r}\right] = \frac{\mathcal{I} n_o e}{j\omega\epsilon_o} \frac{d}{dr}\left[\frac{\epsilon^{-jk_p r}}{4\pi r}\right] \cos\theta , \tag{25}$$

where r, θ, and φ and $\underset{\sim}{r}_o$, $\underset{\sim}{\theta}_o$, and $\underset{\sim}{\varphi}_o$ are the spherical coordinates and the corresponding unit vectors. Making use of Eq. (12), we can calculate the magnetic field

$$\underset{\sim}{H} = \hat{\underset{\sim}{H}} = \frac{1}{\mu_o} \nabla \times \hat{\underset{\sim}{A}} = \mathcal{I} \frac{d}{dr}\left[\frac{\epsilon^{-jk_o r}}{4\pi r}\right] \underset{\sim}{r}_o \times \underset{\sim}{z}_o$$

$$= -\mathcal{I} \frac{d}{dr}\left[\frac{\epsilon^{-jk_o r}}{4\pi r}\right] \sin\theta\, \underset{\sim}{\varphi}_o . \tag{26}$$

The modified electric field $\hat{\underset{\sim}{E}}$ is then

$$\hat{\underset{\sim}{E}} = -j\omega \hat{\underset{\sim}{A}} - \nabla \hat{\phi}$$

$$= -\frac{j\omega\mu_o \mathcal{I}}{4\pi r} \epsilon^{-jk_o r} \underset{\sim}{z}_o + \frac{\mathcal{I}}{j\omega\epsilon} \frac{d^2}{dr^2}\left[\frac{\epsilon^{-jk_o r}}{4\pi r}\right] \cos\theta\, \underset{\sim}{r}_o$$

$$- \frac{\mathcal{I}}{j\omega\epsilon} \frac{1}{r} \frac{d}{dr}\left[\frac{\epsilon^{-jk_o r}}{4\pi r}\right] \sin\theta\, \underset{\sim}{\theta}_o$$

$$= \frac{\mathcal{I}}{4\pi r} j\omega\mu_o \left\{ \cos\theta \left[-\epsilon^{-jk_o r} - r k_o^{-2} \frac{d^2}{dr^2}\left[\frac{\epsilon^{-jk_o r}}{r}\right]\right] \underset{\sim}{r}_o \right.$$

$$\left. + \sin\theta \left[\epsilon^{-jk_o r} + k_o^{-2} \frac{d}{dr}\left[\frac{\epsilon^{-jk_o r}}{r}\right]\right] \underset{\sim}{\theta}_o \right\} \tag{27}$$

The electric field is then obtained from Eqs. (6), (25) and (27):

$$\underset{\sim}{E} = \hat{\underset{\sim}{E}} + \frac{\omega_p^2}{n_o e(\omega^2 - \omega_p^2)} \nabla p = \frac{j\omega\mu_o \mathcal{J}}{4\pi r}$$

$$\times \left\{ -\cos\theta \left[\epsilon^{-jk_o r} + rk_o^{-2} \frac{d^2}{dr^2}\left[\frac{\epsilon^{-jk_o r}}{r}\right] + rk_o^{-2}\left[\frac{\omega_p}{\omega}\right]^2 \frac{d^2}{dr^2}\left[\frac{\epsilon^{-jk_p r}}{r}\right]\right] \underset{\sim}{r}_o \right.$$

$$\left. + \sin\theta \left[\epsilon^{-jk_o r} + k_o^{-2} \frac{d}{dr}\left[\frac{\epsilon^{-jk_o r}}{r}\right] + k_o^{-2}\left[\frac{\omega_p}{\omega}\right]^2 \frac{d}{dr}\left[\frac{\epsilon^{-jk_p r}}{r}\right]\right] \underset{\sim}{\theta}_o \right\} \tag{28}$$

The velocity $\underset{\sim}{v}$ can be obtained from Eq. (4)

$$\underset{\sim}{v} = \frac{-(\nabla p + n_o e\underset{\sim}{E})}{jmn_o\omega} = -\frac{\frac{\omega^2}{\omega^2 - \omega_p^2} \nabla p + n_o e\hat{\underset{\sim}{E}}}{j\omega m n_o}$$

$$= \mu_o \frac{e}{m} \frac{\mathcal{J}}{4\pi r} \left\{ \underset{\sim}{r}_o \cos\theta \left[\epsilon^{-jk_o r} + rk_o^{-2} \frac{d^2}{dr^2}\left[\frac{\epsilon^{-jk_o r} + \epsilon^{-jk_p r}}{r}\right]\right] \right.$$

$$\left. - \underset{\sim}{\theta}_o \sin\theta \left[\epsilon^{-jk_o r} + k_o^{-2} \frac{d}{dr}\left[\frac{\epsilon^{-jk_o r} + \epsilon^{-jk_p r}}{r}\right]\right]\right\}. \tag{29}$$

For large values of r, we can approximate $\underset{\sim}{H}$, $\underset{\sim}{E}$, p, and $\underset{\sim}{v}$ by their asympotic forms:

$$\underset{\sim}{H} \approx jk_o \mathcal{J} \frac{\epsilon^{-jk_o r}}{4\pi r} \sin\theta \, \underset{\sim}{\varphi}_o \tag{30}$$

$$\underset{\sim}{E} \approx \frac{j\omega\mu_o \mathcal{J}}{4\pi r} \left\{ r_o \cos\theta \left(\frac{\omega_p}{\omega}\right)^2 \left(\frac{c}{a}\right)^2 \epsilon^{-jk_p r} + \underset{\sim}{\theta}_o \sin\theta \, \epsilon^{-jk_o r} \right\} \tag{31}$$

$$p \approx \frac{-k_p n_o e \mathcal{J}}{\omega \epsilon_o} \frac{\epsilon^{-jk_p r}}{4\pi r} \cos\theta , \tag{32}$$

$$\underset{\sim}{v} \approx -\mu_o \frac{e}{m} \frac{\mathcal{J}}{4\pi r} \left\{ + \underset{\sim}{r}_o \cos\theta \left(\frac{c}{a}\right)^2 \epsilon^{-jk_p r} + \underset{\sim}{\theta}_o \sin\theta\, \epsilon^{-jk_o r} \right\}. \tag{33}$$

The power density in the far field can now be evaluated:

$$\underset{\sim}{S} = \underset{\sim}{S}_o + \underset{\sim}{S}_p = \mathrm{Re}\left[\underset{\sim}{E} \times \underset{\sim}{H}^* + p\underset{\sim}{v}^* \right] \tag{34}$$

Since only the r component of $\underset{\sim}{S}$ is necessary for power calculation, we have

$$S_r = \mathrm{Re}\left[E_\theta H_\phi^* + p v_r^* \right]$$

$$= \sin^2\theta \frac{k_o \omega \mu_o}{(4\pi r)^2} \mathcal{J}^2 + \frac{k_p n_o e^2 \mu_o \mathcal{J}^2}{\omega \epsilon_o m (4\pi r)^2} \cos^2\theta \left(\frac{c}{a}\right)^2 . \tag{35}$$

Evaluating the total radiated power, we obtain

$$P = P_o + P_p , \tag{36}$$

$$P_o = \frac{4}{3} \cdot \frac{k_o \omega \mu_o}{8\pi} \mathcal{J}^2 , \tag{37}$$

$$P_p = \frac{2}{3} \cdot \frac{k_p \omega \mu_o}{8\pi} \left[\frac{\omega_p}{\omega}\right]^2 \left(\frac{c}{a}\right)^2 \mathcal{J}^2 . \tag{38}$$

A quantity of interest is the ratio of power in the plasma wave to that in the optical wave:

$$\frac{P_p}{P_o} = \frac{1}{2} \frac{k_p}{k_o} \left(\frac{c}{a}\right)^2 \left[\frac{\omega_p}{\omega}\right]^2 = \frac{1}{2} \left(\frac{c}{a}\right)^3 \left[\frac{\omega_p}{\omega}\right]^2 . \tag{39}$$

IV. CURRENT DISTRIBUTION ON A FINITE SPHERE

In order to avoid the difficulties associated with the coherence of the radiation from the disturbance in the immediate neighborhood of the oscillating dipole, we may consider the problem of radiation from a prescribed current distribution on the surface of a rigid sphere. Alternatively, we may consider the problem of a radiating point dipole embedded at the center of a rigid dielectric sphere of finite size surrounded by an infinite plasma medium. In the former case, the tangential magnetic field at the surface of the sphere is determined by the prescribed current distribution. In the latter case, the fields external to the dielectric sphere can be related to the results that we shall obtain for the prescribed current distribution on a rigid sphere.

Let us choose the current distribution on the surface of a rigid sphere of radius b such that the tangential magnetic field at the surface of the sphere will be precisely the magnetic field of a point dipole in an infinite plasma on the surface r = b, that is,

$$\underset{\sim}{H}(b,\theta,\varphi) = -\mathcal{J}\left[\frac{d}{dr}\left[\frac{\epsilon^{-jk_o r}}{4\pi r}\right]\right]_{r=b} \sin\theta\ \underset{\sim}{\varphi}_o \ . \tag{40}$$

Due to the rigidity of the sphere, we have to satisfy the boundary condition:

$$v_r = 0\ , \quad r = b\ . \tag{41}$$

The optical field is uniquely determined by the prescribed tangential magnetic field on the surface of the sphere r=b and by the requirement of outgoing waves at infinity. If the tangential magnetic field on the sphere r=b is given by Eq. (40), then the optical field for r > b is identical with that previously found for a dipole in an infinite plasma. We can then find the plasma field by applying the boundary condition (41); by making use of Eq. (29), it can be written as follows:

$$\frac{\partial p}{\partial r} = -\frac{n_o e}{\omega^2}(\omega^2 - \omega_p^2)\,\hat{E}_r, \quad r = b\ . \tag{42}$$

Inserting the expression for $\hat{E}_r$ for Eq. (27) into Eq. (42), we obtain

$$\left.\frac{\partial p}{\partial r}\right|_{r=b} = \frac{j\mu_o(\omega^2-\omega_p^2)\, n_o e \ell \cos\theta}{4\pi b\omega}\left[\epsilon^{-jk_o r} - \frac{r^2}{k_o^2}\frac{d^2}{dr^2}\left[\frac{\epsilon^{-jk_o r}}{r}\right]\right]_{r=b} \tag{43}$$

Now the pressure distribution is uniquely determined by the value of the normal derivative $\partial p/\partial r$ on the sphere $r = b$, since it satisfies the wave equation

$$\nabla^2 p + \frac{\omega^2 - \omega_p^2}{a^2}\, p = 0 \tag{44}$$

and the Sommerfeld boundary condition at infinity. In order to satisfy all the above requirements, the pressure must have the form

$$p(r,\theta) = C\,\frac{H^{(2)}_{3/2}(k_p r)}{\sqrt{r}}\cos\theta\,, \tag{45}$$

where $H^{(2)}_{3/2}$ denotes the Hankel function of the second kind of order 3/2. Equating the derivative of Eq. (45) to the right-hand side of Eq. (43), we find the constant C to be

$$C = \frac{jn_o e(\omega^2-\omega_p^2)\mu_o}{2\pi b\omega k_o k_p}\cdot\frac{\epsilon^{j(k_p-k_o)b}\left(1+\dfrac{1}{jk_o b}\right)}{1+\dfrac{2}{jk_p b}-\dfrac{2}{k_p^2 b^2}}\,. \tag{46}$$

We can compare this pressure wave with the pressure wave generated by a point dipole. Since the spatial dependence is the same in both cases, we find the ratio of pressure due to current distribution on a rigid sphere to pressure due to a point dipole:

$$\left|\frac{p_{sphere}}{p_{dipole}}\right| = \left|\frac{1+\dfrac{1}{jk_o b}}{1+\dfrac{2}{jk_p b}-\dfrac{2}{k_p^2 b^2}}\right|\cdot\frac{2a^2}{c^2(k_o b)}\,. \tag{47}$$

Since the power ratio is equal to the square of the magnitude of the pressure ratio, and since the ratio of the power radiated by the dipole in the acoustic wave to that power radiated in the optical wave was calculated before, we obtain the ratio of acoustic power to optical power radiated by a current distribution on the sphere:

$$\frac{P_p}{P_o} = \frac{2a}{c}\left(\frac{\omega_p}{\omega}\right)^2 \frac{(k_o b)^{-2} + (k_o b)^{-4}}{1 + 4\,(k_p b)^{-4}} . \tag{48}$$

We can distinguish between three ranges of parameters in which this expression simplifies:

1) $k_o b << 1$, $k_p b << 1$,

2) $k_o b << 1$, $k_p b >> 1$,

3) $k_o b >> 1$, $k_p b >> 1$.

In the first case, when the sphere is small compared to both optical and plasma wavelengths, the power ratio (48) reduces to that obtained previously for a point dipole. In the second case, when the sphere is large compared to the plasma wavelength, but small compared to the optical wavelength, we obtain

$$\frac{P_p}{P_o} \approx \frac{2a\,(\omega_p/\omega)^2}{c\,(k_o b)^4} , \tag{49}$$

which may be either large or small. In the third case, in which the sphere is large compared to both plasma and optical wavelengths, we have

$$\frac{P_p}{P_o} \approx \frac{2a\,(\omega_p/\omega)^2}{c\,(k_o b)^2} , \tag{50}$$

which is always small.

The special case occurring when the radius of the sphere is equal to the Debye shielding distance, or $b\omega_p/a = 2\pi$, falls in the first of the three cases discussed above.*

*Since Landau damping was not taken into account, it is recognized that the range of validity of this theory is restricted to frequencies near ω_p.

V. POINT SOURCE IN A SPHERICAL VOID IN A PLASMA

If we place a point dipole at the center of a rigid spherical cavity of radius b in a plasma (the cavity can be free space or dielectric), the magnetic field distribution on the interface must have the form

$$\underset{\sim}{H}_t = C \sin\theta\, \underset{\sim}{\varphi}_o \tag{51}$$

where C is a constant which would be determined by the parameters of the problem. Once the constant C is specified, the optical field exterior to the sphere (r > b) is determined. Hence, following the procedure of Section IV, the normal derivative of pressure on the surface of the sphere is determined, and we can finally calculate the entire acoustic field in the region r > b. The ratio of power in the plasma wave to that in the optical wave is independent of the constant C, since this constant appears as a factor in all fields. Hence, the power ratios previously calculated for a current distribution on a sphere apply equally well to the case at hand.

REFERENCE

1. L. Oster, "Linearized Theory of Plasma Oscillations," *Rev. Mod. Phys.*, Vol. 32, No. 1, pp. 141-168 (January 1960).

ON A VARIATIONAL PRINCIPLE FOR PLASMAS

S. Gartenhaus
Purdue University, Lafayette, Indiana

By making use of certain properties of Liouville's equation for a classical, many-particle system, a mathematical correspondence is set up between this equation and that of Schrödinger. This similarity is then employed to set up, for the classical system, a variational principle which is the exact counterpart of the time-dependent Hartree-Fock method in the quantum mechanical case. For practical applications, the variational principle requires the specification of a trial function whose form, however, is completely arbitrary. In particular, a trial function consisting of a product of single particle functions yields directly the collisionless Boltzmann equation with the electromagnetic field terms determined in the familiar, self-consistent way. Preliminary work has been done on the problem of short-range correlations, and it has been found with the aid of a particular trial function that only a Maxwellian velocity distribution corresponds to equilibrium.

Dr. Bernstein, in a paper given at this meeting (see page 19), described the procedure used and the assumptions required to derive the equations of magnetohydrodynamics starting with the Boltzmann-Vlasov equation. For a plasma consisting of a single-species, this equation is

$$\frac{\partial f}{\partial t} + \underset{\sim}{v} \cdot \frac{\partial}{\partial \underset{\sim}{r}} f + \frac{e}{m} \left[\underset{\sim}{E} + \underset{\sim}{E}_i + \underset{\sim}{V} \times (\underset{\sim}{B} + \underset{\sim}{B}_i) \right] \cdot \frac{\partial}{\partial \underset{\sim}{v}} f = 0, \tag{1}$$

where $\underset{\sim}{E}$ and $\underset{\sim}{B}$ represent any external electromagnetic fields, and where $\underset{\sim}{E}_i$ and $\underset{\sim}{B}_i$ are the solutions of Maxwell' s equations with charge and current density given by the formulas

$$\rho = e \int d\underset{\sim}{v}\ f; \qquad \underset{\sim}{j} = e \int d\underset{\sim}{v}\ \underset{\sim}{v}\ f. \tag{2}$$

A convenient physical way of describing Eq. (1) is by means of the statement:

Each particle in the plasma moves along a trajectory which is determined by the forces due to the external fields plus an average force produced by the fields due

---

Presented at the Symposium on Electromagnetics and Fluid Dynamics of Gaseous Plasma, Polytechnic Institute of Brooklyn, April 4, 5, 6, 1961

to all of the other particles.

This statement, which is evidently equivalent to Eq. (1), is unfortunately restrictive in that it does not enable us to generalize this equation in order, for example, to take into account effects due to short-range correlations. The fact that Eq. (1) cannot be a complete description of the plasma follows from the observation that in the absence of external fields, any function of the velocity alone satisfies Eq. (1) while intuitively we know that at equilibrium the distribution function must be Maxwellian.

To overcome this incompleteness of the Boltzmann-Vlasov equation, it is natural to attempt to add the well-known collision integrals to the right-hand side of Eq. (1). As was stated in Dr. Tidman's paper (see page 111), this leads to some very complicated mathematics. In addition it is not obviously correct since some of the effects due to the collisions have already been included on the left-hand side of Eq. (1). A second approach, which may be used to overcome this incompleteness of Eq. (1), was presented by Prof. Burgers, (see page 81), who started with the chain of equations which relate the several particle distribution functions to each other. By assuming that the corrections to Eq. (1) were small, he obtained the two-particle distribution function at equilibrium in the form

$$F_2 = F_1(\underset{\sim}{v}_1) F_1(\underset{\sim}{v}_2) \left\{ 1 - \frac{e^2}{kt} \frac{\exp\left[- \left| \underset{\sim}{r}_1 - \underset{\sim}{r}_2' \right| / \lambda \right]}{\left| \underset{\sim}{r}_1 - \underset{\sim}{r}_2 \right|} \right\} \quad (3)$$

where $F_1(\underset{\sim}{v})$ is a Maxwellian distribution, λ is the Debye shielding distance, and T is the temperature. As we have seen, both of these methods, although yielding very simple equilibrium formulas, are, in general, very complex mathematically.

I would now like to discuss an alternate way for describing the dynamics of a plasma. This method is not as rigorous as that considered by Burgers, but it is, on the other hand, very general, and may allow for a simplified mathematical treatment without leaving out too much in the way of physical essentials. As we shall see, the Boltzmann-Vlasov equation is a direct consequence of this formulation. Thus there is an alternate way of describing Eq. (1) in words, and we are in a position to generalize the equation in various ways. This work is, at present, in a preliminary state and only the essential ideas and some of the first results will be presented here.

For reasons of simplicity, let us consider a system consisting of a very large number, say N, of electrons immersed in given external electromagnetic fields which may include a static background of positive charge. Correct to order $1/c^2$, the Hamiltonian for the system is

$$H = \sum_{i=1}^{N} \left\{ \frac{1}{2M} \left[\underset{\sim}{p}_i - \frac{e}{c} \underset{\sim}{A}(\underset{\sim}{r}_i, t) \right]^2 + e\phi(\underset{\sim}{r}_i, t) \right\}$$

$$+ e^2 \sum_{i<j} \left\{ \frac{1}{r_{ij}} - \frac{1}{2m^2c^2} \left[\frac{\underset{\sim}{p}_i \cdot \underset{\sim}{p}_j}{r_{ij}} + \frac{\underset{\sim}{p}_i \cdot \underset{\sim}{r}_{ij} \underset{\sim}{p}_j \cdot \underset{\sim}{r}_{ij}}{r_{ij}^3} \right] \right\} \tag{4}$$

where $\underset{\sim}{A}$ and ϕ are the potentials describing the external fields. In terms of the given Hamiltonian, Liouville's equation for the total distribution function $F^{(N)}(t)$ is given by

$$\frac{\partial F^{(N)}}{\partial t} = LF^{(N)}, \tag{5}$$

where the operator L is given in terms of H by the formula

$$L = \sum_{i=1}^{N} \left\{ \frac{\partial H}{\partial \underset{\sim}{r}_i} \cdot \frac{\partial}{\partial \underset{\sim}{p}_i} - \frac{\partial H}{\partial \underset{\sim}{p}_i} \cdot \frac{\partial}{\partial \underset{\sim}{r}_i} \right\}. \tag{6}$$

We have written Liouville's equation in the form of Eq. (5) in order to emphasize the essential similarity between it and the Schrödinger equation. This identification follows by virtue of the anti-hermitian nature of the operator L. Furthermore, since Liouville's equation is not only linear and homogeneous, but also involves only first-order derivatives, we conclude the very important fact that an arbitrary function of a solution is also a solution. This latter property, taken together with the mathematical correspondence between Eq. (5) and the Schrodinger equation, suggests that we define a new function, $u^{(N)}(t)$, whose modulus is equal to the square root of the non-negative distribution function $F^{(N)}(t)$; that is

$$F^{(N)}(t) = | u^{(N)}(t) |^2. \tag{7}$$

We have written this definition thus in order to emphasize the fact that we shall allow $u^{(N)}(t)$ to have a phase $\phi^{(N)}(t)$ which need not be restricted a priori in any way. The reason for this arbitrariness in the phase is, of course, due to the fact that all physically measurable quantities are given in terms of averages over the distribution function by expressions of the form

$$\overline{M}(t) = \int d\Omega\, M^{(N)}\, F^{(N)}(t) = \int d\Omega\, M^{(N)} \left| u^{(N)}(t) \right|^2, \quad (8)$$

and all of these are independent of the phase $\phi^{(N)}(t)$.

We now exploit this arbitrariness in the phase of $u^{(N)}$ by demanding that $\phi^{(N)}(t)$ itself satisfy Liouville's equation. Since $|u^{(N)}|$ also satisfies Eq. (6) it follows that $u^{(N)}(t)$ is also a solution of the equation

$$\frac{\partial u^{(N)}}{\partial t} = L\, u^{(N)}. \quad (9)$$

Thus, bearing in mind that $\phi^{(N)}$ is not observable, we see that a complete description of the electron gas can be given equally well in terms of $u^{(N)}$ in place of the distribution function $F^{(N)}$. Therefore, let us turn our attention towards obtaining approximate formulas for $u^{(N)}$.

The above-noted similarity between Eq. (9) and the Schrödinger equation, as well as that between $u^{(N)}(t)$ and the wave function for a quantum-mechanical system, now suggests that for the present classical problem we attempt to use the very same techniques that have found such wide application for stationary-state phenomena in many-particle quantum systems. In particular, the Hartree-Fock method of self-consistent fields immediately comes to mind. A time-dependent version of this method appropriate for our purposes is expressed by the following statement.

The quantity V defined by the formula

$$V = \left[u^{(N)}, \left[L - \frac{\partial}{\partial t} \right] u^{(N)} \right] \quad (10)$$

and considered as a functional of various complex functions $u^{(N)}(t)$, each of which is normalized to unity

$$\left[u^{(N)}, u^{(N)} \right] = 1, \quad (11)$$

is stationary about the solution of Eq. (9).

In this formulation, we have made use of the notation

$$(f, g) = \int d\,\Omega\, f^* g, \quad (12)$$

where the integration is carried out over all of phase-space. The proof of the equivalence of this variational principle for independent variation of both $u^{(N)}$ and $u^{(N)*}$ is straightforward and is very similar to Fock's original proof.

To make use of this variational principle in a practical way, it is necessary to construct a trial function. In general, this function will contain a set of parameters whose variation will yield the best distribution function of the given form. At this point, only two types of trial functions have been explored in any detail. The first of these reproduces the Boltzmann-Vlasov equation in its entirety, and thus shows that this variational principle yields the same results as are obtainable by more intuitive arguments. The second of these trial functions is of interest for the cases in which short-range correlations are small, but not entirely negligible. Let us briefly consider both of these.

For the case of an electron gas immersed in the electromagnetic fields $\underset{\sim}{E}$, and $\underset{\sim}{B}$, the Boltzmann-Vlasov equation follows from the variational principle by use of the trial function

$$u^{(N)}(t) = \prod_{i=1}^{N} u(x_i, t), \tag{13}$$

where the complex function u is normalized to unity,

$$(u, u) = 1, \tag{14}$$

and depends on the coordinates and momenta $x_i \equiv (\underset{\sim}{r}_i, \underset{\sim}{p}_i)$, of a single particle only. We substitute the trial function in Eq. (13) into Eq. (10), make use of Eq. (14) and the Hamiltonian in Eq. (4). We then find, by varying the functional form of u*, that the best form of u will satisfy Eq. (1), with charge and current densities now given in terms of u and u* by the formulas

$$\begin{aligned} \rho(\underset{\sim}{r}, t) &= Ne\left[u(x', t), \quad \delta(\underset{\sim}{r} - \underset{\sim}{r}')\, u(x', t)\right], \\ \underset{\sim}{j}(\underset{\sim}{r}, t) &= Ne\left[u(x', t), \quad \underset{\sim}{v}' \quad \delta(\underset{\sim}{r} - \underset{\sim}{r}')\, u(x', t)\right]. \end{aligned} \tag{15}$$

Actually, one finds that u satisfies Eq. (1) with several extra terms; however, it is easily seen that these terms are purely imaginary and may be removed by a propitious choice of phase. Moreover, regardless of such additional terms, if one multiplies the equation for u by u*, and adds the result to its own complex conjugate, these spurious terms cancel out and one also finds that the single-particle distribution function f(x, t), which according to Eqs. (7) and (13) is given by

$$f(x, t) = |u(x, t)|^2, \tag{16}$$

satisfies Eq. (1) exactly. Thus we have shown that by use of a product trial function, the variational principle directly yields the Boltzmann-Vlasov equation. In carrying out the details of this derivation one must, of course, consistently neglect terms of order $1/c^3$.

For the case of a plasma consisting of more than one species, (say, of electrons and of a single type of ion) the appropriate trial function is given by

$$u^{(N)}(t) = \left[\prod_e u(x_e, t)\right] \left[\prod_I v(x_I, t)\right] . \tag{17}$$

The detailed application of the variational principle for this case is only slightly more complicated than the above, in that we must carry out separate variations of both u* and v* and use an appropriately mor general form of the Hamiltonian. Again one obtains the well known an physically expected results. That is, $|u|^2$ and $|v|^2$ both satisfy Eq. (1) with different e/m values, of course, but now the charge and current densities inherent in these equations are generated by the particles of both species.

The second type of trial function, which has been examined in some detail, is applicable to a system of identical particles which interact by means of two-particle, repulsive forces. For reasons of simplicity, we shall neglect all magnetic effects and assume that the particles interact only by means of a central potential $V\left[|\underset{\sim}{r}-\underset{\sim}{r}'|\right]$. The trial function is taken to be of the form

$$u^{(N)}(t) = \frac{1}{[N!]^{1/2}} \left\{ \prod_{i=1}^{N} u(x_i, t) \right\} \text{Det} \left\{ v_i (\underset{\sim}{r}_j, t) \right\} \tag{18}$$

where the ij-th element of the determinant is given by the i-th function v_i and depends only on the coordinates (but not the velocity) of the j-th particle and the time. For reasons of convenience, we introduce the functions U_i (x, t) which are defined by

$$U_i (x, t) = u (x, t)\, v_i (\underset{\sim}{r}, t), \tag{19}$$

and are assumed to form a mutually orthonormal set, that is

$$(U_i, U_j) = \delta_{ij}. \tag{20}$$

In the following, independent variations of each of these functions U_i

will be made. One must bear in mind that the trial function in Eq. (18) makes good physical sense, that is the probability of finding two particles close together is vanishingly small regardless of their velocities, only if U_i can be factored as in Eq. (19) with one factor, u, independent of the index i, and the second independent of the velocity.

The one and two-particle distribution functions that result from the trial function in Eq. (18) are of some interest and may be calculated in a straightforward way. We find, by use of Eq. (20), the results

$$f_1(x, t) = \frac{1}{N} \sum_i |U_i(x, t)|^2 \tag{21}$$

and

$$\begin{aligned} f_2(x, x', t) = {} & f_1(x, t)\, f_1(x', t) \\ & - \frac{1}{N^2} \sum_{i,j} U_i^*(x, t)\, U_j^*(x', t)\, U_i(x', t) U_j(x, t). \end{aligned} \tag{22}$$

Because of the orthogonality of the functions U_i and the fact that the number of particles is very large, it is reasonable to expect that, except for $\underset{\sim}{r} \approx \underset{\sim}{r}'$, the second, or exchange, term in the formula for f_2 will be small compared to the first term. Of course, for $\underset{\sim}{r} = \underset{\sim}{r}'$, the exchange term will cancel the first term. Thus, we conclude that the trial function in Eq. (18) can be expected to be a good approximation for those physical situations for which f_2 can be written as a product of two one-particle distribution functions plus a small correction. In this sense, the trial function in Eq. (18) may be viewed as yielding a first-order correction to the Boltzmann-Vlasov equation.

The equations that govern the evolution of the functions U_i, are obtained by inserting the trial function in Eq. (18) into the variational principle. Making use of Eq. (20), and again dropping all LaGrange multipliers and other irrelevant phase factors, we obtain the system of equations

$$\begin{aligned} \frac{\partial U_i}{\partial t} : + \underset{\sim}{v} \cdot \frac{\partial}{\partial \underset{\sim}{r}} U_i + \frac{1}{m} \sum_j \left[U_j(x', t), \underset{\sim}{F}(\underset{\sim}{r} - \underset{\sim}{r}')\, U_j(x', t) \right] \cdot \frac{\partial U_i}{\partial \underset{\sim}{v}} \\ - \frac{1}{m} \sum_j \left[U_j(x', t), \underset{\sim}{F}(\underset{\sim}{r} - \underset{\sim}{r}')\, U_i(x', t) \right] \frac{\partial}{\partial \underset{\sim}{v}} U_j = 0, \end{aligned} \tag{23}$$

where $\underset{\sim}{F}$ is expressed in terms of the given central potential by the formula

$$F\,(\underset{\sim}{r}-\underset{\sim}{r}') = -\frac{\partial}{\partial \underset{\sim}{r}}\, V\left[|\underset{\sim}{r}-\underset{\sim}{r}'|\right]. \tag{24}$$

It should be noted that Eq. (23) represents a set of coupled, non-linear, integrodifferential equations, and at first sight seems rather formidable. However, because of Eq. (20), it is easily seen that, in general, the fourth term in Eq. (23) is very small compared to the third term, and thus the former may safely be treated as a small perturbation. Further, with this small term neglected, Eq. (23) is essentially identical with Eq. (1).

In order to see this a little more clearly, let us multiply Eq. (23) by U_i^*, add the result to its own complex conjugate, and sum over the index i. Making use of Eqs. (21) and(22), we obtain the familiar result

$$\frac{\partial f_1}{\partial t} + \underset{\sim}{v}\cdot\frac{\partial}{\partial \underset{\sim}{r}} f_1 + \frac{1}{m}\int dx'\; \underset{\sim}{F}\,(\underset{\sim}{r}-\underset{\sim}{r}')\cdot\frac{\partial}{\partial \underset{\sim}{v}} f_2\,(x, x', t) = 0. \tag{25}$$

In this formula, that contribution to f_2 that arises by virtue of the fourth term in Eq. (23) is entirely accounted for by the second and sma term in Eq. (22). Consequently, it is plausible to expect that the exchange term in Eq. (23) must also be small. In passing, it is of interest to note that in the present context, Eq. (25) is merely an identity among those functions U_i which satisfy Eq. (23), and is therefore not tc be interpreted as an indeterminate equation taken from the familiar hierarchy.

Most of the initial efforts in a study of Eq. (23) have been directed towards obtaining equilibrium solutions. It has been found that the function U_i given by the formula

$$U_i = f\,(\underset{\sim}{v})\; \exp\left\{i\, \underset{\sim}{k}_i \cdot \underset{\sim}{r}\right\}, \tag{26}$$

where the parameters $\underset{\sim}{k}_i$ are a set of N distinct wave vectors, will satisfy Eq. (23) for certain choices of these parameters provided that $f(\underset{\sim}{v})$ is Gaussian. In particular, with the selection of wave vectors implied by the formula

$$\frac{1}{V}\sum_i \longrightarrow \int \frac{d\underset{\sim}{k}}{(2\pi)^3}\,\frac{\alpha^4}{\left[\alpha^2 + k^2\right]^2}, \tag{27}$$

where V is the volume of the gas ($V\rightarrow\infty$), we find that for very short-range forces, $f(\underset{\sim}{v})$ must be a Maxwellian with root-mean-square velocity given by

$$\overline{v^2} = \frac{n_o \gamma}{m} , \tag{28}$$

where γ is the volume integral of the potential and n_o is the particle density. The latter may be expressed in terms of the parameter α introduced in Eq. (27) by the formula

$$n_o = \frac{\alpha^3}{8\pi} . \tag{29}$$

Similarily, for the case of the Coulomb-potential we find again that $f(\underset{\sim}{v})$ must be Maxwellian with root-mean-square velocity now given by

$$\overline{v^2} = \frac{\eta \omega_p^2 m}{\alpha^2} , \tag{30}$$

where ω_p is the plasma frequency and η is a dimensionless factor which is essentially constant and has a numerical value $\approx$ 0. 3. The fact that Eqs. (28) and (30) contain no free parameters corresponding to temperature is due to our choice of wave-vector distribution in Eq. (27) which contains only the one free parameter α. By selecting distributions with more parameters than we have used above, flexibility in the choice of temperature is regained.

Thus we see that equilibrium distributions corresponding to the trial function in Eq. (18) are obtainable. These distributions are an improvement over those obtained from the Boltzmann-Vlasov equation in that, regardless of the range of the forces, the velocity distribution must be Maxwellian. The one and two-particle distribution functions themselves may be obtained by substituting Eq. (26) into Eqs. (21) and (22) to yield

$$\begin{aligned} f_1 (x, t) &= \frac{n_o}{N} f^2 (\underset{\sim}{v}), \\ f_2 (x, x', t) &= \left[\frac{n_o}{N}\right]^2 f^2 (\underset{\sim}{v}) \; f^2 (\underset{\sim}{v}') \left[1 - \exp\left\{- 2\alpha \mid \underset{\sim}{r}-\underset{\sim}{r}' \mid\right\}\right] , \end{aligned} \tag{31}$$

where $f^2(\underset{\sim}{v})$ is Maxwellian. The two-particle distribution function has the form one would expect on physical grounds and has been anticipated by the trial function in Eq. (18). Furthermore, f_2 has a form very similar to that in Eq. (3). Indeed the latter may be obtained by using the Fourier transform of the square root of the Debye potential as a weight function in Eq. (27). Thus we see that the present method is sufficiently general to include some previously obtained results. On the other hand, a great deal of further study with various types of tria functions is still required before a claim can be made for the general usefulness of this variational principle.

POWER AND ENERGY RELATIONS IN BIDIRECTIONAL WAVEGUIDES*

Paul Chorney†
Electrical Engineering Department and
Research Laboratory of Electronics
Massachusetts Institute of Technology

Some new general theorems on the propagation properties of a certain broad class of lossless, passive, uniform waveguides are developed. This broad class is referred to as "bidirectional." Two important cases of bidirectional waveguides are: 1) those containing isotropic materials; 2) those containing gyrotropic materials with the gyrotropic axis along the waveguide axis. A feature of the materials considered is that they are, in general, dispersive. The theorems interrelate group velocity, phase velocity, power, energy, and "pseudo energy." The term "pseudo energy" is used to distinguish the true energy from the energy-like terms which appear in the complex form of Poynting's theorem; for the case of dispersive media, true energy does not appear as such in the complex form of Poynting's theorem.

As an illustration, these theorems are applied to the plasma-filled waveguide. Some general properties of the dispersion character are revealed.

I. INTRODUCTION

Many authors have dealt with the exact theory of propagation in waveguides loaded with cold, lossless, anisotropic plasmas. The application of a dc magnetic field along the axis of a plasma-loaded waveguide introduces an anisotropy which is gyrotropic. The most general treatments of propagation in uniform waveguides containing gyrotropic media with longitudinal magnetization are given by Gamo,[1] Van Trier,[2] and Suhl and Walker.[3] These papers, which consider general gyrotropic media (i. e., simultaneously gyroelectric and gyromagnetic), establish the techniques of the exact mathematical treatments of the problem. Limited approximation techniques of solution have also been introduced, notably perturbation theory[4,5] and quasi-statics.[6,7] The exact theory, even for the simplest configurations (e. g., a circular waveguide completely filled with a uniform gyroelectric plasma) results in involved transcendental determinantal equations. The approximation techniques

* This work was supported in part by the U. S. Army Signal Corps, the Air Force Office of Scientific Research, the Office of Naval Research, and the National Science Foundation.

† Presently at Microwave Associates, Inc., Burlington, Massachusetts.

Presented at the Symposium on Electromagnetics and Fluid Dynamics of Gaseous Plasma, Polytechnic Institute of Brooklyn, April 4, 5, 6, 1961

readily yield tractable dispersion relations and field solutions. However, perturbation theory is limited to incremental changes, and quasistatics is limited to plasmas with plasma and cyclotron frequencies small compared with the empty-waveguide cutoff frequency.

It turns out that uniform waveguides that contain plasmas with longitudinal magnetization are members of a general waveguide class, for which we coin the term "bidirectional." This paper discusses some properties of bidirectional waveguides. As an illustration of the implications of these properties, a waveguide, uniformly filled with a longitudinally magnetized plasma, will be discussed. The theory presented here does not necessarily ease the difficult mathematics encountered in the exact computation of the modes of propagation. However, the theory does aid in understanding the results of computations, as it lends insight and intuition into the nature of the propagation phenomena. Also, some predictions of the qualitative behavior of the dispersion character become evident.

II. BIDIRECTIONAL WAVEGUIDES

We consider a uniform waveguide of arbitrary cross section (Fig. 1). The waveguide walls may be composed of perfect electric conductors, perfect magnetic conductors, or both. The boundary conditions at the walls are

$$\bar{n} \times \bar{E} = 0 \qquad (1)$$

on perfect electric conductors, and

$$\bar{n} \times \bar{H} = 0 \qquad (2)$$

on perfect magnetic conductors, where $\bar{n}$ is the unit normal vector at the waveguide wall. The material filling the waveguide is characterized by the permittivity and permeability tensors

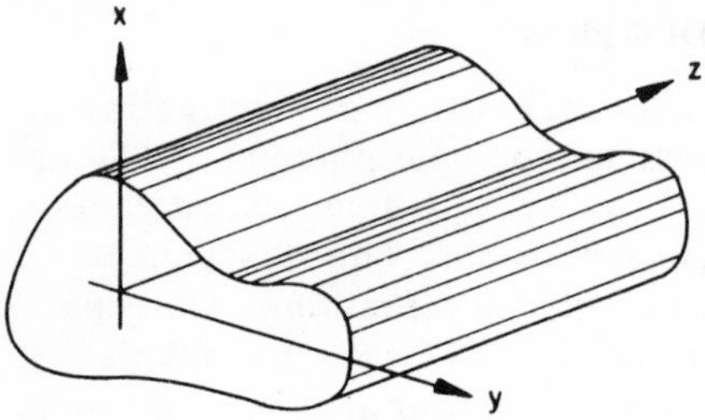

Fig. 1 Uniform waveguide with general cross section

$$\bar{\bar{\epsilon}}(x, y) = \begin{bmatrix} \epsilon_{11} & \epsilon_{12} & 0 \\ \epsilon_{21} & \epsilon_{22} & 0 \\ 0 & 0 & \epsilon_{33} \end{bmatrix}, \qquad (3)$$

and

$$\bar{\bar{\mu}}(x,y) = \begin{bmatrix} \mu_{11} & \mu_{12} & 0 \\ \mu_{21} & \mu_{22} & 0 \\ 0 & 0 & \mu_{33} \end{bmatrix} . \tag{4}$$

The material may be inhomogeneous with respect to the waveguide cross section; however, for a given transverse coordinate, the materials are independent of z. A general feature of the materials under consideration is that we allow them to be dispersive, i.e., their permeabilities and permittivities may be frequency-dependent. For lossless, passive media the diagonal terms of the tensors are pure-real, and the off-diagonal terms are complex conjugates of each other. For lossless gyrotropic media, the 1-1 and 2-2 diagonal terms are equal and the off-diagonal terms are pure-imaginary. The fields in this waveguide are governed by Maxwell's equations in complex form:

$$\nabla \times \bar{H} = j\omega\bar{\bar{\epsilon}} \cdot \bar{E} , \tag{5}$$

$$\nabla \times \bar{E} = -j\omega\bar{\bar{\mu}} \cdot \bar{H} . \tag{6}$$

We assume that the z-dependence is of the form $\exp(-\Gamma z)$, where Γ is a complex propagation constant, and all the fields vary as, for example,

$$\bar{E}(x,y,z) = \hat{E}(x,y)\, e^{-\Gamma z} , \tag{7}$$

where the circumflex denotes that the z-dependence has been removed from a field quantity. We may separate Maxwell's equations into transverse and longitudinal components with the result

$$\nabla_T \hat{H}_z + \Gamma \hat{H}_T = j\omega\bar{i}_z \times \bar{\bar{\epsilon}}_T \cdot \hat{E}_T , \tag{8}$$

$$\nabla_T \hat{E}_z + \Gamma \hat{E}_T = -j\omega\bar{i}_z \times \bar{\bar{\mu}}_T \cdot \hat{H}_T , \tag{9}$$

$$\bar{i}_z \cdot (\nabla_T \times \hat{H}_T) = j\omega\,\epsilon_{33} \hat{E}_z , \tag{10}$$

$$i_z \cdot (\nabla_T \times \hat{E}_T) = -j\omega\mu_{33} \hat{H}_z . \tag{11}$$

The subscripts T and z respectively denote transverse and longitudinal components. The 2×2 sub-tensors that contain the transverse elements of the permittivity and permeability tensors are also denoted by the subscript T.

We note the following: suppose we replace

$$\begin{aligned} \Gamma &\text{ by } -\Gamma ,\\ \hat{E}_T &\text{ by } \mp \hat{E}_T ,\\ \hat{H}_T &\text{ by } \pm \hat{H}_T ,\\ \hat{E}_z &\text{ by } \pm \hat{E}_z ,\\ \hat{H}_z &\text{ by } \mp \hat{H}_z . \end{aligned}$$

Then Eqs. (8) to (11) remain unchanged and the boundary conditions (Eqs. (1) and (2)) also remain unchanged. Thus we conclude that the dispersion relation for Γ is the same as that for $-\Gamma$, i.e., the dispersion relation must be an even function of Γ. Hence, *if a wave propagates as* $\exp(-\Gamma z)$, *it is possible to excite another wave of basically the same field structure that propagates as* $\exp(+\Gamma z)$. This statement is the basic definition of the property of bidirectionality. Expressed mathematically, if a wave with fields of the form

$$\overline{E}_+ = \left[\hat{E}_T + \overline{i}_z \hat{E}_z \right] e^{-\Gamma z} , \tag{12}$$

$$\overline{H}_+ = \left[\hat{H}_T + \overline{i}_z \hat{H}_z \right] e^{-\Gamma z} , \tag{13}$$

can be excited in a bidirectional waveguide, then it is also possible to excite a wave, traveling in the opposite direction, with fields of the form

$$\overline{E}_- = \left[\mp \hat{E}_T \pm \overline{i}_z \hat{E}_z \right] e^{+\Gamma z} , \tag{14}$$

$$\overline{H}_- = \left[\pm \hat{H}_T \mp \overline{i}_z \hat{H}_z \right] e^{+\Gamma z} . \tag{15}$$

The subscripts plus and minus denote, respectively, the forward-traveling and backward-traveling waves. We recall that the only restriction that makes a waveguiding system bidirectional is the form of the permittivity and permeability tensors given by Eqs. (3) and (4). Some examples of bidirectional waveguides are 1) those containing isotropic materials and 2) those containing gyrotropic materials with the gyrotropic axis along the waveguide axis.

It should be pointed out that this concept of bidirectionality is consistent with the results of Villeneuve,[8] who showed that both $+\Gamma$ and $-\Gamma$ are eigenvalues of Maxwell's equations when the gyrotropic material is aligned with the waveguide axis.

III. PSEUDO-ENERGY AND POWER IN LOSSLESS BIDIRECTIONAL WAVEGUIDES

We now restrict our attention to lossless, passive, bidirectional waveguides because of the elegant relations that can be derived for them. These relations connect the phase velocity and power flow with a quantity which is defined here as "pseudo energy." The term "psuedo energy" is used to distinguish this quantity from the true energy which it so much resembles in the most general case. The energylike terms that appear in the complex form of Poynting's theorem represent the true energy only when the medium is nondispersive. In the general case where the medium is dispersive, care must be taken in interpreting these energylike terms, for they do not represent the true energy but only parts of it.[9-13] The pseudo energy expresses only the energy stored in the electric and magnetic fields and in the polarization and magnetization of the material. What is omitted for dispersive media is the kinetic energy stored in the motion of the electric and magnetic dipoles; it is just this motion that accounts for the material being dispersive. The pseudo energy merely gives the reactance of the waves. The true energy is that which is transported by the wave at the group, or energy velocity. In this section we deal with pseudo energy; the true energy in purely propagating waves is derived in Section IV of this paper.

We again consider our general bidirectional waveguide, which is now restricted to contain a lossless, passive medium, and we place a perfectly conducting shorting plane at an arbitrary waveguide plane denoted by $z = 0$. Because of the property of bidirectionality, it is possible to set up a standing wave of the form

$$\overline{E}_T = \hat{E}_T \left[e^{-\Gamma z} - e^{+\Gamma z} \right] , \tag{16}$$

$$\overline{H}_T = \hat{H}_T \left[e^{-\Gamma z} + e^{+\Gamma z} \right] , \tag{17}$$

$$E_z = \hat{E}_z \left[e^{-\Gamma z} + e^{+\Gamma z} \right] , \tag{18}$$

$$H_z = \hat{H}_z \left[e^{-\Gamma z} - e^{+\Gamma z} \right] , \tag{19}$$

The standing wave is composed of the forward-traveling or "incident" wave, expressed by Eqs. (12) and (13), and the backward-traveling or "reflected" wave, expressed by the forms of Eqs. (14) and (15) taken with the upper signs. We note that at $z = 0$, the boundary condition that the transverse electric field must vanish is fulfilled. We call th situation "standing-wave" in a very loose sense since Γ is complex in general. The various possible standing waves are shown in Fig. 2.

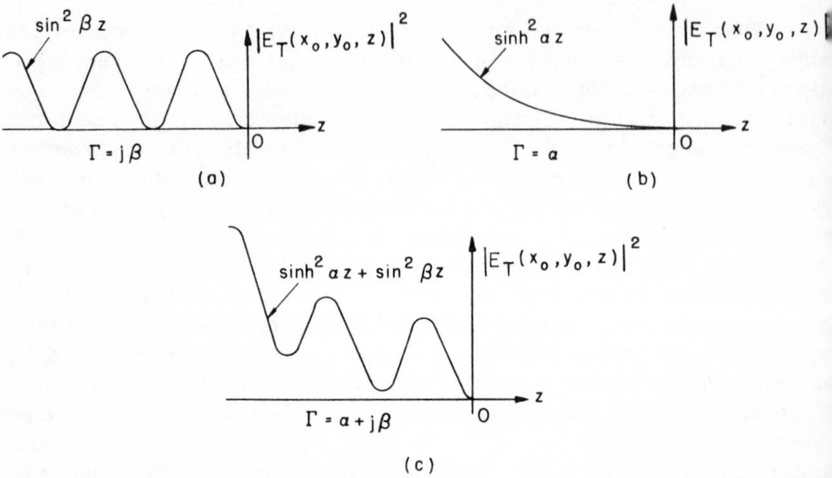

Fig. 2 Standing-wave patterns for (a) propagating, (b) cutoff, and (c) complex waves; z is the variable coordinate; x_o and y_o are fixed.

For lossless, passive, uniform waveguides, the integral form the complex Poynting's theorem requires that

$$\frac{\partial}{\partial z} \int \overline{E} \times \overline{H}^* \cdot \overline{i}_z \, da = -j\omega \int (\overline{H}^* \cdot \overline{\overline{\mu}} \cdot \overline{H} - \overline{E}^* \cdot \overline{\overline{\epsilon}} \cdot \overline{E}) \, da \, . \quad (2($$

The integrations extend over an entire waveguide cross section whos plane is located by the coordinate z. When we apply this form of Poynting's theorem to the fields of the standing wave, Eqs. (16) - (19 and when we let

$$\Gamma = \alpha + j\beta \, , \quad (2$$

we obtain the expression

$$\left[\alpha \cosh 2\alpha z + j\beta \cos 2\beta z\right] \underline{P} = j\omega\left[(U_m - U_e) \cosh 2\alpha z + (U_T - U_z) \cos 2\beta z\right. \quad (2$$

where

$$\underline{P} = \frac{1}{2} \int \hat{E}_T \times \hat{H}_T^* \cdot \overline{i}_z \, da = P + jQ \quad , \quad (2$$

$$U_m = \frac{1}{4} \int \hat{H}^* \cdot \bar{\bar{\mu}} \cdot \hat{H} \, da \quad , \tag{24}$$

$$U_e = \frac{1}{4} \int \hat{E}^* \cdot \bar{\bar{\epsilon}} \cdot \hat{E} \, da \quad , \tag{25}$$

$$U_T = U_{eT} + U_{mT} \quad , \tag{26}$$

$$U_z = U_{ez} + U_{mz} \quad , \tag{27}$$

$$U_{eT} = \frac{1}{4} \int \hat{E}_T^* \cdot \bar{\bar{\epsilon}}_T \cdot \hat{E}_T \, da \quad , \tag{28}$$

$$U_{mT} = \frac{1}{4} \int \hat{H}_T^* \cdot \bar{\bar{\mu}}_T \cdot \hat{H}_T \, da \quad , \tag{29}$$

$$U_{ez} = \frac{1}{4} \int \epsilon_{33} \, |\hat{E}_z|^2 \, da \quad , \tag{30}$$

$$U_{mz} = \frac{1}{4} \int \mu_{33} \, |\hat{H}_z|^2 \, da \quad . \tag{31}$$

The time-average, complex power carried by the incident wave is given by $\underline{P}$; this quantity is underscored to denote that in the general case it is complex; its real part is given by P and its imaginary part by Q. The quantity U_m is the time-average, magnetic pseudo energy stored per unit length in the incident wave; U_e is the similar electric quantity. The contribution of the transverse fields to the time-average pseudo energy stored per unit length in the incident wave is given by U_T, and the contribution of the longitudinal fields is given by U_z.

Since Eq. (22) must be valid for all z, we conclude that the four following relations must hold simultaneously:

$$\alpha P = 0 \quad , \tag{32}$$

$$\alpha Q = \omega(U_m - U_e) \quad , \tag{33}$$

$$\beta Q = 0 \quad , \tag{34}$$

$$\beta P = \omega(U_T - U_z) \quad . \tag{35}$$

From these relations we may state the general theorems listed in Table I for propagating, cutoff, and complex waves in uniform, lossless, passive, bidirectional waveguides.

We see that propagating waves carry pure real power, cutoff waves carry pure reactive power, and complex waves carry no power

Table I: Pseudo energy and power relations in bidirectional waveguides

Propagating Waves	$\Gamma = j\beta$	$\underline{P} = P$	$P = \frac{\omega}{\beta}(U_T - U_z)$	$U_m = U_e$
Cutoff Waves	$\Gamma = \alpha$	$\underline{P} = jQ$	$Q = \frac{\omega}{\alpha}(U_m - U_e)$	$U_T = U_z$
Complex Waves	$\Gamma = \alpha + j\beta$	$\underline{P} = 0$	$U_m = U_e$	$U_T = U_z$

at all, not even reactive. We also see that in propagating waves there is an equipartition between electric and magnetic pseudo energy, a well known result for nondispersive materials. In cutoff waves, there is an equipartition between transverse and longitudinal pseudo energy. And, in complex waves, there is an equipartition between electric and magnetic pseudo energy, as well as between transverse and longitudinal pseudo energy. We note for propagating waves ($\Gamma = j\beta$) that we may now express phase velocity ω/β in terms of the power flow and pseudo energy.

Only a few of the results in Table I have been shown previously for the special case of lossless, passive, nondispersive, isotropic media. Adler has shown that $\underline{P}$ is pure-real for propagating waves and pure-imaginary for cutoff waves.[14] He has also shown that Γ is either pure-real or pure-imaginary and is never complex. However, this rule cannot be extended to lossless, anisotropic media, and thus we must admit that complex propagation constants may exist when the material is anisotropic. Complex propagation constants have been calculated by Tai[15] for transversely magnetized, lossless, ferrite waveguides; however, his system is not bidirectional. But, because complex roots have been found for a lossless, passive, anisotropic waveguide, we should be cautious and examine lossless bidirectional waveguides for complex roots. Such an examination is conducted in the concluding sections of this paper.

IV. TRUE ENERGY AND GROUP VELOCITY IN LOSSLESS BIDIRECTIONAL WAVEGUIDES

An expression for the group velocity of a propagating wave is found from an energy theorem (see Ref. 10, Section V) which, for lossless, passive, uniform waveguides containing dispersive media, gives

$$\frac{\partial}{\partial z} \int \left[\overline{E}_T^* \times \frac{\partial \overline{H}_T}{\partial \omega} + \frac{\partial \overline{E}_T}{\partial \omega} \times \overline{H}_T^* \right] \cdot \overline{i}_z \, da$$

$$= -j \int \left[\overline{E}^* \cdot \overline{\overline{\epsilon}}_\omega \cdot \overline{E} + \overline{H}^* \cdot \overline{\overline{\mu}}_\omega \cdot \overline{H} \right] da \quad . \qquad (36)$$

The quantities $\overline{\overline{\epsilon}}_\omega$ and $\overline{\overline{\mu}}_\omega$ are forms of the permittivity and permeability that give the true time-average energy storage from the fields; they are given by

$$\overline{\overline{\epsilon}}_\omega = \frac{\partial}{\partial \omega} \left[\omega \overline{\overline{\epsilon}} \right] , \qquad (37)$$

$$\overline{\overline{\mu}}_\omega = \frac{\partial}{\partial \omega} \left[\omega \overline{\overline{\mu}} \right] . \qquad (38)$$

We note that for nondispersive media, $\overline{\overline{\epsilon}}_\omega$ and $\overline{\overline{\mu}}_\omega$ reduce to $\overline{\overline{\epsilon}}$ and $\overline{\overline{\mu}}$, respectively.[9-13]

When the fields of a purely propagating wave, given by Eqs. (12) and (13) with $\Gamma = j\beta$, are substituted into Eq. (36), we arrive at the result for the reciprocal of group velocity,

$$\frac{1}{v_g} = \frac{\partial \beta}{\partial \omega} = \frac{W}{P} \quad , \qquad (39)$$

where P is as previously given and W is the total time-average energy stored in the wave per unit length given by

$$W = W_e + W_m \quad , \qquad (40)$$

$$W_e = \frac{1}{4} \int \hat{E}^* \cdot \overline{\overline{\epsilon}}_\omega \cdot \hat{E} \, da \quad , \qquad (41)$$

$$W_m = \frac{1}{4} \int \hat{H}^* \cdot \overline{\overline{\mu}}_\omega \cdot \hat{H} \, da \quad . \qquad (42)$$

An interesting expression may be derived that relates group and phase velocity. From the results of Table I we have

$$P = \frac{\omega}{\beta} (U_T - U_z) \qquad (43)$$

which, when substituted into Eq. (39), yields

$$\frac{\partial \beta}{\partial \omega} = \frac{\beta}{\omega} \, \frac{W}{U_T - U_z} \quad . \qquad (44)$$

We note from Eq. (39) that the group velocity $\partial \omega / \partial \beta$ has the sign of the power flow, since W is always positive as it represents the true energy storage. Positive power flow corresponds to a transport of energy in the same direction as the propagation; negative power flow corresponds to a transport in the opposite direction. In waves with positive dispersion $(\partial \beta / \partial \omega > 0)$, we have the inequality $U_T - U_z > 0$ from Eq. (44); in a wave with negative dispersion, i. e., backward wave $(\partial \beta / \partial \omega < 0)$, we have $U_T - U_z < 0$.

From the theorem stated by Eq. (44), some interesting properties for particular types of bidirectional waveguides may be derived. With this theorem and those listed in Table I, we derive some general properties of a plasma waveguide in Section V.

V. SOME GENERAL PROPERTIES OF PLASMA WAVEGUIDES

As an illustration of the implications of the theorems presented here, we apply them to a waveguide that is completely filled with a uniform, cold, collisionless, longitudinally magnetized plasma. The cross section of the waveguide is arbitrary and the permittivity tensor is given by

$$\overline{\overline{\epsilon}} = \begin{bmatrix} \epsilon_1 & -j\epsilon_2 & 0 \\ j\epsilon_2 & \epsilon_1 & 0 \\ 0 & 0 & \epsilon_3 \end{bmatrix} , \quad (47)$$

where

$$\epsilon_1 = \epsilon_0 \left[1 + \frac{\omega_p^2}{\omega_c^2 - \omega^2} \right] , \quad (48)$$

$$\epsilon_2 = \epsilon_0 \frac{\omega_c}{\omega} \frac{\omega_p^2}{\omega_c^2 - \omega^2} , \quad (49)$$

$$\epsilon_3 = \epsilon_0 \left[1 - \frac{\omega_p^2}{\omega^2} \right] , \quad (50)$$

when the motion of the plasma ions is neglected. The plasma frequen is denoted by ω_p, and the cyclotron frequency is denoted by ω_c. Th permeability is the scalar μ_0.

We must bear in mind that for such a waveguiding system, the modes do not separate into TE and TM solutions, and in general, they simultaneously possess both transverse and longitudinal components of the E and H fields.[1-3] Thus we have all of the pseudo-energy quantities: U_{eT}, U_{mT}, U_{ez}, and U_{mz}.

We note that ϵ_3 is negative for $\omega < \omega_p$ and positive for $\omega > \omega_p$; thus U_{ez} is negative for $\omega < \omega_p$ and positive for $\omega > \omega_p$. Now U_{mT} is always positive; W is also always positive, since it can be shown that $\bar{\bar{\epsilon}}_\omega$ is a positive definite quadratic form. Since U_{ez} is negative for $\omega < \omega_p$ and U_{mT} is always positive, then the quantity $U_{mT} - U_{ez}$ is always positive for $\omega < \omega_p$, and we conclude from Eq. (46) that *if* β *exists for* $\omega < \omega_p$, *then*

$$\frac{\partial \beta}{\partial \omega} > 0 \;;$$

that is to say, $\beta(\omega)$ always has a positive slope for $\omega < \omega_p$. This result is substantiated by the quasi-static solutions[6,7] and by the curves of Schumann.[16]

Next we consider the possibility of the existence of complex propagation constants. We note from Table I the necessary pseudo-energy relations that must be satisfied for complex roots to exist, namely

$$\left.\begin{aligned} U_T &= U_z \\ \text{and} \qquad U_m &= U_e \end{aligned}\right\} \; . \tag{51}$$

This pair of expressions can be manipulated to give an equivalent pair

$$\left.\begin{aligned} U_{eT} &= U_{mz} \\ U_{mT} &= U_{ez} \end{aligned}\right\} \; , \tag{52}$$

which must be simultaneously satisfied for complex Γ. Now since U_{ez} is negative for $\omega < \omega_p$ and positive for $\omega > \omega_p$, and U_{mT} is always positive, then we conclude that *if complex propagation constants exist, they must occur for* $\omega > \omega_p$.

On the basis of these theorems, it is also possible to deduce the field structure of a wave for particular conditions. Suppose we have a cutoff, $\beta = 0$, for some frequency ω_0 such that $0 < \omega_0 < \omega_p$. Then at the cutoff frequency ω_0 the pseudo-energy conditions that must be met are the same as for complex roots and are given by Eq. (52). This follows from an examination of Eqs. (32) through (35). We conclude that at this cutoff frequency a longitudinal E field cannot exist since U_{ez} would be negative if it did exist. Consequently, the transverse H field vanishes and the field is composed of merely a longitudinal H field and a transverse E field. This is indeed true, as can be shown from the exact field solution.[1,2,3]

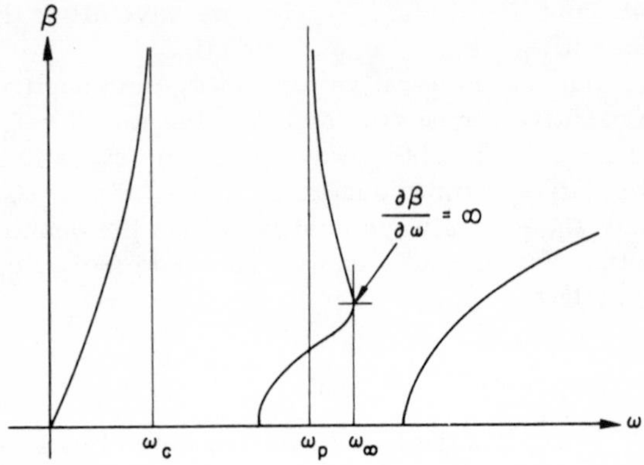

Fig. 3 Sketch of non-quasistatic plasma-waveguide dispersion

Other results may be derived from these theorems. One that poses an interesting question is now discussed. Some recent computations performed by Wang and Hopson[17] indicate that $\partial\beta/\partial\omega = \infty$, for finite β under certain conditions. A dispersion relation showing this behavior is sketched in Fig. 3; the frequency at which $\partial\beta/\partial\omega = \infty$ is denoted by ω_∞. The modes under consideration are the circularly symmetric ones that occur in the plasma-filled circular waveguide; these modes do not exhibit Faraday rotation because of their degenerate symmetry. It seems that this behavior $(\partial\beta/\partial\omega = \infty)$ is exhibited when the cutoff frequency of the empty-waveguide TM_{01} mode becomes comparable to or less than either ω_p or ω_c, depending upon which is greater.

At ω_∞ we have the pseudo-energy relations given by Eqs. (51) and (52), which are the same as those needed for complex propagation constants. We reach this conclusion from Eq. (44) because we must have $U_T = U_z$ in order that $\partial\beta/\partial\omega = \infty$ for finite β and finite energy storage W. The question is now posed: is this the onset of a complex propagation constant ? Apparently, only direct computation can completely answer this question; such computations have not been performed, to the author's knowledge.[18] But an argument based on the nature of mode coupling[19] would indicate that this is the onset of complex roots, i. e., complex roots on a frequency band, the lower bound of which is ω_{co}. Presumably the modes that are coupled are the backward wave, which we have from the quasistatic analysis, and the empty waveguide mode whose cutoff frequency is less than, say, the plasma frequency.

The coupling of modes is sketched in Fig. 4. The originally

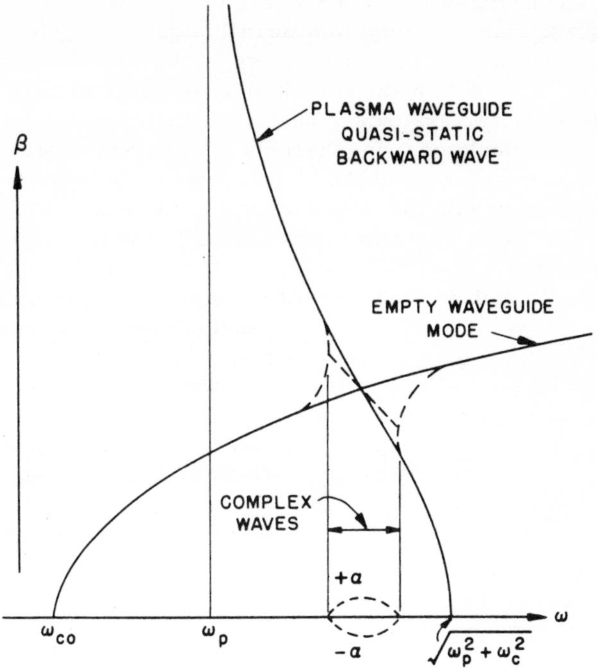

Fig. 4 Weak coupling of empty-waveguide mode with quasistatic, plasma-waveguide, backward wave; ω_{co} is the cutoff frequency of the empty-waveguide TM mode.

unperturbed separate modes are indicated by solid lines. The perturbations due to mode coupling are indicated by broken lines. In the region where the two unperturbed modes are synchronous, complex waves are shown. The imaginary part of Γ (i.e., β) is approximately the arithmetic mean between the two unperturbed modes, according to the theory of weak coupling. The values of the real parts (i.e., $\pm\alpha$) are small compared with β for weak coupling.

According to the theory of coupling of modes, these modes couple to give complex roots. However, we invoke this principle in a heuristic manner here: the coupling of modes theory cannot be used to obtain quantitative results, since being a first-order theory, it applies to weak coupling, and we obviously have very strong coupling. But from the points of view of both the pseudo-energy theorems and coupling of modes, there is a strong suspicion aroused that the plasma-filled waveguide exhibits complex propagation constants.

To illustrate that complex propagation constants are possible in lossless, passive, bidirectional waveguides, we consider the composite waveguiding system shown in Fig. 5. We have a plasma-filled waveguide coupled through a uniform slot in the wall to a large empty waveguide. We choose the cutoff frequency of the plasma waveguide, when it is empty and unslotted, to be very large compared with $(\omega_p^2 + \omega_c^2)^{1/2}$; thus the quasi-static solution is valid in this sub-waveguide. We choose the cutoff frequency of the large empty waveguide, when it is unslotted to be below ω_p. With a sufficiently narrow slot, we have weak coupling between the two systems. The interaction between the two systems may be calculated from Pierce's coupling-of-modes theory. Because the backward wave of the plasma waveguide is synchronous at a certain frequency with the forward wave of the empty waveguide, they couple to give complex propagation constants for the composite system as shown in Fig. 4.

It should be noted that complex roots are not peculiar to lossless passive waveguides containing plasmas. They arise whenever backward-wave structures are coupled to forward-wave structures. We recall, from the theorems in Table I, that complex waves carry zero net power. Thus there is no violation of power conservation even though the fields may be growing (decaying) exponentially with z. The local Poynting vector in some portions of the cross section of a waveguiding system grows (decays) exponentially with z and carries power in the direction of propagation. However, the local Poynting vector in other portions also grows (decays) exponentially with z, but it carries power in the opposite direction. The forward power flux and the backward power flux are equal so that the net power flow is zero. When we have a complex propagation constant that would indicate exponentially growing (decaying) fields in the composite waveguide of Fig. 5, power grows (decays) exponentially with z and flows in the forward direction in the large empty sub-waveguide. However, an equal amount grows (decays) exponentially with z in the plasma sub-waveguide and flows in the backward direction, so that the total power flow across the entire cross section of the composite waveguide is zero.

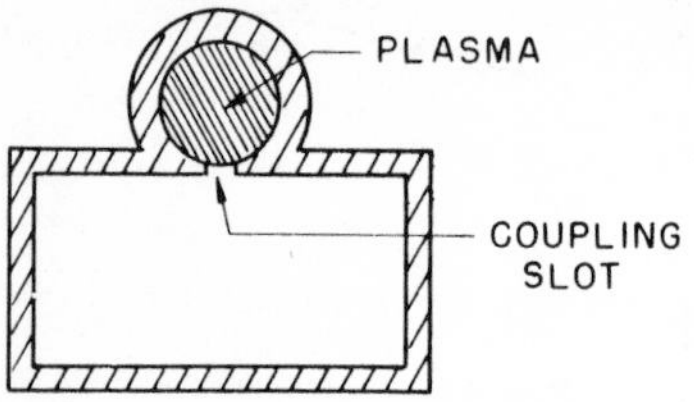

Fig. 5 Cross section of a plasma-filled waveguide coupled to a large, empty waveguide through a uniform, narrow slot

VI. DISCUSSION

We pointed out the existence of the general class of uniform waveguides, which we called bidirectional because it is possible to excite in them modes that propagate with the same dispersion in either direction; these waveguides, incidentally, are not necessarily reciprocal. For bidirectional waveguides that are lossless and passive, we obtained the theorems presented in Table I. These results were derivable because it is possible to set up standing waves in bidirectional waveguides. It is very interesting that the examination of a standing wave leads to new information about the individual traveling waves that comprise the standing wave.

For dispersive media we differentiated between true energy storage and that which we defined as pseudo energy. The discrepancies between these were first noted by Brillouin[9] who, for the case of dispersive isotropic dielectrics, explained that the difference was due to the kinetic energy stored in the motion of the bound charges. A similar explanation holds, of course, for general anisotropic dispersive materials where the difference manifests itself in the kinetic energy stored in the mechanical vibrations of the electric and magnetic dipoles.

It is well known that group velocity can be expressed in terms of the true energy storage and the power flow in a purely propagating wave, as in Eq. (39).[9, 12] We pointed out here that phase velocity can be expressed in terms of pseudo energy and power flow. As a result, we were able to derive a useful theorem relating group velocity and phase velocity directly through the true energy and the pseudo energy. Other useful results were the theorems on equipartition of pseudo energy in cutoff and complex waves.

The theorems were applied to a plasma-filled waveguide in order to illustrate their use in interpreting the dispersion character. Particularly, it was shown that when $\partial\beta/\partial\omega = \infty$ for finite β, the equipartitions of pseudo energy suggested that this condition might indicate the onset of complex roots. It was argued heuristically that the coupling-of-modes theory supports the suspicion of the onset of complex propagation constants.

From the illustrative example of the plasma waveguide we have demonstrated some of the applications of the bidirectional waveguide theorems. As shown, these theorems add some insight and intuition to the nature of propagation phenomena. As a result, they aid in interpreting computations and in making qualitative predictions of dispersion characteristics.

ACKNOWLEDGMENT

The author is grateful to Professor L. D. Smullin for his encouragement and supervision and to Professors W. P. Allis and H. A. Haus for their helpful suggestions.

REFERENCES

1. H. Gamo, "The Faraday Rotation of Waves in a Circular Waveguide," *J. Phys. Soc. Japan*, Vol. 8, pp. 176-182 (March-April 1953).

2. A.A. Th. M. VanTrier, "Guided Electromagnetic Waves in Anisotropic Media," *Appl. Sci. Res.*, Sec. B, Vol. 3, pp. 305-371 (1953).

3. H. Suhl and L. R. Walker, "Topics in Guided-Wave Propagation through Gyromagne-

tic Media, Part I – The Completely Filled Cylindrical Guide," *Bell Sys. Tech. J.*, Vol. 33, pp. 579-659 (May 1954).

4. H. Suhl and L. R. Walker, "Topics in Guided-Wave Propagation through Gyromagnetic Media, Part III – Perturbation Theory and Miscellaneous Results," *Bell Sys. Tech. J.*, Vol. 33, pp. 1133-1194 (September 1954).

5. A. D. Berk, "Variational Principles for Electromagnetic Resonators and Waveguides," *Trans. I.R.E.*, Vol. AP-4, pp. 104-111 (April 1956).

6. A. W. Trivelpiece and R. W. Gould, "Space Charge Waves in Cylindrical Plasma Columns," *J. Appl. Phys.*, Vol. 30, pp. 1784-1793 (November 1959).

7. L. D. Smullin and P. Chorney, "Propagation in Ion Load Waveguides," *Proceedings of the Symposium on Electronic Waveguides*, (New York: Polytechnic Press, April 1958) pp. 229-247.

8. A. T. Villeneuve, "Orthogonality Relationships for Waveguides and Cavities with Inhomogeneous Anisotropic Media," *Trans. I.R.E.*, Vol. MTT-7, pp. 441-446 (October 1959).

9. L. Brillouin, "Wave Propagation and Group Velocity," (New York: Academic Press, Inc., 1960).

10. A. Tonning, "Energy Density in Continuous Electromagnetic Media," *Trans. I.R.E.*, Vol. AP-8, pp. 428-434 (July 1960).

11. T. Hosono and T. Ohira, "The Electromagnetic Energy in a Dispersive Medium," *Proc. I.R.E.*, Vol. 48, pp. 247-248 (February 1960).

12. S. M. Rytov, "Some Theorems on the Group Velocity of Electromagnetic Waves," *J. Experimental and Theoretical Phys.* (U.S.S.R.), Vol. 17, pp. 930-936 (1947).

13. P. L. Auer, H. Hurwitz, Jr., and R. D. Miller, "Collective Oscillations in a Cold Plasma," Report No. 58-RL-2020, General Electric Research Laboratory (August 1958).

14. R. B. Adler, "Properties of Guided Waves in Inhomogeneous Cylindrical Structures," Tech. Rep. 102, Research Laboratory of Electronics, Massachusetts Institute of Technology (May 27, 1949).

15. C. T. Tai, "Evanescent Modes in a Partially Filled Gyromagnetic Rectangular Waveguide," *J. Appl. Phys.*, Vol. 31, pp. 220-221 (January 1960).

16. W. O. Schumann, "Uber Wellenausbreitung in Plasma zwischen zwei unendlich gut Leitenden Ebenen in Richtung eines aufgepragten aussern Magnetfeldes," *Z. angew. Phys.*, Vol. 8, pp. 482-485 (1956).

17. C. C. Wang and J. E. Hopson, "Electromagnetic Wave Propagation in Gyro-Electric Plasmas," Sperry Gyroscope Co., Second Scientific Report, Contract No. AF19 (604)-5555 (April 1960).

18. Computations showing the existence of complex propagation constants have been made since the presentation of this paper (P. Chorney "Power and Energy Relations in Bidirectional Waveguides," Sc. D. Thesis, Massachusetts Institute of Technology, August, 1961).

19. J.R. Pierce, "Coupling of Modes of Propagation," *J. Appl. Phys.*, Vol.25, pp. 179-183 (February 1954).

INTERACTION BETWEEN MAGNETIC FIELDS AND MOVING PLASMAS*

W. H. Bostick
Department of Physics,
Stevens Institute of Technology
Hoboken, New Jersey

Experimental results and theoretical descriptive models will be given for various configurations where plasmas move in magnetic fields, with and without a background conducting medium. Constant velocity, accelerated motion and flute type instabilities will be discussed.

I. BEHAVIOR OF PLASMOIDS IN A MAGNETIC FIELD IN VACUUM

Loss of Plasma by a Plasmoid as It Proceeds Across a Magnetic Field

A plasmoid[1, 2] produced by firing a pulsed plasma gun across a magnetic field in a good vacuum has the general shape shown in Fig. 1(a). A program of precise measurements of the ion (and electron) density distributions n(x, y, z, t) has never been carried out, but a reasonable set of ion density distributions is indicated in Fig. 1. Measurements have shown that the plasmoid expands rapidly in the z-direction. As time passes, this expansion, of course, reduces the value of n(x, y, z, t), as will the ion-electron recombination. This reduction of n(x, y, z, t) has been indicated in Fig. 1(a) at a time $t_2 > t_1$. The scale of the distribution, h_z, in the z direction increases. The rate of increase of h_z, $\dot{h}_z$, essentially characterizes a one-dimensional explosion in the z direction. Measurements show that the scale of the distributions in the x and y directions, h_x and h_y, remain relatively constant for a period of about 10 microseconds, at least, while h_z typically increases from about 0.5 cm to 50 cm within this interval of time. The relative constancy of h_x and h_y indicates that the electron temperature is about $5 \times 10^5\ ^\circ K = 50ev$ since $1/\sigma = 1.29 \times 10^2\ Z(\ell n\Lambda)/T^{3/2}$ ohm meters $= 4 \times 10^2/T^{3/2}$ ohm meters and since the penetration distance of the plasma into the field, and vice versa, $b = (t/\mu\sigma)^{1/2}$. Also in the cases experimentally observed, $b < 0.3$ cm for $t = 2 \times 10^{-5}$ sec. The ratio of diffusion rates parallel and perpendicular to the field can be estimated from existing experi-

*Work supported by AFOSR, AFCRC and AEC.

Presented at the Symposium on Electromagnetics and Fluid Dynamics of Gaseous Plasma, Polytechnic Institute of Brooklyn, April 4, 5, 6, 1961

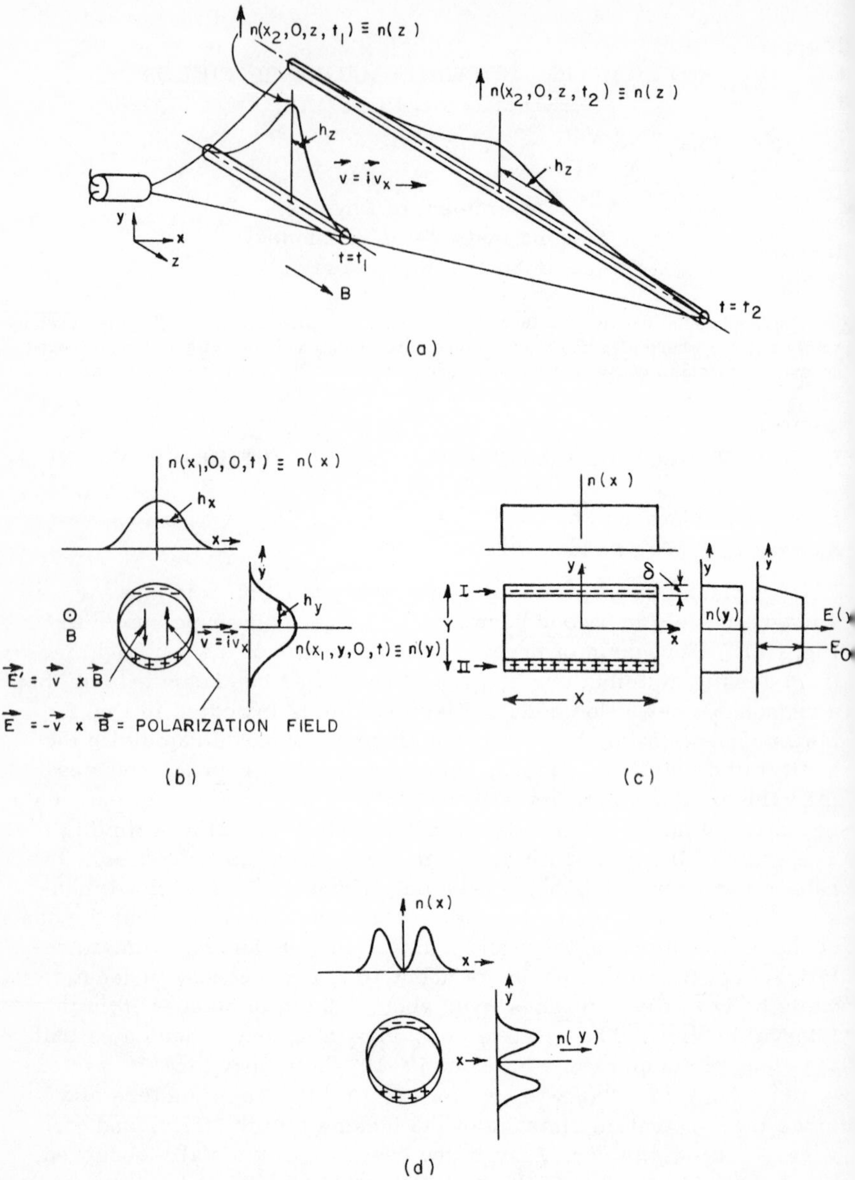

Fig. 1. (a) General shape of a plasmoid as it is projected across a magnetic field with a velocity $\vec{i}v_x$; (b) Cross section of a plasmoid with polarization; (c) Idealized cross section of plasmoid; (d) Plasma density distribution as suggested in certain experiments where the plasma loop current from the two-wire button source produces a magnetic field which opposes the dc field.

ments on plasmoids to be at least about 200. From these experiments it appears that within a well formed plasmoid, no flute-type instabilities are operative to augment the expansion of the plasma across the field, and that diffusion processes alone govern the expansion of the plasmoid in x and y directions. Coupling-loop measurements of the magnetic field reduction within the plasmoid in the region C of Fig. 2, indicate that the value of $\beta = \left[nkt/(B^2/2\mu)\right]$ is less than one per cent at most. This low value of β, coupled with the fact that the plasmoid is free to expand in the z direction, makes it extremely improbable that flute-type instabilities would occur.

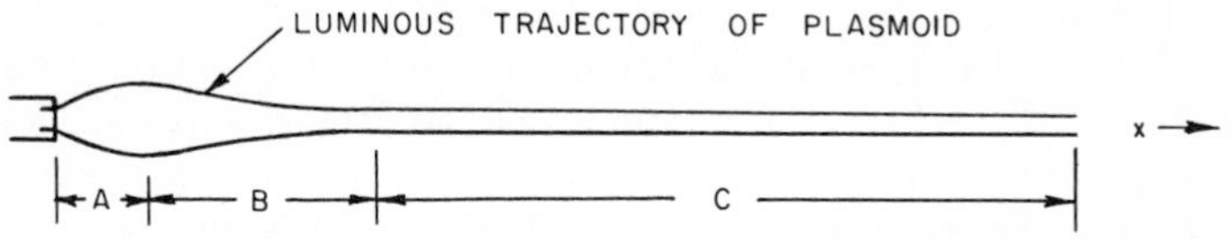

Fig. 2. Luminous trajectory of a plasmoid obtained by a time-exposure photograph of the passage of a plasmoid across the magnetic field. The camera is pointed in the z direction and focused on the z= 0 plane. Light from the luminous trajectory endures for several microseconds after the plasmoid has passed.

Some measurements on certain plasmoids formed by a two-wire button source where the current loop from the source produces a magnetic field opposing the dc magnetic field, suggest that the plasma density distributions n(x) and n(y), are those given in Fig. 1(d). Since this more complex phenomenon is not well understood, we shall consider only simpler distributions n(x) and n(y) of the type shown in Fig. 1(b).

Time-exposure photographs taken in the z direction of the passage of a plasmoid across the magnetic field show the pattern of luminosity diagrammed in Fig. 2. The pattern of luminosity endures for several microseconds after the plasmoid has passed. The luminosity represents the presence, for several microseconds, of a relatively stationary plasma that can give some recombination light and whose electrons can produce the excitation in the residual gases. To this plasma, which is left behind the plasmoid and which gives a luminous trajectory of the plasmoid, we owe a considerable debt of gratitude because the phenomenon enables us to follow experimentally the track of plasmoids by a simple photographic technique. Furthermore, the spacing of the two lines of luminosity left by the plasmoid, as shown in Fig. 2, is indicative of the dimension of the plasmoid in the y direction, and thus records a history of the size of the plasmoid.

The initial shaping of the plasmoid during its formation at the gun and its breakaway from the gun takes place in region A of Fig. 2. This complex process has scarcely been studied experimentally. One can only surmise what happens in region A. In region B, the diameter of the plasmoid apparently decreases with time as it proceeds in the x direction. This decrease in diameter is to be expected because of the decrease of the ion density n at z= 0 due to the rapid expansion in the z direction. In region C, the plasmoid seems to retain approximately the same diameter. One can interpret this to mean that the value of n at z= 0 continues to decrease (but not so rapidly as in region B) and the electron temperature remains high enough to cut diffusion across the magnetic field to a very low value.

Although the analysis of the y-dimension of the plasmoid as a function of time would provide a very interesting problem in plasma physics, our limited objective here is to examine the process whereby the plasmoid leaves behind the two tracks of plasma as it traverses the magnetic field in a good vacuum (= 10^{-5} mm Hg). The pattern of luminosity left behind when a plasmoid passes through a conducting medium provided by an ionized gas at about 10^{-3} mm Hg pressure, where braking currents and deflecting Hall currents can flow, is still a different problem.

As indicated in Fig. 1(b), a plasmoid with a roughly circular cross section, moving across the field $\vec{B} = \vec{j}B_z$ with a velocity $\vec{v} = \vec{i}\,v_x$, generates an electric field $\vec{E}' = -\vec{j}E_y = \vec{v} \times \vec{B}$ in the moving frame in which the plasmoid is immersed. The plasmoid that is a conductor will obviously polarize almost immediately so as to eliminate the electric field within it by adding to $\vec{E}'$ the polarization field $\vec{E} = \vec{j}E_y$ which, inside the plasmoid, is the field observed in the laboratory frame of reference.

It is this field $\vec{E}$ in the laboratory frame which enables both positive ions and electrons to perform their trochoidal drift

$$\vec{v} = (\vec{E} \times \vec{B})/B^2$$

in the x direction. Most of the population of the plasmoid as seen from the laboratory frame enjoys this same electric field $\vec{E}$ and hence is able to execute the trochoidal drift. In the highly idealized plasmoid of Fig. 1(c), where fringing effects of the polarization field $\vec{E}$ are assumed to be negligible ($X >> Y$) and where the ion density distributions in the x and y directions are cut off very sharply, there are the regions I and II where the polarization charges have accumulated. The plot of the polarization electric field $\vec{E}(y)$ is given in Fig. 1(c), from which it can be seen that ions and electrons in this layer do not have the full value of $\vec{E}$ to permit them to have the full drift velocity $\vec{v} = (\vec{E} \times \vec{B})/B^2$. For example, the plasma on the extreme outer layers of regions I and II will have a drift velocity of zero; the plasma with a y coordinate corresponding to the center points of the regions will have a drift velocity of $\vec{v}/2$, etc. The thickness of these regions, for the idealized case of Fig. 1(c) is, by the Gaussian theorem, related to E by

$$ne\delta = \epsilon_o E \quad \text{or} \quad \delta = \frac{\epsilon_o E}{ne} = \frac{\epsilon_o vB}{ne} .$$

The rate of loss of plasma from the plasmoid can then be computed by assuming that half the plasma in regions I and II is lost in the plasmoid's traversal of its own width in the x direction. Thus

$$XY \frac{dn}{dt} = XY \frac{dn}{dx}\frac{dx}{dt} = XY \frac{dn}{dx} v = -n\delta v,$$

or

$$n = n_o e^{-\frac{\delta vt}{XY}} = n_o e^{-\frac{\delta x}{XY}}$$

With typical numbers;

$$n = 10^{12}/cm^3 = 10^{18}/m^3,$$

$$v = 4 \times 10^6 \text{ cm/sec} = 4 \times 10^4 \text{ m/sec},$$

$$B = 10^4 \text{ gauss} = 1 \text{ W/m}^2,$$

$$\delta = \frac{10^{-9} \times 4 \times 10^4}{36\pi \times 10^{18} \times 1.6 \times 10^{-19}} \cong 2.5 \times 10^{-6} m = 2.5 \times 10^{-4} cm.$$

This value of δ is very small, and a plasmoid with a dimension Y = 1 cm would have to traverse a distance

$$x = X/(2.5 \times 10^{-4}) = 4000 X$$

in order to drop to 1/e of its original ion density. It is now obvious that the original assumption that all of the plasma was moving across the field with the same velocity $\vec{v}$ is only an approximation because the plasma in layers I and II is left behind. The problem must be solved in a self-consistent manner by a series of approximations. For the second step in the solution by approximation, one can start with the distribution for $E_1(y)$ produced by Fig. 1(c), which results in the second-approximation velocity distribution $v_1(y)$ shown in Fig. 3. This new velocity distribution which can be expected to alter the polarization field to something like $E_{11}(y)$, will further alter the velocity distribution to $v_{11}(y)$ as shown, etc. Although we have not attempted a quantitative treatment of these approximations, it is apparent that the effective value of δ will be larger than that given by $\delta = \epsilon_o E/ne$.

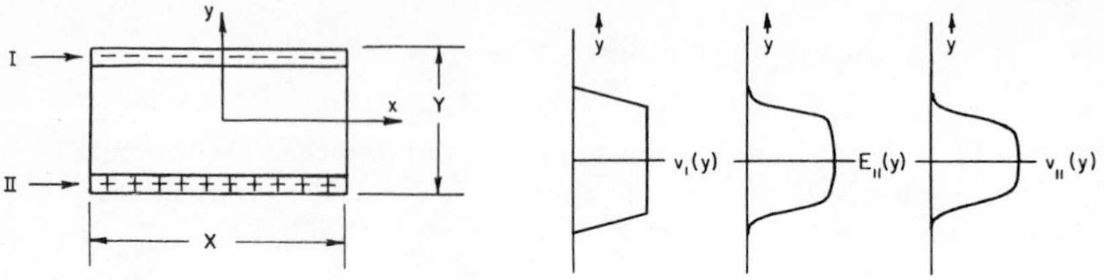

Fig. 3. Successive approximations in the calculation of E(y) and v(y)

As the plasma in layers I and II is left behind, more positive charge is lost from layer II and more negative charge is lost from layer I, thereby constituting a current density $\vec{j}$. The current density provides a $\vec{j} \times \vec{B}$ force density which is a retarding force on the motion of the plasma across the magnetic field. In principle, this retarding force can slightly reduce the speed of the plasmoid as a whole or can drastically change the speed of the small fraction of the plasmoid that occupies regions I and II. This retarding force is much smaller in magnitude than that which occurs when the plasmoid proceeds through a conducting medium formed by an ionized gas at a pressure of about 10^{-3} mm Hg. In this latter case, the braking currents can drastically reduce the velocity of the plasmoid as a whole and can bring about deflection of the plasmoid into a spiral trajectory through the Hall currents that flow.

The magnitude of the retarding current density $\vec{j}$ when the plasmoid proceeds in a good vacuum can be calculated as follows: If ρ_S is the surface charge density in region I or II in Fig. 1(c), $\epsilon_0 E = \rho_S$, and

$$j = \rho_S v = \epsilon_0 E_0 v = \epsilon_0 v^2 B = \frac{10^{-9}}{36\pi} \times 16 \times 10^8 \times 1$$

$$\cong 1.4 \times 10^{-2} \text{ amps/m}^2,$$

$$\text{for } v = 4 \times 10^4 \text{ m/sec and } B = 1\text{W/m}^2.$$

The force density $\vec{j} \times \vec{B} = \epsilon_0 v^2 B^2$.

Then

$$\frac{dv}{dt} = - \frac{\epsilon_0 v^2 B^2}{nm_i},$$

the solution of which gives

$$\frac{1}{v} - \frac{1}{v_o} = \frac{v_o - v}{v\,v_o} = \frac{\epsilon_o B^2}{nm_i}\, t \; .$$

For a plasmoid made primarily of Ti or Cu ions where

$$m_i \cong 10^{-22}\ \text{gms} = 10^{-25}\ \text{kg, for } t = 10^{-5}\ \text{sec, } v \cong v_o,$$

$$\frac{\Delta v}{v_o} = \frac{v_o - v}{v_o} = \frac{v\epsilon_o B^2 t}{nm_i} = \frac{4 \times 10^4 \times 10^{-9} \times 1 \times 10^{-5}}{10^{18} \times 10^{-25} \times 36\pi} \cong 4 \times 10^{-5},$$

which is a very small fractional reduction in velocity.

If the retarding force $\vec{j} \times \vec{B}$ does not retard the plasmoid as a whole but, on the average, changes the drift velocity v of half the ions and electrons in layers I and II from v to zero, then

$$\vec{j} \times \vec{B} = \epsilon_o v^2 B^2 = nm_i\, \delta(\Delta v)\, v = nm_i\, \delta v^2,$$

or

$$\delta = \frac{\epsilon_o B^2}{nm_i} = \frac{10^{-9}}{36\pi} \times \frac{1}{10^{18} \times 10^{-25}} = \frac{10^{-2}}{36\pi}$$

$$\cong 10^{-4}\ \text{m} = 10^{-2}\ \text{cm},$$

which is to be compared with the value of 2.5×10^{-4} cm given by $\delta = \epsilon_o E/ne$. Indeed the two values of δ can be equal only if $v = eB/m_i = \omega_i$; or if the gyrofrequency of the positive ion is numerically equal to the drift velocity. This condition would correspond to

$$v = \frac{1.6 \times 10^{-19} \times 1}{10^{-25}} = 1.6 \times 10^6\ \text{m/sec.}$$

The ion density n must be greater than a certain minimum if the plasma is to proceed across the magnetic field as a whole and not as individual charged particles. The limiting value of n is given by

$$E = \frac{ne\delta}{\epsilon_o} \geqslant |\vec{v} \times \vec{B}| \, ,$$

or

$$n \geqslant \frac{\epsilon_o vB}{e\delta}$$

where δ must be less than Y, the transverse dimension of the plasmoid.

The model of Fig. 1(c) which we have used in these calculations is highly idealized. A realistic experimental approach to the determination of the value of δ would be by photographic means to measure carefully the thickness of each of the pairs of lines in photographs such as those represented by Fig. 2. An earnest attempt should be made to put this type of measurement on a quantitative basis. In the meantime, it is possible to take a more realistic theoretical approach to the determination of δ than we have thus far done.

First, let us observe that δ can never be smaller than the gyroradius of the electron

$$r_e = \frac{m_e v_e}{eB} \cong \frac{10^{-30} \times 1.8 \times 10^{6}}{1.6 \times 10^{-19} \times 1} = 10^{-5}\,\mathrm{m} = 10^{-3}\,\mathrm{cm}$$

for a 10 ev electron. Thus this calculated value of r_e is somewhat greater than the value of $\delta = \epsilon_o E/ne$. However r_e should be considered a lower limit of δ. One might at first sight consider δ also to be lower-limited by r_i, the gyroradius of the positive ions. For an ion velocity,

$$v_i \cong 10^{7}\,\mathrm{cm/sec} = 10^{5}\,\mathrm{m/sec},$$

$$r_i = \frac{m_i v_i}{eB} = \frac{10^{-25} \times 10^{5}}{1.6 \times 10^{-19}} = 0.06\ \mathrm{m} = 6\ \mathrm{cm}.$$

However, the photographic measurements indicate that δ is about 0.1 cm, and it is thus obvious that space-charge effects can be more influential than the ion Larmor radius in producing the thickness of a layer.

The value of δ cannot be less than the Debye length

$$r_o = \left[\frac{kT}{4\pi e^2 n}\right]^{1/2} = 6.9\left[\frac{T}{n}\right]^{1/2}\ \mathrm{cm}$$

where T is given in ^{o}K and n in cm^{-3}. Thus, for our case,

$$n = 10^{12}/\mathrm{cm}^3 \text{ and } T \cong 10^{5},$$

$$r_o = 6.9 \times \left[\frac{10^{5}}{10^{12}}\right]^{1/2} = 21 \times 10^{-4}\ \mathrm{cm} = 2.1 \times 10^{-3}\ \mathrm{cm}$$

for the plane layer of Fig. 1(c). For a cylindrical plasmoid, δ would be about twice as great. The value 2.1×10^{-3} cm is an order of magnitude greater that $\delta = \epsilon_0 E/ne = 2.5 \times 10^{-4}$ cm, and is comparable to the Larmor radius of the electron.

If we now compute the rate of attrition of the plasmoid's population on the basis of $\delta = r_0 = 6.9\ (T/n)^{1/2}$ cm for Fig. 1(c),

$$XY \frac{dn}{dt} = - n\delta v = - 6.9\ T^{1/2}\, n^{-1/2} v,$$

or

$$n_0^{1/2} - n^{1/2} = \frac{3.45\ T^{1/2}\ vt}{XY}.$$

Thus for $t = 10^{-5}$ sec, $T = 10^5$ °K, $v = 4 \times 10^6$ cm/sec, and $n_0 = 10^{12}$/cm,

$$n_0^{1/2} - n^{1/2} = 3.45 \times 3 \times 10^2 \times 4 \times 10^6 \times 10^{-5} = 4 \times 10^4$$

Obviously, $n_0 \cong n$, and hence

$$(n_0^{1/2} - n^{1/2})(n_0^{1/2} + n^{1/2}) \cong 4 \times 10^4 \times 2\, n_0^{1/2},$$

or

$$n_0 - n \cong 8 \times 10^{10}, \quad \text{and} \quad \frac{n_0 - n}{n} \cong 0.08.$$

Thus even with this larger value of δ given by the Debye length, the proportional loss of plasma population by making the track is small in an interval of time of 10^{-5} sec.

The magnitude of δ might be also estimated to be equal to or greater than the thickness of the Rosenbluth or Ferraro sheath, which is somewhat greater than the Debye length. However

$$\beta = nkT/(B^2/2\mu_0)$$

is much less than 1 for the plasmoids with which we have experimental experience, and Rosenbluth sheaths are usually calculated for circumstances where $\beta \rightarrow 1$. At any rate we should be able to state that for the values of $n = 10^{12}/cm^3$ and $T = 10^5$ °K, the lower limit to the value of δ must be about 2×10^{-3} cm.

Let us now consider the cylindrically shaped plasmoid Fig. 1(b) instead of the idealized geometry of Fig. 1(c). In the plasmoid frame of reference, the plasmoid is placed in the electric field $\vec{v} \times \vec{B}$. Since it is a conductor, it polarizes so that the electric field within it is zero and the potential inside it is constant. The resultant electric field pattern in the plasma and in the laboratory frames of reference are shown in Figs. 4(a) and (b).

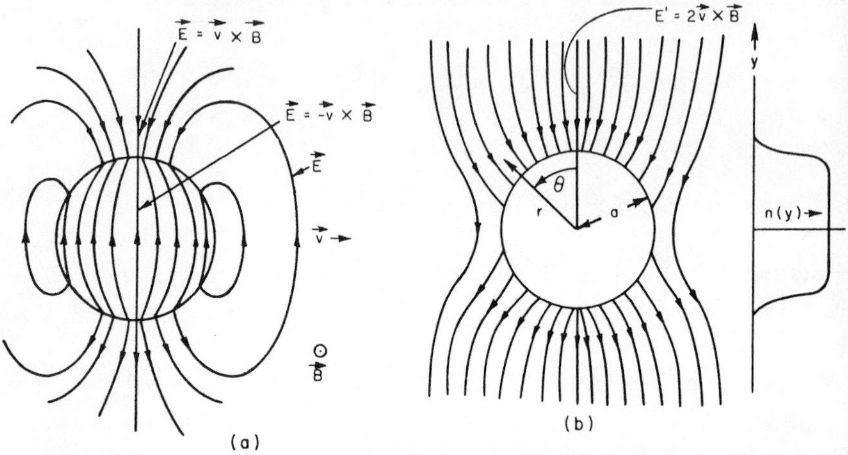

Fig. 4. (a) Electric field $\vec{E}$ in and surrounding the plasmoid in the laboratory frame of reference; (b) Electric field $\vec{E}'$in the plasmoid frame of reference

If the potential ϕ on the cylindrical plasmoid* is considered to be zero, then in the plasmoid frame of reference outside the cylinder,

$$\phi = E_o r \cos\theta \left[1 - \frac{a^2}{r^2}\right],$$

with the coordinates as indicated and

$$E'_r = -\frac{\partial\phi}{\partial r} = E_o \cos(1 + a^2/r^2)$$

$$E'_\theta = -\frac{1}{r}\frac{\partial\phi}{\partial\theta} = E_o \sin\theta\,(1-a^2/r^2)$$

and the surface charge

$$\rho_s = \frac{2\epsilon}{4\pi} E_o \cos\theta$$

where ϵ_o is the dielectric constant. The resultant drift velocity $\vec{v}'$ in the plasmoid frame of reference is then $\vec{v}' = (\vec{E}' \times \vec{B})/B^2$

*This analysis has been given by Hillman Dickinson of Stevens Institute of Technology.

At $r = a$ and $\theta = \pi/2$,

$$E' = 0 \quad \text{and} \quad v' = 0,$$

and the plasma is expected to move along with the plasmoid. However, for $\theta = 0$ and $r = a$,

$$E' = 2E_o \quad \text{and} \quad \vec{v}' = -\frac{2\vec{E}_o \times \vec{B}}{B^2}$$

Since the value of δ is finite, and we might also expect an ion density distribution n(r) as shown in Fig. 4(b). Some of the plasma will be in the region $r = a$ and, at $\theta = 0$ or $\theta = \pi$, will be thrown back with a velocity $|2\vec{v}_0|$ in the plasmoid frame of reference or a velocity $|\vec{v}_0|$ in the laboratory frame of reference. Evidence of this backfire has been observed with probes placed behind the plasma guns, and with Kerr cell photographs (see Fig. 5).

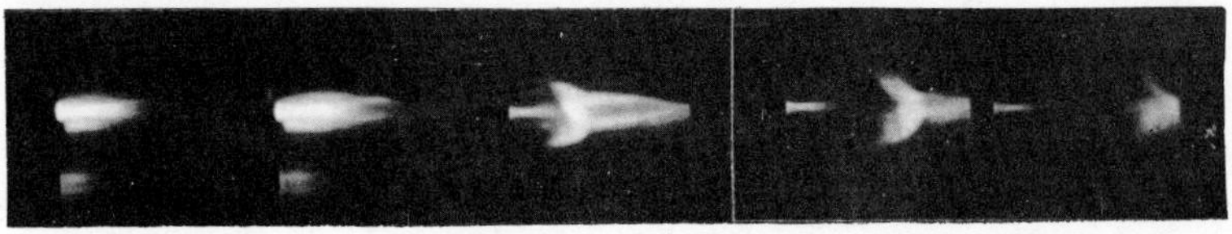

Fig. 5. Successive Kerr cell photographs (taken by Dickinson and Di Marco of Stevens Institute of Technology) of a plasma gun firing (left to right) across a magnetic field, but into the gradient B. Note the "backfire" associated with the motion of the plasma across the field. Time delays are 4, 5, 8, 10, and 12 μsec. B = 12000 gauss at the maximum value of the field and the gun is placed 10 cm away from the maximum field position

II. CHANGE OF VELOCITY OF A PLASMOID IN A MAGNETIC FIELD WITH A GRADIENT

The deflection[1, 2] or scattering of two plasmoids when they are fired at one another across a magnetic field B in a vacuum is a dramatic example of what happens when plasmoids suddenly encounter a gradient in B. Here also there is not only a sudden gradient in B provided by the currents $\vec{j}$ which the plasmoids cause to flow in each other, but also the $\vec{j} \times \vec{B}$ forces which produce both substantial retarding forces and (through the Hall electric field) deflecting forces.

A less complex situation is provided by a plasmoid moving in a vacuum across a field $\vec{B}$ which contains a gradient,

$$\text{grad } |\vec{B}| = \vec{i}\,(\partial B/\partial x),$$

produced by currents completely external to the plasmoid itself. The magnetic moment of an ion or electron is given by $\mu = kT/B$ and is considered to be a constant or adiabatic invariant so long as B does not change appreciably over a Larmor radius. The temperature T can refer to either the ions or the electrons. If πa^2 is the cross-sectional area of the plasmoid, the number of ions per unit length of the plasmoid is $N = n\pi a^2$, where n is the ion density.

The force produced by grad B on a unit length of the ions of the plasmoid is then

$$-\frac{n\pi a^2 kT}{B} \text{ grad } B = -\frac{NkT}{B} \text{ grad } B$$

and the energy per unit length of the plasmoid is NkT. Similar equations can be written for the electrons. The total force and energy are, of course, the sum of those of the ions and electrons. Now if plasma is to be compressed only in the directions x and y perpendicular to the field B, the plasma is a two-dimensional gas with $\gamma = 2$ and $n \sim 1/\pi a^2 \sim T \sim B$.

Simple energy considerations then enable us to calculate the field B_2 to which a plasmoid can penetrate if at B_1 it has a temperature T_1 (assumed here to be the sum of the ion and electron temperatures), a translational macroscopic kinetic energy per unit length $(KE)_1 \cong 1/2\,(N_1 m_i v_1^2)$ associated with its drift velocity v_1, and values n_1 and a_1. The total energy, W_T, of the plasmoid must remain constant, and we assume for simplicity that no particles per unit length are lost, i. e., that N is constant. Thus

$$W_T = (KE_1) + NkT_1 = (KE_2) + NkT_2 = (KE)_2 + NkT_1\,(B_2/B_1).$$

If $(KE)_2$ is to approach zero,

$$B_2 = \frac{\left[(KE)_1 + NkT_1\right] B_1}{NkT_1} = \left[1 + \frac{(KE_1)}{NkT_1}\right] B_1$$

$$= \left[\frac{1 + \frac{1}{2} N m_i v_1^2}{NkT_1}\right] B_1 = \left[\frac{1 + \frac{1}{2} m_i v_1^2}{kT_1}\right] B_1$$

This acceleration and deceleration of plasmoids in fields with gradients has been observed photographically and by means of probes. It is now suggested that by determining the field B_2 to which the plasmoid will penetrate, the temperature T can be measured.

The equation of motion of a unit length of plasmoid in grad B is

$$Nm_i \frac{dv(x)}{dt} = Nm_i \frac{dv(x)}{dx} \frac{dx}{dt} = Nm_i v \frac{dv}{dx} = - \frac{NkT}{B} \text{ grad B.}$$

if B is of the form

$$B = B_1 \left(1 + \frac{x}{h}\right), \quad \left|\text{grad } B\right| = \frac{dB}{dx} = \frac{B_1}{h} .$$

and

$$v \frac{dv}{dx} = - \frac{kT}{m_i h(1 + x/h)}$$

or

$$v^2 = - 2 \frac{kT}{m_i} \ell n \left[1 + \frac{x}{h}\right] + C.$$

At

$$x = 0, \quad v = v_o, \qquad \text{so} \quad C = v_o^2.$$

Thus

$$v^2 = v_o^2 - \frac{2kT}{m_i} \ell n \left[1 + \frac{x}{h}\right] .$$

Any practical field configuration, of course, involves not only a grad B in the x direction but also in the z direction. The plasmoid will thus be compressed in the z direction as well as in the x and y directions and hence will no longer be a strictly two-dimensional gas.

The lack of two-dimensionality alters the amount of geometrical compression experienced by the plasma, but does not change the value of B_2 to which it can penetrate. When $\gamma = 5/3$

$$\pi a^2 \sim \frac{1}{T^{3/2}} \sim \frac{1}{B^{3/2}} .$$

Also, in assuming that N is a constant, we have neglected the very rapid expansion of the plasma which occurs in the z direction. If grad B is strictly in the x direction, this loss of plasma will permit the diameter of the plasmoid to be shrunk to a value less than that given by $\pi a^2 \sim 1/B$, but the depth to which the plasmoid can penetrate into the higher field region will still be unaltered.

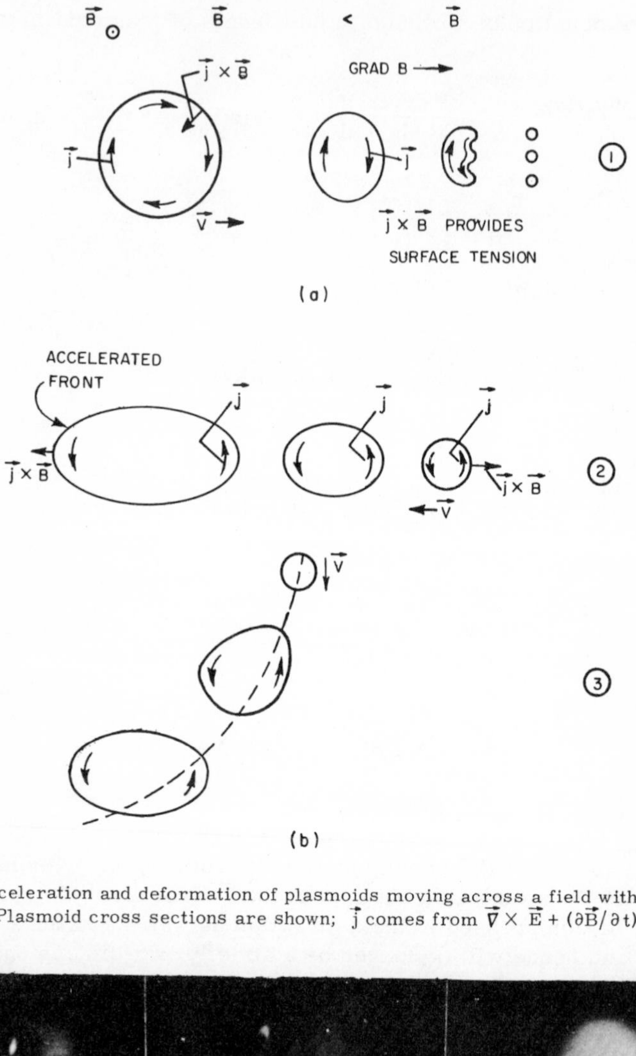

Fig. 6. Acceleration and deformation of plasmoids moving across a field with a gradient. Plasmoid cross sections are shown; $\vec{j}$ comes from $\vec{\nabla} \times \vec{E} + (\partial\vec{B}/\partial t) = 0$.

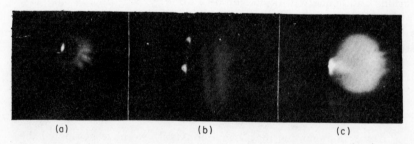

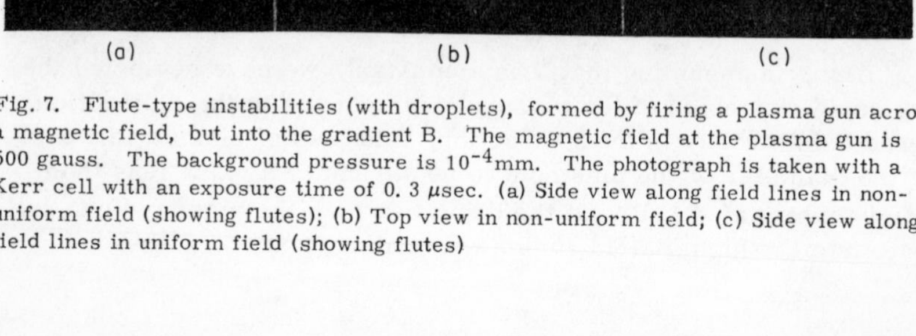

Fig. 7. Flute-type instabilities (with droplets), formed by firing a plasma gun across a magnetic field, but into the gradient B. The magnetic field at the plasma gun is 500 gauss. The background pressure is 10^{-4}mm. The photograph is taken with a Kerr cell with an exposure time of 0. 3 μsec. (a) Side view along field lines in non-uniform field (showing flutes); (b) Top view in non-uniform field; (c) Side view along field lines in uniform field (showing flutes)

By firing the plasmoid perpendicular to the field gradient, as shown in Fig. 6(b), the plasmoid is accelerated in the direction of -grad B. The trajectories of plasmoids thus fired* have been observed to be deflected as shown in the diagram. With some refinement, this technique can also be used to measure the average temperature of a plasmoid.

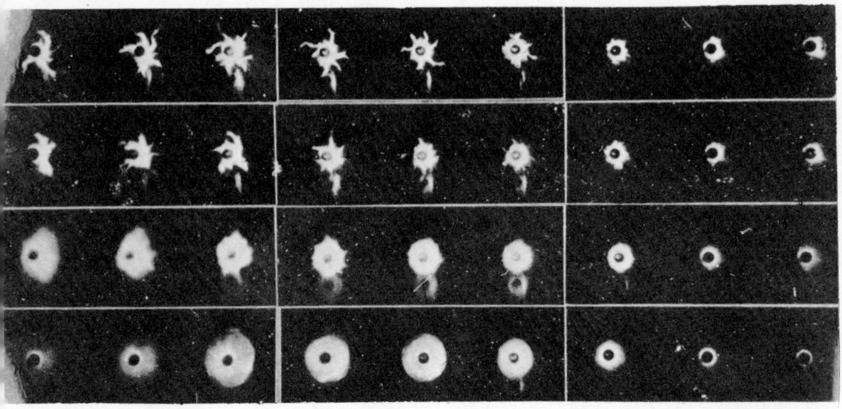

	0.770 webers/m	0.525 webers/m	0.141 webers/m	0.051 webers
1	5 μ sec	2 μ sec	2 μ sec	2 μ sec
2	6 "	5 "	4 "	4 "
3	7 "	7 "	6 "	7 "
4	9 "	9 "	8 "	9 "
5	12 "	11 "	10 "	11 "
6	13 "	13 "	12 "	12 "
7	15 "	15 "	14 "	14 "
8	19 "	19 "	18 "	18 "
9	23 "	23 "	23 "	23 "

Fig. 8 Development of apparent Rayleigh-Taylor instability in a plasma cylinder expanding radially across an existing magnetic field. Kerr cell 0.2 μsec exposure time photographs are taken at vacuum pressure = 5×10^{-4}mm under the conditions shown in the table above. The times given are the delays after firing the plasma gun before the photograph. The experimental arrangement is shown in Fig. 1. The black circle in the center of the picture is the barrier that causes the plasma to expand radially.

The generation of flute-type instability with subsequent "droplet" formation[5] has been observed by firing a plasmoid across a magnetic field with a gradient in the presence of a background medium (Fig. 7). The sequence in the formation of these flutes and droplets is suggested in Fig. 6(a). The generation of flute-type instabilities in plasma explosions in a magnetic field has been dramatically demonstrated by H. Dickinson, et. al. (see Fig. 8).

* H. Dickinson, with W. H. Bostick, J. Di Marco and S. Koslov (Stevens Institute of Technology), paper submitted to Physics of Fluids.

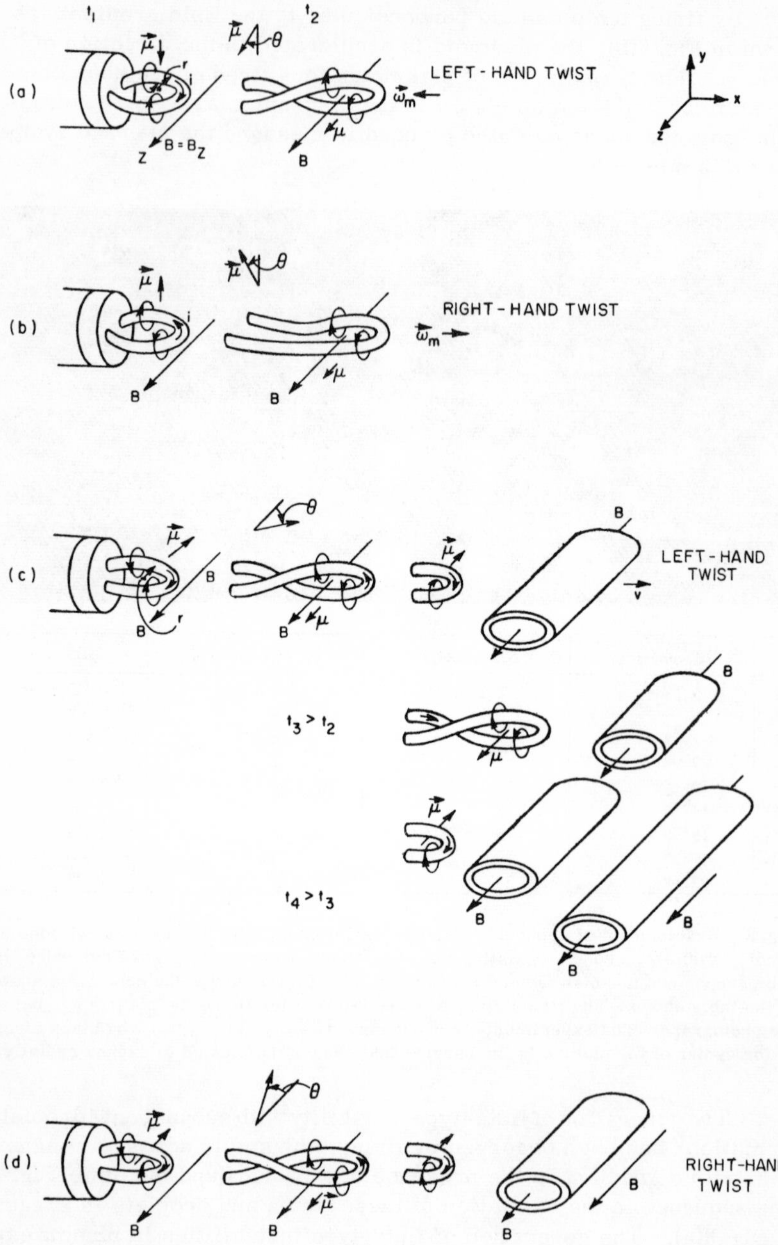

Fig. 9. Various possible deformations of the plasma loop current from a button gun fired perpendicular to a magnetic field B.

III. EXAMINATION OF THE BEHAVIOR OF THE LOOP CURRENT OF PLASMA NEAR THE BUTTON GUN

In attempting to analyze the behavior of the plasma loop current near the button gun, let us first take the case where the button gun is initially oriented as shown in Fig. 9(a). Here the plasma formed at the tip of the wires is confined by the pinch field h due to the current i, and produces a magnetic moment $|\vec{\mu}| \cong \pi r^2 i$. The torque τ on this magnetic moment is $\vec{\mu} \times \vec{B}$ which will produce a right-hand twist in the case of Fig. 9(b) and a left-hand twist in the case of Fig. 9(a). The moment of inertia is written $I \cong mr^2/2$, where m is the mass of the plasmoid in the ring, and a calculated period for the oscillation of the plasmoid loop about its equilbrium position is

$$T = 2\pi \sqrt{\frac{I}{|\vec{\tau}|}} = 2\pi \left[\frac{mr^2/2}{\pi r^2 \, iB} \right]^{1/2} = 2\pi \left[\frac{m}{2iB}\right]^{1/2} .$$

The time required to swing through $\theta = \pi/2$ is

$$\frac{T}{4} = \frac{\pi}{2} \left[\frac{m}{2iB}\right]^{1/2} .$$

For a typical case $m = 10^{-8}$ grams $= 10^{-11}$kg, $i = 10^3$ amps, and $B = 0.5 W/m^2$. Then

$$T/4 = \pi/2 \left[\frac{10^{-11}}{0.5 \times 10^3}\right]^{1/2} \cong 2 \times 10^{-7} \text{ sec.}$$

For $m = 10^{-7}$ gms, $T/4 = 6 \times 10^{-7}$ sec. For lower values of i and B, the value of T/4 is correspondingly larger. The energy of orientation of $\vec{\mu}$ in $\vec{B}$ is $\vec{\mu} \cdot \vec{B}$ and a value $|\mu B|$ will be released as kinetic energy in the y and z directions. This value is

$$|\mu B| = \pi r^2 iB = \pi \times 10^{-5} \times 10^3 \times 0.5 \text{ joules} \cong 1.5 \times 10^{-2} \text{ joules}$$

$$= 1.5 \times 10^{+5} \text{ ergs,}$$

for $r = 0.33$ cm $= 0.33 \times 10^{-2}$ m. Now if the plasma is formed of metal ions like Ti or Cu, then $m_i = 10^{-22}$ grams and the total number of ions in the plasmoid is $10^{-8}/10^{-22} = 10^{14}$. The energy per ion pair in the y and z directions then becomes

$$\frac{1.5 \times 10^5}{1.6 \times 10^{-12} \times 10^{14}} = 10^3 \text{ ev/ion pair.}$$

If this energy were concentrated in the z-direction, it would correspond to a speed of $\sim 5 \times 10^6$ cm/sec.

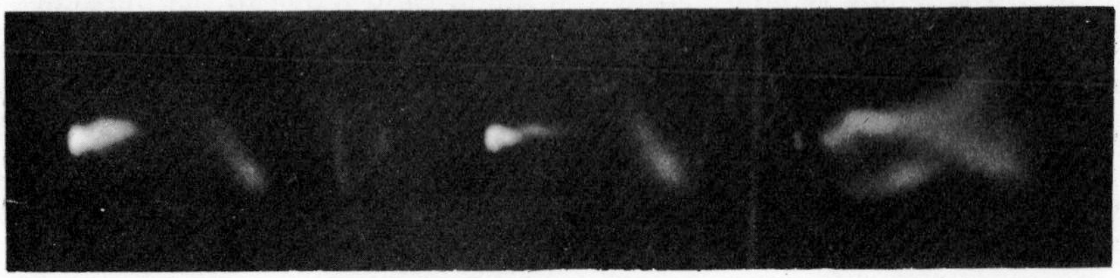

Fig. 10. A Kerr cell photograph of the twisting process predicted in Fig. 9 (by Dickinson and Di Marco, Stevens Institute of Technology)

Time exposure photographs (taken in the -z direction) of the profile of a button gun oriented as shown in Fig. 9(a) provide evidence that the twisting actually occurs. The plasma is also observed by probes to spread in the + z and -z direction with speeds between 3×10^6 cm/sec and 10^7 cm/sec. The fraction of the rotational energy in the y direction can be effectively transferred to some of the electrons, at least, through the formation of a Rosenbluth sheath around the plasmoid.

With the button gun oriented as shown in Fig. 9(a) a left-hand twist is to be expected.

With the button gun oriented as shown in Fig. 9(c), the magnetic moment $\vec{\mu}$ of the loop current is anti-parallel to $\vec{B}$ and the orientation is thus unstable to any angular rotation, $+\theta$ or $-\theta$. Presumably it can become a right-hand or left-hand plasmoid depending on the direction in which the initial perturbation from neutrality starts the rotation. The initial energy of orientation of the button gun in Fig. 9(c) and 9(d) is twice what it is for Fig. 9(a) and 9(b), and the former should therefore exhibit a speed in the z direction $\sqrt{2}$ times greater than that of the latter. This experimental comparison has not yet been performed. The details of the development of the plasmoid which expands in the + z and -z directions as shown in Fig. 9(c) and 9(d) have never been followed with Kerr cell photography because the speed of the plasma is too great and the light emitted is too weak. This twisting has, however, been observed when the plasma is projected across a background conducting medium; in this case the twisting forms a helical jet, due to the dragging of the field lines B, the speed is substantially reduced, and the light intensity is considerably enhanced (see Fig. 10).

Probe measurements show that the plasma breaks into the plasmoids, which are like two dimensional droplets, as shown in Figs. 9(c) and 9(d). Time-exposure photographs taken in the -y direction and probe measurements show that there is a rapid expansion in the +z and -z directions for the arrangement of Figs. 9(c) and 9(d). It is a reasonable hypothesis to assume that the droplet or plasmoid is separated from the rest of the plasma at the first cross-over of the twist, as indicated in Figs. 9(c) and 9(d). It can readily be perceived that the orientation of $\vec{\mu}$ from the anti-parallel to the parallel position is equivalent to a field-mixing operation whereby the reverse field on the inside of the plasma loop current disappears, and the interior of the loop is then occupied by a field parallel to B. Such a field-mixing operation would lead to a heating of the electrons to temperatures comparable to the energy which would be picked up by the ions if the plasmoid flips. If we expect this field-mixing to occur by a straightforward quiescent ohmic diffusion process with the conductivity σ of the plasma calculated from the Spitzer formula, the penetration distance b in a time t through a material with conductivity σ, for a field diffusing process, is $b = (t/\mu_0\sigma)^{1/2}$ in mks units. Spitzer's relationship for the conductivity gives

$$\frac{1}{\sigma} = \frac{1.29 \times 10^2}{T^{3/2}} Z \, \ell n \Lambda \text{ ohm m} \cong \frac{4 \times 10^2}{T^{3/2}} \text{ ohm meters}$$

with T in °K. For an electron temperature of about 10 ev ≅ 10^5 °K,

$$\frac{1}{\sigma} = \frac{4 \times 10^2}{(10^5)^{3/2}} = \frac{4 \times 10^2}{(10^{-1})^{3/2} \times (10^6)^{3/2}} \cong \frac{4 \times 10^2}{3 \times 10^{-2} \times 10^9}$$

$$\cong 1.3 \times 10^{-5} \text{ ohm meters.}$$

If b, the diameter of the plasma thread is ~ 0.3 cm = 3×10^{-3} meters,

$$t = b^2 \mu\sigma = \frac{9 \times 10^{-6} \times 4\pi \times 10^{-7}}{1.3 \times 10^{-5}} \cong 10^{-6} \text{ sec.}$$

If the plasmoid were traveling at 4×10^6 cm/sec, it would have traversed 4 cm by this time. The computed time for its flipping is less than 10^{-6} sec but is of the same order of magnitude. Experimental evidence indicates that the flipping actually does occur.

If the field-mixing should occur through diffusion of the dc field B into the center of the plasma loop rather than by the rotation or flipping of the loop, the field energy released would appear as plasma thermal energy and would cause the rapid expansion in the z direction as the flipping process also does.

The rates of expansion of the plasmoids in the z-direction should be studied experimentally with the current in the plasma loop in the direction shown in Fig. 9(c) and also in the opposite direction. Such a comparison should shed more light on the mechanism of the rapid expansion in the z direction.

IV. PROJECTION OF PLASMA ACROSS A MAGNETIC FIELD IN THE PRESENCE OF A BACKGROUND CONDUCTING MEDIUM

When a button gun is fired across a magnetic field as shown in Figs. 9(c) and 9(d), but in the presence of a background conducting medium provided by a low pressure (~10^{-3} mm) ionized background gas, the behavior is considerably altered. The background gas is rendered ionized, and hence conducting, by the ultra violet radiation coming from the gun. If the retarding effects upon the plasma are small, we might expect a curvature of the trajectory of the plasmoid due to Hall effects. Indeed, if two plasmoids are bounced off one another in the presence of an otherwise good vacuum (~10^{-5} mm), the currents resulting from a combination of the Lorentz and the Hall electric fields produce a collision somewhat like an elastic collision of two balls of the same mass. (See Fig. 12.)

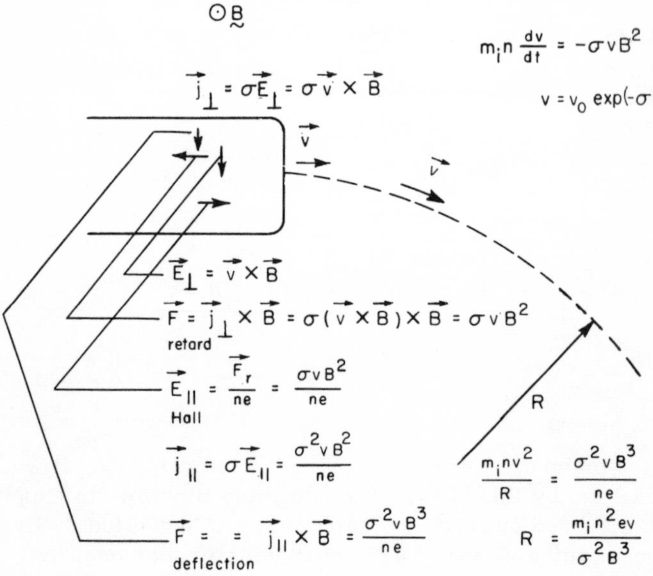

Fig. 11. A simple analysis illustrating how the Hall effect can produce curvature of the trajectories of a plasmoid as it proceeds across a uniform field in the presence of a background conducting medium

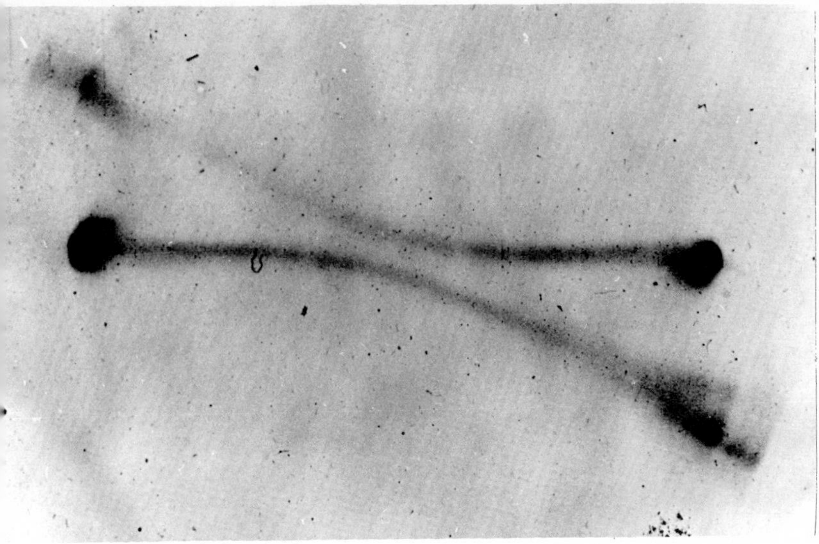

'ig. 12. Time exposure of the trajectories of two plasmoids as they are projected .cross a magnetic field (where the pressure is 10^{-5} mm Hg) and bounce off one another. 'he deflection of these two plasmoids is a dramatic example of the Hall effect.

An experimental investigation which should be carried out is that of measuring the degree of elasticity of these plasmoid collisions. Since the collision time-duration (~2×10^{-7} sec) is known, one could calculate the effective conductivity of the plasma perpendicular to the magnetic field. In essence, the magnetic Reynolds number could be experimentally determined. These plasmoids collide as if they were single entities because, although their density distribution n(z) is as shown in Fig. 1, the two button guns, and hence the center of the distribution, are lined up in the z direction. Thus every element of plasmoid length in the z direction collides with a corresponding element of its same mass in the other plasmoid. An entirely different situation would occur if the two button guns that produce the colliding plasmoids were displaced from one another by several cm in the z direction. Under these circumstances the more massive elements of one plasmoid will, through the magnetic field, collide with the less massive elements of the other plasmoids. Such an experiment might be a way to study the density distribution of the plasmoid in the z direction.

If the background conducting medium is provided not by another moving plasmoid, but by the low-background-pressure ionized gas, the greater plasmoid density at low values of z (see Fig. 1) has more

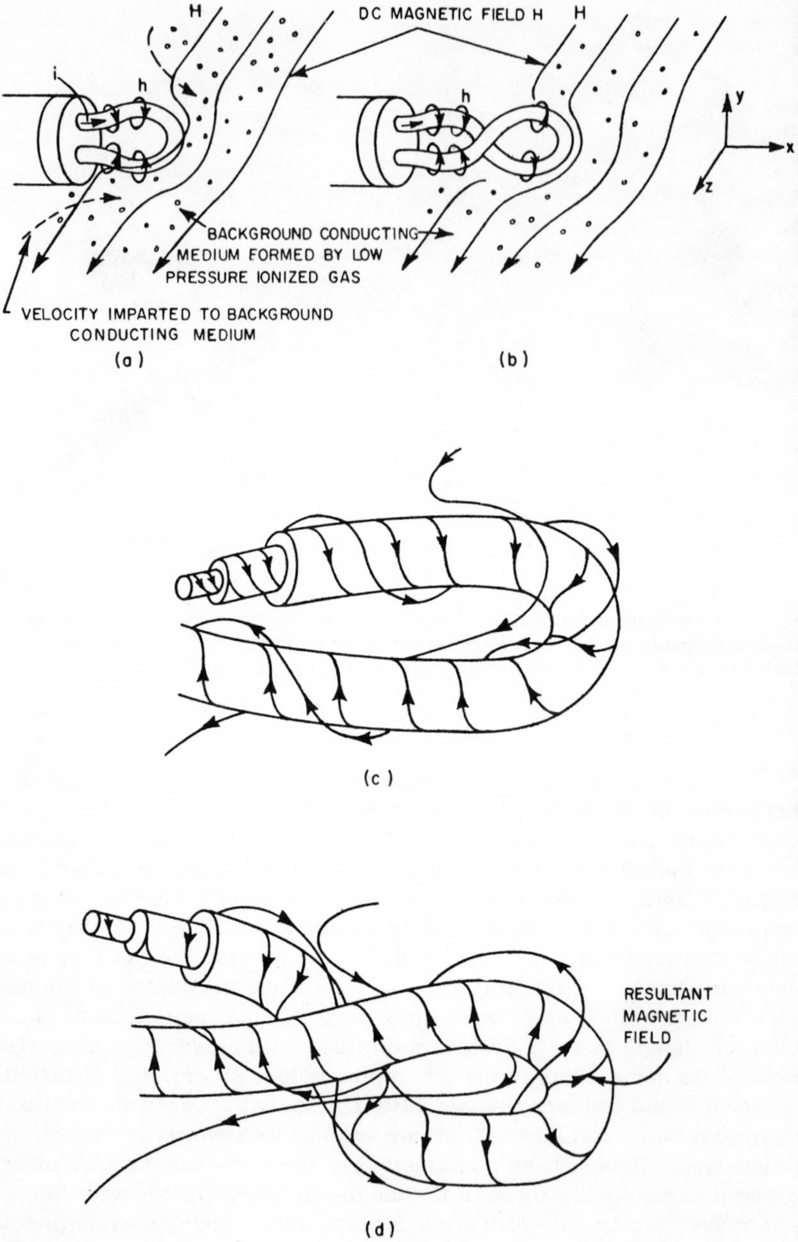

Fig. 13. Deformation of the plasmoid expected when a background conducting medium is present

nomentum density than wings of the plasmoid. However, the retard-ng force density j X B resulting from currents driven by the electric ield $\vec{E} = \vec{v} \times \vec{B}$, is the same along the z length of the plasmoid. Thus he plasmoid will move in the x direction faster at z = 0 than at large 'alues of z, and the plasmoid will jet as shown in Fig. 13. It is to be expected that flipping of the loop will occur under these circumstances. ndeed, it is under these circumstances that the flipping and resultant wisting of the plasmoid occur. The photograph taken by Dickinson et al, (Fig. 10) shows the conventional plasmoid proceeding through a good vacuum, and following it in its ionized wake is a twisted plasmoid, wherein the dc field lines of B have been dragged.

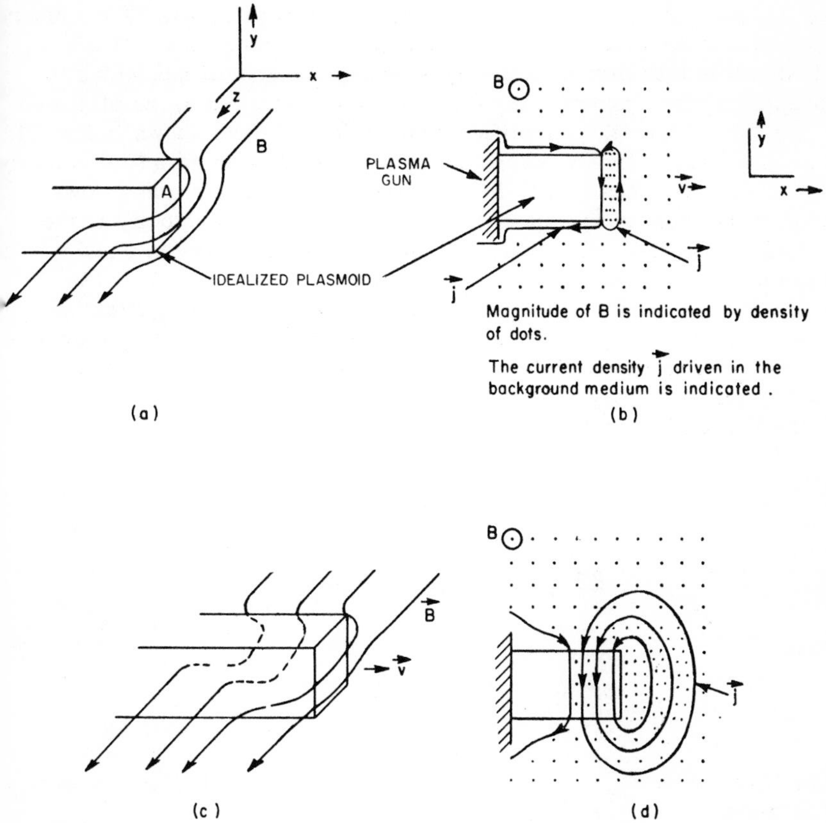

Fig. 14. Idealized plasmoid projected across a magnetic field with background con-ducting medium of density less than that of the plasmoid. Parts (a), (b) represent a high conductivity regime where the skin depth is low; (c), (d) represent a lower con-ductivity regime where the dragged field can slip part way through the plasmoid.

Now the magnitude of the magnetic Reynolds number will determine to what extent the dragged field lines will be permitted to slip through the moving plasmoid back to their previous positions. If the magnetic Reynolds number is $\gg 1$, all the dc lines of B encountered will be dragged and kept within the plasmoid jet during its traversal of the chamber (~10 cm). If the magnetic Reynolds number is low, most of the lines encountered will have slipped through the plasmoid during its passage.

The number of the lines of B encountered per second depends upon the speed of the plasmoid and upon the y dimension of the plasmoid (see Figs. 13, and 14). For simplicity, let us assume that the conductivity of background conducting medium and plasmoid are sufficiently high so that essentially none of the field lines are permitted to slip through the plasmoid jet during the passage across the chamber The field lines weigh virtually nothing; and the momentum of the plasmoid is transferred to the less dense background gas which is dragged by the magnetic field lines which are dragged by the plasmoid.

Let us take the simplified geometrical picture shown in Fig. 14. The plasmoid of frontal cross-sectional area A with an initial velocity v_o sweeps up a mass $\rho A v$ in unit time. Much of this mass flows around the front of the plasmoid jet and travels at a velocity in the laboratory system with an x component anywhere between 0 and v. Let us take a rough estimate of $v/2$ for this average velocity at which the mass $\rho A v$ is dragged. The momentum exchanged per second with the background plasma is then $\rho A v^2/2$. The effective cross-frontal area is obviously somewhat greater than A. We can take it as 2A, and therefore the momentum exchanged per second is $\sim\rho A v^2$. If the mass of the plasmoid is m,

$$-m\frac{dv}{dt} = \rho A v^2 .$$

Then

$$\frac{dv}{v^2} = -\frac{\rho A}{m}\,dt, \quad \text{and at } t = 0,\ v = v_o.$$

Thus

$$\frac{1}{v} - \frac{1}{v_o} = \frac{\rho A t}{m} .$$

The time taken for v to be reduced from v_o to $v_o/2$ is $t_{1/2} = m/\rho A v_o$. The distance traversed is

$$\int_{t=o}^{t=t} v\,dt = \int_o^t \frac{dt}{\left[\frac{\rho A t}{m} + \frac{1}{v_o}\right]} = \frac{m}{\rho A}\left[\ell n\left[\frac{\rho A t}{m} + \frac{1}{v_o}\right] - \ell n\,\frac{1}{v_o}\right]$$

For a typical case, at $p = 10^{-3}$ mm of air, $n \cong 7 \times 10^{13}$ and the atomic weight = 14. The ion weight is therefore

$$\sim 14 \times 1.6 \times 10^{-24} \text{ gm and } \rho = 7 \times 10^{13} \times 14 \times 1.6 \times 10^{-24}$$

$$= 1.6 \times 10^{-7} \text{ gm/cm}^3$$

If

$$v_o = 5 \times 10^6 \text{ cm/sec},$$

$$m = 10^{-7} \text{ gm, and } A = 1 \text{ cm}^2,$$

$$t_{1/2} = \frac{10^{-7}}{1.6 \times 10^{-7} \times 1 \times 5 \times 10^6} = 0.12 \times 10^{-6} \text{ sec}.$$

The time $t_{1/11}$ taken for v_o to be reduced to $v_o/11$ is 10 times $t_{1/2}$, and this $t_{1/11}$ is thus 1.2 μ sec. The corresponding values for $m = 10^{-8}$ gms are $t_{1/2} = 0.012 \times 10^{-6}$ sec and $t_{1/11} = 0.12 \times 10^{-6}$ sec.

These values are of the same order of magnitude as was estimated from our experimental experience. It can be readily seen that the deceleration depends upon ρ of the background medium. Thus a measurement of the deceleration of a plasmoid or its range in a magnetic field could be used as a measure of the ion density of the background plasma. It can also be seen that, to a first order of approximation, the rate of deceleration does not depend upon B although the frontal area A assumed by the plasmoid will depend significantly upon B. It can be seen that the magnetic field intensity directly in front of the plasmoid can be markedly increased, and that these field lines will soak into the plasmoid as they are dragged along. As the plasmoid is twisted, the field lines will be twisted up into it. An attempt to describe this is made in Fig. 13. The twisting is expected to produce the over-all helical twist, which is experimentally observed in Kerr cell pictures. Experimental observations indicate that the deceleration is increased with the background pressure and hence with ρ, and that the wavelength of the helix decreases with ρ.

It can be seen from Figs. 13 and 14 that a forked tail of plasma is to be expected, and these forked tails are commonly observed. The models we have drawn of the plasmoids in these figures also indicate that the dragged portion of the background conducting medium is also incorporated into the helically twisting plasmoid along with the dragged magnetic field lines. This dragged plasma along with the plasma from the gun, is compressed and thus adiabatically heated as the dragged magnetic field lines are compressed by the dragging procedure. The resulting electron temperatures are apparently high enough to permit the plasmoid to keep its shape and boundaries for at least 50 μ sec and probably 100 μ sec. The corresponding conductivity can again be estimated from $b = (t/\mu_0 \sigma)^{1/2}$ where now $b \cong 0.5$ cm = 0.5×10^{-2} m and $t = 5 \times 10^{-5}$ sec.

Thus

$$\sigma = \frac{t}{\mu_0 b^2} = \frac{5 \times 10^{-5}}{0.25 \times 4\pi \times 10^{-7} \times 10^{-4}}$$

$$\cong 2 \times 10^{6} \text{ mhos/m and } \frac{1}{\sigma} = 0.5 \times 10^{-6} \text{ ohm meters.}$$

The corresponding value of T_e is 90 ev or ~ 90, 000 °K. If a value of t = 100 μ sec is chosen, the value of T_e is about 150 ev. The energy for heating the plasma is, of course, extracted from the origi nal kinetic energy of projection of the plasma and also from the energ of orientation of its loop-current magnetic dipole in the dc field B.

It can be seen from Figs. 9(c) and (d) and Fig. 13, that if the loop in its unstable orientation in the field happens to start a left-hand twist (Fig. 5(c)) the $\vec{\mu} \times \vec{B}$ torque will continue to produce at least a 180° left-hand twist. However, if the loop should start a right-hand twist, the torque will produce at least a 180° right-hand twist (Fig. 9(d)). It would seem to be a matter of chance (or actually a small amount of plus or minus angular deviation from zero) as to whether a right-hand or left-hand twist results. A right-hand twist of the two strands of plasmoid will result in a gross right-hand helical deformation of over-all shape; this helical deformation is observed with stereo Kerr cell pictures. When two plasmoids are projected across a magnetic field and conducting medium towards one another and join in the center to form a barred spiral configuration, it is observed that they are always both either right-handed or both left-handed. This peculiar coincidence can be understood in terms of the coupling of the magnetic moments of the two plasmoids; minimum potential energy will occur when they both twist right-handedly or both twist left-handedly. They behave like two trained acrobats who watch each other: when one makes a move with his right hand the other makes the same move with his right hand etc., so that they may clasp each other securely when they come together. Spiral galaxies observed edge-on have a sigmoid or ∽ shape, like an integral sign lying on its side. This is evidence that the two galactic arms are helically shaped and that they are both either right-handed or left-handed. The author[5-7] has already advanced the hypothesis that the formation of galactic arms comes essentially from two galactic plasmoids converging toward the galactic center in the same manner in which our laboratory plasmoids come together. This hypothesis not only explains the general two-dimensional shape of a barred spiral galaxy, but now also explains the helical shape of the galactic arms.

V. DRAGGING OF MAGNETIC FIELD LINES WHEN PLASMA IS PROJECTED ALONG THE AXIS OF SYMMETRY OF A MAGNETIC FIELD WHICH HAS A RADIAL COMPONENT

Figure 15 shows a situation in which the plasma gun can be fired into a good vacuum and the magnetic field lines will still be dragged because of the axial symmetry and the radial component of the magnetic field. The effects of the rotation produced by firing the coaxial plasma crater gun in an axial magnetic field will not be considered at this time.

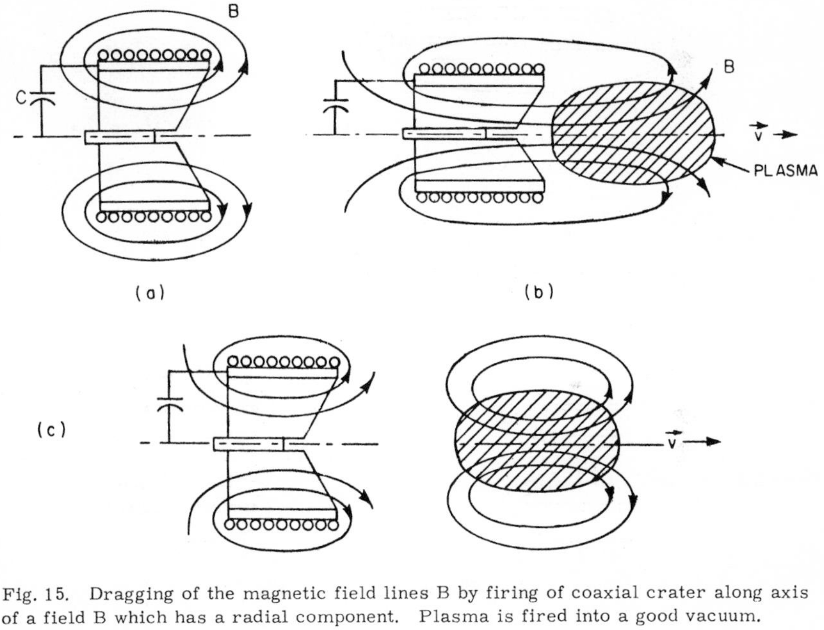

Fig. 15. Dragging of the magnetic field lines B by firing of coaxial crater along axis of a field B which has a radial component. Plasma is fired into a good vacuum.

To analyze the situation represented by Fig. 15 in an idealized geometry, let us consider the two rigid conducting cylingers of Fig. 16 which are telescoped on one another. They have practically the same radius, $r_1 = r_2 = r$, and the same length, ℓ. Initially, at $t = 0$, they are both threaded with the same flux, $B_o \pi r^2$, due to a current which has been flowing in the outer fixed cylinder (No. 1). However at $t = 0$ the inner cylinder (No. 2) is given an amount of axial kinetic energy equal to $1/2\ mv_o^2$ in the +x direction, where m_2 is the mass of cylinder No. 2. If the current in the one-turn current sheet of cylinder No. 1 is i, then $B = \mu_o i/\ell$ and since $\ell > 2r_o$, the energy stored, is approximately $W_B = (B^2/2\mu_o)\pi r^2 \ell$. The axial displacement of cylinder No. 2 is x.

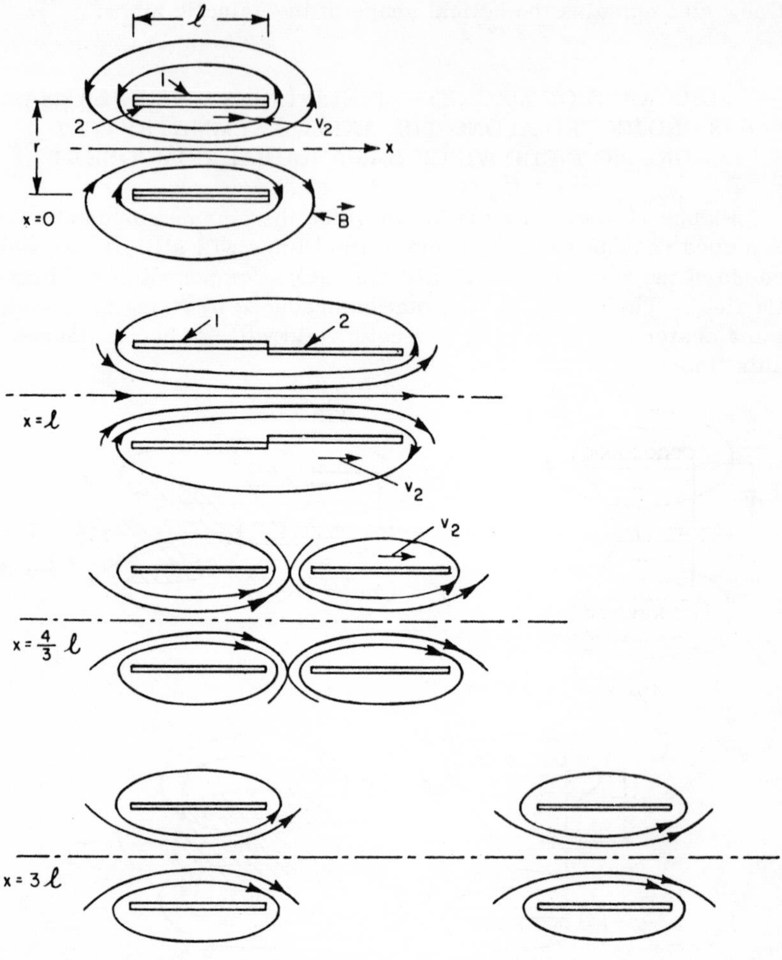

Fig. 16. Idealized representation of Fig. 15

Let us now consider the force which tends to hold the cylinders together axially in the regime $0 < x < \ell$.

The restoring force is

$$\frac{dW_B}{dx} = \frac{B^2}{2\mu_0}\pi r^2 \frac{d\ell'}{dx} = \frac{B^2}{2\mu_0}\pi r^2 = \frac{\mu_0^2 i^2 \pi r^2}{2\mu_0 \ell^2} = \frac{\mu_0 i^2 \pi r^2}{2\ell^2}$$

where $\ell' = \ell + x$ and the magnetic energy stored is $(B^2/2\mu_0)\pi r^2 \ell'$. Since the total energy must remain constant,

$$\frac{1}{2}\, mv^2 + \frac{B^2}{2\mu_0}\pi r^2 \ell' = \frac{1}{2}\, mv_0^2 + \frac{B^2}{2\mu_0}\pi r^2 \ell\ ,$$

The value of $(1/2)\, mv^2$ at $x = \ell$ is then

$$\frac{1}{2} mv^2 = \frac{1}{2} mv_o^2 - \frac{B_o^2}{2\mu_o} \pi r^2 \ell .$$

The equation of motion during this regime is

$$m \frac{dv}{dt} = - \frac{B^2}{2\mu_o} \pi r^2 ,$$

which represents uniform deceleration.

When the cylinders have separated a distance $x \gg \ell$, the magnetic energy content is exactly twice what it was at $t = 0$, that is, $B = B_o$ in both cylinders; this is approximately the magnetic energy content when $x = \ell$. Hence, practically all of the loss of kinetic energy to magnetic energy occurs in the region $0 < x < \ell$.

If cylinder #2 has finite conductivity, and hence a resistance R, an inductance L, and hence an L/R time-constant, there will be the following regimes:

Regime A:

$$\frac{1}{2} mv_o^2 < \frac{B_o^2}{2\mu_o} \pi r^2 \ell$$

then

$$\bar{v} \cong v_o/2 ,$$

and if

$$t = (\ell/\bar{v}) < L/R,$$

cylinder #2 will not escape from the magnetic field which threads the cylinder. The energy $(B_o^2/2\mu_o)\, \pi r^2 \ell$ is essentially the binding energy of the system involving cylinders #1 and #2 and the magnetic field.

Regime B:

$$\frac{1}{2} mv_o^2 > \frac{B_o^2}{2\mu_o} \pi r^2 \ell .$$

Then $\vec{v} \cong v_o$, and $t_{x=\ell} \cong \ell/\vec{v} \cong \ell/v_o$. If $t_{x=\ell} < L/R$, the velocity of escape is that given by the equation for the infinite conducting case. If $t_{x=\ell} > L/R$, the velocity of escape will be that corresponding to the restoring force being active over a displacement length $x \cong (L/R)\, v_o$, and the increase in magnetic energy will be

$$\frac{B_o^2}{2\mu_o} \pi r^2 \frac{L}{R} v_o .$$

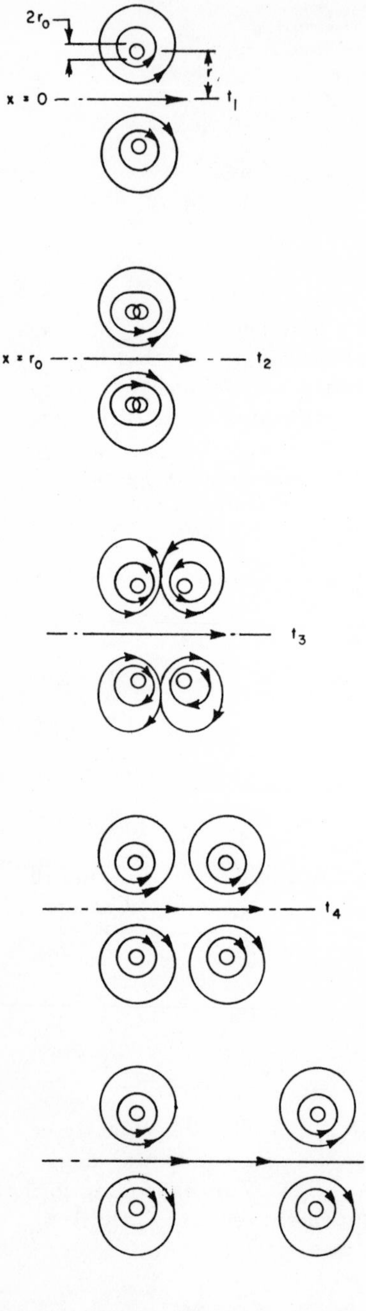

Fig. 17 Same process as that of Fig. 16, but with loop-coils instead of cylindrical coils

In an orthogonal pinch type of plasma gun which squirts plasma out the end, it is obvious that the binding energy of plasma to the coil involves that magnetic flux which has diffused into the plasma and which threads the coil.

Another idealized geometry is that of two conducting loop coils as shown in Fig. 17. For the interval $r_0 < x < r$, the force F_x between the two is practically that between two wires of length $2\pi r$ carrying a current i, and having a spacing x; $F_x \cong \mu_0 i^2 r/x$. Thus

$$W_{B \atop x=r} \cong \int_{x=r_o}^{x=r} \frac{\mu_o i^2 r}{x} dx$$

$$\cong \mu_0 i^2 r \ell n \frac{r}{r_0}$$

This can be compared with

$$W_0 = \frac{1}{2} Li^2 \cong \frac{1}{2} \mu_0 r i^2 \ell n \frac{r}{r_0},$$

the original magnetic energy, where $L \cong \mu_0 r \ell n (r/r_0)$. The final magnetic energy is $2W_0$ when $x >> r$ (see Fig. 17); hence practically all the loss of kinetic energy and gain in magnetic energy occurs in the interval $r_0 < x < r$. The same considerations concerning the time constant L/R for loop No. 2 apply here as for the two cylinders in Fig. 16.

As the plasma is slowed down by the magnetic field, we can expect flute instabilities to occur. The time available for them to occur is of the order of ℓ / v_0 and the efolding time constant of the instability is $(2\pi\lambda/g)^{1/2}$.

If the binding energy is greater than the initial kinetic energy and instabilities develop, it is quite possible that the instability jets that develop will drag some of the magnetic field, and that the plasma will exhibit jets with shreds trailing behind.

It is now obvious that if cylinder No. 2 or loop No. 2 (which are really idealized plasmoids of Figs. 16 and 17) have time constants $L/R >> x/v_o$, they will continue to contain a large fraction of their dipole flux BA over the distance of travel x, even though the flux should produce an expansion of the plasmoid.

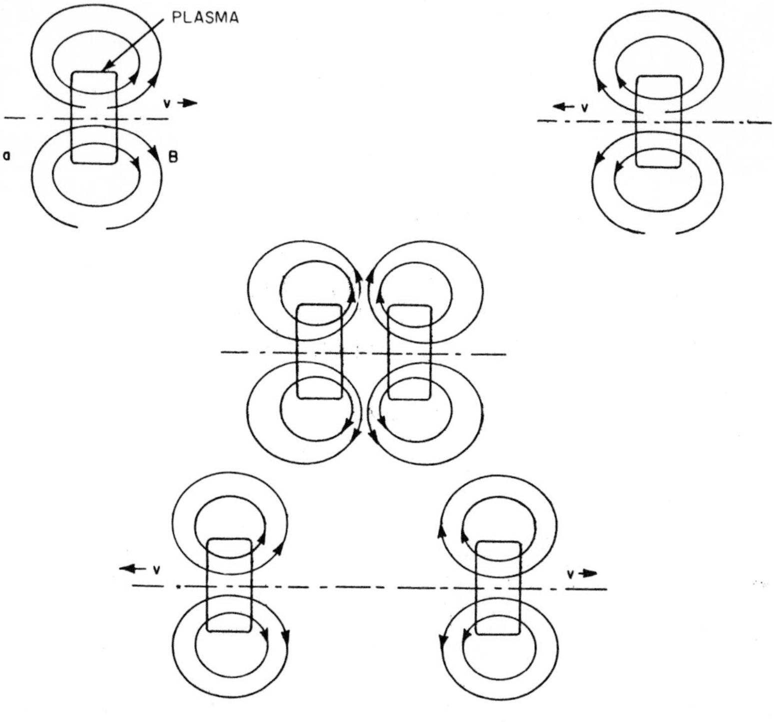

Fig. 18. Predicted collision of two plasma toruses

Let us see what would happen if two such plasmoids would be projected towards one another, as shown in Fig. 18(a), with the fields B oriented as shown. When the plasmoids come together, they would build up a magnetic cushion and bounce back from each other. If instabilities develop from the rapid acceleration, they will form jets, interpenetrate, and exhibit shreds which trail the jets.

If the two plasmoids have their fields oriented as shown in Fig. 19, the magnetic binding energy will accelerate them toward one another and they will pass through one another and separate again on the other side.

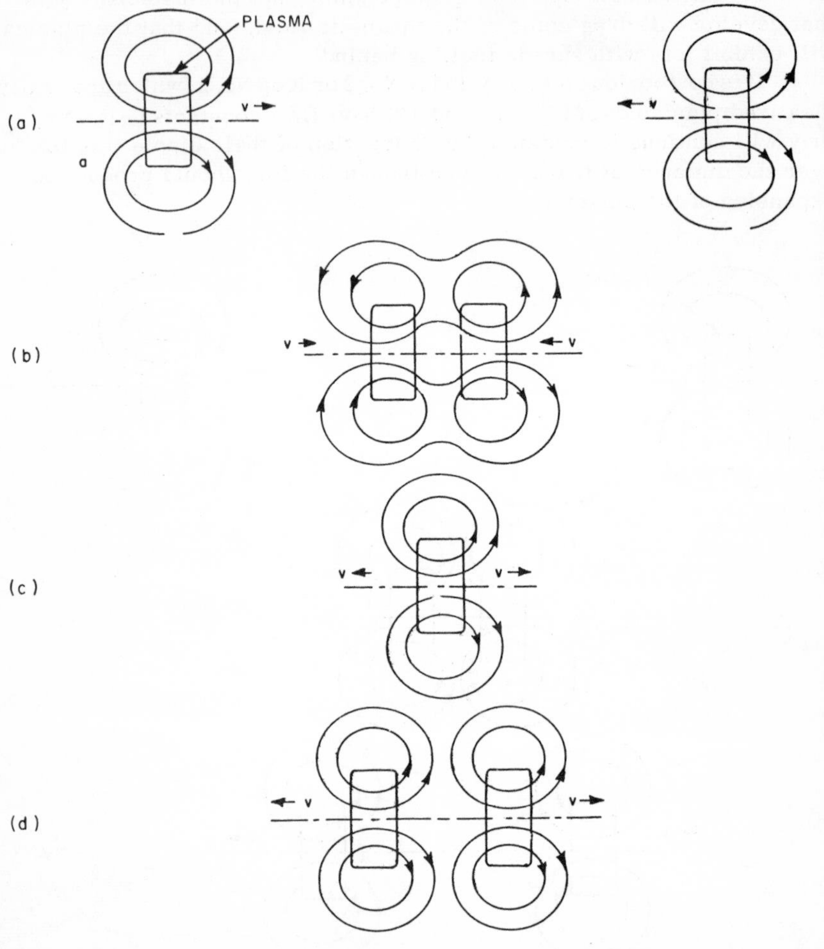

Fig. 19. Collision of two plasma toruses with their magnetic moments in the same direction (otherwise the same as in Fig. 18)

VI. COLLISION OF PLASMOIDS WHERE ROTATION IS INVOLVED

Let us consider the case where there is an axially impressed, dc magnetic field along the entire path of the plasmoids, as shown in Fig. 20. If the driving-current pulses in the two coaxial crater guns are opposite in direction, the rotations will also be opposite in direction as shown in the figure. The resulting radial electric fields are opposite in direction and, when the two plasmoids encounter one another, will drive currents as shown to produce the azimuthal, toroidal magnetic field illustrated. This azimuthal field will be compressed by the oppositely directed axial moments of the two plasmoids, and hence will decelerate the plasmoids. If instabilities grow in this deceleration, Kerr cell photographs should then show, in general, shreds of plasma and magnetic field appearing as forked tails behind a leading head or apex.

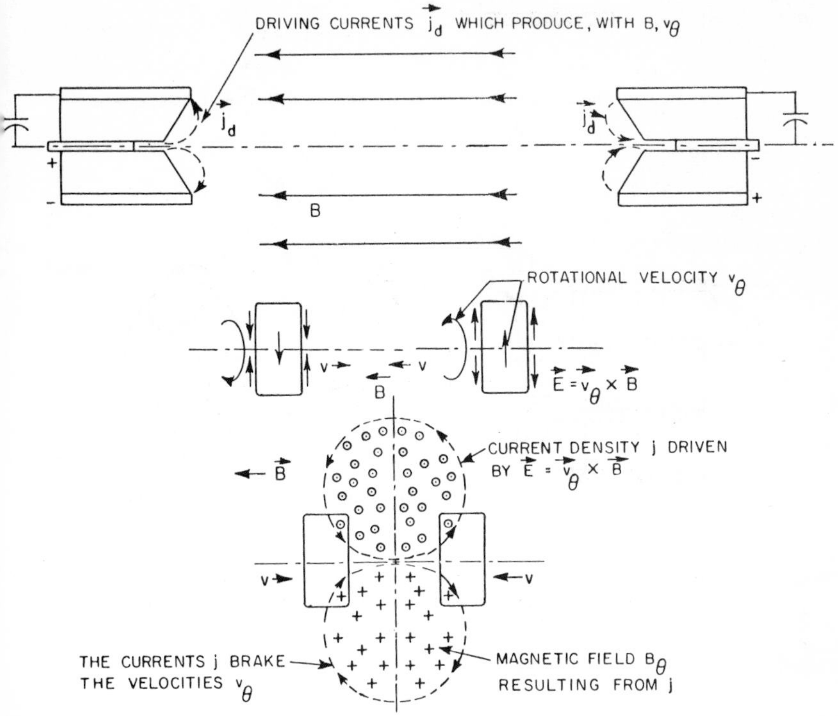

Fig. 20. Predicted collision of two rotating toruses where an axial magnetic field is employed

If the driving current pulses in the coaxial crater guns with the arrangement shown in Fig. 20 have only one-half cycle of current and are in the same direction, the effect of rotation will be negligible and the two plasmoids will pass through each other without interaction. This is true only if the two guns are originally perfectly lined up on the same magnetic field lines. If they are offset, for example, by one radius of the gun, then on the overlapping portions the electric fields will drive currents which will again produce some transverse magnetic field when the plasmoids collide. Again instabilities will be expected and these should produce Kerr cell photographs with the plasma exhibiting apexes with dragged-out tails.

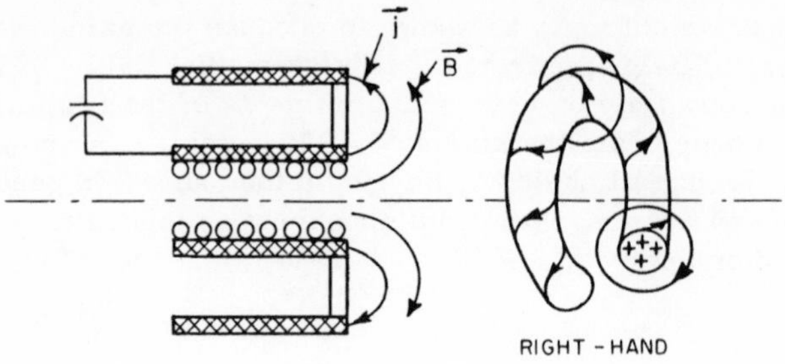

Fig. 21. Firing of one-half-cycle of current with $\vec{B}$ and $\vec{J}$ as shown

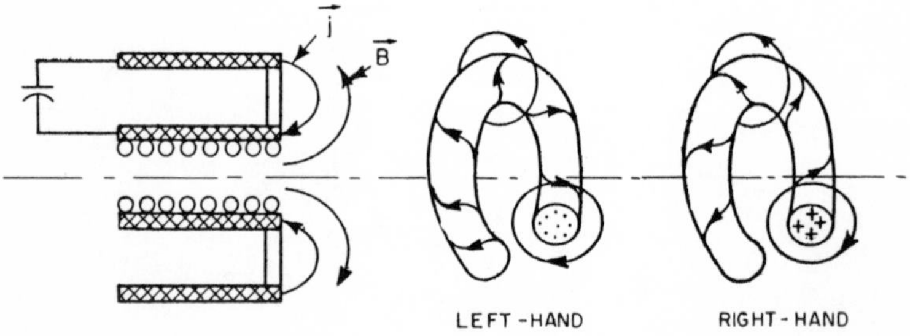

Fig. 22. Firing of two half-cycles current where the poloidal field $\vec{B}$ is unchanging in time, but the $\vec{J}$, and hence the toroidal $\vec{B}$ reverses direction

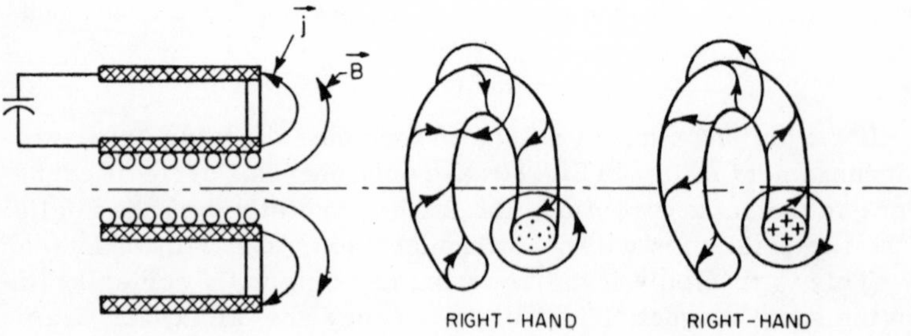

Fig. 23. Firing of two half cycles where the coil for the poloidal $\vec{B}$ and the electrodes are connected in series

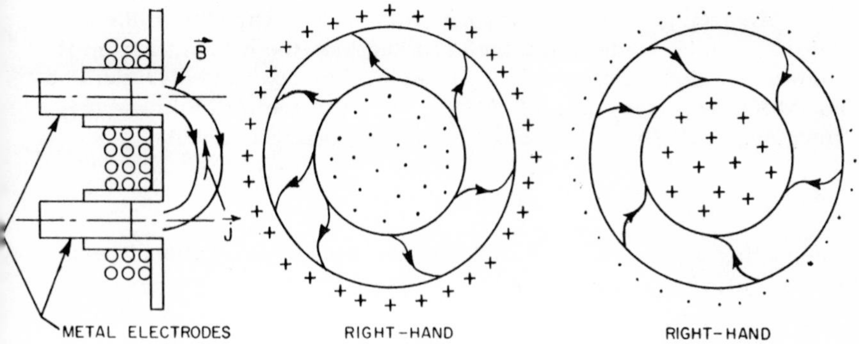

Fig. 24. Firing two half cycles with coil and electrodes in series.

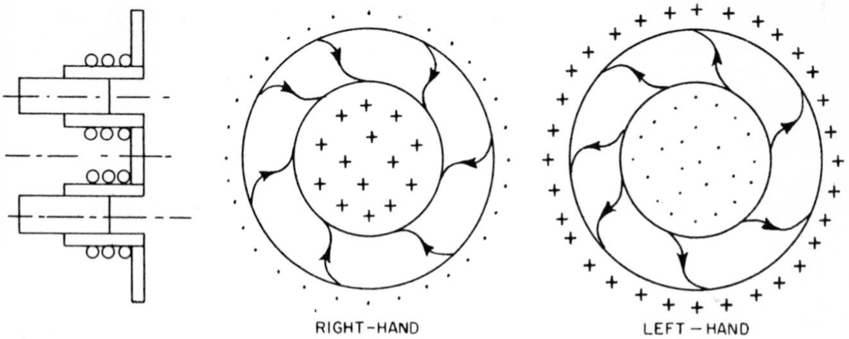

Fig. 25. Firing two half-cycles with the current in the coil unchanged, but the current though the electrodes reversing

If the current pulses in each coaxial crater gun are effectively two half-cycles and the guns are lined up perfectly on the same magnetic field line, and the direction of the first half cycle of current is the same in each gun, the plasmoids formed by the first half-cycle in each gun will be expected to pass through each other and interact with the plasmoids formed by the second half-cycle in the opposing guns. Two interacting zones should then be observed. Indeed, it is quite possible that the plasmoids coming off one gun, but having two half-cycles of current, will be linked with each other by the currents driven by the oppositely directed radial electric fields. These azimuthal magnetic fields will be compressed by the coming together of the two oppositely directed azimuthal configurations if two such guns are now fired at each other. An interaction and possible instabilities should be observed.

An estimate of the rotational velocity compared with the axial velocity can be made. In a typical situation, the current i from the center electrode to the outer cylinder of the coaxial crater gun is about 4000 amps for $\Delta t = 2 \times 10^{-6}$ sec and the magnetic field is 10^4 gauss = $1 W/m^2$. The mass m of the plasma is about

$$20 \times 10^{-6} \text{ gms} = 2 \times 10^{-8} \text{ kg}.$$

The radius of the gun is about 1 cm; therefore the rotational peripheral velocity will be given by

$$v \cong \frac{iB\Delta t}{m} \cong \frac{4 \times 10^3 \times 1 \times 2 \times 10^{-6}}{2 \times 10^{-8}}$$

$$\cong 2 \times 10^5 \text{ cm/sec},$$

which is about one order of magnitude lower than the translational velocity along the axis of the plasma gun.

Figures 21 - 25 represent suggestions concerning various types of plasma guns which can be used to incorporate both the poloidal and toroidal magnetic fields in a plasmoid.

VII. A TOROIDAL MODEL OF AN ELEMENTARY PARTICLE SUGGESTED BY PLASMOIDS

The tendency of plasma to form into filaments or shreds (see Fig. 1, for example) suggests that the basic matter in the elementary particle may be in the form of a filamentious torus (see Fig. 26) where the torus carries a charge e which circulates with v = c. Then

$$|\vec{E}| = (E_r) = (\vec{H}) \; (= H_\theta) = \frac{e}{\pi \mu R} .$$

The field energy E_f is given in Fig. 26. The configuration of Figs. 26(a) or 26(b) can conceivably be constructed of a very thin gravitationally stabilized fiber, whose gravitational potential energy is E_g, is given in Fig. 26. A more complete description[4] of this type of particle has now been published. The parameters of such particles can be adjusted so as to give approximately the correct values of the mass, the magnetic moment, the spin, and the g factor for both the electron and the proton.

VIII. APPLICATION OF INFORMATION ON PLASMOIDS TO GALACTIC ARMS FORMATION

Descriptions have already been given of the manner in which

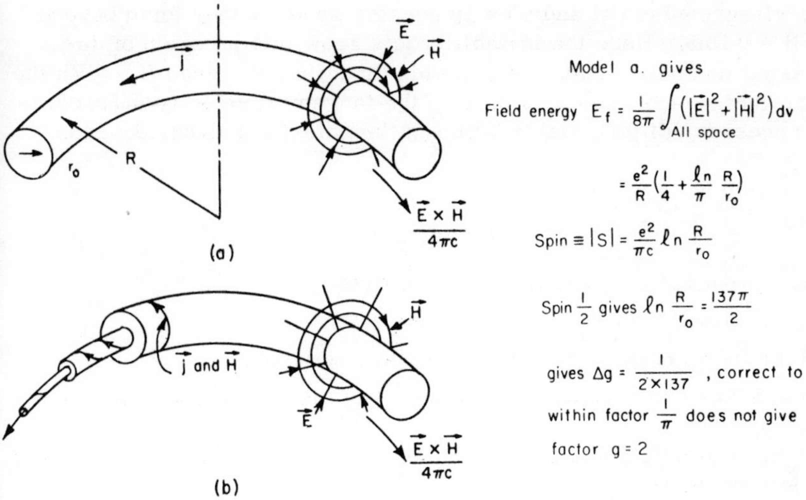

Model a. gives

Field energy $E_f = \dfrac{1}{8\pi} \displaystyle\int_{\text{All space}} \left(|\vec{E}|^2 + |\vec{H}|^2\right) dv$

$= \dfrac{e^2}{R}\left(\dfrac{1}{4} + \dfrac{1}{\pi}\ln\dfrac{R}{r_0}\right)$

Spin $\equiv |S| = \dfrac{e^2}{\pi c}\ln\dfrac{R}{r_0}$

Spin $\dfrac{1}{2}$ gives $\ln\dfrac{R}{r_0} = \dfrac{137\pi}{2}$

gives $\Delta g = \dfrac{1}{2\times137}$, correct to

within factor $\dfrac{1}{\pi}$ does not give

factor $g = 2$

(a)

(b)

Fig. 26. Gravitational stabilization of fiber; gravitational potential energy is

$$E_g = -\frac{e^4 G}{\pi^3 c^4 R_g^3}\ \ell n^3 \frac{R_g}{r_{og}}$$

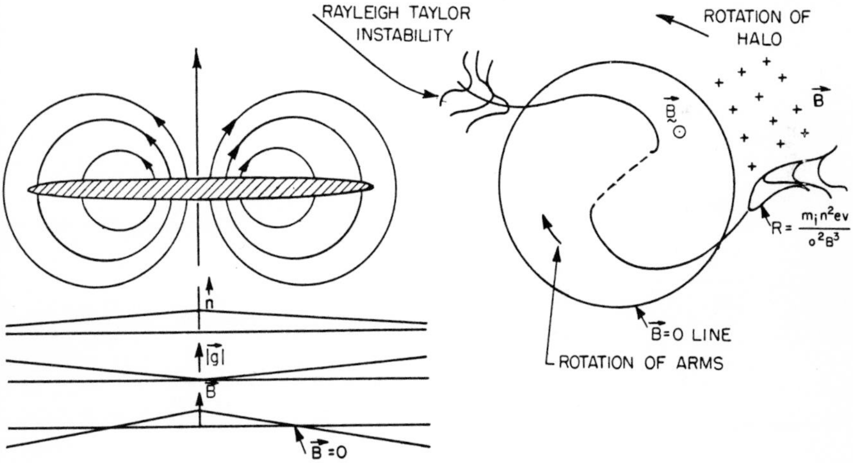

Fig. 27. Formation of galactic arms

colliding plasmoids (in the laboratory) can produce galactic configurations,[5, 6, 7] and the parallelism between this and actual galactic formation has been drawn. The more recent laboratory information on twisting plasmoids (Fig. 9) curvature due to Hall effect and the speed of Rayleigh-Taylor instability jets can now be used to fill out this picture. As Fig. 27 indicates, the Rayleigh-Taylor instability jets will grow fastest and pick up greater speed if they form beyond the B = 0 line. Here the instability jets grow into a region of decreasing magnetic field, i. e., in this direction of - grad B. With the Hall effect, the jets can also pick up the tangential velocity and produce the necessary differential rotation in the galaxy for dynamo action.

REFERENCES

1. W. H. Bostick, *Phys. Rev.*, Vol. 104, p. 292 (1956).
2. W. H. Bostick, *Phys. Rev.*, Vol. 106, p. 404 (1957).
3. H. Dickinson, et al., *Phys. of Fluids*, Vol. 3, p. 480 (1960).
4. Gravity Research Foundation Essay Contest 1961 (first prize), New Boston, New Hampshire.
5. W. H. Bostick, "Electromagnetic Phenomena in Cosmical Physics," *Inst. Ast. Union Symposium.*
6. W. H. Bostick, *Rev. Mod. Phys.*, Vol. 30, p. 1090 (1958).
7. W. H. Bostick, *Trans. N. Y. Academy of Sciences*, Vol. 20, p. 79 (1957).

INTERACTION BETWEEN SLOW PLASMA WAVES AND AN ELECTRON STREAM

V. J. Kislov, E. V. Bogdanov
Institute of Radioelectricity and Electronics,
Academy of Sciences, U. S. S. R.

At present research is being carried out to find new physical means of amplifying and generating microwaves. One of these means is the use of plasma.

This paper relates the results of theoretical and experimental studies on possible mechanisms by which a non-relativistic electron stream may be made to interact with plasma in a magnetic field.

I. GENERAL CONSIDERATIONS AND THE CRITERIA OF SEPARATING SLOW E AND H WAVES

Let us consider a system consisting of two regions. The inner region comprises a cylinder of radius a filled with plasma and an electron stream of the same radius penetrates into it. The outer region comprises unbounded plasma having a concentration different from that in the inner region. The magnetic field is directed along the axis of this system. The electron stream is focused by a magnetic field and has only longitudinal components for the ac electron velocity v_e and ac current density j_e, which are much smaller than the corresponding dc values.

We will assume that all variable quantities contain the factor $\exp\left[i(\omega t - \gamma_z)\right]$. The set of field equations is as follows:

$$(\text{curl } \vec{H})_i = i\omega \epsilon_{ik} E_k + j_{ei}$$
$$\text{curl } \vec{E} = - i\omega \mu_o \vec{H} . \tag{1}$$

From the continuity and motion equations, and assuming the usual linear approximation, we have:

$$j_{ei} = \frac{\rho_o \eta E_z}{i\omega\left[1-\gamma/\gamma_e\right]^2} \tag{2}$$

Presented at the Symposium on Electromagnetics and Fluid Dynamics of Gaseous Plasma, Polytechnic Institute of Brooklyn, April 4, 5, 6, 1961

where ρ_o is the charge density, γ_e is the electron wave number, and η is the charge-to-mass ratio of the electron.

If, by using the expression obtained for the current density as a field function, we introduce into the tensor ϵ_{ik}, the active term associated with the existence of an electron stream, the set of equations becomes homogeneous:

$$(\text{curl}\, \vec{H})_i = i\omega\epsilon_{ik} E_k,$$

$$(\text{curl}\, \vec{E}) = i\omega\mu_o \vec{H}, \tag{3}$$

and the tensor components have the following form:[1]

$$\epsilon_{ik} = \epsilon_o \begin{bmatrix} \epsilon_r & \epsilon_\phi & 0 \\ -\epsilon_\phi & \epsilon_r & 0 \\ 0 & 0 & \epsilon_z \end{bmatrix} = \epsilon_o \begin{bmatrix} 1 - \dfrac{b}{1-\alpha^2} & \dfrac{-ib\alpha}{1-\alpha^2} & 0 \\ \dfrac{ib\alpha}{1-\alpha^2} & 1 - \dfrac{b}{1-\alpha^2} & 0 \\ 0 & 0 & 1 - b - \dfrac{b_e}{\left(1-\dfrac{\gamma}{\gamma_e}\right)^2} \end{bmatrix} \tag{4}$$

where $b = \omega_p^2/\omega^2; \quad b_e = \omega_{pe}^2/\omega^2; \quad \alpha = \omega_H/\omega$.

ω_p being the plasma frequency, ω_{pe} the plasma frequency of the electron stream, and ω_H the cyclotron frequency of the electrons.

We will seek a solution to the set of Eqs. (3), which is symmetrical in angle. For this case Maxwell's equations can be written as follows:

$$\frac{\partial E_r}{\partial z} - \frac{\partial E_z}{\partial r} = -i\omega\mu_o H_\phi \tag{5}$$

$$-\frac{\partial H_\phi}{\partial z} = i\omega\epsilon_r E_r + i\omega\epsilon_\phi E_\phi \tag{6}$$

$$\frac{1}{r}\frac{\partial}{\partial r}(rH_\phi) = i\omega\epsilon_z E_z \tag{7}$$

$$-\frac{\partial E_\phi}{\partial z} = -i\omega\mu_o H_r \tag{8}$$

$$\frac{1}{r}\frac{\partial}{\partial r}(rE_\phi) = -i\omega\mu_o H_z \tag{9}$$

$$\frac{\partial H_r}{\partial z} - \frac{\partial H_z}{\partial r} = i\omega\epsilon_r E_\phi - i\omega\epsilon_\phi E_r \tag{10}$$

For $\epsilon_\phi = 0$ (when $H = 0$ or $H = \infty$), Eqs. (5) to (7) describe E-waves, and Eqs. (8) to (10) describe H-waves.

In the inner region I, Eqs. (5) to (10) have a solution of the form

$$\left.\begin{aligned} E_z^{(1)} &= E_{zo}^{(1)} I_o(Tr) \\ E_r^{(1)} &= E_{ro}^{(1)} I_1(Tr) \end{aligned}\right\} e^{i(\omega t - \gamma z)} \tag{11}$$

while in the outer region, the solution is of the form:

$$E_z^{(2)} = E_{zo}^{(2)} K_o(\tau r)\, e^{i(\omega t - \gamma z)}, \text{ etc.}, \tag{12}$$

where I and K are modified Bessel functions.

From Eqs. (8) to (10) we obtain the following (when taking Eq. (11) into account):

$$E_{\phi o} = \frac{\epsilon_\phi}{\epsilon_r + \dfrac{T^2 - \gamma^2}{k_o^2}} E_{ro}. \tag{13}$$

From Eqs. (5) to (10) it is seen that the E and H waves are connected through ϵ_ϕ. With $\epsilon_\phi = 0$,

$$\begin{aligned} T_E^2 &= \gamma^2 \frac{\epsilon_z}{\epsilon_r} - k_o^2 \epsilon_z , \\ T_H^2 &= \gamma^2 - k_o^2 \epsilon_z . \end{aligned} \tag{14}$$

Substituting Eq. (11) into Eqs. (5) to (10), we obtain an equation from which T can be determined:

$$\underbrace{\left[T^2 - \left[\gamma^2 \frac{\epsilon_z}{\epsilon_r} - k_o^2 \epsilon_z\right]\right]}_{\text{E-waves}} = -\gamma^2 \frac{\epsilon_z}{\epsilon_r} \frac{\epsilon_\phi^2}{\epsilon_\phi^2 + \epsilon_r \underbrace{\left[\epsilon_r + \frac{T^2 - \gamma^2}{k_o^2}\right]}_{\text{H-waves}}} . \qquad (15)$$

Let us evaluate the right-hand side of Eq. (15) taking the value $(T^2)_o = \gamma^2 (\epsilon_z/\epsilon_r) - k_o^2 \epsilon_z$ as a zero approximation. Neglecting terms of the order $(k_o/\gamma)^4$ we obtain:

$$\frac{T^2 - (T^2)_o}{(T^2)_o} = -\frac{1}{1 + \frac{\epsilon_r^2}{\epsilon_\phi^2} + \frac{\gamma^2}{k_o^2 \epsilon_\phi^2}(\epsilon_z - \epsilon_r)} \equiv \frac{k_o^2}{\gamma^2} \frac{b}{1-\alpha^2} . \qquad (16)$$

For values far from cyclotron resonance with $b/(1-\alpha^2) \ll \gamma^2/k_o^2$, the correction to the zero approximation due to the right-hand side is small and $T^2 = \gamma^2 (\epsilon_z/\epsilon_r)$.

Let us return to Maxell's equations and evaluate the coupling of E and H waves in the fields, taking the ratio $\epsilon_\phi E_\phi/\epsilon_r E_r$ (see Eq. (6)).

From Eqs. (13) and (16) it follows that this ratio is equal to

$$\frac{k_o^2}{\gamma^2} \frac{b}{1-\alpha^2} \ll 1 .$$

Thus, the criterion for separating slow E and H waves is the following inequality:

$$\frac{k_o^2}{\gamma^2} \frac{\omega_p^2}{\omega^2 - \omega_H^2} \ll 1 . \qquad (17)$$

A strong coupling between E and H waves appears only at cyclotron resonance, where $\omega_p^2/(\omega^2 - \omega_H^2)$ is of the order γ^2/k_o^2. Further on we will disregard the range near cyclotron resonance, and will assume slow E and H waves as being separated.

Equating the tangential components of the field at the boundary of the cylinder r = a, we obtain the dispersion equation for slow E waves:

$$\frac{\epsilon_{z1}}{Ta}\frac{I_1(Ta)}{I_0(Ta)} = -\frac{\epsilon_{z2}}{\tau a}\frac{K_1(\tau a)}{K_0(\tau a)} \tag{18}$$

where

$$\epsilon_{z1} = 1 - b_1 - b_e/\left[1-(\gamma/\gamma_e)\right]^2, \quad \epsilon_{z2} = 1 - b_2,$$

$$T^2 = \gamma^2 \frac{1-b_1 - \dfrac{b_e}{(1-\gamma/\gamma_e)^2}}{1-\left[b_1/(1-\alpha^2)\right]}, \qquad \tau^2 = \gamma^2 \frac{1 - b_2}{1-\left[b_2/(1-\alpha^2)\right]}.$$

Equation (18) has two groups of growing solutions. The first group corresponds to the growth of space-charge density waves. The second group corresponds to the amplification of slow traveling waves, which can also be propagated in the system when there is no electron stream. We will examine the first group of solutions.

II. INTERACTION OF A MODULATED ELECTRON STREAM WITH AN INDUCED PLASMA WAVE

The first group of solutions was considered in Reference 4 for the case of homogeneous plasma in an infinitely strong magnetic field. In this section we will consider the case of a finite magnetic field. Let us note, first of all, that with $b_1 = b_2$ and $b_e = 0$, Eq. (18) has no solutions, that is, there is no propagation of slow E waves in the system without an electron stream. For homogeneous plasma in a magnetic field dispersion, Eq. (18) has the form:

$$T_1 a \frac{J_1(T_1 a)}{J_0(T_1 a)} = \begin{cases} \tau a \dfrac{K_1(\tau a)}{K_0(\tau a)}, & \tau^2 > 0 \\[2ex] -\tau_1 a \dfrac{H_1^{(2)}(\tau_1 a)}{H_0^{(2)}(\tau_1 a)}, & \tau_1^2 > 0, \end{cases} \tag{19}$$

where $T_1^2 = -T^2$, $\tau_1^2 = -\tau^2$, and $H_0^{(2)}$ is a second-order Hankel function.

If we seek a solution for which γ is close to γ_e and take $\gamma = \gamma_e$ in the right-hand side of Eq. (19), then the right-hand side of Eq. (19)

will turn out to be a known function of $\gamma_e a$, b and α^2, after which the values of Ta are found. Further, by taking account of the expression for Eq. (18), we find the propagation constant, which can be written as follows:

$$\gamma = \gamma_e \left[1 \pm \frac{\omega_{pe}}{\omega} (p + iq) \right] . \quad (20)$$

From this we obtain the amplification per unit of length equal to $G_e = 8.7\,\gamma_{pe}\,q$ where $\gamma_{pe} = \omega_{pe}/v_e$.

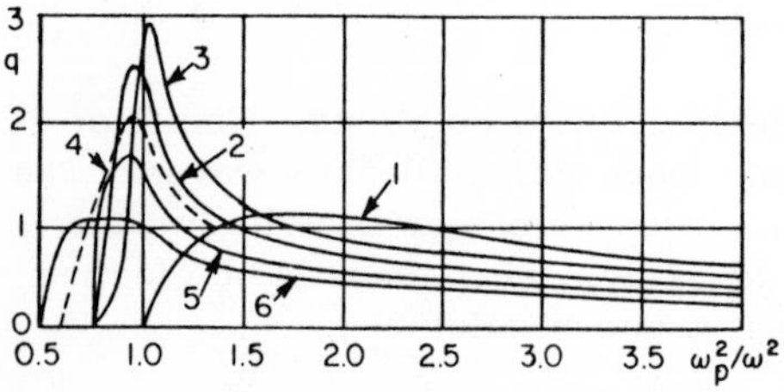

	ω_H^2/ω^2	$\gamma_e a$
1	∞	2
2	0.25	2
3	0.25	4
4	0.40	2
5	0.25	1
6	0.50	1

Fig. 1. Curves for the amplification parameter q as a function of ω_p^2/ω^2 for different values of ω_H^2/ω^2 and γ_e a

Curves of the quantity q as a function of ω_p^2/ω^2 are presented in Fig. 1 where the quantities ω_H^2/ω^2 and $\gamma_e a$ are parameters. As is seen from the curves, the presence of a magnetic field reduces the resonance peak and broadens the region of interaction. The critical frequency, above which amplification occurs, is shifted towards the range of higher frequencies according to the relationship

$$\omega_{crit}^2 = \omega_p^2 + \omega_H^2 ,$$

if $\omega_H^2 < \omega^2$. In the range beyond cyclotron resonance $\omega_{crit} = \omega_p$. Amplification also increases with the parameter $\gamma_e a$. Taking into account the finite dimensions of the electron stream may reduce the amplification by several orders.

The physics behind this mechanism is similar to the process that occurrs in inductive wall amplifiers. Under the influence of the ac fields of a modulated electron stream, charges are induced in the plasma and the electron stream is bunched in the field of these charges with instability as the result. The usual space-charge-wave process is characterized by the frequency $\omega_{pe} = (\eta \rho_0/\epsilon)^{1/2}$. Instability occurs for $\epsilon < 0$ when the frequency becomes imaginary and the oscillatory solution turns into the exponentional solution. The traveling wave of the induced charges is associated only with the modulated electron stream and cannot exist in the system without it. The results of research into the mechanism of interaction between an electron stream and an induced plasma wave are discussed in Reference 4.

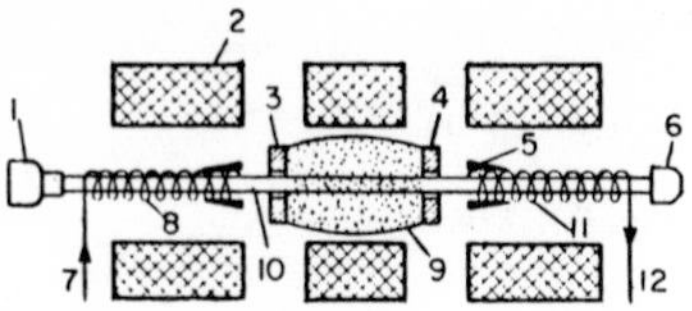

1. electron gun
2. magnetic coils
3. cathode
4. anode
5. attenuator
6. collector
7. hf input
8. modulation helix
9. plasma
10. electron stream
11. demodulation helix
12. hf output

Fig. 2. Schematic diagram of the experimental setup

We will now discuss the influence of the magnetic field. The experimental setup (see Fig. 2) is similar to that described in Reference 4, except that an additional magnetic coil is placed in the region of discharge. This coil is capable of changing the field in the plasma region without altering the conditions for focusing the electrons in the modulating sections. Measurements were made in the centimeter and decimeter bands, and the qualitative characteristics of the experimental and theoretical curves are in good agreement. Quantitatively, the absolute values for the amplification compare well, although the peak and left boundary of the curve is not so saliently expressed as in the theory. (See Figs. 3 and 4.)

III. INTERACTION OF AN ELECTRON STREAM WITH A TRAVELING PLASMA WAVE

Let us now examine the second group of solutions to Eq. (18), considering the system without an electron stream. Propagation of waves in such systems (plasma waveguides) has been studied in several works.[2, 3]

As was shown in Section II above, separation of slow E and H waves occurs throughout the entire region where the magnetic field varies, except for a narrow band near cyclotron resonance. This enables us to carry out a simpler and more effective analysis of slow waves, including the case of a finite magnetic field (compare with Reference 6).

We will assume $b_e = 0$ in Eq. (18). Then

$$T = \gamma \sqrt{\frac{1 - b_1}{1 - \frac{b_1}{1 - \alpha^2}}}, \qquad \tau = \gamma \sqrt{\frac{1 - b_2}{1 - \frac{b_2}{1 - \alpha^2}}}$$

The dispersion equation is written as follows:

$$- \sqrt{\frac{(1-b_1)\left[1 - \frac{b_1}{1-\alpha^2}\right]}{(1-b_2)\left[1 - \frac{b_2}{1-\alpha^2}\right]}} \cdot \frac{I_1(Ta)}{I_0(Ta)} = \frac{K_1(\tau a)}{K_0(\tau a)} \tag{21}$$

if $T^2 > 0$, and

$$\sqrt{\frac{(1 - b_1)\left[\frac{b_1}{1-\alpha^2} - 1\right]}{(1 - b_2)\left[1 - \frac{b_2}{1 - \alpha^2}\right]}} \cdot \frac{J_1(T_1 a)}{J_0(T_1 a)} = \frac{K_1(\tau a)}{K_0(\tau a)}, \quad T_1^2 > 0 \tag{22}$$

where $T_1^2 = - T^2$.

When $\tau^2 < 0$, radiation occurs; we will not consider this case.

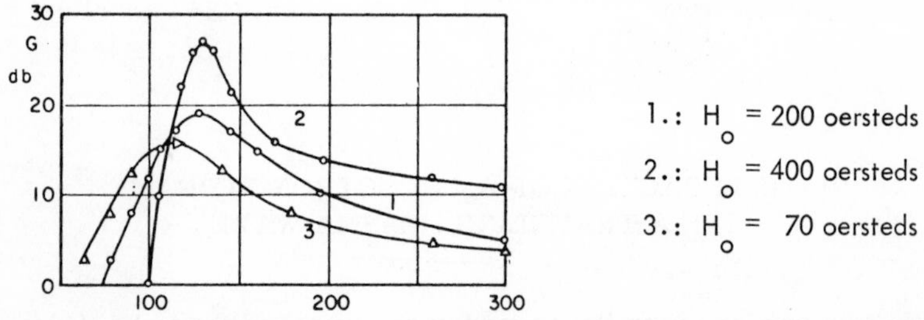

Fig. 3. Curves for the amplification as a function of the discharge current for different values of the magnetic field with a signal frequency of 380 mc.

Equation (21) corresponds to surface waves, in which the field has its maximum at the boundary r = a and drops off when going away from it, just as with ordinary slow-wave structures. Equation (22) corresponds to volume waves, in which the field magnitude is a maximum along the axis of the system. This type of slow wave does not have any analog among ordinary slow-wave structures. For example, for a plasma column in a vacuum ($b_2 = 0$) four cases are possible:

1) When $b_1 > 2 - \alpha^2$, $\alpha^2 < 1$, surface waves are propagated. The critical point where the phase velocity equals zero can be determined from the equality $b_1 = 2 - \alpha^2$. The dispersion in this case is positive.

2) When $b > 1$ and $\alpha^2 > 1$, volume waves are propagated. The dispersion in this case is also positive.

3) When $\alpha^2 < 1$ and $1 - \alpha^2 < b < 1$, volume waves which are also backward waves are propagated with negative dispersion. The group velocity in this case has its maximum and drops off at the boundaries of the region.

4) When $b_1 < 1 - \alpha^2$ and $\alpha^2 < 1$, no slow waves are propagated.

Let us consider the propagation of slow waves in a plasma channel waveguide ($b_1 = 0$, $b_2 \neq 0$). Equation (21) takes the form:

$$\frac{I_1(\gamma a)}{I_0(\gamma a)} = \frac{K_1(\tau a)}{K_0(\tau a)} \sqrt{(b_2-1)\left[\frac{b_2}{1-\alpha^2} - 1\right]} . \tag{23}$$

Here, propagation exists only for $1 < b_2 < 2 - \alpha^2$ with $\alpha^2 < 1$. The waves are of the surface type and their dispersion is negative.

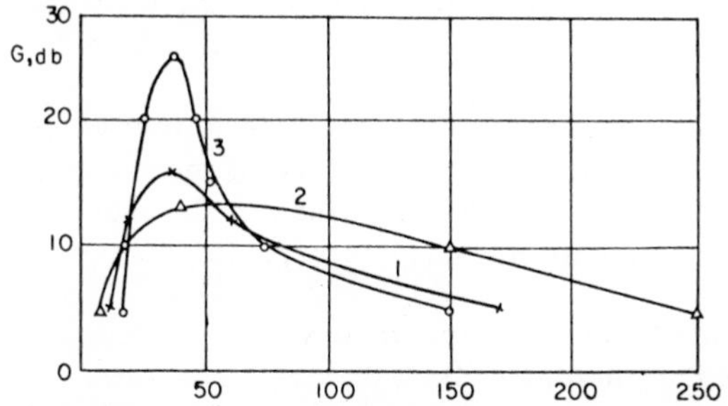

1.: H_o = 300 oersteds
2.: H_o = 30 oersteds
3.: H_o = 400 oersteds

Fig. 4. Curves for the amplification as a function of the discharge current for different values of the magnetic field with a signal frequency of 2800 mc.

In the more general case described by Eq. (21), there are two plasmas with b_1 and b_2. The conditions for propagation of surface waves follow from the inequalities:

$$T^2 > 0, \quad \tau^2 > 0, \quad \sqrt{\frac{(b_1-1)\left[\frac{b_1}{1-\alpha^2} - 1\right]}{(1-b_2)\left[1 - \frac{b_2}{1-\alpha^2}\right]}} \geq 1 . \tag{24}$$

The equal sign in the last relationship corresponds to a critical point with infinitely large retardation. After reduction, the last inequality can be expressed as follows:

$$\begin{aligned} b_1 + b_2 &\geqslant 2 - \alpha^2, \qquad \text{for} \qquad b_1 > b_2 \\ b_1 + b_2 &\leqslant 2 - \alpha^2 \qquad \text{for} \qquad b_1 < b_2 \end{aligned} \tag{25}$$

Moreover, in view of the first two inequalities, we obtain additional conditions: $b_2 = 1 - \alpha^2$ for $b_1 > 1$, while $b_1 < 1 - \alpha^2$ for $b_2 > 1$, That is, in one of the regions the concentration must be small (let us say $b_2 < 1 - \alpha^2$), while in the other region it should be rather large ($b_1 > 1$). When the inner plasma is the denser, the dispersion curve is located to the right of the critical point

$$b_1 + b_2 = 2 - \alpha^2, \qquad 2 - \alpha^2 - b_2 < b_1 < \infty$$

and the dispersion is normal. When the outer plasma is the denser, the dispersion curve is located to the left of this point ($1 < b_2 < 2-\alpha^2 - b_1$) and the dispersion is anomalous.

The conditions for the propagation of volume waves in the general case are similar to the conditions for their propagation in a plasma column considered above, except that the following condition is imposed on the outer plasma $\tau^2 > 0$. This occurs when $b_2 > 1$ or $b_2 < 1 - \alpha^2$.

We have examined the propagation of slow waves in piecewise homogeneous plasma and have determined the nature of their dependence on the plasma concentration and the magnitude of the magnetic field. Let us now consider the interaction between an electron stream and a traveling plasma wave.

Just as is done in traveling-wave-tube theory, we will expand the dispersion equation of the plasma - electron stream system near the point $\gamma = \gamma_0$, where γ_0 is the phase constant of a "cold" wave.

As an example, let us consider the interaction between the electron stream and a wave traveling in a plasma cylinder with no magnetic field present.

For $b_2 = 0$ and $\alpha = 0$, Eq. (18) takes the form:

$$(b - 1)\sqrt{1 + \frac{b_e}{(b-1)(1 - \gamma/\gamma_e)^2}} \cdot \frac{I_1(Ta)}{I_0(Ta)} = \frac{K_1(\gamma a)}{K_0(\gamma a)} . \tag{26}$$

Expanding Eq. (26) in a series about the point $\gamma = \gamma_0$ for small disturbances introduced by the electron stream, we obtain the following cubic equation:

$$(\gamma a - \gamma_0 a)\left[\frac{\gamma a}{\gamma_e a} - 1\right]^2 = - b_e\, m\,(\gamma_0 a)\ ,$$

$$m\,(x) = \frac{1}{2}\ \frac{(x\,F)'}{(b-1)\,F' - \phi'}\ ,\quad F(x) = \frac{I_1}{I_0}\ ,\quad \phi(x) = \frac{K_1}{K_0} \tag{27}$$

where $F'(x) = 1 - \frac{I_1^2}{I_0^2} - \frac{1}{x}\frac{I_1}{I_0}$, $\phi'(x) = \frac{K_1^2}{K_0^2} - 1 - \frac{1}{x}\frac{K_1}{K_0}$.

Equation (27) is valid for $|\gamma - \gamma_0| \ll \gamma_0$. In the region of synchronism with $\gamma_e = \gamma_0$ this equation has an increasing solution. The gain factor per unit of length is given by the formula:

$$G_e = 8.7\,\gamma_e\, q, \tag{28}$$

($q = (2/\sqrt{3})\,C$, where C is Pierce's amplification parameter, and q is the imaginary part of the quantity $(\gamma/\gamma_e - 1)$ determined from Eq. (27).

The gain factor G_e varies with b for constant values of $\gamma_e a$ and b_e in the following way. Maximum amplification occurs at $\gamma_0 = \gamma_e$. To the left of this point with decreasing b the amplification drops off quickly. The right section of the curve is flatter.

The optimum value for amplification is determined by

$$G_{e_{max}} = 8.7\,\gamma_e\,\frac{\sqrt{3}}{2}\sqrt[3]{\frac{m}{\gamma_e a}\, b_e}\ . \tag{29}$$

Curves for optimum values of q are represented in Fig. 5. For large $\gamma_e a$, the asymptotic formula for $G_{e\,max}$ has the form:

$$G_{e_{max}} = 8.7\,\gamma_e\,\frac{\sqrt{3}}{2}\sqrt[3]{\frac{\gamma_e a}{2}\, b_e} \tag{30}$$

(with $\gamma_e a = 10$, Eq. (30) has an accuracy of 3%). From Eq. (29), we see that the amplification rises with frequency (due to increasing γ_e) with $\gamma_e a$ and with b_e. The latter quantity is proportional to the current density in the stream.

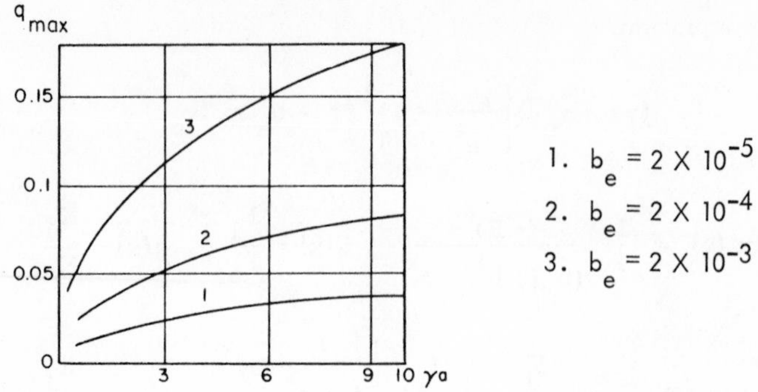

Fig. 5. Curves for the optimum value of the parameter q as a function of γa.

In the more general case where a finite magnetic field is applied along the axis of the plasma column so that $\alpha \neq 0$, the dispersion equation near the point of synchronism can be written as follows:

$$(\gamma a - \gamma_0 a)\left[\frac{\gamma a}{\gamma_e a} - 1\right]^2 = -\frac{\frac{1}{2} b_e \left\{ F\sqrt{\frac{(b/1-\alpha^2) - 1}{b - 1}} + \gamma_0 aF' \right\}}{(b - 1) F' - \phi'} \tag{31}$$

where $\gamma_0 a$ satisfies the equation for the "cold" system.

A similar examination can be carried out for the case of interaction of sheet electron streams with plasma. When there is no magnetic field or plasma in the outer region, the solution of Maxwell's equations is as follows. For the inner region,

$$H_y = H_{yo} \sinh Tx \qquad \left[\frac{H_y}{E_z}\right]_1 = \frac{i\omega\epsilon_{z1}}{T} \tanh Tx . \tag{32}$$

$$E_z = E_{zo} \cosh T_x$$

For the outer region, the fields are proportional to $e^{-\tau|x|}$ and $(H_y/E_z)_2 = i\omega\epsilon_0/\tau$, where

$$T^2 = \gamma^2 \frac{b + \frac{b_e}{(1 - \gamma/\gamma_e)^2} - 1}{b - 1}, \qquad \tau^2 = \gamma^2, \ \epsilon_z = 1 - b - \frac{b_e}{(1 - \gamma/\gamma_e)^2}$$

The dispersion equation takes the form:

$$- \epsilon_z \frac{\tau}{T} \tanh Ta = 1 . \tag{33}$$

When there is no electron stream,

$$(b - 1) \tanh \gamma_o a = 1 . \tag{34}$$

Expanding the equation in a series for small disturbances caused by the presence of an electron stream and taking into account only small terms of the first order, we come to the following equation for determining γ

$$\left[\frac{\gamma a}{\gamma_e a} - 1\right]^2 (\gamma a - \gamma_o a) = - \frac{1}{2} \frac{b_e}{b-1} \left[\frac{\tanh \gamma_o a}{1 - \tanh^2 \gamma_o a} + \gamma_o a \right] \tag{35}$$

where $\gamma_o a$ is related to the plasma concentration in accordance with Eq. (34).

In traveling-wave-tube theory, the effectiveness of interaction is characterized by the coupling impedance. Let us calculate these coupling impedances for the different types of plasma waves.

The coupling impedance on the axis is determined by the expression

$$K = \frac{E_{zo}^2}{2\gamma^2 P_z} , \tag{36}$$

where E_{zo} is the field magnitude on the axis; P_z is the total power transmitted along the axis.

$$P_z = \pi \operatorname{Re} \int_0^\infty E_r H_\rho^* \, r \, dr . \tag{37}$$

For surface waves in a plasma column, the expression for the coupling impedance takes the form

$$K = \frac{R_o \gamma a}{2\pi k_o a} \; \frac{1}{I_o^2 (Ta) \left\{ \epsilon_r A_1 (Ta) + A_2 (\gamma a) \right\}} \tag{38}$$

where

$$1/R_0 = \sqrt{\epsilon_o / \mu_o} , \qquad k_o = \omega / c ,$$

$$A_1(x) = \frac{1}{2} x^2 \left[\frac{I_1^2(x)}{I_0^2(x)} - 1 + \frac{2}{x} \frac{I_1(x)}{I_0(x)} \right],$$

$$A_2(x) = \frac{1}{2} x^2 \left[1 - \frac{K_1^2(x)}{K_0^2(x)} + \frac{2}{x} \frac{K_1(x)}{K_0(x)} \right].$$

For space waves,

$$K = \frac{R_0}{2\pi} \frac{\gamma a}{k_0 a} \frac{1}{J_0^2(T_1 a)\left\{\epsilon_r A_3(T_1 a) + A_2(\gamma a)\right\}}, \quad (39)$$

where

$$A_3(x) = \frac{1}{2} x^2 \left[1 + \frac{J_1^2(x)}{J_0^2(x)} - \frac{2}{x} \frac{J_1(x)}{J_0(x)} \right].$$

Figure 6 gives the dependence of these impedances on γa with $k_0 a = 0, 1$ for different types of waves in plasma. For comparison, the impedance curve of an ordinary helix is also presented.[5]

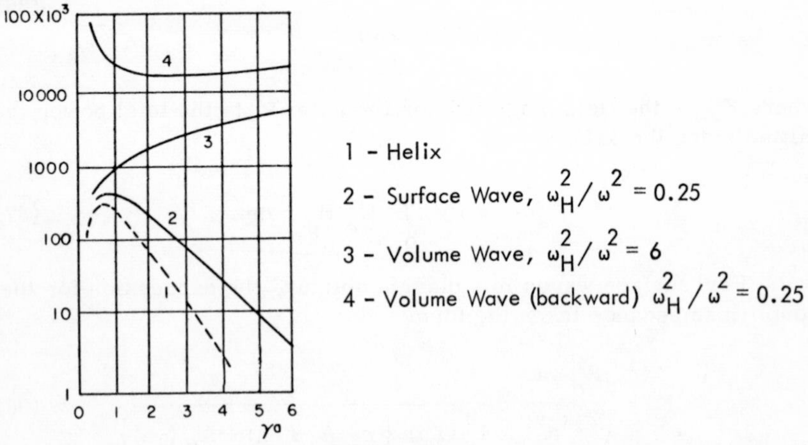

Fig. 6. Values of the coupling impedance on the axis for different types of waves in a plasma column and helix as a function of γa for $k_0 a = 0.1$.

The shape of the curves for surface waves in plasma coincide with that for the helix. The impedance of the plasma waves is greater however, for large values of γa.

The curves for volume waves are of special interest. The impedance in this case increases with γa. The coupling impedances are large, being several orders higher than the impedances for a spiral with the same radius.

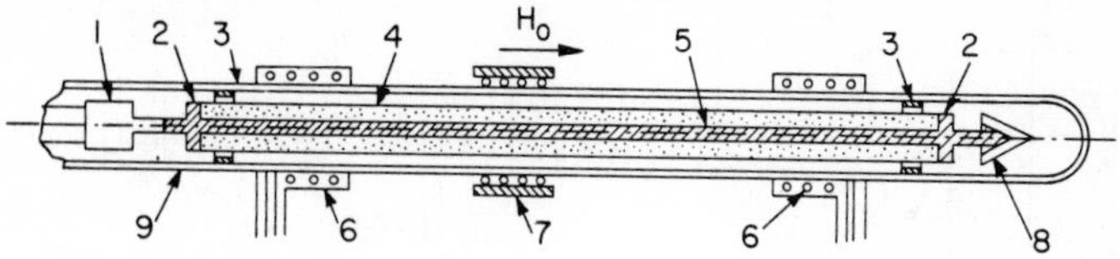

1. Electron gun
2. Discharge cathode
3. Discharge anode
4. Plasma
5. Electron stream penetrating into the plasma
6. Helix coupling devices
7. Helix attenuators
8. Collector

Fig. 7. Schematic diagram of the experimental set up for studying the interaction between an electron stream and a traveling plasma wave.

Interaction of an electron stream with a traveling plasma wave was obtained experimentally. Let us examine the results obtained. The diagram for the experimental setup is given in Fig. 7. A discharge gap is used for obtaining the plasma column. It consists of two ring-shaped cathodes and two anodes maintained at the same potential. The discharge electrons are kept from drifting transversely by a magnetic field. On the other hand, they are held back in the region around the cathode by its negative potential. An electron stream was injected along the axis of discharge. Helix couplers were used to excite waves in the plasma column.

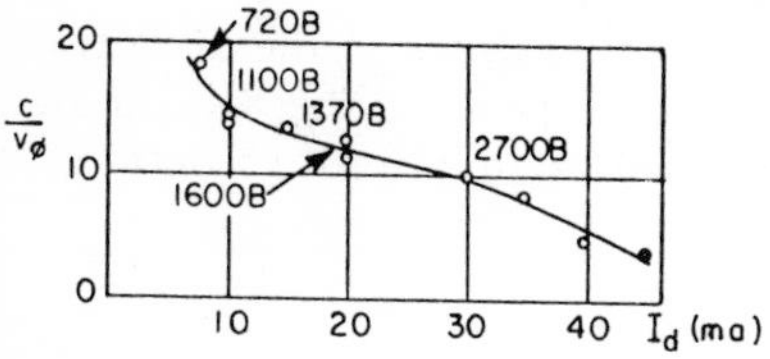

Discharge U = 50 V
H_0 = 300 oersteds

Fig. 8. Experimental curve for the slow down c/v_ϕ as a function of the discharge current

The signal was applied during the discharge. The retardation of the waves was measured by the standing-wave method. The dependence of this retardation on the discharge current is presented in Fig. 8. Measurements were made at a frequency of 1000 mc and a large retardation of up to $c/v_\phi = 24$ was obtained.

When the electron stream was turned on, amplification of the passed signal was obtained. Before the stream was turned on, the signal was transmitted with an attenuation of about 10-20 decibels.

However, with the electron stream, a real amplification of 25 decibels was obtained. Optimum electron interaction was obtained just when the stream velocity equalled the phase velocity of the slow electromagnetic wave. How the amplification depends on the electron stream velocity is shown in Fig. 9.

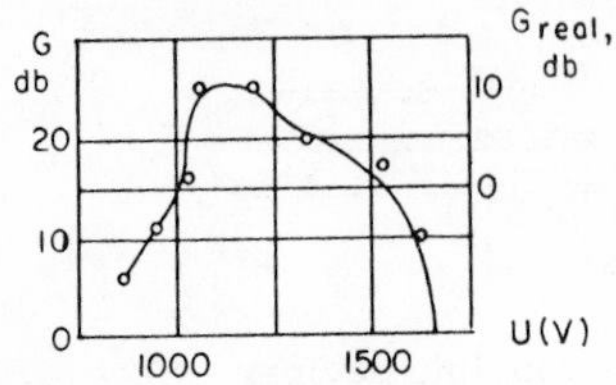

f = 1000 mc   Discharge I = 12.5 ma
H = 900 oersteds   Discharge U = 60 V
I_{beam} = 1.2 ma

Fig. 9. Experimental curve for the amplification as a function of the electron streams voltage

The following parameters represent conditions of effective amplification:

Electron stream current = 2 ma; electron stream voltage = 450 v; radius of the plasma cylinder = 0.4 cm; length of the interaction space = 8 cm; λ = 30 cm, whence $k_0 a$ = 0.084, γa = 2, K= 2140 ohms, C = 0.134, N = 6.1, G = 47.3 × CN - 20 = 20 decibels (the losses in the drift region were taken to be about 10 decibels).

This is in good agreement with the amplification obtained experimentally.

IV. INHOMOGENEOUS PLASMA

It is known that certain difficulties are encountered in the practical construction of plasma waveguides having a homogeneous concentration and sharply defined boundaries. Therefore, the propagation of waves in inhomogeneous plasma is of great interest.

Let us consider an inhomogeneous gyrotropic plasma located between two parallel infinite metal plates, the distance between them being 2a. The magnetic field points along the plates in the direction of the Z axis, and the plasma is inhomogeneous along the X-axis and unbounded along the Z-axis. From Maxwell's equations we obtain for a slow E wave

$$\frac{\partial^2 E_z}{\partial x^2} + \frac{\partial \epsilon_x}{\partial x} \frac{1}{\epsilon_x} \frac{\partial E_z}{\partial x} - \gamma^2 \frac{\epsilon_z}{\epsilon_x} E_z = 0 , \tag{40}$$

where $\epsilon_x = 1 - \frac{b(x)}{1 - \alpha^2}$ and $\epsilon_z = 1 - b(x)$

are the components of the tensor of the dielectric permeability and

$b(x) = \left[\omega_p^2/\omega^2\right] f(x)$ is a certain function of x. It is not possible to obtain an exact analytical solution to Eq. (40) with the aid of known functions even with the simplest expressions for $\epsilon(x)$. Therefore, we will solve Eq. (40) approximately by means of Halerkin's method. Let us introduce a new independent variable $u = \gamma x$ and transform the equation to its self-conjugate form:

$$\frac{\partial\left[\epsilon_x \frac{\partial E_z}{\partial u}\right]}{\partial u} - \epsilon_z E_z = 0. \tag{41}$$

Assuming that

$$f(x) = 1 - \left[x^2/a^2\right],$$

we have

$$b(u) = b_0\left[1 - \frac{u^2}{(\gamma a)^2}\right],$$

$$\epsilon_x = 1 - \frac{b_0\left[1 - \frac{u^2}{(\gamma a)^2}\right]}{1 - \alpha^2},$$

$$\epsilon_z = 1 - b_0\left[1 - \frac{u^2}{(\gamma a)^2}\right],$$

$$\sigma = \gamma a,$$

$$p^2 = \sigma^2\left[1 - \frac{1-\alpha^2}{b_0}\right] = \sigma^2\beta,$$

$$p_0^2 = \sigma^2\left[1 - \frac{1}{b_0}\right] = \sigma^2\beta_0.$$

Making use of these new designations, Eq. (41) takes the form:

$$L(E_z) \equiv (u^2 - p^2)\frac{\partial^2 E_z}{\partial u^2} + 2u\frac{\partial E_z}{\partial u} + (p_0^2 - u^2)(1-\alpha^2)E_z = 0.$$

The boundary conditions are $E_z\Big|_{\pm\sigma} = 0.$

We will seek an approximate solution in the form of a polynomial satisfying the boundary conditions

$$E_z = (u^2 - \sigma^2)(a_1 + a_2 u + \cdots)$$

and limit ourselves to a first approximation. In this case Halerkin's equation takes the form

$$\int_{-\sigma}^{\sigma} L(E_z)(u^2 - \sigma^2)\, du = 0.$$

After integrating, we determine the eigenvalues

$$\sigma^2 = -\frac{7/6}{1-\alpha^2} \frac{b_o - 5/2(1-\alpha^2)}{b_o - 7/6} \tag{42}$$

By using a cosine approximation ($E_z = a_1 \cos \frac{\pi u}{2\sigma} + \cdots$), we obtain the following result

$$\sigma^2 = -\frac{1.32}{1-\alpha^2} \frac{b_o - 2.15(1-\alpha^2)}{b_o - 1.15}. \tag{43}$$

The dispersion equation obtained enables us to determine the region where slow E-space waves exist for any value of the magnetic field. Let us consider the limiting cases of $H = 0$ and $H = \infty$. When there is no external magnetic field, we have the following from Eq. (43):

$$(\gamma a)^2 = -\frac{1.32(b_o - 2.15)}{b_o - 1.15}. \tag{44}$$

Wave propagation takes place for relative concentrations $b_o = \omega_p^2/\omega^2$ lying between $b_o = 1.15$ and $b_o = 2.15$. The dispersion is normal. The point for infinitely large retardation corresponds to $b_o = 1.15$. For an infinitely large magnetic field,

$$(\gamma a)^2 = -\frac{1.32 \times 2.15}{b_o - 1.15}.$$

Starting with $b_o = 1.15$ up to $b_o = \infty$, traveling waves exist with a normal dispersion. The following picture holds true for a finite magnetic field: when α^2 varies from 0 to 1, the range $1.15-2.15(1-\alpha^2)$ becomes smaller, and for $\alpha^2 = 0.46$ it degenerates into a point. Here the dispersion is normal. For further growth of α^2, the range becomes wider at the small concentration end starting from the point 1.15. Here waves are propagated with an anomalous dispersion. For

$\alpha^2 > 1$, waves propagate similarly to the case of an infinitely large magnetic field. The points near $\alpha^2 = 1$ are not considered.

Let us now consider slow E waves in a cylindrical waveguide filled with plasma having an inhomogeneous concentration along its cross section. The initial set of equations has the form:

$$-i\gamma E_r - \frac{\partial E_z}{\partial r} = -i\omega\mu_o H_\phi ,$$

$$-i\gamma H_\phi = i\omega \epsilon_r E_r , \tag{45}$$

$$\frac{1}{r} \frac{\partial}{\partial r} (rH_\phi) = i\omega \epsilon_z E_z .$$

For slow waves, we can therefore neglect the term on the right-hand side of the first of Eqs. (45).

$$\frac{\partial}{\partial r} \left(r \epsilon_r \frac{\partial E_z}{\partial r}\right) - \gamma^2 r \epsilon_z E_z = 0.$$

Introducing the same designations as in the case of surface waves, we obtain the following dispersion equation for the parabolic approximation $E_z \cong a_1 (\sigma^2 - x^2)$:

$$(\gamma a)^2 = -\frac{3}{2} \frac{1}{1-\alpha^2} \frac{b_o - 7(1-\alpha^2)}{b_o - 3/2} . \tag{46}$$

By taking the cosine series $E_z = a_1 \cos(\pi x/2\sigma) + \cdots$ as our base system, we come to the following equation:

$$(\gamma a)^2 = -\frac{1.77}{1-\alpha^2} \cdot \frac{b_o - 6.25(1-\alpha^2)}{b_o - 1.45} . \tag{47}$$

The conditions for propagation in the cylindrical and plane cases are quite close. In the cylindrical case the propagation band (with respect to the relative concentration b_o) is about two times wider.

Thus, in the cylindrical, just as in the plane case, the inhomogeneous concentration of plasma over the cross section of the waveguide enables slow space waves to propagate not only in the presence of a magnetic field, but also when there is no magnetic field.

Let us see how the extent of inhomogeneity in the cross section of the plasma waveguide influences our problem. We have studied the case where the concentration was equal to zero at the wall ($u = \sigma$), that is, $b = b_o \left[1 - (u^2/\sigma^2)\right]$. The case for slower change in the concentration can be described by the function $b = b_0 \left[1 - (u^2/\sigma_1^2)\right]$, where $\sigma_1 > \sigma$. With isotropic plasma (H = 0) this reduces, for example, to

$$\epsilon_1 = \frac{b_0}{\sigma_1^2}\left\{ x^2 - \sigma_1^2\left[1 - \frac{1}{b_0}\right]\right\},$$

that is, β increases by $\mu^2 = (\sigma_1^2/\sigma^2) = (R/r)^2$ times, where r is the size of the waveguide, and R is the radius of concentration drop off. Expression (46), with $\alpha = 0$, takes the following form:

$$(\gamma a)^2 = -\frac{5\mu^2 - 3}{2\,(\mu^2 - \frac{1}{7})} \cdot \frac{b_0 - \dfrac{5\mu^2}{5\mu^2 - 3}}{b_0 - \dfrac{\mu^2}{\mu^2 - \frac{1}{7}}}. \tag{48}$$

From (48) it is seen that for $\mu^2 = 1$, we obtain the same result as above. As was expected for $\mu^2 = \infty$, (homogeneous filling) no waves are propagated. When a small gradient of the concentration appears, $\mu^2 \gg 1$, near the point $b_0 = 1$, a small band appears $\Delta b \simeq 1/2\mu^2$. which expands with the inhomogeneity.

It is interesting to note that for $\mu^2 = -1$, when the concentration at the center is a minimum

$$(\gamma a)^2 = -\frac{7}{2}\,\frac{b_0 - 5/8}{b_0 - 7/8}.$$

From this we see that volume waves with an anomalous dispersion are propagated.

REFERENCES

1. J. L. Alpert, V. L. Ginsberg, E. L. Feiberg, *The Propagation of Radio Waves*, (Moscow: *GITTL*, 1953).

2. J. B. Feinberg, M. F. Gorbatenko, *J. Theoret. Phys.*, (U.S.S.R.) May 1959.

3. L. M. Pyatigorski, *Trans. Kharkov State University*, Vol. 6, p. 23, (1955).

4. E. V. Bogdanov, V.S. Kislov, Z. S. Chernov, *Radiotechnica i eloctronica*, No. 2, (1960).

5. S. D. Gvozdover, *The Theory of Ultra-high Frequency Electronic Tubes*, (Moscow: *GITTL*, 1956).

6. A. W. Trivelpiece, R. W. Gould, *J. Appl. Phys.*, Vol. 30, No. 11, p. 1784 (1959).

7. L. V. Kantorovitch, V. I. Krilov, *Approximate Methods of Advanced Analysis*, (Moscow: *GITTL*, 1949).

8. G. A. Postnov, *Radiotechnica i electronica*, No. 10, (1960).

THEORY AND EXPERIMENTS FOR THE ROLE OF SPACE-CHARGE IN PLASMA ACCELERATION

R. V. Hess, J. Burlock, J. R. Sevier and P. Brockman
NASA, Langley Research Center, Langley Field, Virginia

The role of space charge in plasma acceleration is discussed for a variety of accelerator designs. It is shown that the effects of space charges and eddy currents are coupled to each other, and the effects on plasma acceleration are discussed. Experimental studies of a coaxial plasma acceleration device reveal the role of space charges in building up oscillations and extra diffusion mechanisms. The possible role of space charge in obtaining electron emission from cathodes above the thermionic level without arc spots is experimentally demonstrated for the so-called hollow cathode configuration.

I. INTRODUCTION

One of the major differences between the motion of non-ionized gases and that of ionized gases or plasmas concerns the fact that positive and negative charges can interact with each other by electrostatic or Coulomb effects. It is the purpose of this paper to single out those aspects of the broad subject of space-charge interaction which apply to the subject of plasma acceleration. For example, the role of space-charge effects between electrons and ions instrumental in imparting directed motion to the ions falls in this category. Also included is the coupling between space-charge effects and eddy currents, which plays an important part where variations of fluid or electromagnetic properties occur. The problem of instabilities arising from currents applied perpendicularly to magnetic fields, a condition that is fundamental with a $\vec{j} \times \vec{B}$ plasma accelerator, is also discussed, based on experiments for a particular coaxial plasma acceleration device. Finally, the possible role of space-charge in obtaining electron emission from cathodes above the thermionic level without formation of arc spots is experimentally demonstrated for the so-called hollow cathode configuration. With such an emission mechanism, damage to the electrode material in long-time operation could be reduced. The major emphasis in this paper is on experiments and theory in continuous plasma acceleration with electrodes and, to a lesser degree, without electrodes. The role of space-charge in pulsed plasma acceleration was discussed by Dr. Lovberg at the November, 1960 meeting of the Plasma Physics Division of the Physical Society in Gatlinburg.

Presented at the Symposium on Electromagnetics and Fluid Dynamics of Gaseous Plasma, Polytechnic Institute of Brooklyn, April 4, 5, 6, 1961

NOTATION

$\vec{B}$ = magnetic induction

d = Debye shielding distance

$\vec{E}$ = electric field

$\vec{E}'$ = electric field relative to axes moving with the fluid, $\vec{E}' = \vec{E} + \vec{v} \times \vec{B}$

e = charge of positive ion

f = fraction of atoms not ionized, $1/f = (1 + n_e/n_n)$

$\vec{H}$ = magnetic field

$\vec{j}$ = current density

k = Boltzmann constant

M = Mach number

M_0 = Mach number at the accelerator entrance where x = 0

M_x = Mach number at a distance x from the accelerator entrance

m = mass

n = particle density

p = pressure

Q = heat

r_L = Larmor radius

T = temperature

t = time

$\vec{v}$ = velocity

r, θ, z = cylindrical coordinate system

x, y, z = rectangular coordinate system (Fig. 1)

$\beta = \kappa_e/(\kappa_e + \kappa_i)$

γ = ratio of specific heats, c_p/c_v

ε = interaction parameter, related to collision time by

$$\epsilon_{ie} = \frac{m_i m_e}{(m_i + m_e)} \frac{1}{n_i \tau_{ie}} ;$$

$$\epsilon_{in} = \frac{m_i m_n}{(m_i + m_n)} \frac{1}{n_n \tau_{in}} ;$$

$$\epsilon_{en} = \frac{m_e m_n}{(m_e + m_n)} \frac{1}{n_n \tau_{en}} .$$

ϵ_0 = permittivity of free space

K = Hall coefficient, $K \equiv (1 - 2f\beta)/n_e e \approx 1/n_e e$

$\kappa = 1/\omega_e \tau_{ei}$

$\kappa_e = 1/\omega_e \tau_{en}$

$\kappa_i = 1/\omega_i \tau_{in}$

Λ = ion slip coefficient,

$$\Lambda \equiv f^2/n_e eB(\kappa_e + \kappa_i) \approx 2\tau_{in}/m_i n_e$$

Λ_0 = value of Λ at x = 0

λ = mean free path

μ = magnetic permeability

ρ = density

σ_0 = conductivity in the absence of a magnetic field

τ_{ei} = mean collision time between electrons and ions

τ_{en} = mean collision time between electrons and neutrals

$\bar{\tau}_e = \left(\frac{1}{\tau_{ei}} + \frac{1}{\tau_{en}}\right)^{-1}$

τ_{in} = mean collision time between ions and neutrals

ω = cyclotron frequency, $\frac{eB}{m}$

An arrow over a symbol means the symbol is a vector quantity.

SUBSCRIPTS

e = electron

i = ion

n = neutral

x, y, z refers to rectangular coordinate system

r, θ, z refers to cylindrical coordinate system

II. DEVELOPMENT OF EQUATIONS FOR SPACE-CHARGE DISTRIBUTION AND EDDY CURRENTS

Meaning of Equations for Particle Motion

The equations of motion of the electrons, ions and neutrals, given in Reference 1, Eq. (48.7) are, neglecting temperature gradient terms,

Electrons

$$n_e m_e \frac{D\vec{v}_e}{dt} + \nabla p_e + n_e n_i \epsilon_{ei}(\vec{v}_e - \vec{v}_i) + n_e n_n \epsilon_{en}(\vec{v}_e - \vec{v}_n) = -n_e e(\vec{E} + \vec{v}_e \times \vec{B}) \quad (1)$$

Ions

$$n_i m_i \frac{D\vec{v}_i}{dt} + \nabla p_i + n_i n_e \epsilon_{ie}(\vec{v}_i - \vec{v}_e) + n_i n_n \epsilon_{in}(\vec{v}_i - \vec{v}_n) = n_i e(\vec{E} + \vec{v}_i \times \vec{B}) \quad (2)$$

Neutrals

$$n_n m_n \frac{D\vec{v}_n}{dt} + \nabla p_n + n_n n_e \epsilon_{ne}(\vec{v}_n - \vec{v}_e) + n_n n_i \epsilon_{ni}(\vec{v}_n - \vec{v}_i) = 0 \quad (3)$$

$$\nabla \cdot \vec{E} = \frac{e}{\epsilon_o}(n_i - n_e) \quad (4)$$

The right side of the equations of particle motion represents the input accelerating force on the particles; the terms on the left-hand side involving $D\vec{v}/dt$ represent the output in acceleration; the remaining terms give the friction by collision between particles. The electric field $\vec{E}$ represents both an externally imposed field or fields built up by charge separation according to Gauss' law (or Poisson's equation), Eq. (4). The so-called "Rosenbluth sheath"[2] refers to the collisionless reflection of a low-density plasma stream from a magnetic field, where the interaction between electrons and ions is entirely due to space-charge effects. Here we are making the same approximation that is often made for the case of ambipolar diffusion (see Ref. 3, p. 56) and elsewhere,[2] where, in the equations of motion, the charge concentrations of electrons and ions n_e and n_i can be assumed approximately equal. Since an electric field must be produced by space charge separation, the motion of the ions is tied to that of the electrons; however, some difference in space charges must be permitted to build up. Gauss' or Poisson's equation, (4), indicates that a charge difference $n_e - n_i$ of, say, $10^9/\text{cm}^3$ will produce very large fields even if electrons and ions separate only by very small distances. If we have an absolute charge density of say, $n_e = 10^{13}/\text{cm}^3$ even for $(n_e - n_i) = 10^9/\text{cm}^2$, then n_i will differ from n_e only by a negligible amount. The space-charge distribution can be determined from the distribution of the electric field given through the equation of motion as a first step (a very good one except in sheath regions near the plasma edges) without the necessity of substituting the difference in charge concentrations back into the equation of motion.

Equations for Distribution of Space Charges and Eddy Currents

According to Gauss' law, (Eq. (4)), the space-charge $n_e - n_i$ is expressed through $\nabla \cdot \vec{E}$. In order to obtain expression for $\nabla \cdot \vec{E}$, the "generalized Ohm's law" of Eq. (A - 1) in the Appendix is re-written in the form

$$\vec{E} = \vec{j}/\sigma_o - \vec{v} \times \vec{B} + K(\vec{j} \times \vec{B}) - \Lambda\,(\vec{j} \times \vec{B}) \times \vec{B}\ . \tag{5}$$

Taking the divergence of Eq. (5) and noting that $\nabla \cdot \vec{j} = 0$ and $\nabla \cdot \vec{B} = 0$, there follows

$$\begin{aligned}(n_e - n_i)\frac{e}{\epsilon_o} &= K\vec{B} \cdot \nabla \times \vec{j} + (\vec{v} - K\vec{j}) \cdot \nabla \times \vec{B} - \vec{B} \cdot \nabla \times \vec{v} \\ &\quad + \vec{j} \cdot \nabla \left[\frac{1 + \sigma_o \Lambda B^2}{\sigma_o}\right] + (\vec{j} \times \vec{B}) \cdot \nabla K - \vec{B} \cdot \nabla(\Lambda \vec{B} \cdot \vec{j})\ .\end{aligned} \tag{6}$$

The expression for the eddy currents represented by $\nabla \times \vec{j}$ can be obtained by writing $\vec{j}$ in explicit form, (see Eq. (A-6)) which is conveniently re-written here:

$$\begin{aligned}\vec{j} = \frac{\sigma_o}{(\sigma_o KB)^2 + (1 + \sigma_o \Lambda B^2)^2} &\Big\{(1 + \sigma_o \Lambda B^2)\vec{E}' - \sigma_o K(\vec{E}' \times \vec{B}) \\ &+ \left[(\sigma_o K)^2 + \sigma_o \Lambda (1 + \sigma_o \Lambda B^2)\right](\vec{E}' \cdot \vec{B})\,\vec{B}\Big\}\ ,\end{aligned} \tag{7}$$

where

$$\vec{E}' = \vec{E} + \vec{v} \times \vec{B} .$$

The general expression for $\nabla \times \vec{j}$ can be obtained by taking the curl of Eq. (7); however, the resulting equation is very involved and does not clarify the situation, and will therefore not be presented here. It is instructive, however, to present the simplified case where $\vec{E}$ and $\vec{v}$ are perpendicular to $\vec{B}$, and the coefficients of $\vec{E}'$ and $\vec{E}' \times \vec{B}$ in Eq. (7) are taken to be constants. The resulting expression for $\nabla \times \vec{j}$ is:

$$\nabla \times \vec{j} = \frac{\sigma_0}{(\sigma_0 KB)^2 + (1 + \sigma_0 \Lambda B^2)^2} \left\{ (1 + \sigma_0 \Lambda B^2)\, \nabla \times (\vec{v} \times \vec{B}) - K\sigma_0\, \nabla \times (\vec{E} \times \vec{B}) + K\sigma_0\, \nabla \times (B^2 \vec{v}) \right\} \tag{8}$$

where

$$\nabla \times (\vec{v} \times \vec{B}) = (\vec{B} \cdot \nabla)\vec{v} - \vec{B}(\nabla \cdot \vec{v}) - (\vec{v} \cdot \nabla)\vec{B} ,$$

$$\nabla \times (\vec{E} \times \vec{B}) = (\vec{B} \cdot \nabla)\vec{E} - \vec{B}(\nabla \cdot \vec{E}) - (\vec{E} \cdot \nabla)\vec{B} ,$$

$$\nabla \times (B^2 \vec{v}) = \nabla B^2 \times \vec{v} + B^2 (\nabla \times \vec{v}) .$$

One of the most striking results in the space-charge distribution of Eq. (8) is that the space-charge distribution is coupled with the eddy currents in a term containing the Hall coefficient, $K\vec{B} \cdot \nabla \times \vec{j}$. In reverse, it is, of course, indicated from Eq. (8) that $\nabla \times \vec{j}$ is coupled to a term $K\sigma_0 \vec{B}(\nabla \cdot \vec{E})$. This coupling of space-charge distribution and eddy current distribution through the Hall effect is, of course, of considerable importance for low-density, high-magnetic-field plasma accelerators with nonuniformities in magnetic fields where $\omega_e \tau_e$, representing the Hall effect, may be large.

For example, this may be the case for electrodeless plasma accelerators where the plasma is accelerated by moving magnetic mirrors or cusps produced by traveling waves. The above steady-state equations apply approximately if one sits on the moving mirror and the plasma is accelerated by slip relative to the magnetic field, as in an asynchronous motor. The plasma acceleration in such a scheme depends more or less on a sheath near the mirror surface where the electrons pull the ions along by space-charge effects. The existence of eddy currents short-circuits some of the space-charge effects, since the latter must drive some of these currents.

Several other effects can be directly seen from the equations. It is instructive to discuss the space-charge distribution and eddy-current distribution for the relatively simple case of the rectangular $\vec{j} \times \vec{B}$ accelerator.

III. APPLICATION TO RECTANGULAR PLASMA ACCELERATOR

General Remarks

The rectangular accelerator follows the principle of the linear electric motor. The metal moves in the x-direction driven by a uniform current in the y-direction interacting with a uniform magnetic field in the z-direction (Fig. 1). For a plasma, where the particles have more individuality, the conditions must be specified more closely. If we want the $\vec{j} \times \vec{B}$ force per vol. and the acceleration of the center of mass to be purely in the x-direction, we must specify that Hall currents in the x-direction are zero. This can be achieved by segmenting the electrodes and providing separate power sources to each electrode so as to force currents to flow solely in the y-direction across the channel; that is, $j_x = 0$. This approach has been suggested[4] for generators and has been successfully used for accelerators.[5] The condition that $j_x = 0$, is best fulfilled for small ratios of electrode width to channel height;[6] evidently, for infinitely long conducting electrodes, Hall currents could flow in the x-direction.

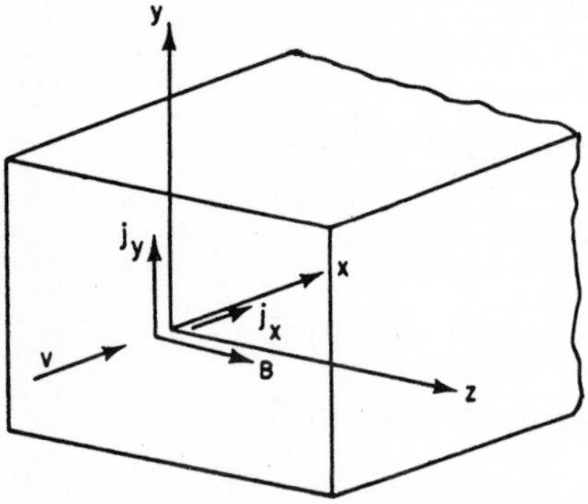

Fig. 1 Geometry of rectangular plasma accelerator

Physically speaking, the flow of the Hall current is suppressed by the fact that space-charges can build up in the x-direction which, in turn, produce an electric field E_x which suppresses the flow of current in the x-direction. The external imposition of an electric field E_x as discussed in Ref. 5 is not a requirement in this case, except perhaps for withholding the build-up of Hall currents near the electrodes if the latter are made too long. Of course, with the use of an external E_x field, the danger of overcompensation and the creation of short-circuits between the segmented electrodes also exists.

The fact that the center of mass is forced to accelerate in the x-direction does not mean that all the individual particles will move exactly in the x-direction. For example, the ions may have a small y-component (Eq. A-17) and thus some particles may be lost to the wall. If we want to force the ions in the x-direction, we have to use a Hall current component in the x-direction; under such conditions the imposition of an external E_x field would be required. Of course, the condition of center of mass acceleration purely in the x-direction is then violated (cf., Ref. 7). However, slight pressure gradients could always have compensating effects. For the practical design of an accelerator these differences are often small and can be ignored.

Space-Charge Distribution

For the rectangular accelerator, with $j_x = 0$, and $\vec{B}$ directed along the z-axis, the space-charge distribution $(n_e - n_i) = (\epsilon_0 / e)\, \mathrm{div}\, \vec{E}$ simplifies to

$$
\begin{aligned}
(n_i - n_e) &= \frac{\epsilon_0}{e}\left[\frac{\partial E_x}{\partial x} + \frac{\partial E_y}{\partial y}\right] \\
&= KB_z \frac{\partial j_y}{\partial x} + \frac{\partial}{\partial y}(v_x B_z) - \frac{\partial}{\partial x}(v_y B_z) \\
&\quad + j_y \frac{\partial}{\partial x}(KB_z) + j_y \frac{\partial}{\partial y}\left[\frac{1 + \sigma_0 \Lambda B^2}{\sigma_o}\right]
\end{aligned}
\tag{9}
$$

For the case of quasi-one-dimensional flow, where variations in the y-direction are ignored, and using $f \approx 1$ and thus $v_y \approx 0$, with $\kappa_e << \kappa_i$ (see Appendix), there results, using Eqs. (A-12) through (A-14),

$$
\begin{aligned}
(n_i - n_e) &= \frac{\epsilon_0}{e}\frac{dE_x}{dx} = \frac{\epsilon_0}{e}\frac{d}{dx}\left[\frac{j_y}{\sigma_0}\omega_e \bar{\tau}_e\right] \\
&= \frac{\epsilon_0}{e}\frac{d}{dx}\left[\frac{\omega_e \bar{\tau}_e (E_y - v_x B_z)}{1 + 2\omega_e \bar{\tau}_e \omega_i \tau_{in}}\right],
\end{aligned}
\tag{10}
$$

For the case of plasma acceleration (assuming constant temperature and constant area for the acceleration (see Appendix)) Eq. (10) becomes

$$(n_i - n_e) = \frac{\epsilon_o}{e} \frac{d}{dx} \left[\frac{\omega_e \bar{\tau}_e}{1 + 2\omega_e \bar{\tau}_e \omega_i \tau_{in}} \frac{v_x B_z}{\gamma M_x^2 - 1} \right] . \qquad (11)$$

Equation (11) indicates that the space-charge distribution along the channel is a function of several parameters which may vary continuously. Thus, through the existence of the Hall effect, a smooth variation of the space charge is possible rather than just sheaths near the beginning and the end of the accelerating section. The situation here is somewhat different from that in Ref. 8, where the effect of a magnetic field on the acceleration of the plasma of a discharge embedded in a non-ionized gas is discussed. It should be emphasized that from a certain practical viewpoint it is desirable to keep changes in σ_0 down when entering the accelerator region. The reason is known from arc discharges in magnetic fields which tend to deform or blow out because not enough ionized material enters the discharge to replenish that accelerated away from the discharge by the magnetic field and to satisfy steady continuity for a non-deformed discharge. Of course, the use of a pre-ionized flow (obtained by seeding with alkalis) entering a magnetic field will create eddy-current losses, but so will a distortion of the discharge, along with other dangers. Furthermore, the eddy losses can be controlled by shaping the magnetic field.

Eddy Current Distribution

For the rectangular accelerator with $\vec{B}$ purely in the z-direction, $\nabla \times \vec{j}$, representing the eddy currents, is still sufficiently simple so that we can write it with all terms. Taking the curl of Eq. (7) gives, for this case, with $\kappa_e << \kappa_i$; and $f \approx 1$ and $v_y \approx 0$,

$$\left[\frac{\partial j_y}{\partial x} - \frac{\partial j_x}{\partial y} \right] =$$

$$= \frac{\sigma_0}{\omega_e \bar{\tau}_e} \left[\frac{\partial E_x}{\partial x} + \frac{\partial E_y}{\partial y} \right] + \frac{1}{\omega_e \bar{\tau}_e} \left[(E_y - v_x B_z) \frac{\partial \sigma_0}{\partial y} + E_x \frac{\partial \sigma_0}{\partial x} \right]$$

$$- \frac{\sigma_0}{\omega_e \bar{\tau}_e} \frac{\partial}{\partial y} (v_x B_z) - \frac{j_y}{\omega_e \bar{\tau}_e} \frac{\partial}{\partial x} (\omega_e \bar{\tau}_e) + \frac{j_x}{\omega_e \bar{\tau}_e} \frac{\partial}{\partial y} (\omega_e \bar{\tau}_e)$$

$$- \frac{j_y}{\omega_e \bar{\tau}_e} \frac{\partial}{\partial y} (2\omega_e \bar{\tau}_e \omega_i \tau_{in}) - \frac{j_x}{\omega_e \bar{\tau}_e} \frac{\partial}{\partial x} (2\omega_e \bar{\tau}_e \omega_i \tau_{in}) . \qquad (12)$$

Neglecting ion slip,[9] $\nabla \times \vec{j}$ could also have been obtained by writing

$$j_y = \sigma_0 (E_y - v_x B_z) + \omega_e \bar{\tau}_e j_x \ , \tag{13}$$

$$j_x = \sigma_0 E_x - \omega_e \bar{\tau}_e j_y \ , \tag{14}$$

and by combining to the form, after individual differentiation,

$$\left[\frac{\partial j_y}{\partial x} - \frac{\partial j_x}{\partial y}\right] = (E_y - v_x B_z)\frac{\partial \sigma_0}{\partial x} - E_x \frac{\partial \sigma_0}{\partial y} - \sigma_0 \frac{\partial}{\partial x}(v_x B_z) + j_x \frac{\partial}{\partial x}(\omega_e \bar{\tau}_e) + j_y \frac{\partial}{\partial y}(\omega_e \bar{\tau}_e) \ . \tag{15}$$

Returning to the case with ion slip, the alternative form of Eq. (12) is

$$(1 + 2\omega_e \bar{\tau}_e \omega_i \tau_{in})\left[\frac{\partial j_y}{\partial x} - \frac{\partial j_x}{\partial y}\right] = (E_y - v_x B_z)\frac{\partial \sigma_0}{\partial x} - E_x \frac{\partial \sigma_0}{\partial y} - \sigma_0 \frac{\partial}{\partial x}(v_x B_z) + j_x \frac{\partial}{\partial x}(\omega_e \bar{\tau}_e) + j_y \frac{\partial}{\partial y}(\omega_e \bar{\tau}_e) + j_x \frac{\partial}{\partial y}(2\omega_e \bar{\tau}_e \omega_i \tau_{in}) - j_y \frac{\partial}{\partial x}(2\omega_e \bar{\tau}_e \omega_i \tau_{in}) \ . \tag{16}$$

In this form, the dependency of $\nabla \times \vec{j}$ and $\nabla \cdot \vec{E}$ is only implicitly contained. In this connection it should be pointed out that in the recent literature[9], eddy currents due to Hall effects in a rectangular plasma accelerator have been calculated. Since an integration of the full curl would be very involved, it has been assumed that the only source of the eddy currents is the variation of the j_x or Hall currents in the y-direction. The integration could be performed with a comparatively simple averaging process. Variations of σ_0 and $\omega\tau$ in the x-direction are ignored, and the ion slip terms are neglected. The coupling between space-charges and eddy currents was not brought out, however, in the approach used in Reference 9.

Finally, it should be noted that the more familiar eddy-current effects producing "end losses" for an accelerator have been calculated.[10, 11] In this case, to obtain practical results, in the integrating procedure the eddy currents are assumed to be caused by variations of the currents in the y-direction along the longitudinal or x-direction.

IV. NATURE OF OPERATION OF A COAXIAL PLASMA ACCELERATION DEVICE

Before going into a discussion of space-charge in the coaxial accelerator, a few reasons are given as to why one may want to use such a device instead of the rectangular plasma accelerator previously discussed. In doing so we are repeating some of the discussion given in Reference 12 about such a device, but with a different emphasis.

The rectangular plasma accelerator receives the gas to be accelerated from a high-temperature source, which is usually an arc jet. The plasma from the arc jet is seeded with an easily ionizable alkali metal and subsequently expanded through a supersonic nozzle where it is accelerated (Fig. 1) by the $j_y B_z$ force/vol (e. g., see Ref. 13). The arc jet itself is generally a coaxial device using an axial magnetic field B_z and a radial current density j_r, which exert a $j_r B_z$ force/vol in the azimuthal direction. The latter rotates a radial arc sector with the velocity v_θ as shown in Fig. 2. In Fig. 2

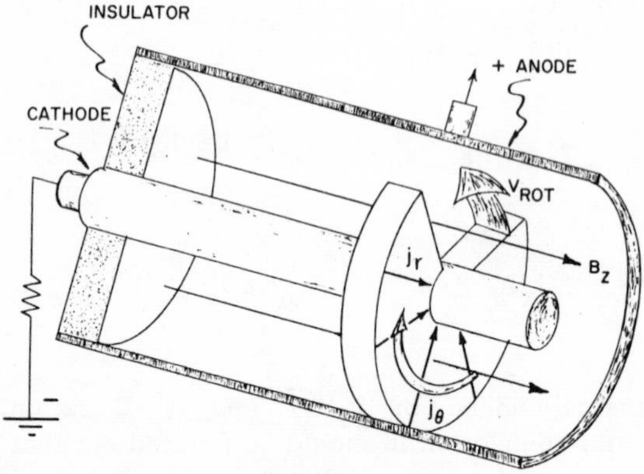

Fig. 2 Plasma rotation and Hall current

a large arc sector, or disc, is shown together with additional azimuthal currents; these features are discussed in a subsequent section. In the conventional arc jet, the rotation of the arc has the purpose of distributing the joule heating of the gas and reducing electrode erosion due to stationary arc spots. The question naturally arises as to whether it would not be possible to use $j_r B_z$ to put work into rotation of the gas and convert energy of rotation directly to energy of translation, rather than to use the arc jet first for thermalizing, together with a subsequent $j_y B_x$ rectangular accelerator. As work is put into rotation, the back emf also reduces the current and thus the electrode losses. The high joule losses, j_r^2/σ_o, near the electrode where the conductivity is low, are thereby also considerably reduced. Of course, the alternative to thermalization by joule heating is thermalization of the rotation by means of viscous or turbulent dissipation at these reduced arc losses.

V. PROCESSES AS PLASMA IS SET INTO ROTATION

In order to put the plasma into rotation, it is generally more efficient to use a uniformly distributed force derived from a current uniformly distributed over an arc disc interacting with the axial magnetic field, rather than using the more or less line-force derived from the current concentrated in an arc spoke.

The processes occurring when a uniformly distributed disc discharge is set into rotation are discussed in Reference 12. Recently, a similar mechanism has been discussed[14] (cf. Ref. 15). Since the presentation of the experiments described in Ref. 14, further experiments have been performed by the authors, these will be described in a subsequent section on "Experiments and Measurements." It should be briefly pointed out that the exploratory experiments described in Reference 12 were performed at comparatively low powers and plasma densities. The experiments described in Reference 14, as well as those more recently performed by the authors, were also performed at higher powers and plasma densities. So far, in all experiments, disc discharges have predominated.

Under the action of the axial magnetic field, the electrons, and to a lesser degree the ions, will deviate from their drift along the radial electric field direction and will perform cycloidal motions along inclined paths (curved because of electric and magnetic field variations in the radial direction). In view of this longer drift path in the magnetic field, the number of ionizing collisions of the electrons is increased, with the magnetic field acting approximately like an increase in pressure. For low pressures, the effect is quite considerable, as in the Phillips ionization gauge. The existence of excessive ionization near the cathode is discussed in the experimental section of this paper.

It seems evident that the deviation of the motions of electrons (and ions) from the radial electric field direction under the influence of the axial magnetic field should reduce the tendency toward a radial breakthrough of arc spokes. It appears that the condition $(\lambda_e/r_{Le}) > 1$ (or the equivalent, $\omega_e \bar{\tau}_e > 1$), should be a reasonable minimal requirement when the electrons are permitted to perform a Larmor rotation before collision. For pressures of 1 atm. and above, of course, very high steady magnetic fields must be used which are becoming available with use of modern techniques. It should be emphasized that the minimal requirement, $\omega_e\bar{\tau}_e > 1$, for the prevention of arc spoke formation is a much stronger condition than is required for a mere reduction of the current in the radial direction due to the presence of a magnetic field. In Section VII below, it is shown that this weaker condition, on which the existence of a Hall current also depends, requires only that $\omega_e\bar{\tau}_e > 0$. It must be remembered, however, that $\omega_e\bar{\tau}_e > 1$ is not the only effect capable of promoting uniform discharges. For example, uniform discharges can be obtained without magnetic fields by thermionic emission of the cathode, especially if aided by distributed pre-ionization in the discharge region. The possibility thus arises that $\omega_e\bar{\tau}_e > 1$ may become a starting requirement which can be considerably reduced to smaller values during steady operation. Another condition for uniform disc discharges at reduced $\omega_e\bar{\tau}_e$ could arise if the arc spoke rotates so fast that it catches up with the decay in ionization.

VI. HALL CURRENT AND ROLE OF SPACE-CHARGE IN ROTATION

The Hall current is given by connecting the azimuthal components of the differential motion between electrons and ions. Since the Hall current is a flow along "streamlines" in the direction of the components of the curved particle path (mostly electrons), a closure of the Hall current is possible as soon as the magnetic field produces the slightest deviation of the particle paths from the radial electric field direction, (that is, when $\omega_e \bar{\tau}_e > 0$). The equations for the radial and Hall currents under influence of a purely axial magnetic field when the ion slip term is included are given in Eqs. (1) and (2) of Reference 12, but are repeated here for convenience:

$$j_r = \frac{\sigma_o (E_r - v_\theta B_z)(1 + 2f^2 \omega_e \bar{\tau}_e \omega_i \tau_{in})}{(1 + 2f^2 \omega_e \bar{\tau}_e \omega_i \tau_{in})^2 + (\omega_e \bar{\tau}_e)^2} \tag{17}$$

$$j_\theta = \frac{\sigma_o (E_r - v_\theta B_z)\, \omega_e \bar{\tau}_e}{(1 + 2f^2 \omega_e \bar{\tau}_e \omega_i \tau_{in})^2 + (\omega_e \bar{\tau}_e)^2} \tag{18}$$

It may be of interest to note that a distortion of the current in the axial direction is also discussed in Reference 14. Since the condition $\nabla \cdot \vec{j} = 0$ must be fulfilled, by looking at Eq. (6) for $\nabla \cdot \vec{E}$ in which $\nabla \cdot \vec{j}$ has been set zero, it is evident that for a distortion of the current, some non-uniformities of the parameters in that equation must exist. Such non-uniformities could be produced easily by any deviation from uniformity over an infinite axial extent: e. g., by a finite length of the electrodes

Where a Hall current exists, no space-charge will build up in the azimuthal direction. The lack of space-charge effects is, in a sense, also a disadvantage since it is harder to accelerate the plasma in the azimuthal direction unless, of course, density, and therefore collision frequency, are high. At excessive densities, however, $\omega_e \bar{\tau}_e$ may become too low, and undesirable arc spokes may form. Of course, certain compromises in the adjustment of the parameters will be required. The possibility of making use of oscillatory random disturbances within the plasma without the formation of arc spots also arises; this is suggested by experiments which will be discussed subsequently. It should be re-emphasized, however, that the existence of a single disruption does not mean that no Hall current at all can flow. As indicated before, the Hall current follows the "streamlines" formed by the azimuthal components of the curved particle motion. Let us assume that an arc spoke has spread over a wide angle: in other words, that the disc has only a small angle interruption. A Hall component can exist within the wide angle arc. Near the ends, a small Hall component can still exist near the conducting walls, but it is reduced toward the region between the walls. The reasoning here is similar to that used for the Hall current distribution for finite electrode segments for generators.[6] More detailed effects are discussed after description of measurements of the plasma in the accelerator.

VII. VARIOUS METHODS FOR STEADY COAXIAL PLASMA ACCELERATION

The methods of plasma acceleration in the coaxial device can be grouped into magnetic and non-magnetic types. The magnetic methods have already been described in detail.[12] Both types make use of the diverging magnetic field, or as it may be called, an open magnetic mirror. In one case, the acceleration is obtained by interaction of azimuthal Hall current with the radial component of the magnetic field (Fig. 3). As has previously been described, the Hall current is obtained from the azimuthal component of the electron drift due to interaction of the radial electric field with the axial magnetic field component. In the other mode of operation, the whole plasma is set into drift rotation. The different centrifugal effects on electrons and ions create a difference in their drift motion, resulting in an azimuthal drift current[16] which should not be identified with the Hall current. Again, the interaction of the azimuthal current with the radial component of the magnetic field will yield an axial acceleration. The force per-unit-volume for plasma acceleration is $j_\theta B_r$. To be exact, more complete expressions for j_θ and j_r must be used than are given in Eqs. (17) and (18) for the purely axial magnetic field and purely rotational flow. The expression for j_θ and j_r when B_r and v_r are included, however, become extremely involved and are not given

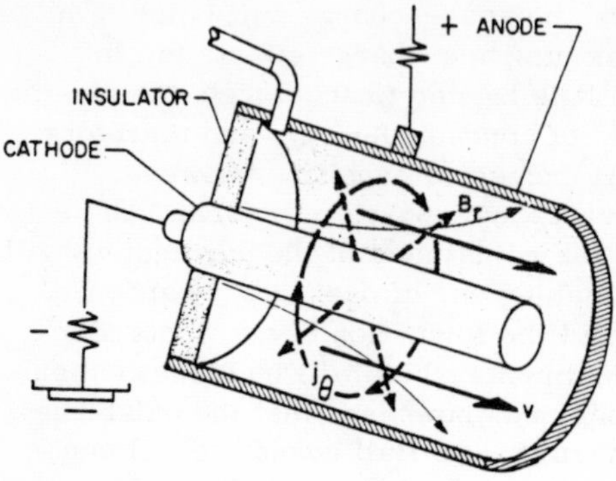

Fig. 3 Plasma acceleration based on Hall current.*

in this paper. An analysis of the accelerator which includes the radial magnetic field is given in Ref. 47.

Experiments can distinguish between plasma acceleration due to Hall current and that due to azimuthal current originating from rotation. The reason is that for Hall-current operation, the direction of acceleration changes with the polarity of the electric field E_r which, in turn, changes the direction of the Hall current j_θ. For a given magnetic field direction, the magnetic field enters in the second power and thus its direction does not enter into the direction of acceleration. The fact that the coaxial device can act in a diamagnetic fashion (pushing the plasma toward the weaker part of the magnetic field) or in a paramagnetic fashion (pushing the plasma into the stronger part of the magnetic field) was shown in a film of experiments presented at the symposium. Evidence for the existence of a Hall current in a coaxial device has also been obtained[14] with magnetic probes during the current delay when shutting off the apparatus.

The push due to rotational drift currents will always be toward the weaker part of the magnetic field. The rotation of the plasma can also be converted to translation by mechanical means. This method is most desirable when the density of the plasma is comparatively high and the per cent ionization is comparatively low. To be exact, the detailed evaluation of this condition is governed by the specific impulse desired. For example, in electrothermal propulsion using more or less conventional arc jet techniques, lithium is a more desirable working medium than hydrogen or helium for specific impulses in the range of 2500 seconds from the point of view of frozen flow efficiency, in spite of the fact that it is more easily ionized.[17, 18] If plasma rotation is required as an intermediate step to axial thrust,

*The analysis of the coaxial Hall current accelerator in this paper is based on a design which inhibits flow of current in the axial direction; this, in turn, requires short or segmented electrodes. The analysis in the Appendix for the convential crossed-field accelerator is also based on this requirement but an explicit statement concerning the coaxial accelerator was omitted in the original presentation of the paper. In the meantime, Ref. 46 has appeared where it was assumed that the accelerator was meant to have long (theoretically infinite) electrodes in which case the axial current flow is not impeded, resulting in low efficiency and low propulsive force. The authors, in a separate paper,[47] have shown in the meantime that for short or segmented electrodes the efficiency of the coaxial accelerator is comparable to that of the conventional crossed-field accelerator at a comparable propulsive force.

the advantage of lithium may become even greater.

Basically, two methods exist for mechanical conversion from rotation to translation. One method deals with conversion through diverging walls, whereby the acceleration is produced by the uncompensated components of the centrifugal force in the direction of the wall. The other method concerns ejection of the plasma tangentially to its rotating motion. Such ejection would be difficult to accomplish in the region where the coaxial electrodes are situated because their disruption from symmetry would cause a tendency towards formation of stationary arcs. The possibility exists of gently pushing the rotating plasma out of the electrode region, either by a slight pressure gradient or by slight magnetic field gradient, whereupon it is tangentially ejected.

VIII. EXPERIMENTS FOR COAXIAL PLASMA ACCELERATION DEVICE

Description and Operating Conditions

The coaxial device in which the plasma was generated and accelerated is shown schematically in Fig. 4, with a photograph given in Fig. 5.

The anode (A) is an integral part of the body of the accelerator, which is constructed of stainless steel. The cathode (C) is made of thoriated tungsten. In the high-power experiment for seeding by easily ionizable materials, the cathode was hollowed to accept the seeding material. The cathode has narrow axial slots through which the vaporized seeding material emerges (in these experiments, lithium). The cathode operating in the temperature range corresponding to thermionic emissions was sufficiently hot to provide vaporization of a seeding material. An apparatus is, however, being built to produce lithium vapor for injection through the cathode structure, and a variety of cathode perforations for the injection will be tried. The pressure in the arc region is regulated by a variable leak. While a variety of gases has been tried, nitrogen and argon were used in these particular experiments.

Previously[12] lower power experiments were conducted using nitrogen, helium, argon, and air at low densities, with and without seeding, to investigate low-power operation with glow discharges and the preventive action of magnetic fields for transition to arc-spot formation.

The large, air-core solenoid (B) is constructed of copper tubing and is water-cooled, using normal tap pressure. Operating from a dc motor-generator set, fields of 5,000 gauss can be produced for indefinite periods and fields of 10,000 gauss can be produced for short periods of time. Solenoids producing higher magnetic fields are under construction.

A solenoid of this type can be used in two ways. First, in the

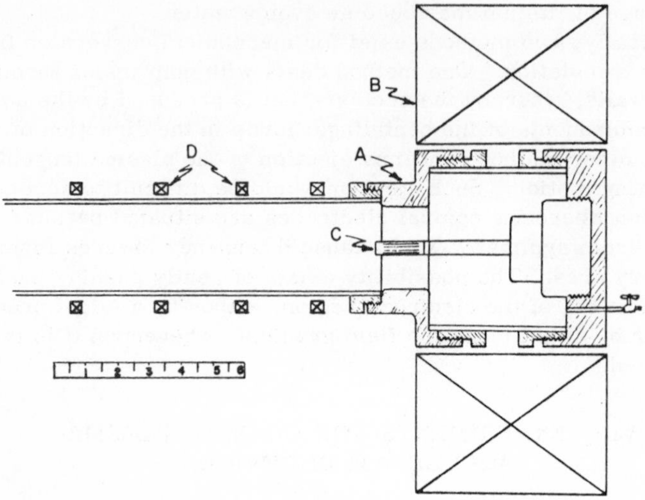

Fig. 4 Schematic view of coaxial plasma accelerator

Fig. 5 Coaxial plasma accelerator

position shown in Fig. 4, and with the addition of a field-shaping ferromagnetic ring, it can produce a slanted field in the region of the arc. This is the field configuration essential for the acceleration of the plasma using the Hall currents or drift currents due to rotation of the plasma.

In the other mode of operation, in which the solenoid is centered over the arc, the device closely resembles the configuration of the rotating arc used in arc jets. Observation has shown that with the more extended axial field region, rotation of the discharge appeared more pronounced. Use of the Helmholtz coil arrangement is also planned for this test. Probe measurements performed in a variety of magnetic field configurations have shown no large potential variations as would occur due to a rotating arc spoke (with moving electrode spots); this suggests the existence of an arc disc. Since the original presentation of this paper, Fastax movies have been made which confirm the existence of an arc disc.

The confining coils (D) produce an axial magnetic field which minimizes plasma motion to the walls of the device and plasma cooling.

A typical run of three minutes continuous operation using lithium vapor at a pressure of 350 μ of Hg and a magnetic field of 3,000 gauss allowed 6.6 kw of power to be put into the arc. The device has been run for shorter times with pressures up to 5 mm of Hg. Probe measurements again suggested the existence of distributed discharge discs. Higher powers were not used in this device since continuous operation presented a danger to the vacuum seals because of overheating. A device is presently being constructed which will not have such power limitations. The use of higher pressures and higher magnetic fields is also being tried in order to study to what pressures the arc disc operation can be extended. As pointed out earlier in this paper, operation at comparatively high pressures (densities) is required for conversion of rotation to translation by solid nozzles.

In planning the injection of an easily ionizable vapor such as lithium, the question arises as to whether one should inject the vapor into the discharge or behind it. If it is injected into the discharge, use can be made of the fact that the electron temperature is higher than the ion temperature; in this way enhanced conductivity can be obtained[19] and the possibility of rotation and formation of an arc disc would also be increased. The use of injection behind the discharge region[13] is desirable if one wants to put the electric power directly into heat without much rotation of the discharge. The use of higher conductivity in the discharge region may also increase the currents to such values that the current input becomes limited by lack of available steady state power supplies. However, the use of very strong magnetic fields in the arc, putting much work into rotation, may again remedy this situation.

IX. MEASUREMENTS OF PLASMA CONDITIONS IN THE COAXIAL DEVICE

While the full potentialities of the high-power, high-density device as an accelerator or as an improved arc jet cannot be evaluated from the low-power, low-density experiments, the latter have shown certain basic mechanisms operating in the device. One is the Hall current and the plasma acceleration due to interaction of this current with the magnetic field. Such Hall currents have also been observed in the high-power and pressure device at Langley Research Center and in that discussed in Reference 14. Furthermore, probe measurements have shown that oscillations will be produced in the discharge in the presence of a magnetic field at low densities as well as at high densities with increased magnetic fields. Similarly, the formation of arc discs at lower and higher densities depends on the magnetic field. The existence of clearly established scaling laws for the Hall current at various densities and the observations of approximate scaling conditions for the other effects, suggest increased significance of the low-density experiments for which, so far, more measurements have been made. Careful experiments are being performed to check possible scaling laws.

X. PROBE MEASUREMENTS

Figure 6 gives a schematic view of the coaxial accelerator, including the position where probe measurements were performed:

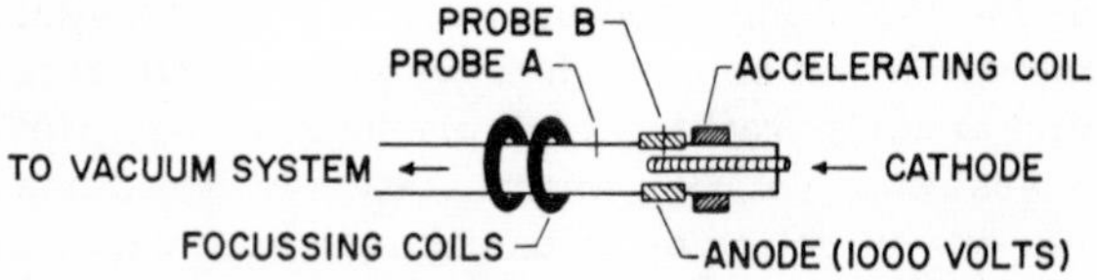

Fig. 6 Low pressure coaxial plasma accelerator

A - outside the accelerating regions and in a region of low magnetic flux; and B - inside the accelerating region. For the low-density device, using Hall currents for acceleration, the magnetic field is, of course, not uniform because the radial magnetic field component, together with azimuthal Hall currents, gives the $\vec{j} \times \vec{B}$ force/vol for axial acceleration. The measurements in this device were taken at pressures from 50 to 300 microns; a few measurements were also taken in the high-power device at pressures of 5 mm at magnetic fields from 3000 to 5000 gauss. The larger number of probe measurements were done with the magnetic field of about 500 gauss in the accelerating region and a voltage drop between the electrodes of about 1,000 volts; the device thus operated in the glow-discharge region. For the plasma acceleration experiments reported in Reference 12, magnetic fields up to 1,000 gauss were used.

The plot in Fig. 7 shows the variation of probe currents with probe voltage of a probe situated at position A outside the accelerator region, 1/4-inch away from the wall.

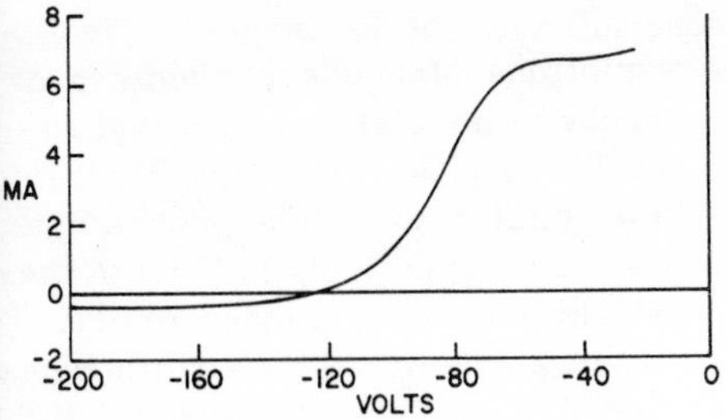

Fig. 7 Probe measurement in the flow region

The probe voltage is referred to the anode. The curve is typical for the Langmuir probe and yields an electron temperature of 10^5 °K and an electron density of

$$n_e = 10^{11}/cm^3$$

at 55μ pressure. The electron density n_e at position A was also measured with 3 cm microwaves and a result of $n_e = 10^{12}/cm^3$ was obtained. Since the microwave measurements give an average over the cross section, and the probe A is 1/4-inch away from the wall, it appears correct to assume that plasma of higher n_e is near the center of the tube. The following measurements inside the accelerator also bear out this fact.

Radial surveys of the plasma potential at position B inside the accelerator region are given in Fig. 8. In the lower curve of Fig. 8, the magnetic field is turned off and the potential distribution is typical of that in a glow discharge. In the upper curve, where the magnetic field is turned on, a considerable change in the distribution of the potential is noted, and the drop in potential is concentrated in a greatly reduced region near the cathode. Visual observations also indicate a considerable increase in brightness near the cathode. Since measurements of electron concentration near the cathode were difficult to undertake (for reasons to be subsequently discussed), the existence of these concentrations of potential variation and brightness represent the strongest, if indirect, evidence of comparatively high electron concentration near the cathode. Further indirect evidence was also obtained from a disc situated at about position B, which was used as a ballistic pendulum to measure the plasma momentum (cf. Ref. 12). The disc was burned in a ring region with the inside diameter about equal to that of the cathode. Using the evidence obtained from measurements suggesting that n_e near the center of the tube outside the accelerator would be larger than $10^{12}/cm^3$, the value of n_e near the cathode inside the accelerator should be even

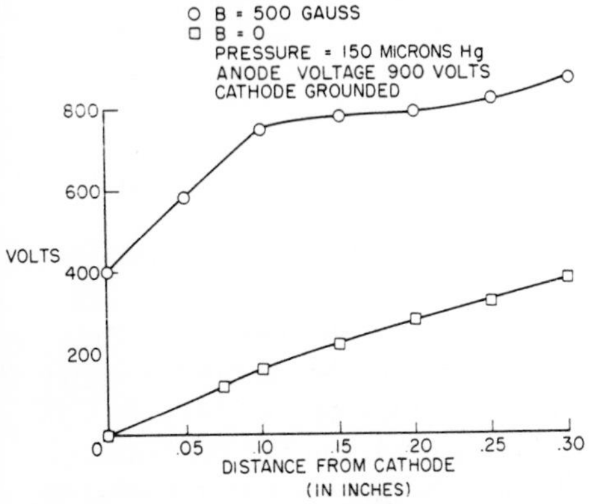

Fig. 8 Plasma potential near cathode

higher. This again shows the strong influence of the magnetic field.

Figures 9 and 10 show the variations of probe currents and probe voltage at two different radial locations of position B inside the accelerator. The probes are located respectively 1/4" from the anode and 1/4" from the cathode. T probe signatures show an influence o the stronger magnetic flux inside th accelerator. The signature shows greater symmetry with respect to t zero current axis in Fig. 9 than in th weaker magnetic flux region in Fig. 7. This is due to the fact that in the presence of the magnetic field the electron current is depressed while the ion current is less affected. For the probe curve in Fig. 9, the upper, almost horizontal, plateau is only comparatively short and is followed by an upward break. This break, which has also been observed in Reference 8, does not occur for the probe curve in Fig. 7 for station A in the weak magnetic field region. The reason for such a break is generally attributed to the occurrence of breakdown near the probe, as the probe begins to act like an anode, relative to the "plasma cathode" around it. The premature breakdown in a magnetic fiel may be due to the increased ionization, caused by the lengthening of the pat of the electrons in the sheath resulting in an increased number of collisions

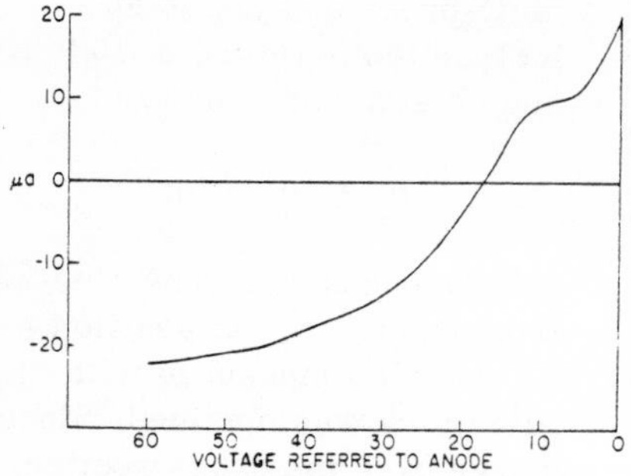

Fig. 9 Probe measurement in accelerator region 1/4" from anode

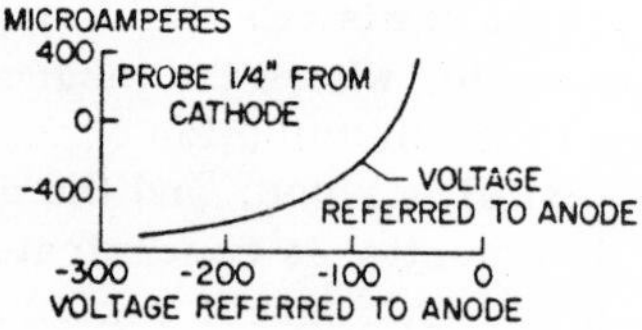

Fig. 10 Probe measurement in accelerator region 1/4" from cathode

For the probe curve (Fig. 10) given by the probe 1/4-inch from the cathode, a leveling toward the lower part of the ion saturation current seems indicated; however, the top break of the curve seems to have disappeared. So far, an attempt to increase the voltage range to find this top has not been successful. In view of the high ionization together with the magnetic field near the cathode, a good possibility exists of breakdown occurring as the full electron saturation current is reached.

Neither probe signature is sufficiently distinct to give a measure of electron concentration; however, indirect evidence previously mentioned suggests that it is very high near the cathode. The electron temperatures of the probe curves near the anode and near the cathode are 10^5 °K and 10^6 °K, respectively. (There would be more than enough potential energy in the discharge for such a temperature.) However, the meaning of temperature in probe measurements becomes somewhat uncertain because of the oscillations introduced into the plasma by the magnetic field interaction with the discharge. It has been argued[8, 20] that oscillations shift the probe curve in such a manner as to give a higher apparent temperature. However, recent studies[21] suggest that the temperature measurements with a Langmuir probe are accurate at oscillation energies lower than or equal to kT_e. In the high-density, high-power device, preliminary measurements indicate that the temperature measurements could be of the same order; careful checks of these results are being made.

A radial survey of oscillations of the plasma potential in the accelerator region is presented in Fig. 11. In the top picture the probe was 0.5" from the cathode and was moved 0.1" towards the cathode between pictures; in the bottom picture, it is .1" from the cathode.

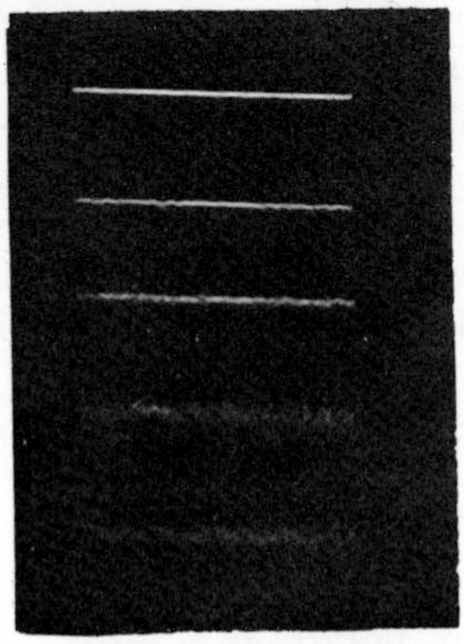

Pressure (μ Hg)	300
Sweep Speed (μ s/cm)	10
Sensitivity (v/cm)	10

Fig. 11 Plasma oscillation survey

Sweep speed is 10μ sec/cm, and sensitivity is 10 volts/cm. The intensity of the oscillations falls off rapidly with increasing distance from the cathode. Under certain conditions, when observing oscillations with a probe at a distance over 0.2" from the cathode, irregular spikes are seen which have a larger magnitude than do the normal oscillations. As the probe is moved towards the cathode, the spikes decrease in magnitude while the normal oscillations increase in magnitude until the spikes can no longer be distinguished. The spikes seem to be caused by the "blobs" of finite-size plasma entities breaking through the magnetic field. The oscillations are highly irregular and cannot be stopped using the oscilloscope sweep. However, a study of single-sweep photographs taken at $10\ \mu$ sec/cm show that the frequency of the oscillations range up to about 10^6/sec. A tentative explanation of the origin of the oscillations is given later.

Oscillations were also observed in the coaxial device previously described using higher powers with higher densities and also with higher magnetic fields. An increase in oscillations connected with an increase in current seemed to occur over a limited region of pressure increase in the low pressure device. In the experiments at high powers and pressures, the cathode emitted thermionically, whereas in the low-pressure experiments the operation was in the glow-discharge range with secondary emission by ion bombardment. The question naturally arises as to whether the higher cathode drop existing in the glow discharge without the magnetic field would not play a part in producing oscillations. Oscillations were still observed with thermionic emission, suggesting that the cathode drop for the glow discharge without the magnetic field does not play an essential part in producing oscillations.

Probe measurements were also undertaken to determine possible coherent motion of disturbances. In particular, the question arose as to whether some rotational motion could be observed for glow-discharge operation, i. e., without arcs. Two probes were placed radially into the accelerator region 60° apart in azimuth. The ac component of the floating probe potentials were displayed on the x and y-axes of an oscilloscope. The fact that a Lissajous figure with the same phase difference appeared indicates that the coherent rotation of an approximately sinusoidal variation in potential could be observed under certain conditions. In Fig. 12, one such Lissajous figure is shown in the

Pressure (μ Hg)	200
Sweep Speed (ms/cm)	2
Sensitivity (v/cm)	10
Magnetic Field (Gauss)	300

Fig. 12 Two probe oscilloscope Lissajou record; probe displacement 60° in azimuth

foreground, while in the background, the oscillations on one probe vs time are displayed. The crests of the coherently rotating potential variations can apparently be identified with a rotation of the previously identified spikes in the probe potential. Since it appears that these spikes correspond to finite plasma entities, or blobs, it seems likely that such blobs could be explained by the fact that they represent perturbations of the coaxial symmetry. Thus, use can be made of space charges to pull the ions behind the electrons, which are being accelerated by the $j_r B_z$ force/vol. It should be emphasized, however, that the amplitudes of the oscillations in the accelerator are not large enough to disrupt the flow of the Hall current. Rotation has been observed in related discharge geometries in Reference 22 and more recently, in Reference 23. The subject of rotations for discharges in magnetic fields is far from closed and a variety of effects seem to be possible.[24, 25]

XI. DISCUSSION OF EXPERIMENTS

Effect of Magnetic Field on Electrode Losses and Electron Emission Effects

One might intuitively feel that due to the existence of a Hall current component, the power lost to the electrodes is reduced even when the total power is made the same with the magnetic field as it was without it. However, the fact that the current between the electrodes deviates from the radial direction, does not in itself change the kinetic energy of the charged particles impinging on the electrodes. The presence of the Hall current, can, however, change the power balance near the electrodes if the microscopic motion is accounted for. Due to the presence of the magnetic field, the electrons may perform part of their drift motion at a distance of the order of the Larmor radius provided that $\lambda_e/r_{Le} \approx \omega_e\bar{\tau}_e > 1$. As a consequence, ionizing collisions occur in the close neighborhood of the cathode and the thickness of the sheath is reduced. This effect is brought out strongly in the experiments. Due to the small thickness of the sheath and the close proximity of a large ion concentration near the cathode surface, emission effects above the effects of thermionic emission may be encouraged, especially the so-called I. F. (Ion Field) field emission mechanism[26] which does not require fields as high as ordinary field emission. Of course, the thermionic emission itself can also be enhanced by the presence of atoms of low ionization potential near the surface of a cathode, which lower its work function. However, for highly ionized regions near the cathode, the other mechanism should begin to predominate. The amplitudes of the oscillations near the cathode may be high enough to stimulate secondary electron emission (note that secondary electron emission due to a variety of oscillations occurs also in the magnetron[27]).

On the other hand, near the anode, if $\lambda_e/r_{Le} \approx \omega_e\bar{\tau}_e > 1$, an electron can only drop approximately through the height of a Larmor radius rather than through that of a mean-free path. The kinetic energy with which the electrons impinge on the anode is thus reduced to approximately that corresponding to the drift velocity; unless changes in $\vec{E}$, enhanced diffusion, or other effects play a large part, this mechanism reduces anode heating. It should be noted that there are, of course, other methods which produce anode cooling; perhaps the most outstanding one is concerned with gas injection through a porous anode.[28] (For a discussion of other forms of electrode losses, see References 14 and 15.)

Amplification of Oscillations and Enhanced Diffusion in Coaxial Accelerator

The review of mechanisms for amplifying oscillations of a plasma in a magnetic field[25] is used as a background for the present discussion, although the present experiments are actually somewhat different in view of a current imposed perpendicularly to the magnetic field. Fortunately, the amplification of oscillations and the resulting enhanced diffusion has received much attention in connection with the containment of thermonuclear plasmas. Taking into consideration that in the present experiments the magnetic lines form either the straight envelopes of a cylinder or are even convex toward the axis in the acceleration section, the existence of flute instabilities, which require magnetic lines to be concave toward the axis, is unlikely. The flute instability is analogous to the Rayleigh-Taylor instability of a fluid supported under gravity by a second, weightless fluid.[29] A convex curvature of the magnetic lines would produce a force opposed to the direction of gravity in the above analogy. On the other hand, centrifugal forces would act in the proper direction for the occurrence of instabilities. However, instabilities were found to exist in the present experiments even when the velocity of rotation of the ions was small; the electrons, whose velocity of rotation is close to their drift velocity, offer only a remote possibility due to their small mass. Furthermore, instabilities have been noted in related experiments (e. g., Reference[25]), where rotation is not a primary effect. In view of the existence of instabilities at relatively low currents, the various pinch instabilities are unlikely prospects. The formation of a non-uniform region, with comparatively high ionization and azimuthal Hall-current components corresponding to high values of $\omega_e\overline{\tau}_e$, would favor the occurence of transverse Helmholtz instabilities and longitudinal two-stream instabilities. The occurence of helical instabilities[30] is also a possibility for the Hall current accelerator where the electric field has a component in the direction of the magnetic field lines.

Recently, a different approach to the instability problem has been developed which is more or less based on the preliminary studies in Reference 20. It is emphasized, in a series of papers from several viewpoints,[31, 32, 33] that only small asymmetries, such as small currents, are required to produce amplification of oscillations in the presence of a magnetic field, in contrast to the two-stream instability with equal ion and electron temperatures, which requires large currents. It is indicated in Reference 31 and references given there that the velocities corresponding to the large currents would have to be above the thermal velocities corresponding to electrons. It is also indicated in these references that the existence of a comparatively low ion temperature will favor the amplification of oscillations at low currents. The low temperatures used in the present experiments, as compared to the thermonuclear case, are conducive to amplification. This is especially so since the electron temperature can be several orders of magnitude higher than the ion temperature. Therefore, in view of their small mass, the electrons can provide good ionization without appreciably raising the ion temperature (cf. References 34 and 19). The amplification of the oscillations is related to the existence of a collision-free plasma. This collision-free state is defined in the presence of a magnetic field as one where the Larmor radii of the charged particles r_{Li} and r_{Le} are smaller than the mean-free paths λ_i and λ_e, which are of the same order. The "electrostatic" requirement that the Debye distance be smaller than the mean-free path must, of course, also be satisfied. The Larmor radii are determined by $r_{Le} = m_e c_e/eB$ and $r_{Li} = m_i c_i/eB$, where c_e and c_i are, respectively, the thermal speed of electrons and ions and $c_{e,i} \sim \sqrt{T_{e,i}}$. The Debye distances for the electrons and ions respectively, are, assuming that $n_e \approx n_i$, $d_e \sim \sqrt{T_e/n_e}$ and $d_i \sim \sqrt{T_i/n_e}$. One may thus obtain collision-free conditions in a plasma at comparatively high densities or a small mean-free path, provided that the magnetic field and the electron concentration are high enough. Since the Larmor radii are also a function of $\sqrt{T_{e,i}}$, the comparatively low temperatures, especially those of the ions, used in the present experiments may provide an especially inviting situation for collision-free conditions. The low temperature of the ions, which have about the same temperature as the neutrals, however, will keep the mean-free path down. As a matter of fact, $\omega_i \tau_{in}$ will become proportional to $\sqrt{T_i}$, assuming constancy of pressure. Thus, for comparatively high pressures, say, 1/10 atm, the condition $\omega_i \tau_{in} > 1$ would be hard to fulfill. The Debye distance of the ions can easily become smaller than the mean-free path even at high pressures; the electron Debye distance is, of course, somewhat larger than that of the ions. These conditions are considerably aided by the comparatively high $n_e \approx n_i$ in the immediate neighborhood of the cathode (at a distance of the order of r_{Le} away). Thus, the possibility exists for amplification of waves in a magnetic field for small currents. Since the region of high ionization is closed on itself, standing waves could build up. It appears that even for comparatively high pressures, the existence of amplified oscillations could cause drift motion and enhanced diffusion across the magnetic field, especially in the neighborhood of this well ionized region. For low pressures, the condition $\omega_i \tau_{in} > 1$ could also be met, thus adding other possibilities for amplification of oscillations. More work is needed for a detailed interpretation of the experiments.

It should be pointed out that the assumption that the enhancement of diffusion can only occur by randomized oscillations across the magnetic field is not quite satisfied. The bulging currents in the axial direction is discussed in Reference 14; such effects would be caused by non-uniformities due to, say, finite electrode extension. Naturally, for the present non-uniform conditions of electric and magnetic fields, some diffusion along the magnetic lines could also occur. Of course, the plasma acceleration itself modifies the diffusion. The existence of an end wall also makes Simon diffusion possible, but it should not be the predominant anomolous diffusion effect here.

Finally, while the mechanism for amplification of oscillations is not yet definite, it may be of general interest to note that the region in which the amplification occurs seems clearly defined, whereas in some other experiments this has not always been obvious. The fact that the oscillations originate in or near the cathode sheath, where the formation of arc spots is controlled, suggests that they could be instrumental in modifying their formation either directly or through enhanced diffusion.

XII. THE HOLLOW CATHODE

Application to Accelerator

A successful plasma propulsion device must operate for extended periods. Unless, like the traveling mirror accelerator, the device operates without electrodes, electrode heating becomes a problem. Severe heating increases the erosion rate, limiting the lifetime of the accelerator.

A considerable amount of heating of the cathode is required if thermionic emission is the only available source of electrons. Thermionic emission has the advantage that it permits the formation of uniform discharges over a large surface rather than in one or more concentrated arc spots. There are, however, some attractive features about arc discharges from spots, such as field-emission processes which permit current densities above those corresponding to thermionic emission. To take advantage of the extra field-emission effect at lower than thermionic temperatures, cathodes with a distribution of serrations or pinpoints have been used.[35, 36] The high electric fields near the points, together with a high degree of ionization there, offer the possibility of arc-spot field-emission effects. The question arises as to whether emission mechanisms other than those which are thermionic could not be forced to occur on a larger surface than that available with pinpoints, with the further possibility of avoiding erosion. The hollow cathode shows promise in this direction.

Since the hollow cathode emits from a cavity, the surface from which the emission takes place is larger than its opening across which he current flows to the anode. For thermionic emission, the hollow cathode thus gives the same current density as flat plate cathode with the area of the opening at a lower temperature of the cavity surface. In view of its cavity geometry, erosion rates are reduced because sputtered material is redeposited on the cavity surface.

Once the discharge has started, the cavity fills with high ion density plasma (Reference 37 gives $n_e \approx 10^{16}/cm^3$ at 1 mm Hg). In effect, the cavity forms an electrostatic confinement condition; multiple reflections of the electrons in the cavity before escaping (Reference 38, p. 114) create a high degree of uniformity and the current runs to a "plasma cathode." The need for arc spots is eliminated even with current densities as high as 25,000 amps/cm^2 for a 200 amp discharge at 1 mm Hg cavity pressure.[39] Emission at the walls cannot be totally explained by thermionic emission, and the high ion densities in the cavity suggest field enhanced thermionic emission or possibly emission of the I. F. (Ion-Field) type.[26] The presence of high-intensity ultraviolet radiation in the cavity suggests significant contributions from photo emission for hollow cathode glow discharges,[40] but for arcs with the smaller voltage drop such a mechanism has been discounted. The uniformity of the current density across the cavity aperture distinguishes the hollow cathode from the high-intensity arc discharge, which emits electrons from concentrated spots. Finally, a combination of the serrated-cathode effect and a multiple hollow-cathode effect may prove to be useful, for the hollows between the points of a serrated cathode can assume a cavity shape, thus utilizing the entire electrode surface. Since the original presentation of this paper, successful experiments with multiple hollow-cathodes have been performed.[48]

Experimental Work with Hollow Cathodes

Preliminary experiments were made with a cathode in the form of a rectangular box 2 inches long, with a 1/2" × 1/2" aperture, fabricated from thin (.010") tungsten sheets to permit the heating deemed necessary in Reference 39. The rectangular box cavity was tested because of its suitability for a rectangular accelerator. A tendency towards vase-like shaping was observed in Reference 41; however, for more recent tests with different cathode materials, such shaping could be avoided. The cathode was mounted in a mycalex body as shown in Fig. 13. When the cover plate is affixed, only the interior of the cavity is visible, thus preventing discharges to the exterior surface. All experiments were made with carbon anodes.

The electrodes were mounted at a gap of 2" in a 3" pyrex cross which was continuously pumped. Both air and nitrogen were bled through a controlled leak to adjust the pressure from 100μ to 10 mm. Chunks of lithium were put in the cathode to give a seeded discharge.

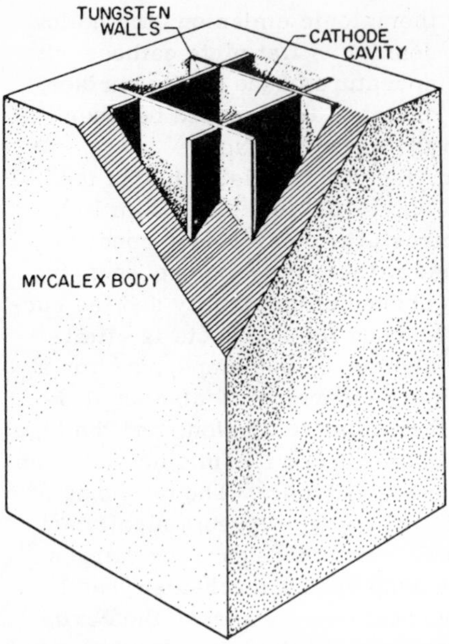

Fig. 13 Sectioned view of the hollow cathode assembly (without cover plate)

A Tesla coil was used to pro mote breakdown which occurred at 200 to 350 volts. Once the discharge settled in the cavity, the Tesla coil could be turned off. Figure 14 shows the hollow-cathode discharge in operation. The discharge operated at $\approx$ 50 volts, with a slight negative characteristic, varying by only 10 to 15 volts as the current was raised from 10 amps to 65 amps (the maximum current to date). No ar spots were observed and the discharge appeared uniform across the aperture. Uniform emission over the interior surface of 2.4 amps/cm^2 (65 amps/27 cm^2) would require a temperature of 2700° K for purely thermionic emission. Across the aperture, $\vec{j} > 40$ amps/cm^2 which, for a flat plate thermionic cathode, woul require $\approx 3200^\circ$ K. Observation inside the cavity suggest a much lower operating temperature, implying that there are other than therr ionic emission processes in the cavity.

Figure 15 shows the cathode assembly (without the mycalex cove plate) after the 50 amp run which marked the failure of an anode. Th cover plate was loosened in this discharge, and arcing to two assembl screws in the mycalex body produced the slight melting observed on the inside edges of the mycalex. Inside the body, the mycalex walls remained smooth with no signs of melting, supporting the low-temper ature operation of the cathode (the melting point of mycalex is $< 1500^\circ$ F). Inside the cathode, pieces of lithium have been deposited on the tungsten walls, but no burning or melting of the tungsten was observable.

Preparations are being made to investigate the behavior of the discharge in a transverse magnetic field at a variety of pressures. The coaxial accelerator will be used as a plasma source to provide th necessary replenishing of ions in the discharge to eliminate "bowing" of the discharge column.

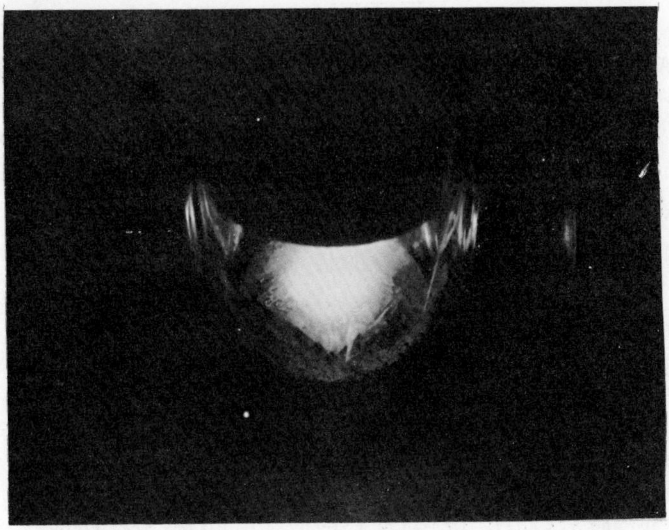

Fig. 14 Hollow cathode in operation

Fig. 15 Hollow cathode after several hours of operation

ACKNOWLEDGMENT

Acknowledgment is made to Messrs. John Malenda and Richard Weinstein for their contributions to the design of the coaxial accelerator and the hollow cathode and for carrying out the experimental wor

REFERENCES

1. W. Finkelnburg and H. Maecker, "Elektrische Bogen und Thermisches Plasma," *Handbuch der Physik,* Vol. XXII (Gasentladung II, Springer, 1956).

2. M. Rosenbluth, "Infinite Conductivity Theory of the Pinch," Los Alamos Scientific Laboratory, Univ. of California, 1954.

3. F. H. Clauser (General Editor), *Plasma Dynamics* (Boston: Addison Welsley, 1960).

4. R. M. Patrick, "Magnetohydrodynamics of Compressible Fluids," Ph. D. Thesis, Cornell Univ., 1956.

5. G. Wood and A. Carter, "Design of a Steady D.C. Plasma Accelerator," *Third Gas Dynamics Symposium: Dynamics of Conducting Gases* (Northwestern Univ. Press, (1960).

6. H. Hurwitz, Jr., R. W. Kilb and G. W. Sutton, "Influence of Tensor Conductivity on Current Distribution in MHD Generator," *J. Appl. Physics,* Vol. 32, No. 2 (Feb. 1961).

7. A. Busemann, "Is Aerodynamics Breaking an Ionic Barrier?" *Proc. Symposium on Electromagnetics and Fluid Dynamics of Gaseous Plasma,* (New York: Polytechnic Press, 1961).

8. W. D. McBee, "A Study of the Influence of a Strong Magnetic Field on an Unconfine Glow Discharge in Air at About 1 mm Pressure," Ph. D. Thesis, Univ. of Michiga 1951.

9. R. J. Rosa, "Physical Principles of Magnetohydrodynamic Power Generation," *The Physics of Fluids,* Vol. 4, No. 2 (Feb. 1961).

10. G. W. Sutton, "Electrical and Pressure Losses in a Magnetohydrodynamic Channel Due to End Current Loops," Aeroscience Lab., General Electric Technical Information Series R59SD431, 1959.

11. F. Fishman, "End Effects in Magnetohydrodynamic Channel Flow," AVCO Researc Report 78, 1959.

12. R. V. Hess, "Experiments and Theory for Continuous Steady Acceleration of Low Density Plasmas," *Proc. XIth International Astronautical Congress* (Stockholm 1960) [Berlin: Springer, 1960].

13. A. Carter, G. P. Wood, A. P. Sabol and R. H. Weinstein, "Experiments in Steady-State High-Density Plasma Acceleration," Second Symposium on the Engineering Aspects of Magnetohydrodynamics. Univ. of Pennsylvania, March 1961.

14. W. E. Powers and R. M. Patrick, "A Magnetic Annular Arc," Second Symposium on the Engineering Aspects of Magnetohydrodynamics. Univ. of Pennsylvania, March 1961.

15. R. R. John and W. L. Bade, "Recent Advances in Electric Arc Plasma Generation Technology," *Amer. Rocket Soc. J.,* Vol. 31, No. 1 (January 1961).

16. O. A. Anderson, et al., "Study and Use of Rotating Plasma," *Proc. 2nd UN International Conference on the Peaceful Uses of Atomic Energy,* Vol. 32.

17. J. R. Jack, "Theoretical Performance of Propellants Suitable for Electrothermal Jet Engines," NASA TN-D-682, March 1961.

18. M. Camac, "Plasma Propulsion Devices," *Advances in Space Sciences,* Vol. 2, (New York: Academic Press, 1960).

19. J. L. Kerrebrock, "Conduction in Gases with Elevated Electron Temperature," Second Symposium on the Engineering Aspects of Magnetohydrodynamics, Univ. of Pennsylvania, March 1961.

20. A. Guthrie and R. K. Wakerling, Editors, *"The Characteristics of Electrical Discharges in Magnetic Fields.* (New York: McGraw Hill, 1949).

21. F. F. Chen, "A Time Resolved Probe Method," Plasma Physics Lab. Princeton Univ., MATT-62, February 1961.

22. H. C. Early and W. G. Dow, "A Crossed Field Ionic Wind Motor," *Conf. on Extremely High Temperatures,* March 1958 (New York: John Wiley and Sons, Inc., 1958).

23. F. F. Chen, "A Hot Cathode Reflex Discharge," *Bull. Amer. Phys. Soc.,* Series II, Vol. 6, No. 2, B11. (March 1961).

24. P. M. Griffin and G. K. Werner, "Spectroscopic Investigations of Doppler Effects in a Luce Type Carbon Arc," *Bull. Amer. Phys. Soc.,* Series II, Vol. 6, No. 2, D12 (March 1961).

25. F. C. Hoh and B. Lehnert, "Diffusion Processes in a Plasma Column in a Longitudinal Magnetic Field," *The Physics of Fluids,* Vol. 3, No. 4 (July-August 1960).

26. G. Ecker and K. G. Muller, "Der Einfluss der Individuellen Feld Komponente auf die Elektronenemission der Metalle," *Zeit. f. Naturforschung,* Band 14a, Heft 5/6, (1959).

27. A. J. Lichtenberg, et al., Univ. of California, Dept. of E.E., Electronics Research Lab. Scientific Report No. 3, 1959.

28. C. Sheer, "Development of Nonconsumable Anode for Fluid Transpiration into High Intensity Arc." Vitro Laboratories KLX – 10179, 1959.

29. M. N. Rosenbluth and C. L. Longmire, "Stability of Plasmas Confined by Magnetic Fields, *Ann. Physics,* Vol. 1, No. 2 (May 1957).

30. B. B. Kadomtsev and A. V. Nedpospasov, "Instability of the Positive Column in a Magnetic Field and Anomalous Diffusion Effect," *J. Nucl. Energy:* Part C, Vol. 1, No. 4 (July 1960).

31. I. B. Bernstein and R. M. Kulsrud, *Physics of Fluids,* Vol. 3, No. 6,(November - December 1960).

32. L. Biermann and D. Pfirsch, "Kooperative Phanomene und Diffusion eines Plasma quer zu einem Magnetfeld," *Zeit. f. Naturforschung,* 15a, Heft 10/12 (1960).

33. H. E. Petschek, "Collision-Free Plasmas," AVCO, AMP 52, November 1960).

34. S. A. Colgate, "Ionization in Crossed Electric and Magnetic Fields," Univ. of California Radiation Lab. Livermore UCRL 6176, March 1961. Also: *Proc. Symposium on Electromagnetics and Fluid Dynamics of Gaseous Plasma,* (New York: Polytechnic Press, 1961).

35. S. T. Demetriades, "Experimental Magnetogasdynamic Engine for Argon, Nitrogen and Air," Second Symposium on the Engineering Aspects of Magnetohydrodynamic Univ. of Pennsylvania, March 1961.

36. D. Ragusa and J. Baker, "Experimental Results With a Direct Current Electromagnetic Plasma Accelerator," Second Symposium on the Engineering Aspects of Magnetohydrodynamics, Univ. of Pennsylvania, March 1961.

37. D. J. Rose, Analysis of a Cavity Discharge in Carbon. Thermonuclear Project Semi annual Report for Period Ending July 31, 1959, ORNL 2802, p. 65.

38. A. von Engel and M. Steenbeck, *Elektrische Gasentladungen,* 2, Band, 1934, Springer.

39. C. Michelson, "A Type of Hollow Cathode Discharge," Thermonuclear Project Semi annual Report for Period Ending July 31, 1959, ORNL 2802, p. 56.

40. P. F. Little and A. von Engel, "The Hollow Cathode Effect and the Theory of Glow Discharges," *Proc. Royal Society of London,* Series A, Vol. 224, p. 209 (1934).

41. A. D. White, "New Hollow Cathode Glow Discharge," *J. Appl. Phys.,* Vol. 30, p. 711 (1959).

42. George P. Wood, et al., "A Theoretical Treatment of the Steady Flow, Linear, Crossed-Field, DC Plasma Accelerator for Inviscid, Adiabatic, Isothermal, Constant-Area Flow," Prospective NASA TN D-924.

43. T. G. Cowling, *Magnetohydrodynamics.* [Interscience Tracts on Physics and Astronomy No. 4 (New York: Interscience, 1957)]

44. A. G. Janes, "Magnetohydrodynamic Propulsion," AVCO Research Report 90, August 1960.

45. N. H. Kemp and H. E. Petschek, "Two-Dimensional Incompressible Magnetohydrodynamic Flow Across an Elliptical Solenoid," AVCO Research Report 26, April 1958.

46. G.W. Sutton and P. Gluerson, "Magnetohydrodynamic Power and Propulsion," ARS Preprint 2005-61, ARS Fourth Biennial Gas Dynamics Symposium (Aug. 1961).

47. J.R. Sevier, R.V. Hess and P. Brockman, "Coaxial Hall Current Accelerator Operation at Forces and Efficiencies Comparable to Conventional Crossed-Field Accelerators," *Amer. Rocket Soc. J.,* Vol. 32, No. 1 (Jan. 1961).

48. R.V. Hess and R.H. Weinstein, "Hollow Cathode Discharge From Multiple Holes and Slots" *Bull. Amer. Phys. Soc.,* Series II, Vol. 7, No. 2, L 9, p. 158, (Feb. 1962).

49. R.H. Weinstein and R.V. Hess, "New Experiments with Hollow Cathode Discharges for Application to Plasma Accelerators" to be presented at the Third Symposium on Engineering Aspects of Magnetohydrodynamics, U. of Rochester (March, 1962).

APPENDIX

The purpose of this Appendix is to present certain relations which are needed in the analysis of acceleration processes and to make use of these relations in obtaining the axial component of electric field, E_x, from which the space-charge distribution can be found. For reasons of simplicity, the particular case considered here is that of the constant-area, constant-temperature, crossed-field accelerator with the further restrictions that the $\vec{j} \times \vec{B}$ body force/vol acts purely in the axial direction. This condition is satisfied when

(1) $j_x = 0$;

(2) $\vec{B}$ is in the z-direction (Fig. 1).

The results given here are identical with those obtained in Reference 42.

This appendix is written to present an alternate approach in which one need not start with the separate equations for particle motion to show the effect of ion slip on important quantities such as v_x, j_y, E_x and the joule heating due to ion slip. The present approach makes use of the well-known form of the generalized Ohm's law,[43] which includes ion slip and the ion contribution to conductivity, and into which the individual equations of motion of electrons, ions and neutrals (indirectly through the center of mass) have already been conveniently combined; this allows the condition $j_x = 0$ to be incorporated easily. The pertinent results can be obtained simply by a modification of the existing equations for constant temperature acceleration[18] using the generalized Ohm's law as a guide in determining the necessary modifications.

If it is desired to obtain the velocities of the individual species, it is, of course, necessary to make use of the equations of motion of the individual species. However, the solution is greatly facilitated by the fact that much of the information needed in the equations has already been found by the preceding analysis using the generalized Ohm's law. Furthermore, since much work appears in the literature for the case $j_x = 0$, several results for the particle motion already appear there (e.g. References 38 and 44).

In Reference 43, the friction coefficients ϵ_{jk} between electrons, ions and neutrals are expressed in terms of the collision times τ_{jk}. The relations can be obtained from Reference 1 and standard relations in kinetic theory (cf. Reference 42). In Reference 43, use is made of the conditions that m_e/m_i is negligible compared to unity, and that $m_i/m_n = 1$. The latter assumption fixes the integer in front of τ_{in} at 2; use of a different ratio would merely change this integer in the pertinent results of the Appendix.

For the case of negligible electron pressure gradient, Eq. (6-22) of Reference 43 may be written (for $\vec{B} = \mu\vec{H}$):

$$\vec{j} = \frac{n_e e \vec{E}'}{(\kappa + \beta\kappa_i) B} - \frac{(1 - 2f\beta)}{(\kappa + \beta\kappa_i) B} (\vec{j} \times \vec{B}) + \frac{f^2}{(\kappa + \beta\kappa_i)(\kappa_e + \kappa_i)B^2} (\vec{j} \times \vec{B}) \times \vec{B} \qquad \text{(A-1)}$$

where $\beta = \kappa_e/(\kappa_e + \kappa_i)$.

Noting that the conductivity in the absence of a magnetic field is given by:

$$\sigma_o = \frac{n_e e}{(\kappa + \beta\kappa_i) B} \qquad \text{(A-2)}$$

(since the terms κ, κ_i, and κ_e are inversely, proportional to B, then B drops out of σ_o),

and defining:

$$K \equiv \frac{1 - 2f\beta}{n_e e}, \quad \Lambda \equiv \frac{f^2}{n_e e B(\kappa_e + \kappa_i)},$$

then Eq. (A-1) can be written:

$$\vec{j} = \sigma_0 \left[\vec{E}' - K (\vec{j} \times \vec{B}) + \Lambda (\vec{j} \times \vec{B}) \times \vec{B} \right] \tag{A-3}$$

which is the usual form of the generalized Ohm's law.

In most cases in the literature, certain small terms appearing in the generalized Ohm's law are justifiably neglected at this point. For example, the ion contribution to the conductivity is usually neglected; in the equation, this is equivalent to neglecting $\kappa_e = 1/\omega_e \tau_{en}$ compared to $\kappa_i = 1/2\omega_i \tau_{in}$. The assumption of a small degree of ionization is equivalent to setting f equal to unity. If these approximations are made, and substitutions are made for the κ's, the constants take the familiar form:

$$\sigma_0 = \frac{n_e e^2}{m_e} \bar{\tau}_e , \qquad K = \frac{1}{n_e e} , \qquad \Lambda = \frac{2\tau_{in}}{m_i n_e}$$

and the expression for the generalized Ohm's law becomes identical with that of Reference 45. In this analysis, however, these small terms will be retained in order to allow comparison with the results of Reference 42, in which these small terms are also retained.

One important result, the expression for joule heating, can be obtained immediately by making the substitution $\vec{E}' = \vec{E} + \vec{v} \times \vec{B}$ and dotting equation (A-3) with $\vec{j}$. The resulting expression can be written (for the case $\vec{j}$ perpendicular to $\vec{B}$):

$$\vec{j} \cdot \vec{E} = (\vec{j} \times \vec{B}) \cdot \vec{v} + \frac{j^2}{\sigma_0} (1 + \sigma_0 \Lambda B^2) \tag{A-4}$$

From the expression (A-4), it can be seen that the power input, $\vec{j} \cdot \vec{E}$, is divided between the rate of work done by the $\vec{j} \times \vec{B}$ body force, and the rate at which energy is dissipated by the joule heating. The joule heating term in (A-4) is greater than the usual heating term, j^2/σ_0, due to the additional heating arising from the ion slip term in Ohm's law. (Note that the Hall-current term does not give rise to additional dissipation.) The ratio of this additional heating to the usual heating, j^2/σ_0, is simply:

$$\sigma_0 \Lambda B^2 = \frac{f^2}{(\kappa + \beta\kappa_i)(\kappa_e + \kappa_i)} \approx 2\, \omega_e \bar{\tau}_e\, \omega_i \tau_{in}$$

as shown in Section 6-52 of Reference 43.

At this point, it is of interest to obtain the electric field distribution in the crossed-field type accelerator for the particular case of one-dimensional, isothermal, constant-area channel flow. The solution of the problem closely follows the treatment of the same problem in Reference 18 except for two exceptions, which will be mentioned below. In the interest of brevity, the entire analysis will not be presented here, only the results.

The first departure from Reference 18 has already been mentioned, namely, the additional joule heating due to ion slip. This difference appears in the energy equation in the term expressing the rate of heat addition per unit mass and is given by

$$\frac{dQ}{dt} = \frac{1}{\rho} \frac{j_y^2}{\sigma_0} (1 + \sigma_0 \Lambda B^2) . \tag{A-5}$$

The other departure from Reference 18 is in the expression for j_y which appears in (A-5), and in the expression for body force in the energy and momentum equations. Solving (A-3) for $\vec{j}$ results in

$$\vec{j} = \frac{\sigma_0}{(\sigma_0 KB)^2 + (1 + \sigma_0 \Lambda B^2)^2} \Big\{ (1 + \sigma_0 \Lambda B^2)\, \vec{E}' - \sigma_0 K \vec{E}' \times \vec{B} + \left[(\sigma_0 K)^2 + \sigma_0 \Lambda (1 + \sigma_0 \Lambda B^2) \right] (\vec{E}' \cdot \vec{B}) \vec{B} \Big\} \qquad \text{(A-6)}$$

For the present case of $\vec{E}$ and $\vec{v}$ perpendicular to $\vec{B}$ and for $j_x = 0$, the following relations are obtained from (A-6).

$$(E_x + v_y B) = \frac{K\sigma_0 B}{(1 + \sigma_0 \Lambda B^2)} (E_y - v_x B_z) ; \qquad \text{(A-7)}$$

$$j_y = \frac{\sigma_0}{(1 + \sigma_0 \Lambda B^2)} (E_y - v_x B_z) . \qquad \text{(A-8)}$$

For both the differences mentioned above, the heating rate and the body force, it is apparent that the present analysis differs from Reference 18 only in the effective conductivity. In this analysis, the conductivity can be considered to be $\sigma_0/(1 + \sigma_0 \Lambda B^2)$ as compared to σ_0 in Reference 18. As might be expected, the final results for j_x and E_y differ only by this ratio. For the case of thermal equilibrium and assuming that $T_e = T_i = T_n$ = constant, σ_0 = constant, the result is

$$j_y = \frac{\sigma_0 v_x B}{1 + \sigma_0 \Lambda B^2} \; \frac{1}{(\gamma M_x^2 - 1} ; \qquad \text{(A-9)}$$

$$E_y = v_x B_z \left[\frac{\gamma M_x^2}{\gamma M_x^2 - 1} \right] . \qquad \text{(A-10)}$$

The result for the Mach-number variation along the channel in the present analysis (and in Reference 42) is somewhat different from a simple modification of the conductivity of Reference 18. The differential equation which expresses the variation of Mach number with x-distance is identical to that of Reference 18 with the modified conductivity mentioned above. However, when integrated, the expressions for M as a function of x become different due to the presence of the variable Λ (which is a function of ion density) in the present analysis. The result, assuming constancy of σ_0 and of n_e/n_n, was first shown in Reference 42 to be

$$\frac{2\sigma_0 B^2}{\rho v_x} x = \left\{ \left[\frac{M_x^2}{M_0^2} - 1 \right] \left[\gamma M_0^2 + \frac{1}{\gamma M_x^2} \right] - 2 \ln \left[\frac{M_x}{M_0} \right]^2 \right\} + \frac{\sigma_o \Lambda_o B^2}{2} \left\{ \left[\frac{M_x^2}{M_0^2} - 1 \right] \left[\gamma M_0^2 + \gamma M_x^2 - 4 \right] + \frac{2 \ln (M_x/M_0)^2}{\gamma M_0^2} \right\} \qquad \text{(A-11)}$$

where M_o and Λ_o refer to the value of these quantities at the entrance of the accelerator, $x = 0$. The quantity ρv_x is the mass flow rate per unit area and is a constant.

In order to obtain the x-component of electric field strength, consider Eq. (A-7):

$$E_x = \frac{K\sigma_o B}{1 + \sigma_o \Lambda B^2} E_y - \left[\frac{K\sigma_o B}{1 + \sigma_o \Lambda B^2} + \frac{v_y}{v_x}\right] v_x B_z .$$

Calculations show that the term $K\sigma_o B/(1 + \sigma_o \Lambda B^2)$ is of the order of unity over a wide pressure range for small degrees of ionization. The ratio v_y/v_x can be determined through the use of the individual particle equations from which Eq. (A-1) is derived. Such calculations have been made using the conditions that, for continuity reasons, the neutrals move only in the x-direction. However, they will not be presented here since the result, as expected, is that $v_y/v_x \ll 1$ for slightly ionized gases, and may therefore be neglected compared to $K\sigma_o B/(1 + \sigma_o \Lambda B^2)$. Note that the assumption of slightly ionized plasma is also made in Reference 42, and certain terms are neglected there in the equations of particle motion before their solution. Thus the expression for E_x simply becomes

$$E_x = \frac{K\sigma_o B}{1 + \sigma_o \Lambda B^2} (E_y - v_x B_z) . \tag{A-12}$$

Substitution of (A-8) and (A-9) into (A-12) results in

$$E_x = (K\sigma_o B) \frac{j_y}{\sigma_o} = \frac{K\sigma_o B}{(1 + \sigma_o \Lambda B^2)} \left[\frac{v_x B_z}{\gamma M_x^2 - 1}\right] . \tag{A-13}$$

For the case of $\kappa_e \ll \kappa_i$, and small degree of ionization, (A-13) can be expressed as

$$E_x = \omega_e \bar{\tau}_e \frac{j_y}{\sigma'_o} = \frac{\omega_e \bar{\tau}_e}{1 + 2\omega_e \bar{\tau}_e \omega_i \tau_{in}} \left[\frac{v_x B_z}{\gamma M_x^2 - 1}\right] , \tag{A-14}$$

where

$$\sigma'_o = (n_e e^2/m_e)\, \bar{\tau}_e .$$

As was mentioned earlier, the equations for the individual species (Eqs. (1)-(4)) can now be used to determine the velocities of the individual species. One other equation will be required, namely:

$$\vec{v} = \frac{\frac{n_e}{n_n}\left(\vec{v}_i + \frac{m_e}{m_i}\vec{v}_e\right) + \vec{v}_n}{1 + \frac{n_e}{n_n}} . \tag{A-15}$$

Equation (A-15) is obtained by equating the momentum of the center of mass to the sum of the individual momenta of ions, electrons and neutrals where the following assumptions have been made: $n_i = n_e$, $m_i = m_n$, and m_e/m_i is negligible compared to unity.

Adding Eqs. (1) and (2) and writing the y-component of the resulting equation, and noting that for the present case $v_{ny} = 0$ and $dv_y/dt = 0$ (since $j_x = 0$), then from (A-15),

$$\frac{dv_{iy}}{dt} + \frac{m_e}{m_i}\frac{dv_{ey}}{dt} = 0 .$$

This results in the following expression:

$$\frac{v_{ey}}{v_{iy}} = - \frac{m_i}{m_e}\frac{\tau_{en}}{2\tau_{in}} \tag{A-16}$$

Expression (A-16) states the well known result for steady-state discharge regions (e. g. , Reference 38, p. 12), and could have been obtained immediately by noting that the ratio of drift velocities is equal to the ratio of mobilities.

From (A-16) and the definition of current, $\vec{j} = -n_e e(\vec{v}_e - \vec{v}_i)$, the individual ion or electron velocities can be obtained in terms of the known current j_y:

$$v_{iy} = \frac{j_y}{n_e e\left[\frac{m_i}{m_e}\frac{\tau_{en}}{2\tau_{in}} + 1\right]} . \tag{A-17}$$

In a similar manner, expressions may be derived for the x-component of velocity. For the present case of $j_x = 0$, then $v_{ex} = v_{ix}$ and the following result is obtained:

$$v_{ix} = v_{ex} = v_x + \frac{\frac{2\tau_{in}}{n_e m_i} j_y B}{\left[1 + \frac{n_e}{n_n}\right]\left[1 + \frac{m_e}{m_i}\frac{2\tau_{in}}{\tau_{en}}\right]} . \tag{A-18}$$

Calculations show that for small degrees of ionization, $v_x \approx v_{nx}$. Thus the ion slip $v_{ix} - v_{nx}$ can be obtained from Eq (A-18) for thermal equilibrium

$$\frac{m_e}{m_i}\frac{2\tau_{in}}{\tau_{en}} \approx \left[\frac{m_e}{m_i}\right]^{1/2} \approx 10^{-2} .$$

For small degrees of ionization, n_e/n_n is of the same order of magnitude; thus, if these two small terms are neglected compared to unity, Eq. (A-17) becomes

$$v_{ix} - v_{nx} = \frac{2\tau_{in}}{n_e m_i} j_y B_z = \frac{2\tau_{in} e}{m_i} E_x , \tag{A-19}$$

which expresses the result that the ion slip is simply the mobility times E_x. Equation (A-19) (which is also obtained in Reference 44) could have been obtained directly from Eq. (2) by neglecting the small terms involving the pressure gradient, the mass-acceleration, and v_{iy}.

PRELIMINARY EXPERIMENTS ON MHD CHANNEL FLOW WITH SLIGHTLY IONIZED GASES

G. W. Sutton and F. Robben
Space Sciences Laboratory, Missle and Space Vehicle Department
General Electric Co., Philadelphia, Pa.

An apparatus has been constructed and operated for the study of magnetohydrodynamic flows and power generation with slightly ionized gases in a channel in an external magnetic field. The source of the plasma is a 2500 kw plasma jet, with nitrogen as the working fluid. Ionization is provided by the injection of powdered potassium carbonate downstream of the arc. The gases then flow through a rectangular channel, 5/8" X 4" X 24" long, with a constant transverse magnetic field of 10,000 gauss. On each narrow side of the channel are four electrodes; each pair of electrodes is switched through four resistances. The measured quantities yielded data on the flow velocity and plasma electrical conductivity that compares favorably with theoretical calculations based on compressible flow with a turbulent boundary layer and variable conductivity. A maximum power of 6 kw and 78 volts open-circuit was obtained.

INTRODUCTION

Direct conversion of the kinetic energy of a partially ionized gas into electrical energy by Faraday induction has been recently demonstrated in experimental magnetohydrodynamic (MHD) generators, in which the electrically conducting gas acts as the moving conductor in a homopolar generator. The experiments thus far verify most of the basic phenomena of the conduction of electricity in thermally ionized gases. This success has resulted in some speculation that preheated air could be burned directly with a fossil fuel; then an easily ionizable element such as potassium could be added to the gas, and the products of combustion could be passed through the MHD generator on a commercial basis.

Toward this end, a number of small exploratory experiments,[4, 5] as well as a number of theoretical analyses of the flow of a conducting gas in a channel,[6-9] were performed at General Electric Company. Simultaneously, the construction of a larger experimental MHD generator was initiated, in order to investigate the associated phenomena on a larger scale and perhaps discover some new phenomena. In this paper, the construction of the generator and the initial MHD experiments are described and compared to theory.

EXPERIMENTAL EQUIPMENT

It was originally planned to heat air in a large plasma jet possessing carbon electrodes. Previous experience with this plasma jet

Presented at the Symposium on Electromagnetics and Fluid Dynamics of Gaseous Plasma, Polytechnic Institute of Brooklyn, April 4, 5, 6, 1961

indicated that the available oxygen in air combined with the carbon from the electrodes to form a gas mixture similar in composition to a combustion gas which might be used in a practical generator. Although a few experiments were performed with air, difficulties were encountered in determining the actual gas composition, and the remaining experiments were performed with nitrogen gas.

The plasma jet used to preheat the nitrogen is a three-phase ac arc.[10] The electrical power is supplied by two inertial generators capable of delivering 10^9 watts of power for a short period of time, and 10^6 watts continuously. The plasma jet is normally operated with 2.5 megawatts for time periods of 10 to 30 seconds, but has been operated as high as 15 megawatts. It consists of a graphite-lined, water-cooled, cylindrical chamber, eleven inches in diameter and three feet high, with three electrodes at the bottom. Graphite electrodes were initially used; however, most of the runs were performed using water-cooled copper electrodes. The nigrogen is admitted to the arc chamber at the bottom, flows around the electrodes, and then flows out the top. An automatic control system maintains a constant pressure in the arc chamber by adjusting the gas flow rate.

Fig. 1 Photograph of experimental MHD generator. Gas flow is from bottom to top.

The MHD generator channel is mounted on top of the arc (see Fig. 1). The heated nitrogen passes from the arc through a graphite nozzle and inlet section into the MHD generator, which is constructed of an insulating refractory material. On opposite sides of the channel are four pairs of graphite electrodes 5. 7 inches long. The over-all length of the generator is 24 inches, and the channel cross section is 4 × 5/8 inches, although initially the width was 3/8 inches. A sectional view of the generator is shown in Fig. 2.

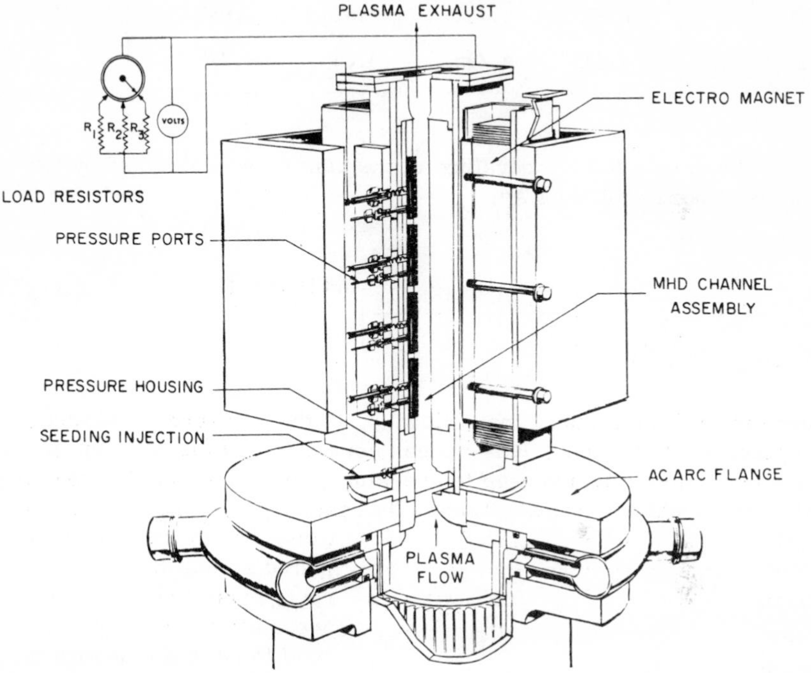

Fig. 2 Schematic diagram of MHD generator, showing top of plasma jet, magnet, and electrodes.

Each pair of electrodes was connected to a separate load cycling circuit. In each circuit, three different load resistances are switched at the rate of three per second. The load resistances are shown in Table 1.

To inject the easily ionizable element, powdered potassium carbonate was blown into the top of the arc chamber. Initially, an aqueous solution of K_2CO_3 was tried, but the spray tip in the arc chamber was burned off as soon as the arc was struck.

The electromagnet has pole faces 4 × 24 inches, with a gap of 2-1/8 inches. With 400 amps in the field coils, the magnetic field is about 11, 000 gauss. The magnet saturates at about 17, 000 gauss.

TABLE 1: MHD LOAD RESISTANCES (Ohms)			
Center		Electrode pair	
1	2	3	4
0.265	0.276	0.263	0.245
1.070	1.153	1.131	1.040
4.315	4.795	4.615	4.295

The stagnation temperature of the plasma was obtained by use of a short nozzle of area A*:

$$\frac{m}{A^{*} p_o} = \left[\frac{\gamma}{RT_o}\right]^{1/2} \left[\frac{2}{\gamma + 1}\right]^{(\gamma+1)/2(\gamma-1)} \tag{1}$$

where m is the measured mass flow, p_o is the measured pressure in the plasma jet chamber, R is the gas constant, γ is the ratio of specific heats evaluated at an average temperature, and T_o is the desired stagnation temperature. Figure 3 shows the resulting temperature calibration. The throat area was adjusted so that the voltage, current, mass flow, and chamber pressure are identical to the conditions in a test with the MHD channel.

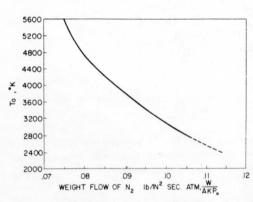

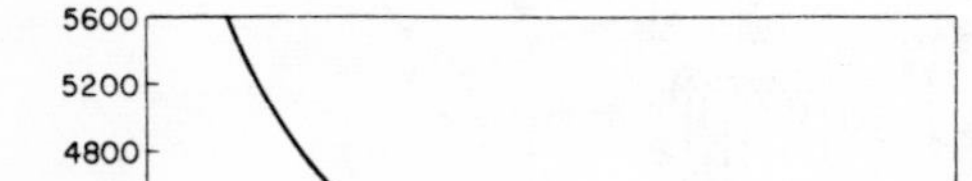

Fig. 3 Temperature calibration curve for nitrogen

EXPERIMENTAL RESULTS

The generator performance during the initial test was somewhat disappointing With a stagnation temperature of 4700°K, a stagnation pressure of 44 psia, and a weight flow of 0. 28 lb/sec, only 300 watts were generated, which was too low by almost two orders of magnitude. An analysis of the data indicated three possible causes of the poor performance, as follows:

1) Gas temperature was too low.

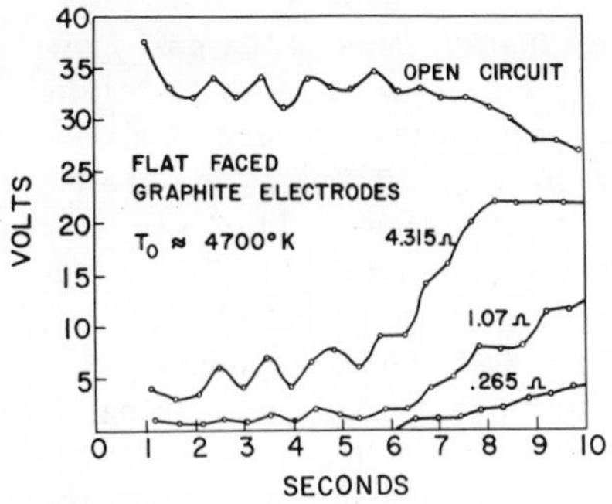

Fig. 4 Voltage across load resistors when using flat-faced graphite electrodes

2) Seed material did not ionize.

3) Electrodes were not emitting electrons.

Careful examination of the voltage records shed considerable light on the problem. Figure 4 shows the voltage for the first pair of electrodes. The initial low voltages indicate a high resistance somewhere in the generator, which gradually decreases during the test. Thus, for the 5 ohm resistor, the internal resistance of the generator has become constant at the end of 8 seconds; but for the one ohm and 0. 25 ohm resistor, the apparent internal resistance was still decreasing. It therefore appeared that the graphite electrodes were emitting by thermionic emmission; they were therefore emission-limited until they achieved a sufficiently high temperature, which took about 10 seconds for the smallest load resistance at the first pair of electrodes. For the electrodes further downstream, where the gas was cooler and the boundary layer thicker, asymptotic voltages were not reached for any of the load resistors.

Figure 4 also shows one-second oscillations in the open circuit

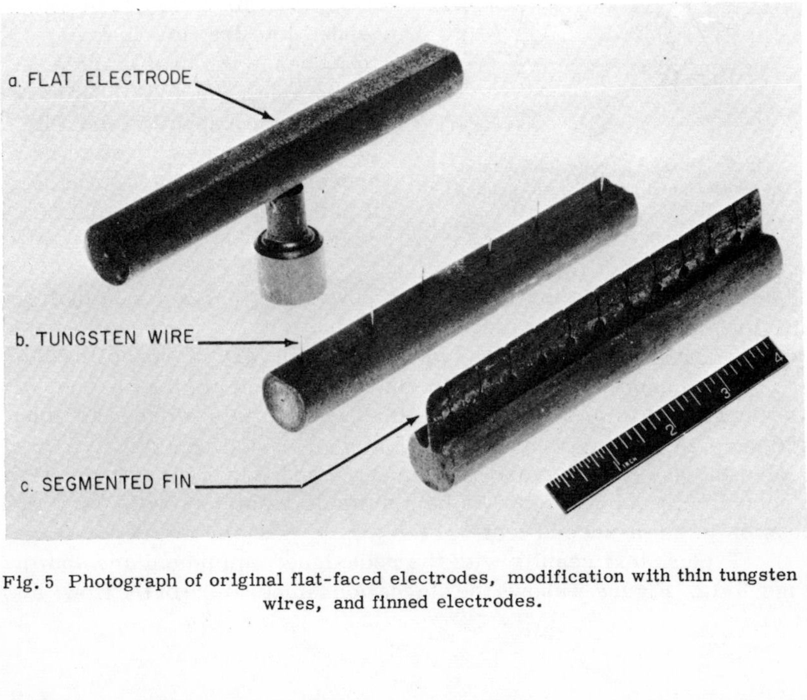

Fig. 5 Photograph of original flat-faced electrodes, modification with thin tungsten wires, and finned electrodes.

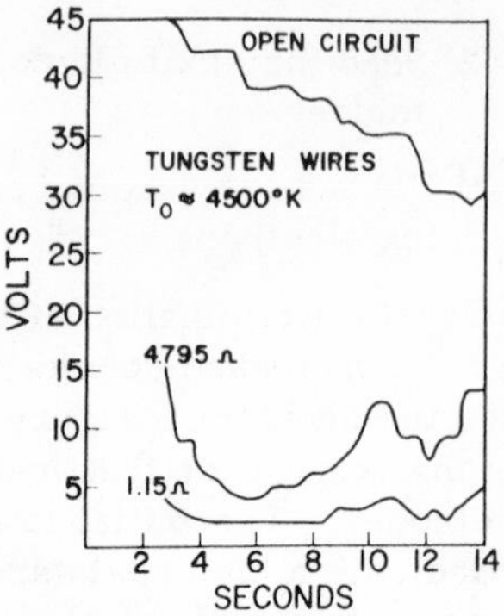

Fig. 6 Voltage across load resistors with tungsten wires inserted into flat-faced graphite electrodes

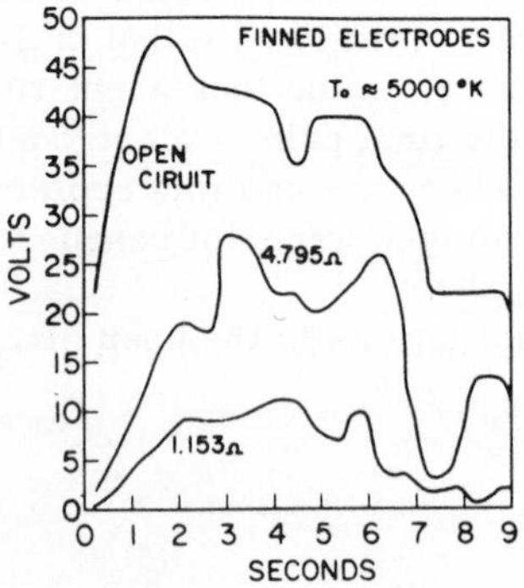

Fig. 7 Voltage across load resistors with finned graphite electrodes

voltage. These were caused by instabilities of the gas-flow regulator, which was stabilized in later tests. There is also a downward trend in the open-circuit voltage. This was apparently caused by leaks and poor gaskets in the plasma jet itself, and disappeared after new gaskets and linings were placed in the arc chamber.

To verify the possibility that the graphite electrodes were emission-limited, an experiment was performed in which thin tungsten wires were inserted in the graphite electrodes (see Fig. 5). Here, the voltage across the 5 ohm resistor was initially high, then decreased due to melting of the tungsten wires; and then increased again as the graphite itself became hot (see Fig. 6).

As a result of these tests, new electrodes were designed with a fin which extended into the flow in order to increase the heat transfer to the electrode and to decrease the thermal capacity (see Fig. 5). This change proved to be successful; see Fig. 7, where it can be seen that the electrodes are operating effectively at the end of about two seconds.

In this test the total generated power was 517 watts, which was still low. It appeared that the plasma conductivity was decreasing rapidly in the downstream direction, which indicated very rapid cooling of the gas by the channel walls. To alleviate this problem, the channel width was increased to 5/8 inch and the inlet section was widened to about 3/4 inch. In addition, the insulator material eroded excessively, which cooled the gas even further. After some additional experimentation, a zircon compound was found to be a suitable insulator, with very little erosion in a ten-second test.

Typical test results with the redesigned equipment are shown in Figs. 8-12. Figure 8 shows the stagnation temperature of the flow, stag-

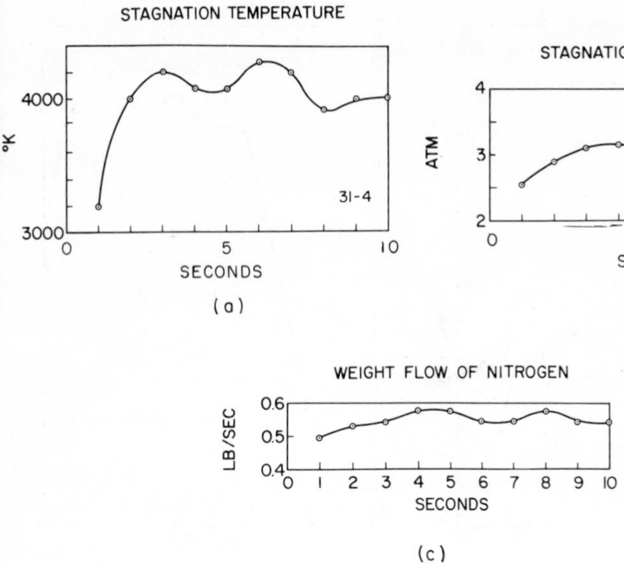

Fig. 8 Test conditions for test 31-4

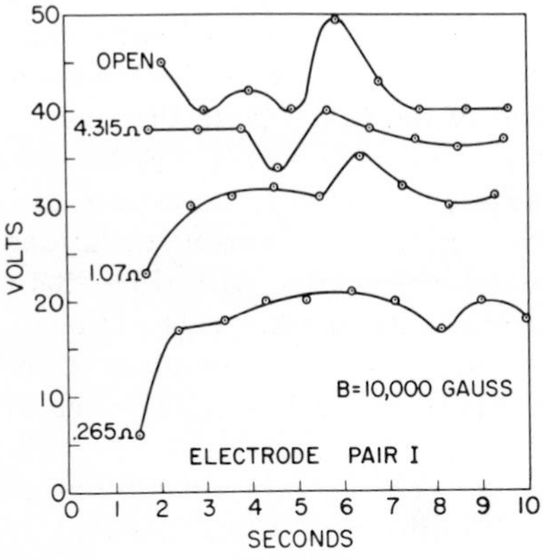

Fig. 9 MHD voltage history for test 31-4.

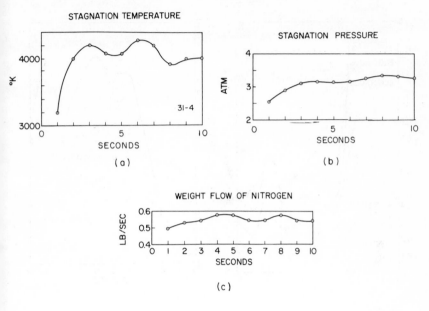

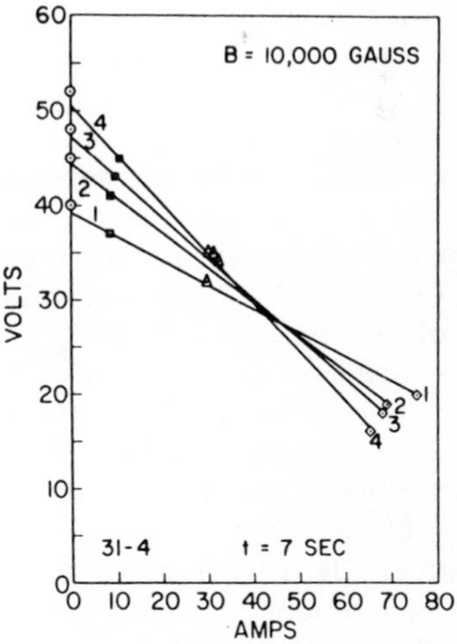

Fig. 10 MHD generator operating characteristics for test 31-4

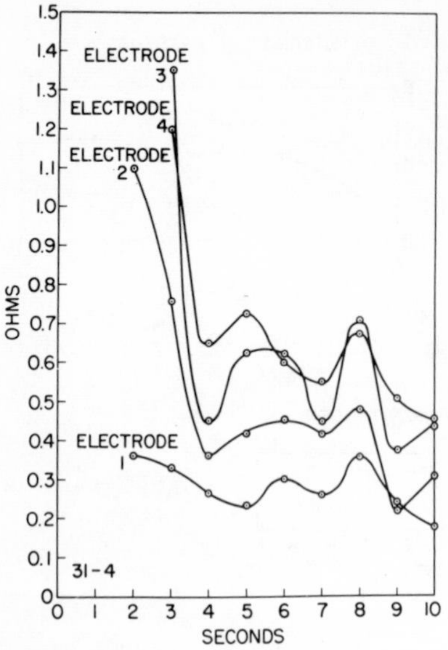

Fig. 11 Plasma resistance between each pair of electrodes for test 31-4.

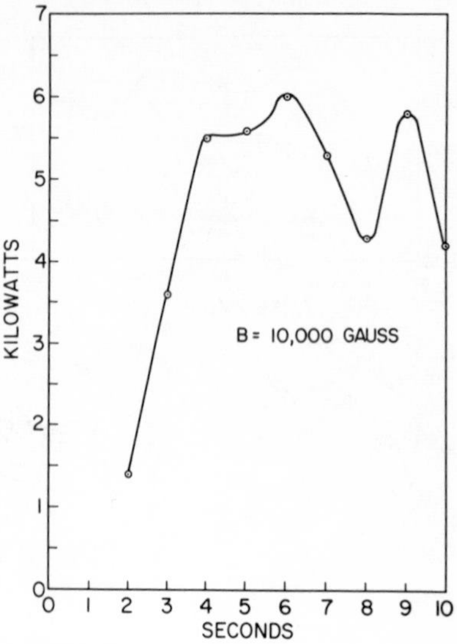

Fig. 12 Total maximum generated power for test 31-4.

nation pressure, and mass flow of nitrogen. There appeared to be some slight oscillations in the test condition, but these were not serious. Note that about four seconds of operation are required to achieve steady operation of the plasma jet. Figure 9 shows a typical voltage record. Again, about four seconds are required to achieve steady operation. The voltage-current characteristics for the four pair of electrodes are shown in Fig. 10 for the seventh second of the test. Note that there appears to be an electrode voltage drop of about one volt. From the slopes of these curves, the plasma resistance between each pair of electrodes can be calculated; this is shown in Fig. 11. Two observations are of interest. First, the plasma resistance varied with time; it is believed that this was caused by fluctuations in the seeding rate as there is no correlation with the total temperature. Second, the plasma resistance increases in the downstream direction, indicating cooling of the plasma by the walls of the channel.

The total power developed in the 0.25 ohm nominal resistors is shown in Fig. 12. A maximum power of 6 kilowatts was generated in this experiment.

Although the initial total pressure was 3 atmospheres, the exit pressure was atmospheric, corresponding to a Mach number of one. Most of the pressure drop is due to friction, as is shown in the next section, "Comparison with Theory." The resulting decrease of gas density in the downstream direction caused the gas velocity to increase, and accounts for the increase in open circuit voltage in the downstream direction (see Fig. 10).

The actual voltage traces were not smooth but were quite noisy (see Fig 13). There are shown the voltages across the four pairs of electrodes, as they are switched between the three load resistors and open-circuit. It can be seen that the noise is in phase between all four pairs; furthermore, the amplitudes are identical. Also, even the open-circuit measurement showed noise. Although it is possible that fluctuations in the seeding caused this noise, it is more likely that the noise is just electrical noise from the plasma jet itself. Additional experiments are planned to determine the cause of the noise. Noise has also been observed in experiments with combustion gases. [11]

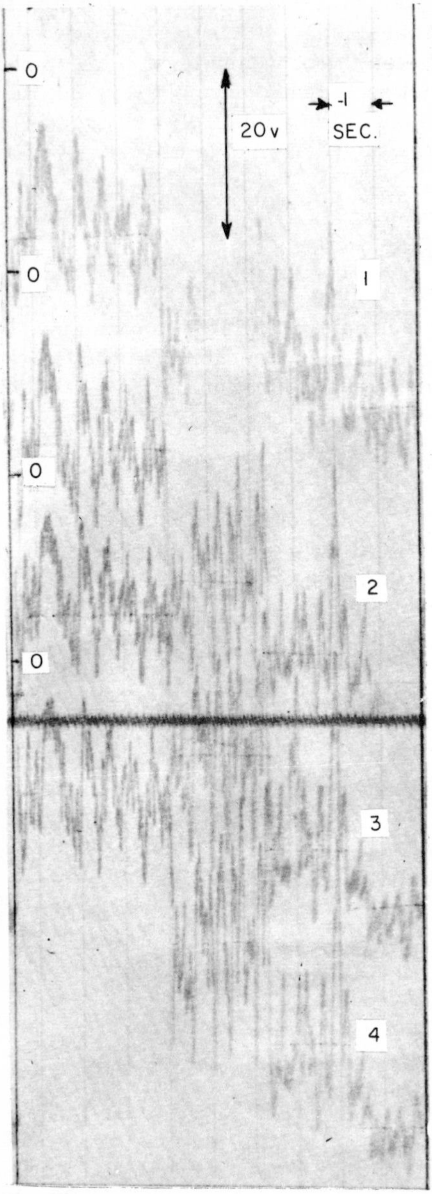

Fig. 13 Oscillograph of load voltage showing high-frequency noise.

COMPARISON WITH THEORY

The model is an ideal compressible gas flow in a straight channel of constant cross section, with friction forces, heat transfer, and Lorentz force. It is assumed that the velocity, density, and all other properities are constant in the main flow at any downstream station, and that the electric current is transverse to the flow. The shear stress τ on the wall is

$$\tau = \frac{1}{2} f \rho V^2 , \tag{2}$$

where f is the friction factor, ρ is the free-stream gas density, and V is the free-stream gas velocity. The heat transfer q to the wall is

$$q = K_h \rho V C_p (T - T_w), \tag{3}$$

where K_h is the Stanton number, C_p

is the specific heat, and T and T_w are the gas and wall temperature, respectively. Reynolds analogy yields $K_h = \frac{1}{2} f$ for a Prandtl number of unity, which is adequate for this treatment. The friction factor for fully developed pipe flow may be taken as 0.008,[12] although it actually depends on the magnetic interaction parameter.[13] A better approximation to the actual result would consider the boundary layer development and variations of the plasma properties in the boundary layer, but the results would be qualitatively the same. In the main flow the gas is assumed to be perfect since the results are applied to nitrogen over a limited temperature range. Thus,

$$p = \rho RT; \quad dh = C_p dT; \tag{4}$$

where p is the pressure, R is the gas constant and h is the gas enthalpy. Equation(4) also assumes that the effect of a small percentage of added seed material is negligible. The momentum equation is, then:

$$dp + \rho V dV + 2D^{-1} f\rho V^2 dx + \sigma V B^2 (1-K)\, dx = 0, \tag{5}$$

where D is the hydraulic diameter, x is the coordinate in the flow direction, σ is the electrical conductivity of the gas, and B is the magnetic field strength. K is the generator loading coefficient defined as the ratio of the voltage to the open-circuit voltage, or $K = E/VB$ where E is the electric field. The energy equation is:

$$dh + VdV + 2D^{-1} f(T-T_w)\, dx + \rho^{-1} VB^2 K(1-K)\, dx = 0. \tag{6}$$

With the use of the continuity relation, ρV = constant, Eqs. (5) and (6) can be combined to yield:

$$dx = \frac{(1-M^2)\, dM^2}{\alpha M^2 \left[1 + \frac{1}{2}(\gamma-1) M^2\right] \left[(2-\tau)\gamma M^2 - \theta\right] + \beta \left[2\gamma - K(\gamma-1)\right] M^4} \tag{7}$$

where

$$\left.\begin{aligned} \alpha &= 2f/D, \\ \beta &= \tau B^2 (1-K)/\rho V, \\ \theta &= (T-T_w)/T_o . \end{aligned}\right\} \tag{8}$$

The stagnation temperature to is given by:

$$dT_o = -\alpha T_o dx - \frac{B^2 K(1-K)}{C_p/R} \frac{\sigma VT}{p} dx . \quad (9)$$

Both(7) and (9) were solved on a digital computer using finite differences.
The conductivity, including the Hall effect is given by:

$$\sigma = \frac{\sigma_o}{1 + (w/2)^2} = \frac{\sigma_o}{1 + (\sigma_o B/n_e e)^2} \quad (10)$$

where the scalar conductivity is given by:

$$\sigma_o^{-1} = \sigma_n^{-1} + \sigma_I^{-1} . \quad (11)$$

The conductivity respectively due to neutrals and ions is given by:

$$\sigma_n = 0.85\, n_e e^2 \left[M_e < C_e > N_n Q\right]^{-1}, \quad (12)$$

$$\sigma_I = \gamma_E \frac{2\,(2KT)^{3/2}}{\pi^{3/2} M_e^{1/2} e^2 \ell n\Lambda} , \quad (13)$$

$$\Lambda = (3/2)\, e^{-3} (K^3 T^3/\pi N_e)^{1/2} . \quad (14)$$

Equations (10) - (14) are derived from the kinetic theory of gases. Equations(10) and (11) are only approximate;[14] Equations(13) and (14) were derived by Spitzer[15] et al. The notation is the same as used by Spitzer. The degree of ionization of the potassium was calculated on the basis of thermodynamic equilibrium which corresponds to small ratios of electric field to pressure. The average neutral cross section was taken to be $Q = 10^{-15} cm^2$.

Calculations were performed for a channel 80 cm long, with the generating section beginning at 12 cm and ending at 75 cm, for a cross-section of 5/8" X 4". End effects were neglected. Since the flow at the exit is sonic, it was necessary to specify the plasma variables at the exit, and integrate Eqs. (7) and (9) up to the entrance.

A number of cases were tried, and the two typical results are given in Figs. 14 and 15. The exit conditions are identical for the two cases, but one is for K = 1 (no load) and the other for K = 0.5, which should represent approximately the point of maximum power. The conductivity was reduced by the Hall effect (Eq. (10)), but it was assumed to be 1500 °K, and the potassium concentration was one mole per cent. The plasma conditions at the exit were chosen to be 1.2 atmospheres

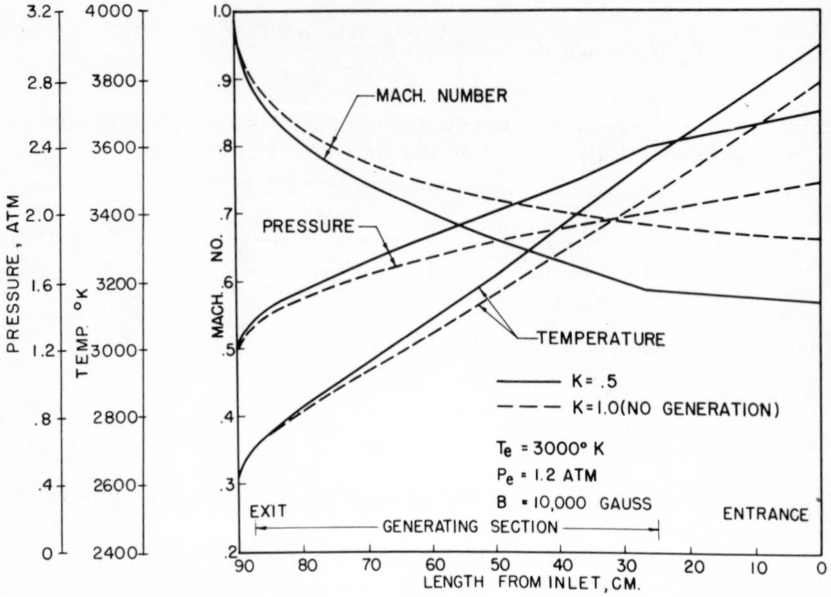

Fig. 14 Theoretical variation in properties along channel with and without power generation for seeded nitrogen. Channel cross section is 5/8 × 4 inches.

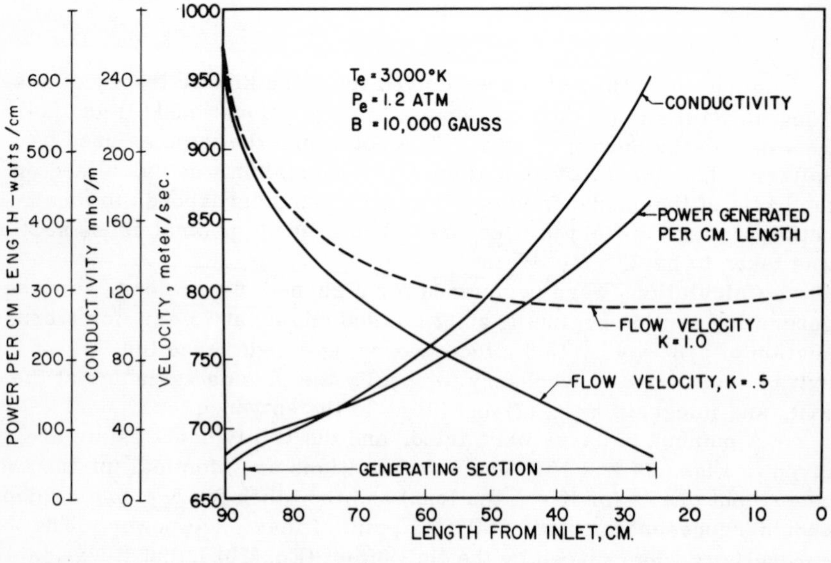

Fig. 15 Theoretical flow velocity, power and electrical conductivity in channel. Channel cross section is 5/8 × 4 inches.

pressure, 3000°K stagnation temperature, and Mach one flow. It is seen that friction and compressibility dominate the flow. The large pressure drop due to friction causes a large decrease in the density which results in an appreciable increase in gas velocity toward the exit. The pressure drop due to Lorentz forces for K = 0.5 is about 50% of the friction pressure drop.

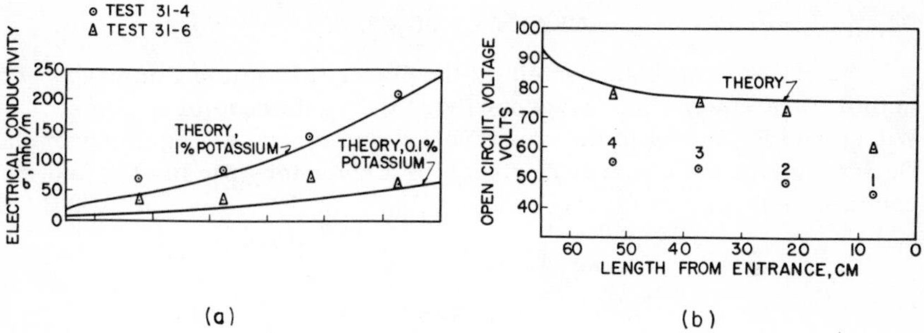

Fig. 16 Electrical conductivity and open-circuit voltage compared with theory.

The theoretical calculation for K = 0.5 gave the result that a total of 14.5 kw was generated, neglecting end effects. This is to be compared with test 31-4 which generated 6.1 kw maximum, and test 31-6 which generated 2.8 kw. Because test 31-6 had a potassium concentration less than 0.5%, with a large uncertainty, a case with identical conditions as stated above, except for 0.1% molar potassium concentration, was computed. The calculated power was then 4.9 kw. In Fig. 16(a) the conductivity vs channel length is shown for the cases K= 0.5 with 1% and 0.1% seeding. Also plotted are the effective conductivities from tests 31-4 and 31-6. Figure 16(b) shows the open-circuit voltage, as deduced from the calculation of flow velocity for the case K = 1.0 and the open circuit voltages measured in tests 31-4 and 31-6. It is seen that test 31-6 agrees fairly well with the theory. The No. 1 electrode voltage is expected to be low due to the end effect. The differences between measured and calculated conductivity could also be due to the actual cross section being closer to 2×10^{-15} cm^2.

In test 31-4, the channel wall material was alumina. It is possible that the alumina became electrically conducting and caused the reduction in the measured open-circuit voltage. The presence of potassium could also cause the electrical conductivity of the alumina to increase. The channel material for test 31-6 was zircon, which apparently did not become electrically conducting.

CONCLUSIONS

A magnet and channel for MHD power experimentation has been

constructed and tested with nitrogen gas seeded with potassium carbonate powder. Within the experimental uncertainties of plasma temperature and composition, the initial MHD experiments compared favorably with theoretical calculations based on a compressible gas with a turbulent boundary layer and variable electrical conductivity. A maximum of 6 kw of power and a maximum open-circuit voltage of 78 volts were generated.

ACKNOWLEDGMENTS

This work was supported by the General Electric Company. The authors gratefully wish to acknowledge the assistance of R. Dale, A. Were, and R. Burns in the construction and test of the equipment; and D. Marquis of the General Engineering Laboratory for his aid and encouragement.

REFERENCES

1. L. Steg and G. W. Sutton, "Prospects of MHD Power Generation," *Astronautics*, Vol. 5, p. 22 (1960).

2. R. J. Rosa, "Physical Principles of Magnetohydrodynamic Power Generation," *Phys. Fluids*, Vol. 4, No. 2, p. 182.

3. H. J. Pain and P. R. Smy, "Experiments on Power Generation from a Moving Plasma," *J. Fluid Mech.*, Vol. 10, No. 1, p. 51.

4. F. C. Foshag and A. E. Were, "Magnetohydrodynamic Power Generation Experiment," General Electric Report TIS R59SD447 (1959).

5. A. E. Were, "Rocket Exhaust MHD Experiment," G. E. Report TIS R60SD381 (1960).

6. G. W. Sutton, "Electrical and Pressure Losses in a Magnetohydrodynamic Channel due to End Current Loops," G. E. Report TIS R59SD431 (1959).

7. G. W. Sutton, "Design Considerations of a Steady, D. C. Magnetohydrodynamic Electrical Power Generator," G. E. Report TIS R59SD432 (1959). Presented at the 1960 SAE-AFOSR Third Astronautics Symposium, to be published by Pergamon Press. SAE Reprint 231.

8. H. Hurwitz, Jr., R. W. Kilb and G. W. Sutton, "Influence of Tensor Conductivity on Current Distribution in an MHD Generator," *J. Appl. Phys.*, Vol. 32, No. 2, p.205 (1961).

9. G. W. Sutton and A. W. Carlson, "End Effects in Inviscid Flow in a Magnetohydrodynamic Channel," to be published by *J. Fluid Mechanics*.

10. F. C. Foshag, "The 2500 KW A-C Air Arc," G. E. Report TIS R59SD311 (1959).

11. V. H. Blackman and M. S. Jones, Jr., "MHD Power Generation Studies in Rectangular Channels," presented at Second Symposium on Engineering Aspects of MHD, Univ. of Penna., March 9, 1961 (to be published by Columbia University Press).

12. S. Goldstein, *Modern Development in Fluid Mechanics* (Oxford University Press, 1938).

13. L. G. Napolitano, "On Turbulent Magneto-Fluid Dynamic Boundary Layers," *Rev. Mod. Physics,* Vol. 32, p. 785 (1960).

14. M. S. Sodha, "Electron Mobility in Partially Ionized Atomic Hydrogen," *Phys. Rev.,* Vol. 113, No. 5, p. 1163 (1959).

15. L. Spitzer, Jr., *Physics of Fully Ionized Gases* (New York: Interscience, 1956).

PLASMA STUDIES IN A SHOCK TUBE*

John W. Daiber and Herbert S. Glick
Cornell Aeronautical Laboratory Inc., Buffalo, N. Y.

Air plasmas produced by shock waves have been studied in the temperature range extending from 3000°K to 5000°K at densities ranging from 0.5×10^{-2} to 1.5×10^{-2} that of standard air density. Microwave reflection measurements from these plasmas have been made at frequencies of 3320 and 9375mc. A major aim of the reflection measurements was to determine whether or not polarization forces on the electron are important. The present results indicate that the Sellmeier theory, in which the polarization forces are assumed to be negligible, is the proper theory for relating electron concentrations and cross sections with macroscopic electrical parameters. In addition, the collision frequencies of electrons in air were found to agree closely with those reported by Lamb and Lin. The data also provided an estimate of the relaxation time for electron formation.

INTRODUCTION

General Discussion of the Problem

A new area of hypersonic research which has received increasing emphasis in recent years deals with the interaction of electromagnetic waves with the plasma sheath surrounding a hypervelocity vehicle which is flying through the terrestrial atmosphere. Two examples of problems in this area which are presently of practical interest are the communication "blackout"[1, 2] and radar cross-section problems.[3]

In order to treat a problem involving the interaction of electromagnetic energy and the plasma sheath surrounding a hypervelocity vehicle, it is generally necessary first to determine the distribution of chemical species about the body, and then to translate this distribution into an equivalent distribution of electrical parameters. During the past decade a large amount of effort has been devoted to the first part of the problem and it is now possible to calculate chemical species distributions with reasonable accuracy for certain simple bodies.[4-8] The second part of the problem is not new to physicists and radio engineers, having received much attention during the early days of radio transmission.[9, 10, 11] However, a basic question has still not been settled unequivocally, and a goal of the present study has been

*This work was supported by the Air Research and Development Command, Rome Air Development Center, Griffis Air Force Base, New York

Presented at the Symposium on Electromagnetics and Fluid Dynamics of Gaseous Plasma, Polytechnic Institute of Brooklyn, April 4, 5, 6, 1961

to provide new data to help decide this question.

The question at issue is whether or not the so-called Lorentz polarization force should be included in the equation of motion of the electron for gaseous plasmas.[12, 13] It is well known that such a force should be included in describing the electrical behavior of dielectrics, and should be omitted in describing the electrical behavior of metals.[10] A gaseous plasma, which is sometimes described as a lossy dielectric, does not clearly fall into either category and theorists in the past have attempted to determine criteria for deciding when this polarization force is necessary. One criterion depends upon whether or not the electrons are bound or free.[11] Another criterion is based on the ratio of the amplitude of the electron motion to the mean spacing between adjacent particles of the plasma.[10] Experimental studies aimed at resolving the question have been ambiguous, chiefly because the plasmas used in the experiments were either ill-defined geometrically or because the electrical and thermodynamic properties of the plasma were not known with sufficient accuracy.[14, 15]

Present Study

With the advent of high-performance shock-tube technology, it is now possible to produce gaseous plasmas that have certain advantages over plasmas produced electrically or by photo-processes such as occur in the ionosphere. The advantages of shock-produced plasmas stem largely from the purely thermal origin of the electrons. Since the gas is mechanically compressed by the shock wave, the gas sample is processed uniformly and rapidly so that the geometry of the plasma is generally well-defined. The equilibrium properties of the plasma are governed by the Rankine-Hugoniot relations which express the conservation of mass, momentum, and energy. Also, if the relaxation zone which measures the "thickness" of the shock is important, it is possible to determine conditions in the nonequilibrium zone by solving the gasdynamical and chemical kinetic equations simultaneously.[16, 17, 18]

A schematic diagram of the present experimental apparatus is shown in Fig. 1. The air plasmas were created by strong shock waves in a shock tube. This shock-created plasma grows in axial dimension as the shock wave propagates down the tube. While the shock-generated plasma is moving along the axis of the shock tube, microwaves are also propagating axially along the shock tube from the opposite direction and collide with the oncoming plasma. The microwaves interact with the plasma and the basic measurement of the experiment is the fraction of the incident power which is reflected.

The amount of microwave power which will be reflected by a plasma depends on the electron plasma frequency, the collision frequency of the electrons with the other gas species, the electron relaxation distance, and the angle of incidence of the microwaves on the

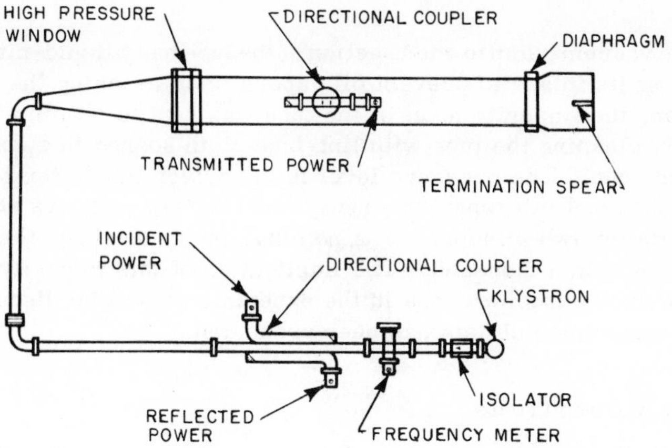

Fig. 1 Microwave schematic for plasma interaction study

plasma. Despite the number of parameters that must be taken into account in analyzing the experimental data, it will be shown that by operating at two microwave frequencies and over a range of plasma temperature and density, it is possible to answer the question of the importance of polarization forces in air plasmas, and at the same time determine the collision frequencies of the electrons and obtain an estimate of the relaxation time for electron formation.

EXPERIMENTAL PROGRAM

Operating Conditions

The driver section of the shock tube was three feet long and the driven section was twenty-one feet long. The inside of the tube was plated with Kanigen, which was found to have a loss of 0. 3db/meter at X-band frequencies. The internal shock tube dimensions were 1-1/2 × 2-1/2 inches.

The shock-tube driver gas was hydrogen at pressures from 150 to 2000 psia, while the driven gas was bottled air obtained from the Olin-Matheson Company which was analyzed by a mass spectrometer and found to contain 21.05% oxygen, 77. 93% nitrogen, 0. 05% carbon dioxide, and 0. 97% argon. The initial driven pressures for the experiments were 1 and 0. 318 mm Hg, as measured by an Alphatron vacuum gauge. The shock Mach number varied from 9. 75 to 13. 42, and the temperature and density of the air behind the incident shock wave varied from 3000 to 5000°K and from 0. 5 × 10^{-2} to 1. 5 × 10^{-2} that of standard air density, respectively. The fraction of particles ionized thus varied from 10^{-6} to 10^{-4} for the present study.

The vacuum pump to each section of the tube had a liquid-nitrogen cold trap at its intake to prevent oil vapors from reaching the tube. In addition, the impurity level of the tube was kept to a minimum by thoroughly cleaning the tube with lint-free cloth soaked in alcohol after every run. The pressure level in the driven tube after pumping was less than 0. 4 microns of mercury and the leak rate was about 1. 3 microns Hg for two minutes. The nominal purity level is, therefore, about one part in a thousand. The implication of this impurity level on the electron concentrations in the experiments will be discussed after the experimental data has been presented.

Plasma Conditions

At the initial air densities of the present experiments, the thickness of the plasma zone which extends from the shock wave to the gas interface separating driven and driver gases is much less than that calculated from ideal gasdynamics.[19] By accounting for boundary-layer effects, Roshko[20] has shown that the plasma thickness can be predicted. For the present shock-tube experiments, this thickness is about 20 cm for the 1 mm Hg runs, and about 6 cm for the 0. 318 mm Hg runs. The plasma thickness required for the microwaves to attenuate to 1/e of their initial value is generally much less than 4 cm for the frequencies used in the present study. Consequently, for the present experiments the plasma may be considered as being semi-infinite, and in interpreting the data no account need be made of the plasma profile at the gas interface. The plasma's cross-sectional area can also be regarded as constant since the boundary layer thickness on the wall of the shock tube is only about 1 mm at a distance of one inch behind the shock wave.[21] The Debye lengths of the plasmas were about 10^{-3} cm.

The passage of the shock wave could be detected readily at various stations along the shock tube by conventional ion gauges. Six gauges were used; these served not only to measure the speed of the shock wave, but also to generate synchronizing signals to the various other components of the system. The output from the three ion gauges closest to the shock-tube end-wall triggered two Berkeley microsecond-interval counters. From these times and the distance between gauges, the wave speed could be measured to within 3/4 per cent. Thus the equilibrium temperature and density of the plasma could be calculated to within 3/4% and 1/2%, respectively. The plasma frequency of the electrons and the collision frequency of the electrons with the other gas species, assuming the collision cross sections given in the literature,[1, 22, 23] could then be determined to within ± 5% and ± 2%, respectively. For the experiments at an initial pressure of 0. 318 mm Hg, this uncertainty in the plasma frequency was unacceptable. Consequently, the microwave ripple, which will be discussed later, was used to measure the shock-wave velocity. This latter method has the additional advantage that the wave speed is measured near the end wall where the reflection measurements are made, and thus no extrapolation of the wave speed is necessary.

Microwave Equipment

A continous microwave signal was produced by a low-power klystron. This signal was transmitted through standard microwave waveguides in the TE_{01} mode to a linear transition section. The transition section was a waveguide taper which changed the guide cross-section dimensions from the standard waveguide size to the 1-1/2 X 2-1/2 inch internal dimensions of the shock tube (Fig. 1). The end wall of the shock tube was a 1-1/2 X 2-1/2 X 0.97 inch fiberglass block fastened with Hysol to the shock tube walls. This fiberglass thickness was selected to give a minimum VSWR (voltage-standing-wave-ratio) at the frequencies used and to withstand the pressure loads created by the shock waves. Two microwave frequencies were used in the present study. One was at 9375 mc in the X-band region, which corresponds to a free-space wavelength of 3.198 cm and to a guide wavelength in the shock tube of 3.304 cm. The power level after the klystron padding was about 1 milliwatt. The other frequency used was in the S-band at 3320 mc, which corresponds to a free space wavelength of 9.03 cm and to a guide wavelength in the shock tube of 12.84 cm. The power output after padding was about 17 milliwatts. Consequently, the peak electric field in the shock tube was 0.2 volts/cm at X-band and 0.9 volts/cm at S-band.

Margenau[24] has established a criterion to determine if the microwaves will disturb the Maxwellian velocity distribution of the electrons. For the distribution to remain Maxwellian, the ratio

$$x_1/\alpha = 24\pi (m/M)(n_e kT/E^2)(f/f_p)^2$$

should be greater than one. For air at 4000°K, the criterion becomes $0.84 \times 10^{-18} (f/E)^2 > 1$. At X-band this ratio is 1850, while for S-band the ratio is 12. A different relation implying a more stringent requirement has been given by Ginzburg and Gurevich.[25] Using this latter criterion and making the conservative assumption that all electron collisions are elastic, it is found that the microwaves still do not affect the electron velocity distribution.

Reflection Measurements

The microwave powers incident upon and reflected by the plasma were measured through a directional coupler located near the klystron (Fig. 1). The detectors were 1N21 and 1N23 crystals which were very nearly perfect square-law detectors when a forward bias current was used.[26] The crystal outputs were fed into a dual-beam oscilloscope which was triggered when the shock wave reached the last ion gauge station.

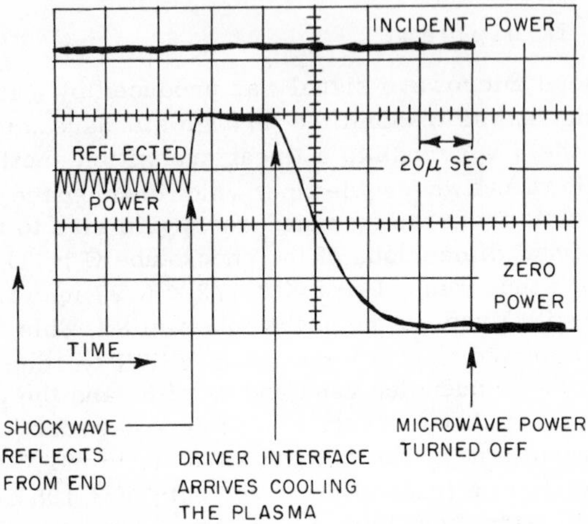

Fig. 2 Typical X-band data. P_1 = 1 mm Hg; M = 12. 1; f/f_p = . 46; f_c/f = . 33.

Figure 2 shows an oscillograph record at X-band for a shock Mach number of 12. 1. The increase in reflected power at the center of the record represents the time at which the shock wave reflects from the fiberglass end-wall window. The reflected power is increased because the plasma has now been processed by both the incident and reflected shock waves, and is consequently at a much higher temperature and density than that gas which has only been processed by the incident shock. The ripple observable in the reflected power is caused by the cavity formed by the fiberglass window and the shock wave going into and out of resonance. The distance the shock wave travels between ripple peaks therefore corresponds to one-half of a guide wavelength. This ripple was displayed on another scope sweeping at 2 μ sec/cm. The period of the ripple could be measured to within 0. 25%, and the shock-wave speed could be measured to within 0. 4%.

The reflected power was also monitored on another oscilloscope, which was triggered by the breaking of the metal diaphragm separating the driver and driven sections of the shock tube. Before the run began, a certain amount of reflected microwave power was being detected. This microwave power came from the reflection of the microwaves by the metal diaphragm. When the diaphragm broke and the experiment began, the reflected power decreased to zero. This falling signal was used as the trigger for the oscilloscope. A typical record from this oscilloscope for an S-band experiment is shown in Fig. 3. The thickness of the oscilloscope trace is due to the peak-to-peak ripple seen in Fig. 2.

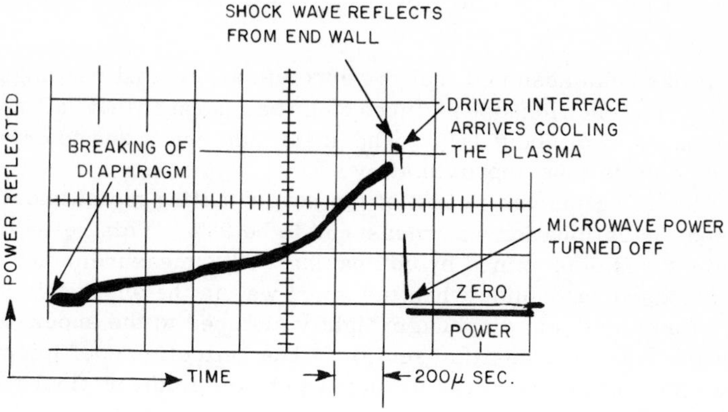

Fig. 3 Typical S-band data. M_S = 12.58; P_1 = 1 mm Hg; f/f_p = .15; f_c/f = 1.03.

Calibration and Errors

The measured reflected and incident power cannot be directly interpreted in terms of a reflection coefficient because of the transmission losses through the waveguides and components. This attenuation loss was measured by placing a metal short of known reflection coefficient in the shock tube at the same station at which the reflection from the shock wave was measured. The plasma power-reflection coefficient, r, is then

$$\log_{10}(r/r_c) = 2\log_{10}(E_{i_c}/E_i) + 2\log_{10}(E_r/E_{r_c})$$

where the subscript c denotes the quantities measured during calibration, the subscript i pertains to incident microwave quantities, the subscript r pertains to reflected microwave quantities, and E is the electric field intensity. Four measurements are therefore necessary to define the power reflection coefficient, i. e., the incident and reflected field intensities during the run, and the incident and reflected field intensities during calibration.

The detector crystal output, C, is directly proportional to the local electric field intensity to some power, i. e.,

$$C = aE^n$$

The value of n for the experiments was quite close to two and was measured immediately after each experiment. Substituting the equation for E in terms of C into the equation defining the reflection coefficient, it is found that

$$| dr/r | \leqslant 4(2/n) | dC/C | + | dr_c/r_c |$$

where it has been assumed that the error in all crystal readings is the same. The oscilloscope pictures could be read such that $dC = \pm 1.5$ for values of C of about 150. The maximum error due to crystal readings only is thus approximately 4%.

The reflection coefficient of the noncontacting metal short which was used for calibration was measured to be 98%. This reflection coefficient was determined by comparing VSWR measurements made in the standard waveguide when the short was in the shock tube to the VSWR of an aluminum diaphragm tightly clamped to the shock-tube side of the tapered transition section. The reflection coefficient of the aluminum diaphragm was assumed to have the theoretical value of unity.

An error is also introduced by averaging the ripple to obtain the incident or reflected crystal readings. In a lossless system, this averaging is justified and introduces no errors. However, the present system is not lossless and the uncertainty in reflection coefficient introduced by ripple is estimated at about 3%.

DATA ANALYSIS

Reflection from a Plane Surface

When a plane electromagnetic wave is normally incident on a semi-infinite plasma with sharp boundaries, a reflected and a transmitted electromagnetic wave are produced. The fraction of the incident power reflected depends on the plasma's index of refraction, η, and extinction coefficient, K, and on the angle of incidence, θ (measured from the normal), which the waves make with the plasma. The expression for the power reflection coefficient, r, is the same as for metallic reflection[27] where

$$r = \frac{(q - \cos\theta)^2 + p^2}{(q + \cos\theta)^2 + p^2}$$

and

$$q\,p = \eta K,$$

$$q^2 - p^2 = \eta^2 - K^2 - \sin^2\theta .$$

The angle of incidence depends both on the free-space wavelength, λ, and on the larger side of the rectangular waveguide dimensions, a . It can be shown[28] that

$$\sin \theta = \lambda / 2a.$$

For the shock tube used in the present study, a= 2.5 inches. Thus at 9375 mc, the angle of incidence is 14. 6°, while at 3320 mc, the angle of incidence is 45. 4°.

The index of refraction and the extinction coefficient are related to the dielectric constant, ϵ , and conductivity, σ, of the plasma. These relations are[1]

$$-\eta^2 = \epsilon / 2 + \frac{1}{2} \left[\epsilon^2 + (2\sigma/f)^2\right]^{1/2}$$

$$K^2 = -\epsilon / 2 + \frac{1}{2} \left[\epsilon^2 + (2\sigma/f)^2\right]^{1/2} .$$

Thus, by knowing the electrical macroscopic properties of the plasma, ϵ and σ , one can calculate the amount of incident radiation of frequency, f , which will be reflected by a plane plasma interface.

Plasma Properties

The equilibrium plasma properties, generally expressed in terms of the electron plasma frequency, f_p, and the electron collision frequency, f_c, can be calculated from the concentrations of the species that are present* and the electron collision cross sections.[1,23]

The plasma frequency, which depends on the number density of the electrons, is[29]

$$f_p^2 = n_e \frac{e^2}{\pi m}$$

where n_e is the number density of electrons, e is the electronic charge, and m is the mass of an electron. The electron collision frequency, f_c, is given by[22]

$$2 \pi f_c = (4/3) \overline{V} \sum_j n_j Q_j$$

where $\overline{V}$ is the average electron speed, n_j is the number density of the jth species, and Q_j is the electron collision cross section with the jth species.

As mentioned previously, the relationship of the parameters, f_p and f_c, with the macroscopic properties, ϵ and σ, has been the

*Equilibrium normal shock wave program supplied by R. E. Duff, Los Alamos, New Mexico.

subject of some controversy in the past. These properties are related through the equation of motion of an electron. For a dielectric medium, a polarizing force must be included in the equation of motion of an electron. For a metallic conductor, the polarization force has been shown to be nonexistent, and the theory for translating microscopic plasma properties into macroscopic electrical parameters for this case is usually called the Sellmeier theory.

The equation of motion for an electron, neglecting polarization forces, may be written heuristically as

$$m \ddot{\xi} = eE - g \dot{\xi}$$

where ξ is the electron displacement in the direction of $\vec{E}$. The viscous resistance coefficient, g, is usually taken[30] as $2\pi m f_c$. Solving the equation of motion for the current density $\vec{J} = -n_e e \dot{\xi}$ and comparing this solution with

$$\vec{J} = (\sigma + i \omega \beta) \vec{E}$$

where $\epsilon = 1 + 4\pi\beta$, it is found that for Sellmeier theory

$$\epsilon = 1 - f_p^2/(f^2 + f_c^2)$$

$$2\sigma/f = f_p^2 f_c/f(f^2 + f_c^2) .$$

If the polarization force is included in the equation of motion of the electron, then it is found that

$$m \ddot{\xi} = e(E + 4\pi P/3) - g \dot{\xi}$$

where

$$P = n_e e \xi$$

The macroscopic plasma properties are then given by

$$\epsilon = 1 - \frac{f_p^2 (1 + f_p^2/3f^2)}{f^2(1 + f_p^2/3f^2) + f_c^2}$$

$$\frac{2\sigma}{f} = \frac{f_p^2 f_c}{f\left[f^2(1 + f_p^2/3 f^2)^2 + f_c^2\right]}$$

These latter relations are commonly called the Lorentz equations.

The reflection coefficients predicted by each theory can then be computed for various values of the ratios f/f_p and f_c/f. The results are shown in Fig. 4 for the case of normal incidence. From this figure it can be seen that there are two regions where the predicted reflection coefficient is markedly different for the two theories. One of these regions is where the normalized wave frequency, f/f_p, is slightly less than unity and the value of f_c/f is sufficiently low; the other region is where f/f_p is much less than unity. The first region is difficult to attain in a shock tube because of the low initial densities necessary to achieve the required values of collision frequency.[19, 20] The second region, in which f/f_p is less than 1/10, requires very strong shock waves.

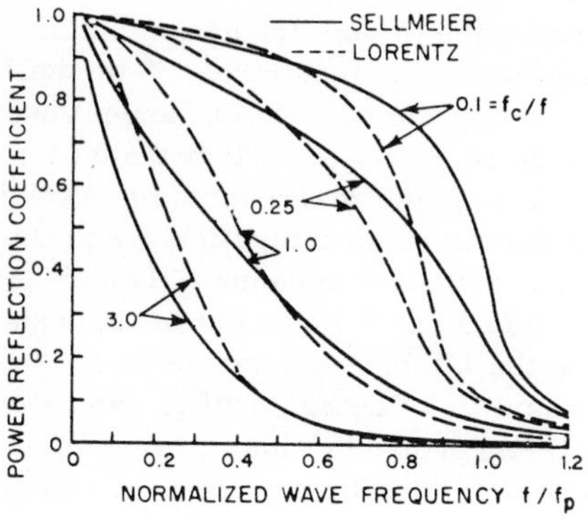

Fig. 4 Reflection from plane interface

Electron Relaxation Effects

In the present experiments, electron relaxation effects are important in determining the reflection properties of the plasma front. As the shock wave advances down the tube, it produces a plasma of known equilibrium temperature and density. However, the gas is not

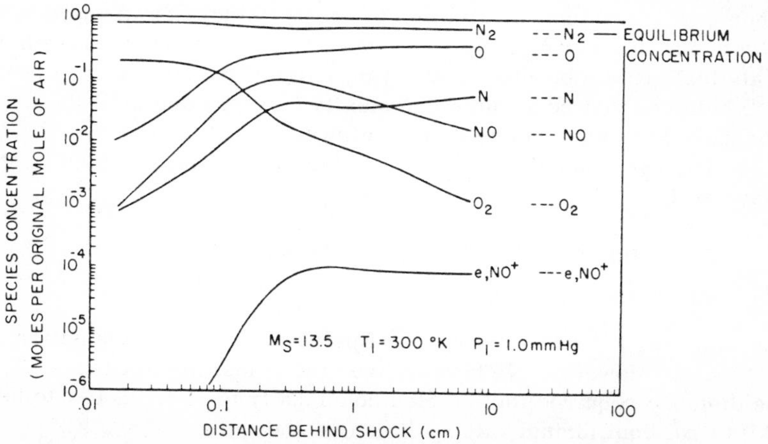

Fig. 5 Species concentration behind normal shock in air, calculated using IBM program of Reference 18, including vibrational nonequilibrium.

instantaneously changed into this new state. Each new species has a relaxation distance associated with its formation; for the electrons, this distance is found to be of the order of one centimeter for the temperatures and densities used in the present experiments[18] (Fig. 5). The thickness of this finite transition region strongly affects the amount of microwave power which is reflected.[31]

In the literature, three solutions are available which account for an arbitrary incidence angle and a particular transition profile. These solutions are the linear ramp solution of Hartree,[32] the half-cycle sinusoidal layer of Beghian,[33] and the hyperbolic tangent profile of Epstein.[34] A characteristic of these solutions is that transition profile geometry is assumed to be that of the macroscopic electrical properties, rather than that of the electron concentration. For the Sellmeier theory, these profiles are the same because f_p^2 (which is proportional to the electron density) can be factored out of the equations defining $1-\epsilon$ and $2\sigma/f$. For the Lorentz theory, no such factorization is possible and the resulting electron profile geometry is therefore different from the electrical property transition geometry. A computational program adequate for either theory for an arbitrary electron transition profile is given in the Appendix.

The variation of reflection coefficient with ramp thickness is shown in Figs. 6 and 7 for equilibrium values of $f/f_p = 0.65$ and $f_c/f = 0.60$. The variation for the hyperbolic tangent profile was found using Epstein's solution; the other four profiles were obtained by the computational program described in the Appendix. The nondimensional transition-zone thickness parameter is taken as Z/λ for the latter profiles. For the profile, $g_1(\zeta)$, Z is defined as the distance over which the electron density changes from 1% to 99% of the final value. This definition of the transition zone for Epstein's solution gives good qualitative agreement with the reflection coefficients predicted by the other profiles. Accordingly, in the present study, the transition zone effects due to electron relaxation have been treated using Epstein's analytical results because of the simplicity of the solution and because it is believed that no greater complexity is warranted until the transition-zone geometry can be better defined.

The variation of dielectric constant with distance which Epstein assumed is

$$\epsilon(x) = \frac{1}{2}(\epsilon + 1) + \frac{1}{2}(\epsilon - 1)\tanh\frac{x}{2Z_0}$$

where $\epsilon(-\infty) = 1$ and $\epsilon(+\infty) = \epsilon$ Epstein calls Z_0 the transition thickness. However, we have defined the transition thickness, Z, as the distance required for the electron density to go from 1%, to 99% of its final equilibrium value. It can be shown that $Z = 9.2\, Z_0$.

Defining $a = 2\pi i(Z_0/\lambda)\cos\theta$ and $b = 2\pi i(Z_0/\lambda)(\epsilon - \sin^2\theta)^{1/2}$,

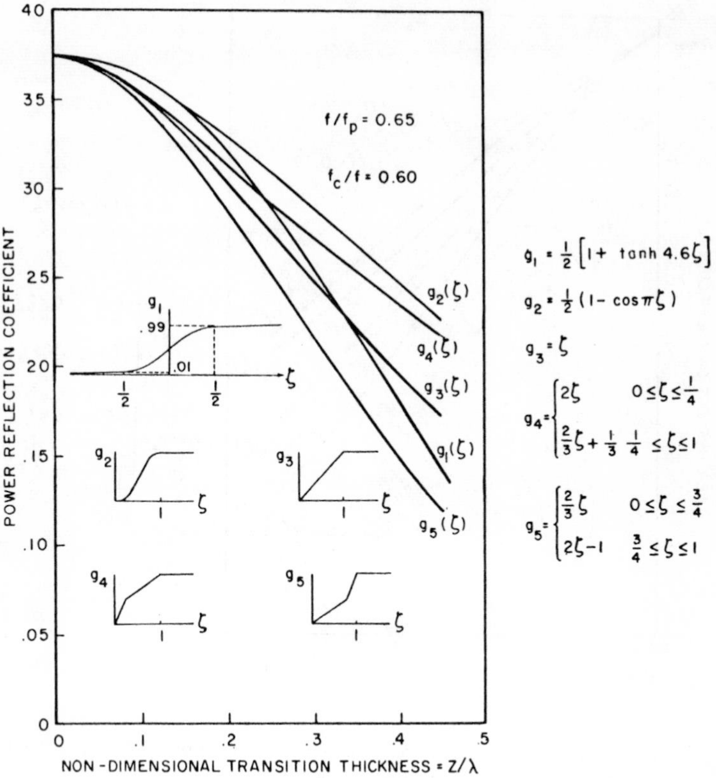

Fig. 6 Reflection from various electron density gradients for Sellmeier theory at normal incidence

Epstein shows that the reflection coefficient is

$$r = \left| \Gamma(2a)\,\Gamma(-a-b)/\Gamma(-2a)\,\Gamma(a-b) \right|^2$$

For the case considered here, this equation reduces to

$$r = r_s \exp 4\,(u_1 - u_2)$$

where

$$u_1 = \mathrm{Re}\left\{ \ln \Gamma(1 - a + b) \right\}, \quad u_2 = \mathrm{Re}\left\{ \ln \Gamma(1 + a - b) \right\}$$

and r_s is the Fresnel reflection coefficient.

Kinetics Calculations

Calculations of the chemical species distributions behind normal shocks have been carried out for the range of the present

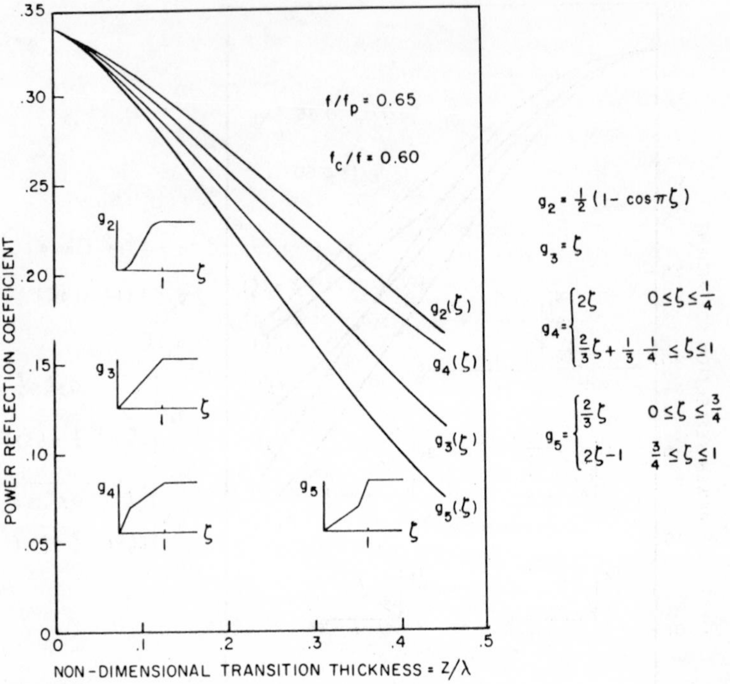

Fig. 7 Reflection from various electron density gradients for Lorentz theory at normal incidence

TABLE I

Overshoots in Plasma Frequency Behind a Normal Shock Wave for Initial Pressures Before the Shock Wave of 0.318 and 1.0 mm Hg.

M_s	P_1 = 0.318 mm Hg $(f_p)_{max}/(f_p)_{eq}$	P_1 = 1.0 mm Hg $(f_p)_{max}/(f_p)_{eq}$
11.0	1.36	1.25
11.6	1.19	—
11.9	1.08	—
12.28	1.03	1.06
13.5	1.05	1.04

experiments. These calculations have employed the best available kinetic data for air and have included the coupling of vibrational excitation with the dissociation reactions.[18, 35] A typical species distribution, which is shown in Fig. 5, is translated into profiles of electron plasma and collision frequency in Fig. 8. The only electron-producing mechanism assumed is

$$N + O \longrightarrow NO^{+} + e^{-}$$

and the reaction rate is taken to be $5 \times 10^{13}\ T^{-1/2} \exp(-31715/T)$ cc/mole -sec.[35, 36] It is seen that the electron plasma frequency overshoots its equilibrium value. The results of several calculations of the overshoot in plasma frequency are shown in Table I, where it is seen that appreciable overshoots in plasma frequency occur in the lower part of the shock Mach number range. However, it will be seen later that some doubt exists as to the proper electron-producing reaction mechanism, and it has been decided in the present theoretical analysis to neglect electron overshoots. The experimental observations have been reported directly so that new data on air kinetics can be conveniently analyzed and compared with the experimental results.

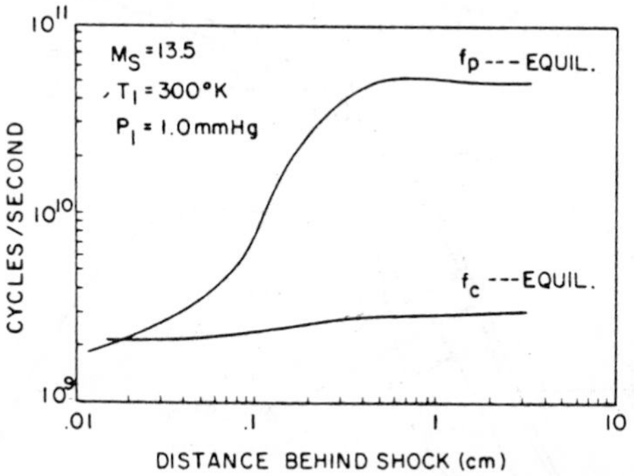

Fig. 8 Calculated plasma frequency and collision frequency distributions behind a normal shock in air

The change in collision frequency is small throughout the electron transition region, so it was neglected. This approximation is poorer at S-band when $f_c/f \approx 1$. However, here the transition-zone thickness is very small compared with a wavelength, so the correction term becomes almost negligible and further refinements are beyond the accuracy of the experimental data. Thus the data were corrected for the electron gradient by using Epstein's solution for the Sellmeier theory. The reduction of the data for Lorentz theory was accomplished with the IBM machine program. The collision frequencies throughout the transition region were calculated using the cross sections of NO,

N_2 and O_2 used in Reference 1 and those of O and N given in Reference 23.

EXPERIMENTAL RESULTS

Polarization Effects

When f/f_p is slightly less than unity and the values of f_c/f are less than 0.5, the reflection coefficients predicted by the Sellmeier and Lorentz theories are quite different. In order to attain the necessary values of f_p at low values of f_c, the shock tube was operated at the initial pressure of 0.318 mm Hg so that f_c/f varied from 0.06 to 0.10. The shock-wave velocity was measured using the ripple in the reflected power. The measured reflection coefficients of X-band microwaves are shown in Fig. 9 as a function of f/f_p. The wave-speed variation causes uncertainty in the values of shock Mach number of ±0.1

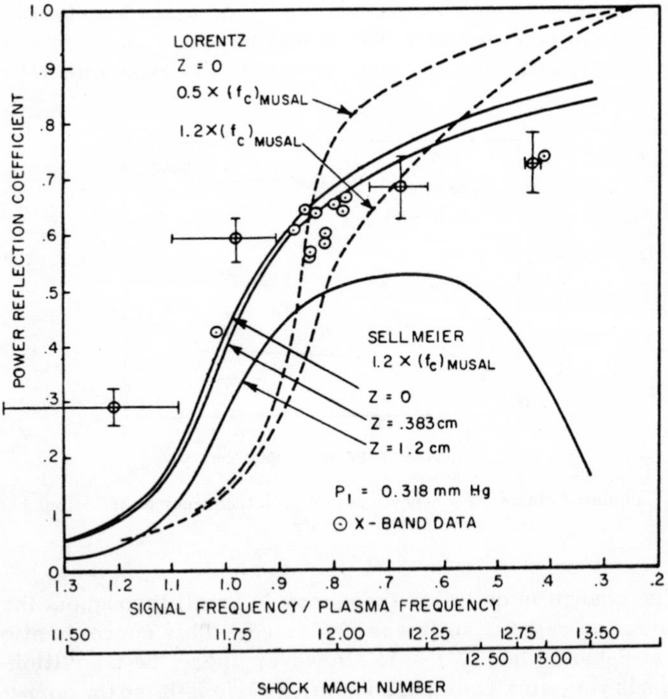

Fig. 9 Reflection coefficient from shock-generated air plasmas. Z is the relaxation distance at M = 13.5.

Also shown in Fig. 9 are two curves of reflection coefficients predicted by the Lorentz theory for a plane plasma interface. Any correction factor added to these theoretical curves to account for electron relaxation effects would decrease the predicted reflected power. When the plasma collision frequencies are taken to be 20% higher than the values tabulated by Musal,[22] i. e., values of collision frequency which agree with those of Lamb and Lin[23] and with the present results (see next section), the predicted curve falls far short of the experimental points. Higher predicted values can be obtained by lowering the collision frequency. However, even for a 50% reduction in collision frequency, there still exist significant differences in measured and predicted reflection coefficients.

The reflection coefficients predicted by the Sellmeier theory for a 20% increase in collision frequency and for a plane interface are also shown in Fig. 9. This curve is very near to being an upper bound of the experimental data, so that a correction factor due to transition thickness can be predicted assuming the Sellmeier theory, while this is not possible assuming the so-called Lorentz theory. Thus, it is concluded that the Sellmeier theory is the proper theory for calculating the electrical properties of air plasmas in the range of the present experiments.

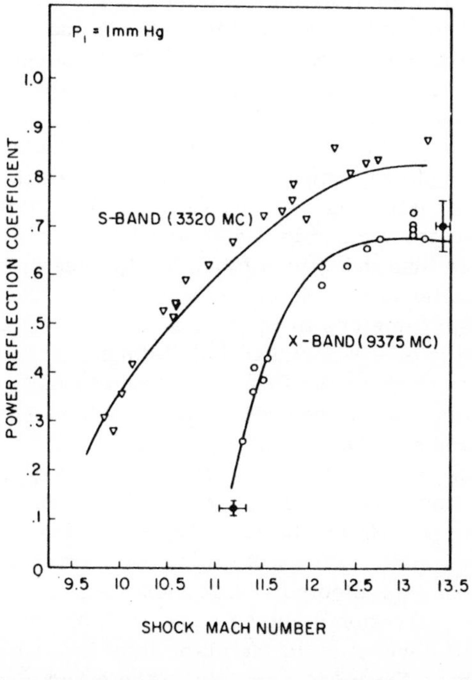

Fig. 10 Power reflection coefficients for air plasmas. Theoretical curves have been calculated using Epstein's theory and values of $f_c = 1.20(f_c)_{Musal}$ and $Z = 0.38$ cm at $M = 13.5$

Collision Frequency and Electron Relaxation Measurements

The variation of the reflection coefficient with shock Mach number is shown in Fig. 10 for experiments with an initial air pressure of 1 mm Hg. For the microwave frequency of 3320 mc, the shock Mach number range of the experiments is from 9. 75 to 13. 25, corresponding to equilibrium temperatures ranging from 3300°K to 4900°K. The range of f/f_p is from 1. 02 to 0. 077, and the range in f_c/f is from 0. 6 to 1. 2. For the runs at 9375 mc, the Mach number range is 11. 2 to 13. 42, corresponding to equilibrium temperatures ranging from 3800°K to 5100°K. The ranges in f/f_p and f_c/f are from 1. 01 to 0. 20, and from 0. 30 to 0. 45, respectively.

The reflection coefficient of electromagnetic waves from a plasma interface in a shock tube depends on four parameters: the ratios, f/f_p and f_c/f, the effective angle of incidence of the microwaves in the shock tube, and the electron relaxation distance. For the present experiments the plasma frequency and angle of incidence can be regarded as known quantities. The electron collision frequency and the electron relaxation distance can then be used as the two adjustable parameters in correlating the Sellmeier theory with the experimental reflection coefficients. The S-band reflection coefficients are relatively insensitive to relaxation distance and may be used to obtain an approximate estimate of the collision frequency. Then, an estimate of the relaxation distance can be made using the X-band data, especially the data in the high-shock Mach number region which is extremely sensitive to relaxation zone length. This procedure was employed in the 1 mm Hg experiments and the following results were found after several iterations: a) The values of collision frequency are equal to those determined by Lamb and Lin,[23] which are approximately 20% higher than the values tabulated by Musal;[22] b) The electron relaxation distance is 0. 38 cm at Mach 13. 5. Using these values of the adjustable parameters in Epstein's solution and assuming that the logarithm of the electron relaxation distance varies linearly with the shock Mach number,[37] the theoretical curves of power reflection coefficient as a function of shock Mach number are shown in Fig. 10 for both the X-band and the S-band experiments. It is seen that the theoretical curves represent the experimental data quite well.

The theoretical power-reflection coefficient curves at an initial pressure of 0. 318 mm Hg can be found by taking into account the electron relaxation distance. Figure 9 shows two curves which correct the Sellmeier theory for electron relaxation distance. One curve, with the electron relaxation distance equal to 0. 383 cm at Mach 13. 5, gives only a small correction to the plane interface reflection case and is slightly above the measured data. The other curve, in which the relaxation distance has been scaled inversely with density, falls far below the experimental data and exhibits a falling off at high values of f_p which is not found in the data. Consequently, the present results indicate that the electron relaxation distance does not scale inversely with density as it would if the only electron-producing mechanism were the reaction, $N + O \rightarrow NO^+ + e^-$, which has been reported by Lin.[17, 36] Thus, it is believed that the kinetics of electron formation in high-temperature air should be re-examined both experimentally and theoretically.

Effect of Impurities

In the present experiments and in those of Lamb and Lin,[23] the nominal purity level of the experiments was sufficiently poor to suggest the possibility that impurities could furnish an appreciable number of electrons. An important result of the present studies is that this impurity problem did not arise and that it is possible to produce a well defined, uncontaminated air plasma in a shock tube with only moderate effort. This conclusion had been reached earlier by Lamb and Lin in their air dc conductivity measurements and was largely justified by the lack of scatter in the data and in the general shape of the curve of the experimental results. The present results serve to make the same conclusions more quantitative. It can be seen from Fig. 4, for example, that if the electron concentration were doubled due to impurity electrons in the low shock Mach number runs where the number of thermally produced electrons is small, $f/f_p \simeq 1$, the measured power reflection coefficient, would change from 10% to over 50%. Such an electron impurity level could be caused, for example, by a sodium concentration of one part in ten thousand. This sensitivity of the reflection coefficient to impurity electrons strongly indicates that such electrons were not produced and that the plasma is one whose properties are well defined.

CONCLUDING REMARKS

The present microwave-plasma interaction results indicate that the polarization forces are negligible in the temperature and density range of the experiments and that the Sellmeier theory can be used for calculating the electrical properties of air plasmas. The criterion of Booker and Berkner[10] predicts that in the range of the present experiments the Lorentz theory would be applicable. The present results, therefore, indicate that this criterion is not correct.

The measured values of electron collision frequency are in excellent agreement with the air dc conductivity measurements of Lamb and Lin.[23] Some of the present data have been obtained at values of the parameter, f_c/f, which is appreciably below unity so that the electron oscillates an appreciable number of times between collisions. These data may therefore be said to provide high-frequency verification of the Sellmeier theory.

The electron relaxation data obtained in the present experiments should be viewed as being of a preliminary nature. It is felt that the data are valid only in providing an estimate of the electron relaxation time. The low-density electron kinetics measurements of Lin and Fyfe[38] are subject to several sources of error which are discussed briefly by the authors. These errors may be sufficiently serious that the values reported should also be regarded as providing only order-of-magnitude validity. The present results do not scale with density in a manner predicted by the results of Lin and Fyfe and it therefore seems clear that the kinetics of electron formation deserves more attention.

The present results demonstrate that it is possible to generate a well-defined thermal plasma in a shock tube. It is felt that measurements which have been made using electrical excitation methods, such as dc and rf discharges, plasma jets, etc., should be repeated in the shock tube and the results compared with the previous ones.

APPENDIX

For harmonic plane electromagnetic waves, Maxwell's equations are

$$\text{div } N^2 \vec{E} = 0$$

$$\text{div } \vec{H} = 0$$

$$\text{curl } \vec{H} = N^2 \dot{\vec{E}}/C$$

$$\text{curl } \vec{E} = - \dot{\vec{H}}/C$$

where N is the complex index of refraction

$$N^2 = \epsilon - i\, 2\sigma/f .$$

These equations can be manipulated to form a vector equation for the electric field intensity, $\vec{E}$,[31]

$$\nabla^2 \vec{E} + k_o^2 N^2 \vec{E} + \nabla\left\{\left[\vec{E} \cdot \nabla N^2\right]/N^2\right\} = 0.$$

If the gradient in the macroscopic plasma properties is only in the z direction, and if the plane of incidence of the electromagnetic waves is the x, z plane, then for electromagnetic waves polarized normal to the plane of incidence, the last term in the equation is zero so that the equation reduces to a vector wave equation. Assuming a separable solution, i. e., $E = E(x)\, E(z)$, it is found that

$$E(x) = \exp\left\{ i\,(2\pi f/c)\, x \sin\theta \right\}$$

where θ is the angle of incidence measured from the normal. Let $\zeta = z/Z$ where Z is the thickness of the transition region; then the equation for $E(\zeta)$ becomes

$$E_{\zeta\zeta} + (k_o Z)^2 \left[f(\zeta) \right]^2 E = 0,$$

where

$$\left[f(\zeta) \right]^2 = \epsilon - \sin^2\theta - i2\sigma/f\,,$$

$$k_o = 2\pi f/c\,.$$

The boundary conditions are continuity in $E(\zeta)$ and the first derivative of $E(\zeta)$. If R denotes the amplitude of the reflected wave for a unit incident wave and $T \exp\left\{ -ik_2 Z (\zeta - 1) \right\}$ denotes the transmitted wave, then

$$E(0) = 1 + R$$

$$E'(0) = i(k_o Z)(R-1)$$

$$E(1) = T$$

$$E'(1) = -i(k_o Z)\, f(1)\, T$$

where f (1) is in the fourth quadrant.

There are many ways of programming the solution to a differential equation and its boundary conditions. The method used in the present study has been to notice that the unknown T could be eliminated from the boundary conditions so that

$$E'(1)/E(1) = -i\,(k_o Z)\, f(1)\,.$$

Thus by guessing both the real and imaginary parts of R, the differential equation was integrated using the Runge-Kutta method. At $\zeta = 1$, the ratio of $E'(1)/E(1)$ was compared with the known boundary condition. The Newton-Raphson method was then used to give a better guess of R. The transmitted wave could then be found using the final value of E(1).

ACKNOWLEDGMENTS

The authors are indebted to many of their colleagues for helpful suggestions made during this research effort. In particular, the assistance of Messrs. Richard Blum and Darold Wobschall in constructing and calibrating the microwave instrumentation and the analytical studies by Mr. Marshall Cohen which contributed to the IBM program of the reflection coefficient solution are gratefully acknowledged. The finite rate normal shock solutions were performed for us by Mr. Paul Marrone utilizing an IBM program which he is presently developing under the sponsorship of the Army Rocket and Guided Missile Agency through the Bendix Aviation Corporation.

REFERENCES

1. S. C. Lin, "A Rough Estimate of the Attenuation of Telemetering Signals Through the Ionized Gas Envelope Around A Typical Re-Entry Missile," AVCO Research Report 74, 1956.

2. J. R. White, "Communication During Re-Entry Blackout," ARS Preprint No. 963-59, November 1959.

3. W. Rotman and G. Meltz, "Experimental Investigation of the Effect of a Hypersonic Environment Upon Electromagnetic Radiation," *Sym. on the Plasma Sheath,* AFCRC-TR-60-108(I), 1959.

4. F. G. Gravalos, I. H. Edelfelt and H. W. Emmons, "The Supersonic Flow about a Blunt Body of Revolution for Gases at Chemical Equilibrium," *Proc. 9th International Astronautical Congress,* Vol. 1 (Amsterdam, 1958).

5. R. E. Duff and N. Davidson, "Calculation of Reaction Profiles behind Steady State Shock Waves II. The Dissociation of Air," *J. Chem. Phys.*, Vol. 31, p. 1018 (1959).

6. N. C. Freeman, "Dynamics of a Dissociating Gas III. Nonequilibrium Theory," AGARD Report No. 133.

7. W. Lick, "Inviscid Flow Around a Blunt Body of a Reacting Mixture of Gases, Part A. General Analysis," TR AE 5810 (AFOSR TN-58-522), 1958. "Part B. Numerical Solutions," TR AE 5814 (AFOSR TN-58-1124), Rensselaer Polytechnic Institute, 1958.

8. W. H. Wurster and P. V. Marrone, "Study of Infrared Emission In Heated Air," Semi-Annual Report, CAL Report No. QM-1373-A-3, December 1960.

9. H. R. Mimno, "The Physics of the Ionosphere," *Rev. Mod. Phys.*, Vol. 9, p. 1 (1937).

10. H. G. Booker and L. V. Berkner, "An Ionospheric Investigation Concerning the Lorentz Polarization – Correction," *Terr. Magn. and Atm. Elec.*, Vol. 43, p. 427 (1938).

11. C. G. Darwin, "The Refractive Index of an Ionized Medium," *Proc. Roy. Soc.*, Vol. 146, p. 17 (1934).

12. W. J. G. Beynon, "Oblique Radio Transmission in Ionosphere, and the Lorentz Polarization Term" *Proc. Phys. Soc. of London,* Vol. LIX, p. 97 (1947).

13. S. Buchsbaum, "Interaction of Electromagnetic Radiation with a High Density Plasma," Doctoral Thesis, Mass. Inst. of Tech., 1957.

14. B. B. Meckel and P. A. Harkins, "Production and Analysis of a Large Diameter Plasma Beam," *J. Appl. Phys.*, Vol. 32, p. 489 (1961).

15. E.A. McLean, et al., "Spectroscopic Study of Helium Plasmas Produced by Magnetically Driven Shock Waves,' *Phys. Fluids,* Vol.3, p.843 (1960).

16. R. E. Duff, "Calculation of Reaction Profiles Behind Steady-State Shock Waves. I. Application to Detonation Waves," *J. Chem. Phys.*, Vol. 28, p. 1193 (1958).

17. K. Wray, et al., "Relaxation Processes and Reaction Rates Behind Shock Fronts in Air and Component Gases," AVCO Res. Rept. 83, 1959.

18. W. H. Wurster and P. V. Marrone, "Study of Infrared Emission in Heated Air," Annual Report. CAL Report No. QM-1373-A-4, June 1961.

19. R. E. Duff, "Shock-Tube Performance at Low Pressure," *Phys. Fluids*, Vol. 2, p. 207 (1959).

20. A. Roshko, "On Flow Duration in Low-Pressure Shock Tubes," *Phys. Fluids*, Vol. 3, p. 835 (1960).

21. H. Mirels, Laminar Boundary Layer Behind Shock Advancing Into Stationary Fluid," NACA TN 3401, March 1955.

22. H. M. Musal, Jr., "Electron Collision Frequency in Equilibrium High Temperature Air," Res. Note 9, Bendix Product Division, May 1960.

23. L. Lamb and S.C. Lin, "Electrical Conductivity of Thermally Ionized Air Produced in a Shock Tube," AVCO Research Rept. 5, February 1957.

24. H. Margenau, "Conduction and Dispersion of Ionized Gases at High Frequencies," *Phys. Rev.*, Vol. 69, p. 508 (1946).

25. V. L. Ginzburg and A. V. Gurevich, "Nonlinear Phenomena in a Plasma Located in an Alternating Electromagnetic Field," *Soviet Phys. Uspekhi*, Vol. 3, p. 115 (1961).

26. A. Staniforth and J. H. Craven, "Improvement in the Square Law Operation of IN23B Crystals from 2 to 11 KMC," *I.R.E. Trans. on Microwave Theory and Techniques*, Vol. MTT-8, p. 111 (1960).

27. J. A. Stratton, *Electromagnetic Theory*. (New York: McGraw-Hill, 1941).

28. C. G. Montgomery, *Technique of Microwave Measurements*. [MIT Rad. Lab. Series, Vol. 11 (New York: McGraw-Hill, 1947)].

29. L. Spitzer, Jr., *Physics of Fully Ionized Gases*, (New York: Interscience, 1956).

30. E. V. Appleton and F. U. Chapman, "The Collisional Friction Experienced by Vibrating Electrons in Ionized Air," *Proc. Phys. Soc.*, Vol. 44, p. 246 (1932).

31. F. A. Albini and R. G. Jahn, "Reflection and Transmission of Electromagnetic Waves at Electron Density Gradients," *J. Appl. Phys.*, Vol. 32, p. 75 (1961).

32. D. E. Hartree, "The Propagation of Electromagnetic Waves in a Stratified Medium," *Proc. Cambridge Phil. Soc.*, Vol. 25, p. 97 (1929).

33. J. A. Saxton, et al., "The Propagation of Metre Radio Waves Beyond the Normal Horizon, Part I. Some Theoretical Considerations, with Particular Reference to Propagation Over Land," *Proc. I.E.E.*, Vol. 98, p. 360 (1951).

34. P. S. Epstein, "Reflection of Waves in an Inhomogeneous Absorbing Medium," *Proc. Nat'l Acad. Sci.*, Vol. 16, p. 627 (1930).

35. J. D. Teare and G. J. Dreiss, "Theory of the Shock Front, III. Sensitivity to Rate Constants," AVCO Res. Note 176, December 1959.

36. S. C. Lin, R. A. Neal and W. I. Fyfe, "Rate of Ionization behind Shock Waves in Air. I. Experimental Results," AVCO Res. Note 210, September 1960

37. S. C. Lin, "Rate of Ionization Behind Shock Waves in Air," AVCO Res. Note 170, December 1959.

38. S. C. Lin and W. I. Fyfe, "Low-Density Shock Tube for Chemical Kinetic Studies," AVCO Res. Rept. 91, July 1960; also *Phys. Fluids*, Vol. 4, p. 238 (1960).

MAGNETICALLY DRIVEN SHOCK WAVES

J. D. Cole and C. Greifinger
California Institute of Technology; The RAND Corporation

Several problems in the theory of magnetically driven shock waves are considered and comparison is made with some experiments.

In the first case a linear accelerator in which the gas is driven down a coaxial tube by radial currents is studied. By the use of snowplow theory for the gas motion the coupled electric circuit and gas motion equations are solved.

In the second case a diverging cylindrical shock wave is produced by a line current increasing linearly with time (inverse pinch machine). The flow is computed both according to snowplow theory and the full magnetohydrodynamic equations for an infinitely conducting gas, with and without initial constant magnetic field.

In the third example a converging cylindrical shock wave is produced by a circumferential current (Scylla). For the case of constant current the snowplow approximation provides a simple solution.

I. INTRODUCTION

In this paper some approximate theories for several devices that drive shocks electromagnetically are discussed and some preliminary comparison with experiment is given. In devices of this type an external electric circuit is coupled to an ionized gas in such a way that it produces a magnetic pressure which acts as a piston to drive the gas. In this way it is possible to produce much higher gas velocities (of the order of 10 cm/μsec) than can be achieved by means of mechanical or gas-dynamic drivers.

The first device discussed is called a linear accelerator. It consists of a coaxial arrangement of electrodes coupled to an external circuit whose main elements are a large capacitor and some inductance (see Fig. 1). During the operation of the device an oscillating current flows through the external circuit and radially in the gas, driving a shock wave and a slug of gas down the tube. The operation of this and similar devices has been discussed by various authors;[1, 2, 3] in particular, the analysis of Dattner[3] is closest to that presented here. The motion of the gas is calculated as a one-dimensional flow according to snowplow theory. The improvement introduced here is a consistent treatment of the energy balance for the gas. Dattner[3] assumed that at any moment the internal energy of the gas is some constant fraction of the kinetic energy; as is shown below, this assumption is not correct. The analyses of the other references differ from ours mainly in considering the mass of gas accelerated to be a constant.

Presented at the Symposium on Electromagnetics and Fluid Dynamics of Gaseous Plasma, Polytechnic Institute of Brooklyn, April 4, 5, 6, 1961

Reference 1, however, also includes dissipative effects due to electrical resistance.

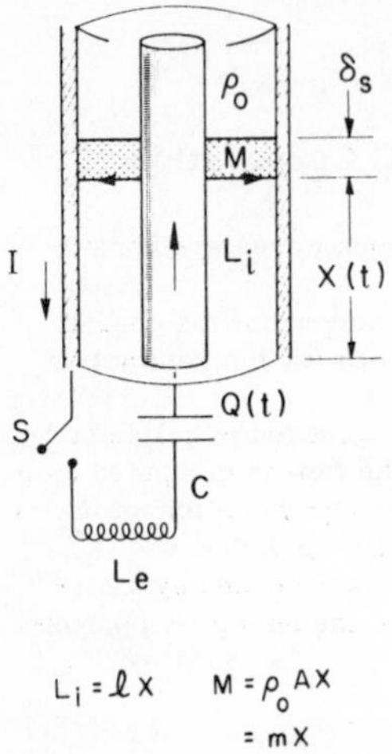

Fig. 1 Diagram of apparatus for linear plasma accelerator

The second device (shown in Fig. 2) has been called an inverse pinch machine.[4] The current from the external circuit runs along an axis and returns through a coaxial sheet, thus driving a cylindrical shock outwards. In the analysis of this device, the effect of the external circuit is uncoupled from the gas-dynamics. In effect, the process is studied for only very small times so that the current is rising linearly with time. The resulting flow has coaxial similarity and can be analyzed both by snowplow theory and gas-dynamic theory for a perfect gas. Details of this theory including the effect of an initial axial magnetic field in the gas have been presented elsewhere.[6] Only some of the results and a comparison with the experiments of Liepmann and Vlases[7] are presented here.

In the third device, called Scylla[5] (Fig. 3), an inward running cylindrical shock wave is

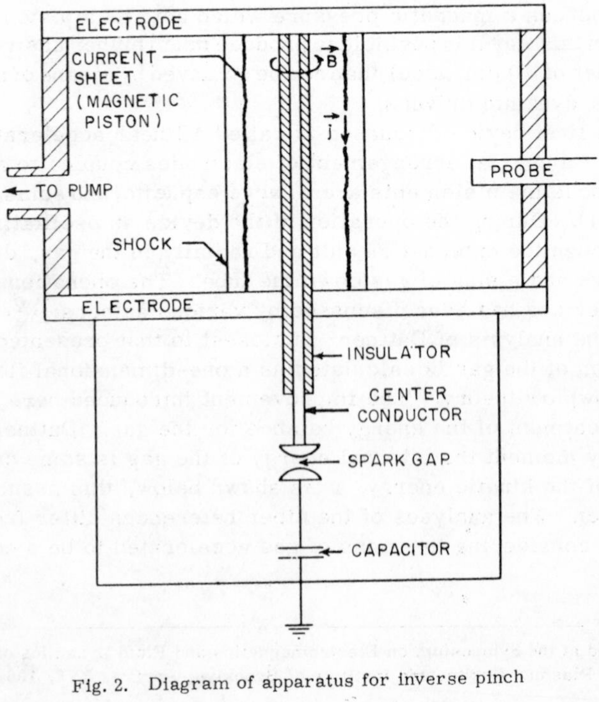

Fig. 2. Diagram of apparatus for inverse pinch

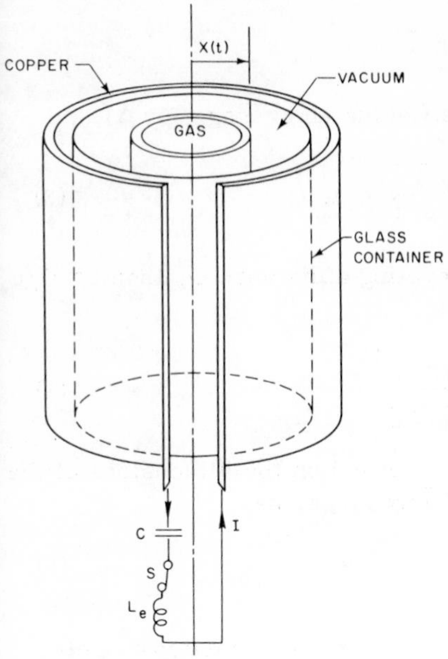

Fig. 3 Diagram of apparatus for Scylla

produced by discharging an azimuthal current around the exterior of the device. It is shown here that if the external circuit can be arranged to produce a current which rises to a constant value in a very short time, then according to snowplow theory, a simple solution with a constant velocity shock results.

Various assumptions are necessary in the analysis of these three devices; one principal assumption is that the gas is infinitely conducting. The generated magnetic field cannot penetrate into the ideal gas; the currents which drive the gas are confined to the interface of the gas and the vacuum field behind. In the actual operation of these devices, current starts to flow because the applied voltage breaks down the gas. Very soon a strong shock wave is formed which ionizes the gas further so that its conductivity may become fairly high, in which case the idealized theory may apply fairly well. A rough estimate for the assumptions may be obtained as follows. An initially thin current sheet may be considered to diffuse into a conductor so that its thickness δ at time t is roughly

$$\delta \sim \sqrt{\frac{t}{\mu\sigma}} \text{ meter ,} \tag{1}$$

where σ = conductivity of the gas (mho/meter); μ = permeability of free space = $4\pi \times 10^{-7}$ henry/meter; t = time (sec).

For a shock, running at roughly constant speed c, the separation Δ of shock and the contact front which carries the current is

$$\Delta \sim (c-u)t, \tag{2}$$

where u = speed of the contact front. For a shock the density ratio

$$\frac{\rho_0}{\rho} = 1 - \frac{u}{c} = \frac{\gamma-1}{\gamma+1} \quad \text{for a very strong shock in perfect gas,}$$

$$> \frac{1}{15} \quad \text{for a real gas (with partial dissociation and ionization)}$$

so that

$$\Delta > \frac{1}{15}\ ct\ .$$

The theory should be valid as long as (taking an average for Δ)

$$\frac{\delta}{\Delta} \cong \frac{10}{c}\sqrt{\frac{1}{\mu\sigma t}} < 1. \tag{3}$$

If we want this to apply to a shock traveling a distance D, then $t \sim D/c$ and

$$\frac{\delta}{\Delta} \sim \frac{10}{\sqrt{\mu\sigma Dc}}\ . \tag{4}$$

Thus, a magnetic Reynolds number R_M based on the dimensions of the device and the shock speed must be fairly large, say,

$$R_M = \mu\sigma Dc > 100\ . \tag{5}$$

For various cases, the shock speed and σ can be related roughly to the initial parameters of gas and circuit and the validity of the infinite conductivity assumption can be roughly checked. For example, for the linear accelerator,

$$D \doteq \frac{1}{3}\ \text{meter}, \qquad c \doteq 5 \times 10^4\ \text{m/sec},$$

so that if $\sigma > 10^4$ mho/meter, then $R_m > 100$. Such conductivities are probably attained when any current flows. The estimates above depend, of course, on the shock itself being fairly thin.

II. LINEAR ACCELERATOR

The performance of the linear accelerator is analyzed under the following assumptions:

1) The gas is infinitely conducting so that the radial driving current is confined to a sheet.

2) The flow is approximately one-dimensional. The distortion of the current due to variation of the magnetic pressure across the annulus is neglected. The sheet is located at X(t). The magnetic force acting on the sheet is calculated in terms of an internal inductance:

$$\begin{aligned} L_i(t) &= \text{internal inductance} = \ell X(t), \\ \ell &= \text{inductance per length} = (\mu/2\pi)\log(d_2/d_1) \\ &\qquad \text{for a circular annulus} \end{aligned} \tag{6}$$

3) The motion of the gas is analyzed according to snowplow theory. The shock is assumed very strong and the compression very large so that δ_S, the thickness of the shock layer, is much less than X(t). All of the gas is assumed to have the velocity of the contact front dX/dt, and the mass in motion at any time is

$$\text{mass in motion} = \rho_0 A\, X(t) = mX(t) \tag{7}$$

where A = area of annulus = $(\pi/4)\cdot(d_2^2 - d_1^2)$ for a circular annulus; ρ_0 = initial density; $\rho_0 A$ = mass swept up per length. The initial pressure is negligible compared to the pressure in the shock layer. It should be noted, as explained below, that the pressure distribution in the shock layer is not constant; the variation across the layer depends on the acceleration of the contact front.

4) All electric resistance and other losses, such as radiation, are neglected. The main dissipative mechanism of the system, the shock wave, is included, however. A study of the energy balance below illustrates the overall losses in the system.

In the operation of the device it is assumed that the gas is initially at rest and the condenser of capacity C has a charge Q_0. The external inductance is L_e. Under these assumptions the device can be described as a coupled electrical-mechanical system. (An analogous description of the ordinary pinch has been given by Killeen and Lippmann.[8]) The equation of motion can be derived from a Lagrangian equation in terms of the generalized coordinates Q(t), X(t). Since the system is not completely conservative (internal energy in the gas, ionization energy, etc., are lost) a generalized nonconservative force must be introduced into the equation for X. Elementary mechanical considerations serve to identify this generalized force. Thus, the coupling between electrical and mechanical parts, as well as the energy balance for the system, is easily found. The Lagrangian L here contains the energy in the field and in the motion of the gas as kinetic energies, and the energy stored in the capacitor as potential energy:

$$L = \frac{1}{2}\, mX\dot{X}^2 + \frac{1}{2}\,(L_e + \ell X)\,\dot{Q}^2 - \frac{1}{2}\,\frac{Q^2}{C}\,. \tag{8}$$

The Lagrangian equations are

$$\frac{d}{dt}\left(\frac{\partial L}{\partial \dot{Q}}\right) - \frac{\partial L}{\partial Q} = \frac{d}{dt}\left\{(L_e + \ell X)\,\frac{dQ}{dt}\right\} + \frac{Q}{C} = 0 \quad \text{(circuit equation)}$$

(9)

$$\frac{d}{dt}\left[\frac{\partial L}{\partial \dot{X}}\right] - \frac{\partial L}{\partial X} = m\frac{d}{dt}\left\{X\frac{dX}{dt}\right\} - \frac{\ell}{2}\left[\frac{dQ}{dt}\right]^2 - \frac{1}{2}m\left[\frac{dX}{dt}\right]^2 = Q_2 \quad \text{(gas-motion equation)} \tag{10}$$

Q_2 is the generalized force not derivable from a potential and it is shown below, by considerations of snowplow theory, that

$$Q_2 = -\frac{1}{2}m\left[\frac{dX}{dt}\right]^2. \tag{11}$$

Thus Eq. (10) equates the time-rate-of-change of momentum $mX(dX/dt)$ with the force produced by magnetic pressure $(\ell/2)\cdot(dQ/dt)^2$. The dissipation produced by Q_2 can be calculated by considering kinetic energy and the work done by a (hypothetical) piston which replaces the current sheet. In the snowplow model, the pressure P on such a piston is equal to the time-rate-of-change of momentum

$$P(t) = \rho_o\frac{d}{dt}\left\{X\frac{d\dot{X}}{dt}\right\} = \rho_o\left[\frac{dX}{dt}\right]^2 + \rho_o X\frac{d^2X}{dt^2}. \tag{12}$$

Equation (12) shows the connection of snowplow theory with Newtonian aerodynamics. The first term on the right of Eq. (12) is pressure immediately behind the shock, while the second is the "centrifugal" force correction. The analogy with gas-dynamic Newtonian theory for flow past a slender body is exact.[9] In fact, based on various models of the gas behavior, this theory can be used to work out some details of the flow in the shock layer. Thus

$$\text{Rate of work} = PA\frac{dX}{dt} = m\left[\frac{dX}{dt}\right]^3 + mX\frac{dX}{dt}\left[\frac{d^2X}{dt^2}\right]. \tag{13}$$

$$\begin{array}{l}\text{Rate of change}\\ \text{of kinetic energy}\end{array} = \frac{d}{dt}\left\{\frac{mX}{2}\left[\frac{dX}{dt}\right]^2\right\} = \frac{1}{2}m\left[\frac{dX}{dt}\right]^3 + mX\frac{dX}{dt}\left[\frac{d^2X}{dt^2}\right] \tag{14}$$

The difference of (13) and (14) yields

$$\text{Rate of energy dissipation} = \frac{1}{2}m\left[\frac{dX}{dt}\right]^3 = -Q_2\left[\frac{dX}{dt}\right] \tag{15}$$

so that Q_2 is indeed given by (11). Thus the equations of motion are

$$\left\{ \begin{aligned} & \frac{d}{dt}\left\{ (L_e + \ell X)\frac{dQ}{dt} \right\} + \frac{Q}{C} = 0 \\ & m\frac{d}{dt}\left\{ X\frac{dX}{dt} \right\} = \frac{1}{2}\ell\left[\frac{dQ}{dt}\right]^2 \end{aligned} \right\} \tag{16}$$

while the energy balance is

$$\frac{1}{2}(L_e + \ell X)\left[\frac{dQ}{dt}\right]^2 + \frac{1}{2}\frac{Q^2}{C} + \frac{m}{2}X\left[\frac{dX}{dt}\right]^2 + \frac{m}{2}\int_0^t \left[\frac{dX}{dt}\right]^3 dt = \frac{1}{2}\frac{Q_o^2}{C}. \tag{17}$$

The first equation of system (16) represents an electric circuit with variable inductance; the second describes acceleration of the gas by magnetic pressure. The total energy available to heat, dissociate, ionize the gas etc., is

$$\text{Internal energy} = \frac{m}{2}\int_0^t \left[\frac{dX}{dt}\right]^3 dt. \tag{18}$$

The initial conditions can be shown to be

$$Q(0) = Q_o, \ \dot{Q}(0) = 0, \ X(0) = 0, \ \dot{X}(0) = 0. \tag{19}$$

A certain non-uniformity is introduced by the fact that the velocity $\dot{X}$ is initially zero, but since the solution shows that the velocity builds up rapidly, this non-uniformity is apparently not too serious. A study of the problem in dimensionless variables shows that operation of the device can be described in terms of a single parameter q_o. Define

$$\text{characteristic length} = \frac{L_e}{\ell},$$

$$\text{characteristic time} = \sqrt{L_e C} = \frac{1}{\text{ringing frequency}},$$

$$\text{characteristic charge} = \sqrt{2m}\, L_e/\ell^{3/2}$$

and dimensionless variables

$$x = \frac{\ell}{L_e}X, \qquad q = \frac{\ell^{3/2}}{\sqrt{2m}\,L_e}Q, \qquad \tau = \frac{1}{\sqrt{L_e C}}t, \tag{20}$$

so that (16) becomes

$$\left\{ \begin{array}{l} \frac{d}{d\tau}\left\{(1+x)\frac{dq}{d\tau}\right\} + q = 0 \\ \\ \frac{d}{d\tau}\left\{x\frac{dx}{d\tau}\right\} = \left(\frac{dq}{d\tau}\right)^2 \end{array} \right\} \tag{21}$$

and the initial conditions are

$$\left\{ \begin{array}{l} q(0) = q_o = \frac{Q_o \ell^{3/2}}{\sqrt{2m}\, L_e} \\ \\ \dot{q}(0) = x(0) = \dot{x}(0) = 0 \end{array} \right\}. \tag{22}$$

A general analytic discussion of system (21) presents formidable difficulties; some general remarks can be made, however. For very small times, $x \ll 1$, so that the external circuit starts to ring freely at its natural frequency. This current may be used to calculate the driving force and the initial motion of the gas. The smaller the value of q_o, the longer this initial state of affairs will persist. If an expansion in terms of q_o is made for $q_o \to 0$, we have

$$\left\{ \begin{array}{l} x(\tau; q_o) = q_o x_1(\tau) + \ldots \\ \\ q(\tau; q_o) = q_o q_1(\tau) + - \end{array} \right\}, \tag{23}$$

and the lowest order equations are

$$\left\{ \begin{array}{l} \frac{d^2 q_1}{d\tau^2} + q_1 = 0 \\ \\ \frac{d}{d\tau}\left[x_1 \frac{dx_1}{d\tau}\right] = \left[\frac{dq_1}{d\tau}\right]^2 \end{array} \right\}, \tag{24}$$

which agree with the initial phase description. The solution of (24) satisfying the initial conditions is

$$q_1 = \cos\tau, \qquad x_1 = \frac{\sqrt{\tau^2 - \sin^2\tau}}{\sqrt{2}}. \tag{25}$$

Due to the varying driving force the velocity and displacement fluctuate but if this approximation can be carried to values of $\tau^2 \gg 1$, then the velocity of the front $(dx_1/d\tau) \rightarrow 1/\sqrt{2}$, If τ becomes too large, however, this initial phase description breaks down and a period of strong coupling occurs. Ultimately, however, the driving force must become small so that the slug of gas will decelerate while conserving its momentum. Thus in the final phase

$$x \sim k\sqrt{\tau}. \tag{26}$$

The varying inductance now drives the external circuit approximately according to

$$\frac{d}{d\tau}\left\{ k\sqrt{\tau}\,\frac{dq}{d\tau} \right\} + q = 0 \tag{27}$$

and the asymptotic solution of (27) for large times is

$$q \sim \tau^{-1/8} \sin\left[\frac{4}{3k^{1/2}}\,\tau^{3/4} - \varphi\right]. \tag{28}$$

A numerical calculation of the solution of the system (21) has been made on an IBM 7090; it bears out the qualitative remarks made above as well as presenting some useful numerical results. The results are given in Figs. 4, 5, 6, 7 and 8 in suitable dimensionless units. A solution carried out for $\tau >> 1$ has also verified the correctness of (28).

A rough check on the theory has been given by some measurements of Dr. T. G. Jones* at the California Institute of Technology.[10] He has measured the shock velocity in air using pressure probes. His circuit and discharge tube parameters are

$$V = 12 \times 10^3\ v, \qquad d_2 = 3'', \qquad d_1 = 1.5'',$$

$$C = 30 \times 10^{-6}\ f, \qquad p_o = 10\mu,$$

$$L_e = 131 \times 10^{-9}\ h, \qquad \ell = 184 \times 10^{-9}\ h/m\ \text{(meas)},$$

so that $\qquad Q_o = 0.36, \qquad q_o = 0.55$

at $X = 12''$

$$(dX/dt)_{obs} = 8.2\ \text{cm}/\mu\text{sec},$$

$$(dX/dt)_{theo} = 14.5\ \text{cm}/\mu\text{sec}.$$

A rough check with prediction of theory is thus obtained. However,

*T. G. Jones, Private communication

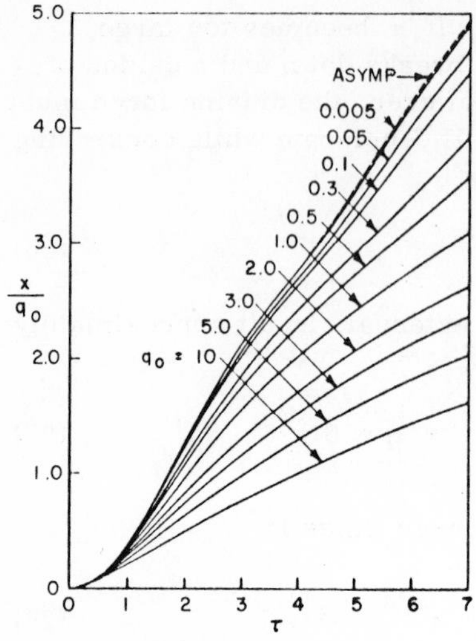

Fig. 4. Position of front as a function of time for various values of q_o

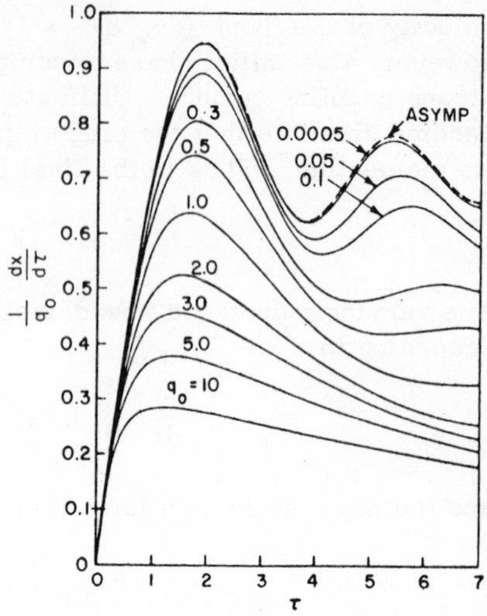

Fig. 5. Velocity of front as a function of time for various values of q_o

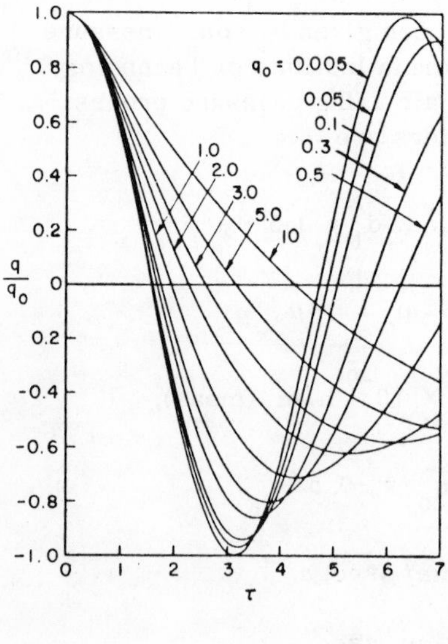

Fig. 6. Charge as a function of time for various values of q_o

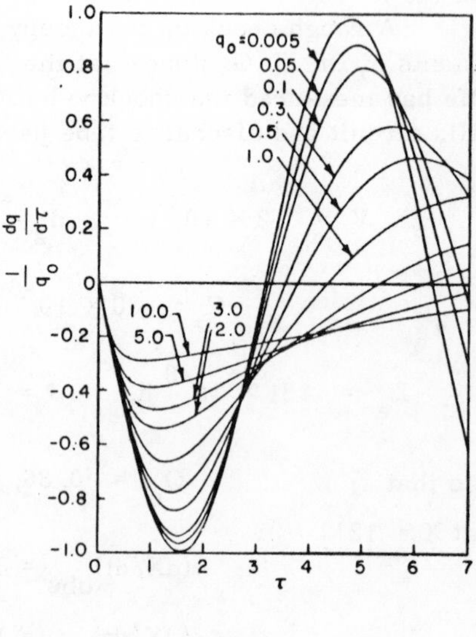

Fig. 7. Current as a function of time for various values of q_o

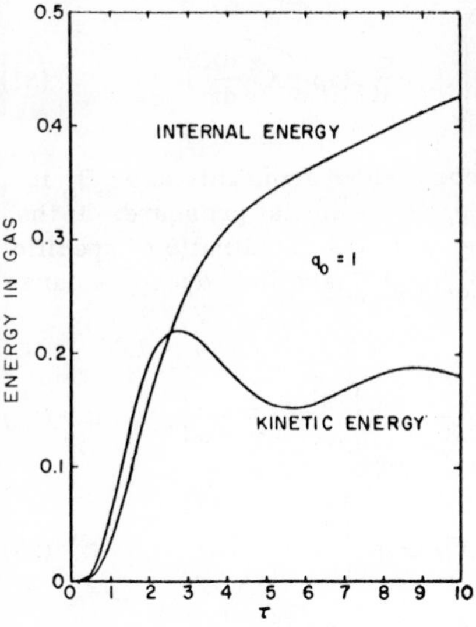

Fig. 8. Energy distribution in the gas as a function of time for $q_o = 1$

there is evidence, obtained by a photograph made using a Kerr cell camera, that the current flow in this experiment was not uniform around the annulus. This is borne out by a certain lack of repeatability of the experiments.

A comparison can also be made with the results of Dattner.[3] Dattner's experiments in H_2 cover the following range of variables:

$C = 12.5 \times 10^{-6}$ f,

$L_e = 57.4 \times 10^{-9}$ h,

$\ell = 266 \times 10^{9}$ h/m

$p = 200 - 1000\ \mu$Hg,

$V = 3$-7 kv,

$q_o = 0.8 - 4.2$,

$\dot{X}_{obs} = 6$-11 cm/μ sec, $\dot{X}_{theo} = 4$-14 cm/μ sec

Dattner reported shock velocities ($\dot{X}_{obs}$) which become constant after about a quarter cycle. $\dot{X}_{theo}$ is the maximum calculated velocity, which also occurs after about a quarter cycle. The agreement is fair. It should also be noted that in both these experiments the magnetic pressure varied appreciably across the annulus, thus leading to further errors.

III. INVERSE PINCH MACHINE

It was seen in Section II that in the initial instants the external circuit rings freely and the current rises linearly with time. For small t the inverse pinch machine behaves essentially the same way when a current is discharged, so that it is assumed here that

$$I = I_o \omega t \tag{29}$$

and the azimuthal field which drives the current sheet out is thus

$$B_\theta = \frac{\mu I_o \omega t}{2\pi r} \tag{30}$$

Within the snowplow model, the equation for the motion of the gas becomes, (where now both an initial pressure and axial magnetic field are included),

$$2\pi X \left[\frac{B_\theta^2}{2\mu} - \frac{B_o^2}{2\mu} - p_o \right] = \frac{d}{dt} \left(\pi \rho_o X^2 \frac{dX}{dt} \right), \tag{31}$$

where X(t) is the distance of the current sheet from this axis; B_o is the initial axial magnetic field; and p_o is the initial pressure. If the sound speed $a_o = (\gamma p_o/\rho_o)^{1/2}$, where γ is the usual ratio of specific heats, and the Alfven speed $b_o = (B_o^2/\mu\rho_o)^{1/2}$ are introduced as parameters, Eq. (31) becomes

$$\frac{d}{dt} \left[X^2 \frac{dX}{dt} \right] = c_o^4 \frac{t^2}{X} - X \left[b_o^2 + \frac{2}{\gamma} a_o^2 \right], \tag{32}$$

where

$$c_o = \left[\mu I_o^2 \omega^2 / 4\pi^2 \rho_o \right]^{1/4} \tag{33}$$

is a quantity with the dimensions of a speed characterizing the circuit and gas. The solutions of Eq. (33) which passes through X(0) = 0, is

$$X = kt,$$

$$k^2 = \frac{1}{4} \left\{ - \left[b_o^2 + \frac{2}{\gamma} a_o^2 \right] + \left[\left[b_o^2 + \frac{2}{\gamma} a_o^2 \right]^2 + 8 c_o^4 \right]^{1/2} \right\} \tag{34}$$

The gas thus moves with the constant speed $dX/dt = k$.

Since the shock velocity is constant, a conical similarity exists and a gas-dynamic solution of the same problem can be obtained. A comparison of the two theories is shown in Fig. 9, where the speed of the contact front obtained from a solution of the full equations is compared with the speed given by the snowplow model. It is seen that there is very good agreement between snowplow theory and the exact solution over the entire range of shock strength.

A comparison of the snowplow results (34) with experiments of Liepmann and Vlases[7] is shown in Fig. 10. There is indeed good agreement verifying the scaling law both with respect to density and current rise.

IV. SCYLLA

In the device known as Scylla, the external circuit drives a circumferential current around the outside of a cylindrical discharge tube (Fig. 3). The resulting axial magnetic field acts like a piston pushing the gas (in which an induced surface current flows, opposite in direction to the primary current) radially inward and leaving behind a cylindrical vacuum region.

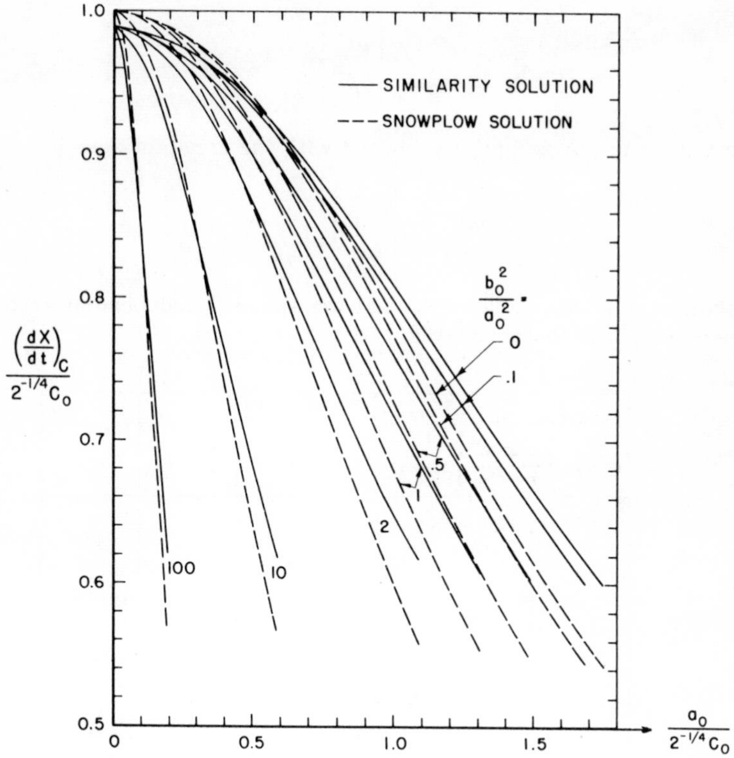

Fig. 9. Comparison of speed predicted by snowplow theory with speed of contact front obtained from a similarity solution of the full equations

If the azimuthal current per unit length is denoted by I, the axial field which drives the current sheet is

$$B_z = \mu I \tag{35}$$

and the snowplow equation of motion becomes

$$2\pi X \frac{I^2}{2\mu} = \frac{d}{dt}\left[\pi \rho_o (X_o^2 - X^2) \frac{dX}{dt}\right] \tag{36}$$

where X(t) is the distance from the axis to the current sheet and X_o is the radius of the tube. This equation is to be solved subject to the boundary condition $X(0)= X_o$. (As in the analysis of the inverse pinch the current I will be considered as a prescribed function of time.)

If the current I(t) is assumed to rise instantaneously from zero to a constant value I_1 (a condition which can be approximated fairly well in practice if the external inductance is made sufficiently small), then Eq. (36) has the simple solution

$$X = X_o - \left[\frac{\mu I_1^2}{2\rho_o}\right]^{1/2} t \,. \tag{37}$$

The gas thus moves radially inward with the constant speed

$$\frac{dX}{dt} = \left[\frac{\mu I_1^2}{2\rho_o}\right]^{1/2} .$$

It should be noted, moreover, that the speed is independent of the dimension X_o of the apparatus.

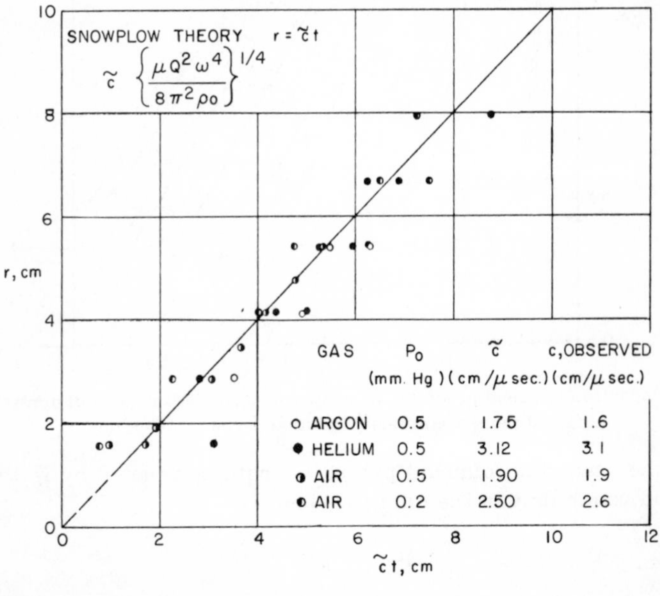

Fig. 10. Comparison of snowplow theory of inverse pinch with experiments of Liepmann and Vlases[7]

For the case considered, the internal energy (18) can be calculated explicitly. The result is

$$\text{Internal energy} = \frac{1}{2}\, m(t) \left[\frac{dX}{dt}\right]^2 \tag{38}$$

where m(t) is again the mass in motion per unit length. It is seen that the internal energy at any time is just equal to the kinetic energy. In this case, then, there is an exact equipartition between kinetic and internal energy.

REFERENCES

1. P. M. Mostov, J. L. Neuringer and D. S. Rigney, "Electromagnetic Acceleration of a Plasma Slug," Plasma Propulsion Laboratory, Republic Aviation Corporation, TR-61-5, February 24, 1961.

2. L. A. Artsimovich, et al., "Electrodynamic Acceleration of Plasma Bunches," *Soviet Physics JET*, Vol. 6, p. 1 (1958).

   I. M. Podgorny, et al., "Study of the Process of Electrodynamic Acceleration of Plasma Bunches II," *Plasma Physics and the Problem of Controlled Thermonuclear Reactions*, Vol. IV, (New York: Pergamon Press, 1960) p.262.

3. A. Dattner, "Acceleration of Plasma," *Proceedings of the Fourth International Conference on Ionization Phenomena in Gases*, Vol. II, (Upsala, 1959) p. 262.

4. O. A. Anderson, et al., "Inverse Pinch Effect," *Phys. Fluids*, Vol. 1, p. 489 (1958).

5. W. C. Elmore, E. M. Little and W. E. Quinn, "Neutrons of Possible Thermonuclear Origin," *Phys. Rev. Letters*, Vol. 1, p. 32 (July 1, 1958).

6. C. Greifinger and J. D. Cole, "On Cylindrical Magnetohydrodynamic Shock Waves," *Phys. Fluids*, Vol. 4, p. 527 (1961).

7. H.W. Liepmann and G. Vlases, "Magnetically Driven Cylindrical Shock Waves," Phys. Fluids, Vol. 4, p.927 (1961)

8. J. Killeen and B. A. Lippmann, "Circuit Dynamics of the Pinch," *J. Appl. Physics*, Vol. 31, p. 1549 (1960).

9. J.D. Cole, "Newtonian Flow Theory for Slender Bodies," *J. Aeronaut. Sci.*, Vol. 24, p. 448 (1957).

SOME PARADOXES OF SUB-ALFVENIC FLOW OF A COMPRESSIBLE CONDUCTING FLUID*

W. R. Sears
Graduate School of Aeronautical Engineering
Cornell University

Steady magnetogasdynamic flows in the category called "aligned-fields flows" may be classified as sub-Alfvenic or super-Alfvenic when the flow speed is respectively, less or greater than the Alfven-wave speed. For plane or axisymmetric sub-Alfvenic flow of a perfectly conducting gas, there are both elliptic and hyperbolic regimes in both the subsonic and supersonic speed ranges. It is shown that these are consequences of the anisotropic propagation properties of magnetosonic waves. One result is a possibility of smooth transition directly from elliptic to hypercritical flow at points in the flow field. Some examples illustrating this phenomenon are shown. An apparent paradox is posed by supersonic-elliptic flow; it is conjectured that this must be resolved by introduction of magnetogasdynamic shock waves, and some possible flow patterns are sketched.

INTRODUCTION

The phenomena to be discussed here fall within a special category of steady flows in which the fluid-velocity field and the magnetic field are both uniform and parallel to one another in the undisturbed regions of flow, i.e., at large distances from obstacles or perturbations. These are called aligned-fields flows. They constitute the idealization of real geometries of several kinds, such as flows through solenoid-wound ducts. Our interest in them however, is not due to their practical importance in technology but is rather a part of a program of study intended to reveal and elucidate the phenomena of magnetofluidmechanics. As we have pointed out elsewhere, [1] the nature of the technical applications of this science is still so unclear as to suggest that such studies are desirable, both in the laboratory and on paper, without much concern for the utility of the configurations studied.

The phenomena we want to discuss are related to the propagation of wave-like disturbances in electrically conducting gases in the presence of a magnetic field. Such waves are neither conventional sound waves nor the well-known Alfven waves of incompressible magneto-

*This research was partially supported by the United States Air Force under Contract AF-49(638)-544, monitored by the Office of Scientific Research, Air Research and Development Command.

Presented at the Symposium on Electromagnetics and Fluid Dynamics of Gaseous Plasma, Polytechnic Institute of Brooklyn, April 4, 5, 6, 1961

hydrodynamics,[1] but are, rather, waves that involve both the compressibility of the fluid and the strength and orientation of the magnetic field, i.e., *magnetosonic waves.* They have been analyzed by a number of writers.[2,3,4,5] The most important conclusions for our purposes are: a) that the propagation of infinitesimal plane waves is anisotropic and depends on the angle between the wave normal and the local magnetic-field vector; and b) that the wave speed is a multi-valued function of this angle. For each value of the angle there is a "fast wave" whose propagation speed is greater than either the speed of sound a or the Alfven speed α (or at least equal to the greater of a and α), an "intermediate wave" whose speed is less than either a or α (or at most equal to the smaller of a and α), and a "slow wave" for which the same statement holds. There is, of course, also the usual ambiguity of sign; i.e., all three waves may propagate either forward or backward for a given wave angle.

The significance of these waves in steady, plane and axisymmetric, aligned-fields flow has been pointed out in earlier papers.[6,7,8] Briefly, this significance is that steady flow past an obstacle or through a channel can set up standing magnetosonic waves in certain speed ranges. This is, of course, analogous to the formation of standing sound waves (Mach waves) by acoustic propagation in conventional gasdynamics. But there are both fast and slow waves,* which makes things more interesting, and there are profound effects of the anisotropy. In conventional gasdynamics the existence of standing waves is related to the flow speed in a very simple way: if the speed is greater than sound speed there are waves; if it is less, there are no waves. Because of the anisotropy, the situation in magnetogasdynamics is considerably more complicated.

NOTATION			
a =	speed of sound	$\mathbf{q}$ =	fluid-velocity vector
A =	Alfven number, q/α	q =	scalar magnitude of $\mathbf{q}$
A_o =	stagnation Alfven number; the value assumed by A in the limit $q \rightarrow 0$	U =	speed of solid body in Fig. 1
		α =	Alfven speed, $H/\sqrt{4\pi\rho/\mu}$
$\mathbf{H}$ =	magnetic-field vector; note that in aligned-fields flow of a perfect conductor $\mathbf{H} \propto \rho \mathbf{q}$	γ =	ratio of specific heats
		θ =	angle between wave normal and direction of $\mathbf{H}$, Fig. 1
H =	scalar magnitude of $\mathbf{H}$	μ =	permeability of fluid
M =	Mach number, q/a	ρ =	mass density of fluid

*The restriction to plane and axisymmetric flows eliminates the intermediate waves.

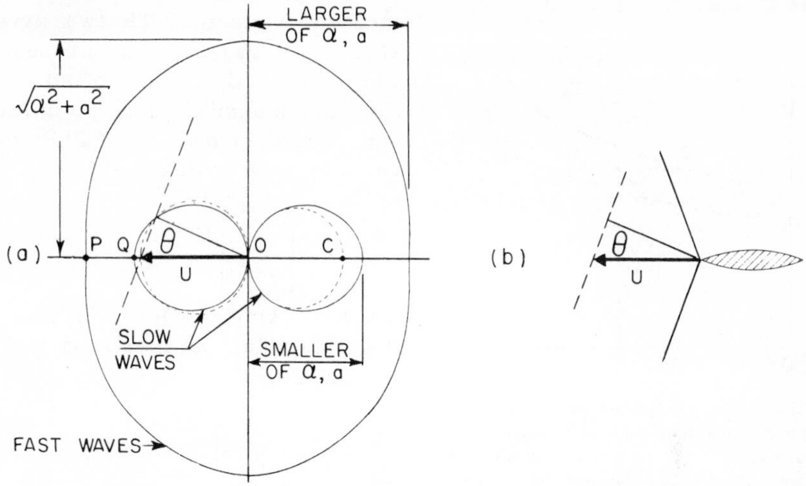

Fig. 1 (a) Wave-speed diagram for fast and slow magnetosonic waves, showing construction used to find standing waves in steady flow at speed U; (b) Sketch of attached waves on body, corresponding to the construction of (a).

To illustrate this complication, Fig. 1 is presented. Fig. 1(a) is a diagram of wave speeds as a function of the inclination θ of the wave normal to the magnetic-field vector H. The curves representing fast and slow waves are shown. Figure 1(b) denotes an object moving steadily with speed U. A wavelet moving steadily with the object will be formed if there is any wave in Fig. 1(a) that propagates at speed $U \cos \theta$ in the direction θ. To find such a wave, one need only construct a circle with the vector U as its diameter, and locate its intersection with the wave-speed diagram, as shown.

It is easy to see that this construction will lead to standing waves for all flight speeds U greater than OP in Fig. 1(a), but will fail to produce such waves for flight speeds between OQ and OP. Clearly, this is because of the particular shapes of the fast-wave and slow-wave diagrams. Furthermore, the shape of the slow-wave diagram is such that there is a minimum speed OC (to avoid confusing the diagram this has been sketched to the right of O instead of to the left), below which the circle of diameter U fails to intersect the wave-speed diagram.

Thus, steady flow at speeds greater than OP and at speeds between OC and OQ produces standing wavelets; flow at other speeds is wave-free. These conclusions are confirmed by steady-flow analyses, for the former cases lead to hyperbolic equations and the latter lead to elliptic equations.

Figure 2 is a diagram, used by both Taniuti and Resler, showing regimes of hyperbolic and elliptic flow in a plot of Alfven number q/α against Mach number, q/a. Flow in this category is isentropic, since

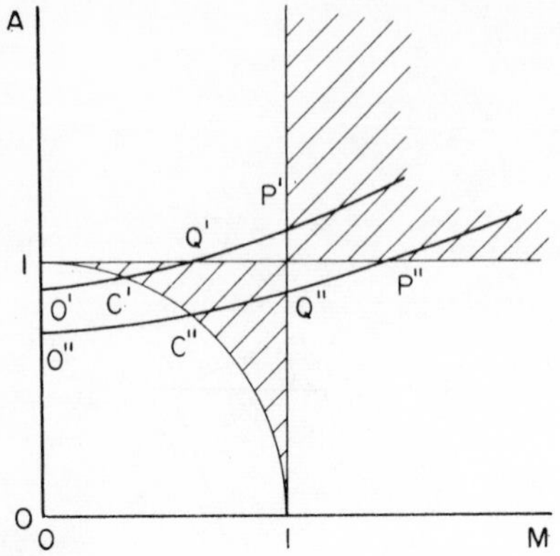

Fig. 2 Taniuti-Resler diagram showing hyperbolic (shaded) and elliptic (unshaded) regimes in isentropic magnetogasdynamic flow. The two curves shown are isentropes having different values of A_o.

both viscosity and electrical resistance are neglected. The two curves sketched in Fig. 2 are isentropes, whose respective values of stagnation Alfven number A_o are different. For the curve O'C'Q'P' this value is greater than

$$\left[\frac{2}{\gamma+1}\right]^{\frac{1/2}{\gamma-1}},$$

while for O"C"Q"P" it is less than this value; an isentrope for A_o equal to

$$\left[\frac{2}{\gamma+1}\right]^{\frac{1/2}{\gamma-1}}$$

would pass through the point $A = M = 1$. The lettering on these curves is intended to facilitate comparison with Fig. 1(a), i.e., the several points have the same significances as the points O, C, P, and Q in Fig. 1(a).

Both the steady-flow analyses[9,10] and the argument using Fig. 1(a) apply either to small-perturbation flow or, locally, to more general categories.

Before proceeding to deduce certain anomalous phenomena from these principles, we wish to emphasize the contrast with conventional gasdynamics. It is clear that the existence or nonexistence of waves is not determined by a simple inequality involving flow speed and propagation speed. For speeds between OQ and OP in Fig. 1(a), for example, there are no waves; yet these speeds all exceed the propagation speeds of slow waves.

THE ELLIPTIC-HYPERCRITICAL TRANSITION

As has been stated, motion at speeds less than OC in Fig. 1(a) cannot produce standing waves; the flow field for such speeds is therefore governed by elliptic differential equations. On the other hand, a speed slightly greater than OC results in waves at a "Mach angle" of nearly zero, i.e., $\theta \approx \pi/2$. Thus there is a transition, at a certain point on a streamline, from wave-free (elliptical) flow to flow that resembles, in some respects, hypersonic flow! A suitable terminology would seem to be *hypercritical* where "critical" refers to the propagation speed of the pertinent magnetosonic waves — in this instance, slow waves propagating in a direction nearly perpendicular to the flow velocity at very low speed. Here, indeed, is a phenomenon which has no counterpart in conventional gasdynamics — the analog would be smooth transition directly from subsonic to hypersonic flow, or vice versa. One seems justified in asking whether such a transition can really be smooth.

Unfortunately, linearized small-perturbation theory casts little light on these matters, just as linearized gasdynamics casts little light on conventional hypersonic phenomena. Mr. Richard Seebass[11] has, therefore, undertaken to extend the technique of the hodograph transformation to this branch of magnetogasdynamics. He finds that the differential equations for the stream function and for a new potential function (the flow is rotational!) are linear in the hodograph plane. One of their elementary solutions is aligned-fields source or sink flow, one example of which is sketched in Fig. 3. This is homentropic, steady, radial, plane flow, bounded at a minimum radius where the speed is sonic, like ordinary compressible source or sink flow, and reaching stagnation conditions at infinite radius. At a certain circle, as shown, the flow undergoes the expected transition from hypercritical to elliptic. The transition is smooth and is characterized simply by the fact that the characteristics, i.e., magnetosonic wavelets, become tangent to the streamlines and end there.

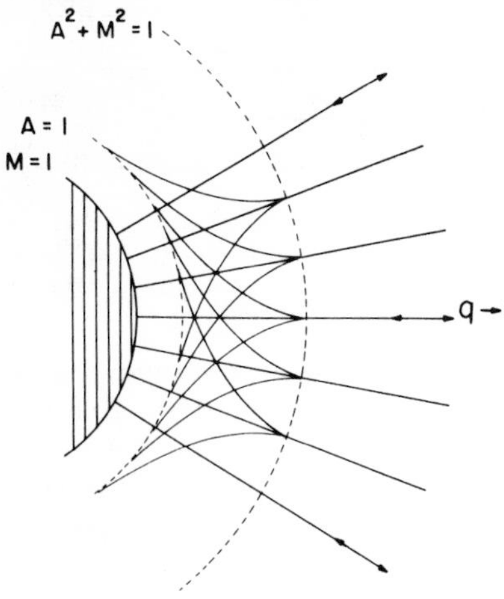

Fig. 3 Subsonic source of sink flow.

$$A_o^2 > \left(\frac{2}{\gamma+1}\right)^{\frac{1}{\gamma-1}}$$

One may anticipate that this will be the character of the elliptic-hypercritical transition in many flow patterns. For example, the transition in a convergent or divergent channel should resemble the flow between two radii in Fig. 3. Mr. Seebass has discovered another exact flow pattern for the particular case $\gamma = 2$ that seems to confirm this. It is shown in Fig. 4.

On physical grounds we expect that flows of similar character must exist for other, more realistic, values of γ. Since Fig. 4 involves a *limit line*, some of the streamlines are without physical meaning and the flow plane is two-sheeted everywhere to the right of the limit line. Nevertheless, there are two families of streamlines that do not intersect the limit line and therefore are meaningful. One of these families consists of all the streamlines to the right of SS'; these are everywhere subcritical, i.e., subsonic-elliptic; they lead from stagnation conditions at upper left to stagnation conditions at lower left (assuming the pattern of Fig. 4 to be continued in its mirror image

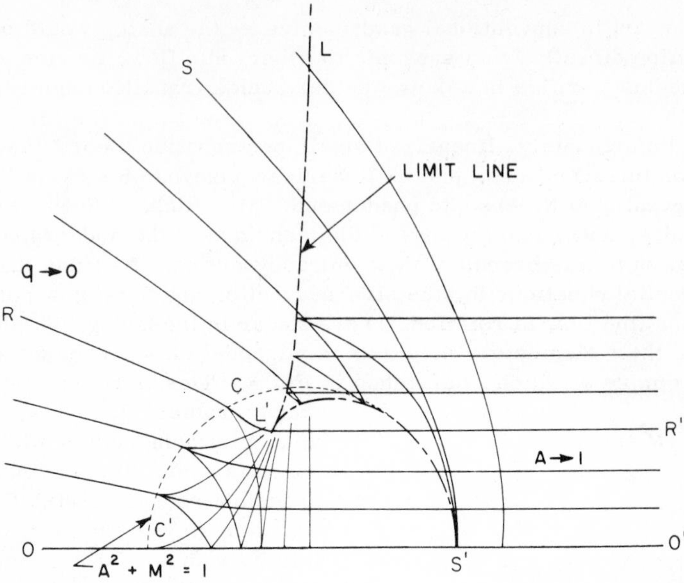

Fig. 4 Flow pattern calculated by Richard Seebass. $A_0^2 = 3/4$ and $\gamma = 2$. In the entire region to the right of the limit line the diagram is two sheeted; one sheet involves, asymptotically, parallel flow at $A = 1$.

below OO'). Thus, this part of the flow plane represents slow, subsonic, magnetogasdynamic flow around a corner. The limit-line segment LL' does not concern this flow; it lies on the other sheet.

The other family of interest consists of the streamlines between OO' and RR'; these constitute a type of nozzle flow from stagnation at the left to Alfvenic flow $(A = 1)$ at the right, with smooth transition at CC' from elliptic to hypercritical. The limit-line segment L'S' does not affect these streamlines, which lie on the other sheet; neither, of course, do the other family of streamlines discussed above. Between RR' and SS' lies a family of streamlines that cross over from one sheet to the other by means of intersections with the limit-line segments; these are of no interest.

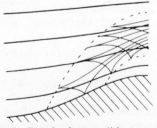

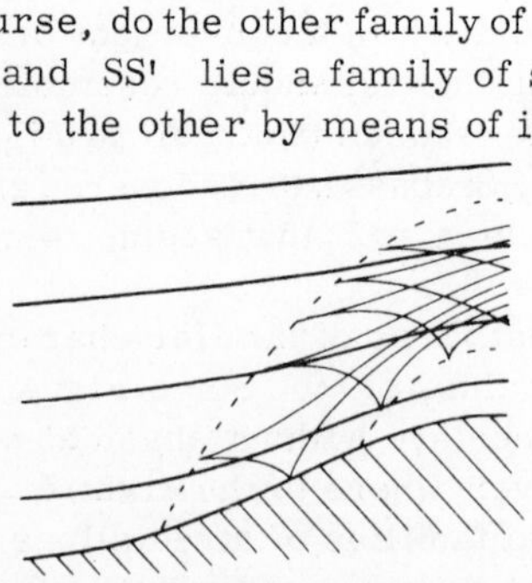

Fig. 5 Sketch of a possible type of "double mixed flow" (only the left half is shown). The flow at far left and at top is subsonic-elliptic.

Mr. Seebass has also identified several vortex-like flows and flow in spirals. One may also speculate on the existence of flows with imbedded supercritical areas, somewhat analogous to transonic flows. Such flows would be expected to resemble the sketch of Fig. 5. At this writing Mr. Seebass has not yet succeeded in analytically identifying such patterns.

WAVE-FREE SUPERSONIC FLOW

Returning to Fig. 1(a), let us now assume that the Alfven speed α is greater than the sound speed a. This is equivalent to saying that the magnetic pressure $\mu H^2/8\pi$ is greater than $\gamma/2$ times the static pressure; thus it is an easily arranged experimental situation. Then, in Fig. 1(a), OP denotes α and OQ denotes a. Flow speeds between OP and OQ, which produce no standing waves, are therefore supersonic speeds.

The equations of steady flow, moreover, confirm these assertions (see references 6, 7, and 12). They reveal that the streamline patterns of such flows are typically elliptic. Locally, or in small-perturbation flows they are related by a simple affine transformation (analogous to the Prandtl-Glauert), to the streamline patterns of incompressible flow. Thus we encounter the anomaly of supersonic flow that has streamlines typical of subsonic flow! It is clear that such flows would involve a reversed variation of pressure and speed, compared with subsonic flows, for the variation of pressure and speed with streamtube area is opposite in subsonic and supersonic flows. Some consequences have been discussed briefly in reference 12. To be sure, this presents a paradox at the stagnation point, which ought to become a point of maximum speed according to this reasoning.

Let us postpone discussion of this dilemma briefly to return to Fig. 5, which also extends into the regime of wave-free supersonic flow. In other words, if the flow of Fig. 5 involves sufficiently great flow speeds locally to exceed the sonic, it must contain, within the imbedded hyperbolic region, an imbedded supersonic area; if $\alpha > a$, this must be elliptic. Figure 5 represents an attempt to sketch such a three-regime flow. If the flow is still further accelerated near the body surface, it must become supersonic-hyperbolic, thus forming a four-regime flow pattern.

MAGNETOGASDYNAMIC SHOCK WAVES

The analogies between conventional gasdynamics and magnetogasdynamics include the phenomena of shock waves. Just as Mach wavelets are replaced in certain situations by conventional shock waves, the standing magnetosonic wavelets described here are sometimes replaced by magnetogasdynamic waves of finite amplitude: magnetogasdynamic shocks. These have been studied by a number of authors (references 13-15, and others). In a study particularly pertinent to our present discussion, Cabannes[15] has investigated the question of the existence of attached oblique shocks. One of the conclusions that can be drawn from his work is the following: there exists a family of "strong" oblique shock waves for which the conditions upstream are those of wavefree supersonic flow, as discussed above, and for which the conditions downstream are in the hyperbolic subsonic regime. In other words, referring again to Fig. 1(a), there are "strong" oblique shocks capable of making a discontinuous transition from regime PQ to regime OQ. Here the word "strong" is used to imply that these are shocks that do not reduce to wavelets as the flow-deflection angle vanishes; rather, they include as one of their members the normal shock wave.

Surely, here lies the explanation of the stagnation-point paradox mentioned above. Near such a point the flow speed must be reduced by a strong, detached shock to subsonic (hyperbolic) values before being accelerated to supersonic (elliptic) conditions again. Figure 6 shows

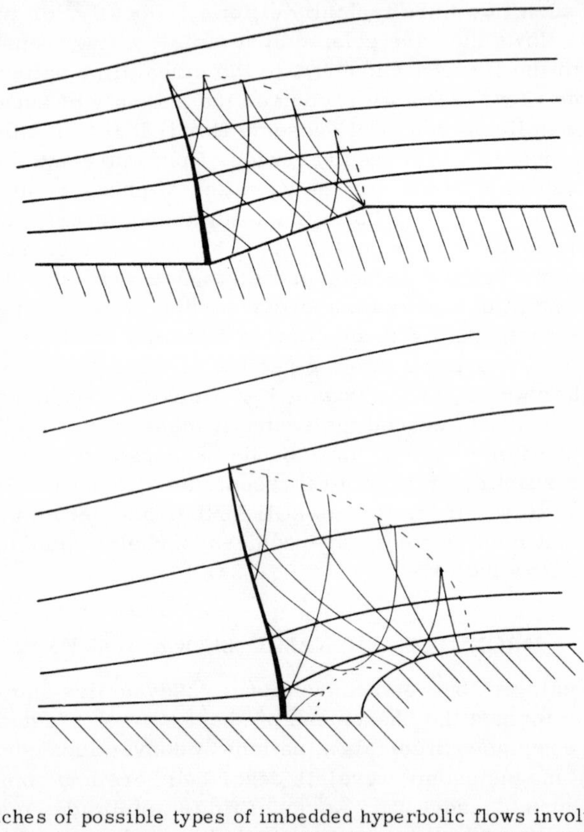

Fig. 6 Sketches of possible types of imbedded hyperbolic flows involving magnetohydrodynamic shock waves. The flow direction is from left to right. At the far left and at top these flows are supersonic-elliptic.

two attempts to sketch the resulting imbedded hyperbolic area; for this purpose a relatively simple geometry has been selected.

The analogy between the imbedded region of Fig. 6 and the imbedded supersonic areas of transonic flow, terminated by shock waves, is tempting. This analogy might be considered a discouraging one from the viewpoint of a theoretician, for transonic flows with imbedded supersonic areas and shock waves have resisted analysis in conventional gasdynamics, and the prospects for analysis of these magnetogasdynamic flows seem even poorer.

CONCLUSIONS

A number of authors have called attention to the analogies that exist between conventional gasdynamics and magnetohydrodynamics. We have examined here, within the special category of aligned-fields flow of ideal conductors, some situations that do not have analogies in conventional gasdynamics — or, at best, require rather startling interpretations to be considered analogous. It seems clear that this complicated branch of fluid mechanics involves many intriguing flow phenomena whose analysis poses formidable theoretical problems.

REFERENCES

1. H. Alfven, "On the Existence of Electromagnetic-Hydrodynamic Waves," *Arkiv for Matematik Astronomi och Fysik,* Vol. 29B, No. 2, 1943; see also *Nature*, Vol.150, pp. 405-406 (1942).
2. N. Herlofsen, "Magneto-Hydrodynamic Waves in a Compressible Fluid Conductor," *Nature,* Vol. 165, p. 1020 (1950).
3. H. C. Van de Hulst, "Interstellar Polarization and Magneto-Hydrodynamic Waves," *Problems of Cosmical Electrodynamics,* Central Air Documents Office No. AD-1103347 (1949).
4. K. O. Friedrichs and H. Kranzer, "Notes on Magneto-Hydrodynamics VIII. Nonlinear Wave Motion," NYO-6486, Inst. Math. Sci., N.Y.U. (July 1958).
5. H. Grad, "Propagation of Magnetohydrodynamic Waves Without Radial Attenuation," NYO-2537, Inst. Math. Sci., N.Y.U., (January 15, 1959).
6. E. L. Resler, Jr. and J. E. McCune, "Electromagnetic Interaction with Aerodynamic Flows," *The Magnetodynamics of Conducting Fluids,* D. Bershader, ed. (Stanford Cal.: Stanford University Press, 1959) pp. 120-135.
7. J. E. McCune and E. L. Resler, Jr., "Compressibility Effects in Magnetoaerodynamic Flows Past Thin Bodies,' *Jour. Aerospace Sci.,* Vol. 27, pp. 493-503 (1960).
8. W. R. Sears, "Some Remarks about Flow Past Bodies," *Rev. Mod. Phys.,* Vol. 32, pp. 701-705; (1960), reprinted in *Magneto-Fluid Dynamics,* F. N. Frenkiel and W.R. Sears, eds., Nat. Acad. Sci - Nat. Res. Council Publ. No.829, (1960).
9. T. Taniuti, "An Example of Isentropic Steady Flow in the Magnetohydrodynamics," *Progress of Theoretical Physics,* Vol. XIX, No. 6, (1958).
10. W. R. Sears and E. L. Resler, Jr., "Theory of Thin Airfoils in Fluids of High Electrical Conductivity," *J. Fluid Mech.,* Vol. 5, pp. 257-273 (February 1959).
11. R. Seebass, "On Transcritical and Hypercritical Flows in Magnetogasdynamics," *Quart. Appl. Mech.,* Vol.19, No.3, pp.231-237 (1961).

12. W. R. Sears, "Sub-Alfvenic Flow in Magnetoaerodynamics," *Jour. Aerospace Sci.*, Vol. 28, pp. 249-250 (1961), (Readers' Forum.)

13. J. Bazer and W. B. Ericson, "Hydromagnetic Shocks,' *Astrophysical Jour.*, Vol. 129, pp. 758-785 (1959).

14. H. L. Helfer, "Magnetohydrodynamic Shock Waves," *Astrophysical Jour.*, Vol. 117, pp. 177-199 (1953).

15. H. Cabannes, "Attached Stationary Shock Waves in Ionized Gases," *Rev. Mod. Phys.* Vol. 32, pp. 973-976; reprinted in *Magneto-Fluid Dynamics,* F. N. Frenkiel and W. R. Sears, eds., Nat. Acad. Sci. - Nat. Res. Council Publ. No. 829, (1960). See also "Sur l'attachement des ondes de choc dans les écoulements a deux dimensions," *C. R. Acad. Sci.* Paris, Vol. 250, pp. 1968-1970 (1960).

IONIZATION IN CROSSED ELECTRIC AND MAGNETIC FIELDS

Stirling A. Colgate
Lawrence Radiation Laboratory, University of California
Livermore, Calfornia

Both in magnetohydrodynamic shocks and in accelerated, partially ionized gas flow across a magnetic field, space-charge separation occurs that establishes very large electric fields in the direction of motion. The width of the current layers associated with the acceleration is never less than the electron Larmor radius with no collisions and is broadened by electron collisions to a width solely determined by the effective resistivity. The electrons gain an energy, regardless of collisions, equal to the electric potential difference across the layer. For $\omega\tau < 1$ (ω = electron cyclotron frequency, τ = collision time), this potential corresponds to the change in kinetic energy of mass motion per ion. For slightly ionized gases, the additional stress of neutral ion collisions within the layer can make the electric potential (and hence gain in electron energy) very large for only modest changes in mass velocity. Thus ionization may occur when the change in kinetic energy of the ions is small compared to the ionization potential.

THE M-LAYER

The simplest current layer in a plasma and magnetic field that has been treated analytically is that of Rosenbluth's M-layer where a cold plasma stream is reflected from a magnetic field.[1] By analyzing the forces exerted on each particle, one can show that the strong magnetic pulse solution of Adlam and Allen[2] falls within the same physical description as do most present shock solutions.[3, 4] The rate of electron ionization in these current layers can then be determined from a knowledge of their structure.

The M-layer (Fig. 1) is created by a magnetic field pushing on a cold ionized plasma with the assumption of no magnetic field in the plasma and no collisions. In the moving frame of the layer, ions and electrons are reflected elastically with a total momentum change of $2v\rho$, where v is the velocity of the layer and ρ the density of the plasma. The momentum flux $2v^2\rho$ must be balanced by the magnetic field pressure $B^2/8\pi$, and since the mass resides in the ions of mass M,

$$2MN\,v^2 = B_o^2/8\pi. \tag{1}$$

Rosenbluth has shown that, in a self-consistent calculation of electric and magnetic fields, a current layer of thickness D,

$$D = \sqrt{mc^2/8\pi Ne^2}, \tag{2}$$

Presented at the Symposium on Electromagnetics and Fluid Dynamics of Gaseous Plasma, Polytechnic Institute of Brooklyn, April 4, 5, 6, 1961

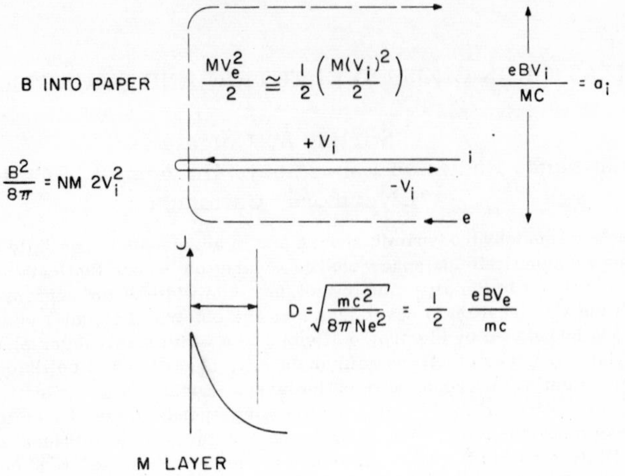

Fig. 1 M-layer

is formed in which the primary stress on the ions is the electrostatic force of charge seperation. The electrons, on the other hand, move in orbits parallel to the layer and across the magnetic field so that the electrostatic stress on the electrons is balanced by the Lorentz force (e/c) ($\vec{v}_e \times \vec{B}$) of the magnetic field. Since the ions are accelerated only by an electrostatic force, the potential difference across the layer V must correspond to the change in the ion kinetic energy.

$$V = eED = Mv_i^2/2; \tag{3}$$

$$\therefore \frac{e}{c} v_e B = Mv_i^2/2D.$$

Assume B is an average field approximately equal to $B_0/2$. Then using (2) and rearranging, we get

$$\frac{mv_e^2}{2} = \left[\frac{Mv_i^2}{2}\right]^2 \frac{4c^2 m}{2e^2 B_0^2} \frac{8\pi Ne^2}{mc^2}, \tag{4}$$

or

$$\frac{mv_e^2}{2} = 1/2 \left[\frac{Mv_i^2}{2}\right]. \tag{5}$$

In other words, the electron kinetic energy when the electron is within the layer must be approximately half the ion kinetic energy relative to the layer. The thickness of the layer must then be self-consistent with the fact that the electrons pick up most of the electrostatic potential of the layer. In other words, the layer is not much thicker than an electron Larmor radius when the electron has the kinetic energy of the ion. To show this, the electron Larmor radius in an average field $B = B_0/2$ is

$$a = \frac{2mv_e c}{eB_0} = \frac{2mc}{B_0 e}\left[\frac{Mv_i^2}{2m}\right]^{1/2} = \left[\frac{2Mv_i^2\, mc^2}{B_0^2 e^2}\right]^{1/2} . \tag{6}$$

However, by Eq. (1)

$$a = \left[\frac{mc^2}{8\pi Ne^2}\right]^{1/2} = D. \tag{7}$$

LARGE MAGNETIC PULSES

In the Adlam-Allen large magnetic pulses, the ions are similarly accelerated by charge separation electric fields, with the difference that the magnetic field exists ahead of and within the pulse (Fig. 2) so that the trajectories must pass through the layer. The layer is still D in thickness, but the electron drift velocity parallel to the layer is now reduced from the perfect diamagnetic M-layer of Rosenbluth because with larger magnetic field the Lorentz stress on the electrons at a given velocity is greater.

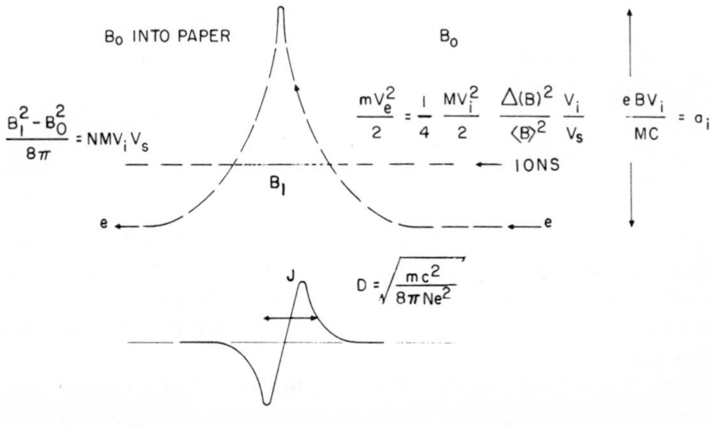

Fig. 2 Large-amplitude hydromagnetic pulse

The equivalent momentum balance is

$$NMv_i v_s = \left[B_{max}^2 - B_{min}^2\right]/8\pi = \Delta(B)^2/8\pi, \qquad (8)$$

where v_i is the change in ion velocity measured in the moving frame v_s of the layer. Electrostatics apply in the frame in which the layer is stationary, in which case Eq. (4) becomes

$$\frac{mv_e^2}{2} = \frac{1}{4}\frac{Mv_i^2}{2}\frac{\Delta(B)^2}{\langle B\rangle^2}\frac{v_i}{v_s}, \qquad (9)$$

where $\langle B \rangle$ corresponds to an average field within the layer. The large pulse solution is no longer valid when the pulse velocity (v_s in this case) becomes twice the Alfven velocity or when

$$v_s = 2\left[\frac{B_{min}^2}{4\pi NM}\right]^{1/2}, \quad \text{or} \quad \frac{\Delta(B)^2}{\langle B\rangle^2} = 2. \qquad (10)$$

This limit approaches the perfect diamagnetic case of Rosenbluth where the electron kinetic energy in the layer is one-half the change in ion kinetic energy.

The thickness of the layer measured in electron Larmor radii becomes (from Eqs. (6) and (8)):

$$a = \frac{mv_e c}{e\langle B\rangle} = \frac{mc}{e\langle B\rangle}\left[\frac{Mv_i^2}{4m}\frac{\Delta(B)^2}{\langle B\rangle^2}\frac{v_i}{v_s}\right]^{1/2}$$
$$= (1/2)\,D\,\frac{\Delta(B)^2}{\langle B\rangle^2}\frac{v_i}{v_s}. \qquad (11)$$

Therefore, in the limit of the strong shock solution where $v_i \rightarrow v_s$ and $\Delta(B)^2 \simeq \langle B\rangle^2$, we recover the results of the diamagnetic case where the layer is an electron Larmor radius thick. For weaker magnetic pulses, the layer becomes a number of Larmor radii thick according to Eq. (11).

Despite the fact that the orbits of the two solutions are not continuously connected, it is nevertheless evident that the layer thicknesses, in terms of electron Larmor radii and the electron energy within the layer, are connected between the two solutions.

COLLISIONLESS SHOCKS

Present theory of collisionless shocks, particularly that due to Gardner et al,[3] has predicted oscillating solutions of the form of a series of waves following behind the principle wave or shock front. The general description of these waves is of the form of a series of the strong pulses already discussed. This picture of a hydromagnetic shock has recently been verified by machine calculations of Auer, Hurowitz and Kilb,[4] in which a series of strong pulses of increasing spacing were observed for Mach number less than 2 and a random wave field composed of such pulses for Mach number greater than 2.

A unifying feature of all these current layer descriptions is that of charge separation electric fields in which the change of kinetic energy of the ions is equal to the electrostatic potential across the shock.

This description applies to the collisionless case, but the layer structure can be expected to change as soon as collisions are included. In particular, as soon as an average of one collision per electron occurs within the layer, we would expect the layer roughly to double in thickness to two electron Larmor radii. In order to calculate this probability, we must know the average path length of an electron within the layer.

By (3) the velocity of an electron within the layer is

$$v_e = \frac{c}{e} \frac{Mv_i^2}{2D \langle B \rangle} , \qquad (12)$$

and the time t spent within the layer must be the same as the ion transit time (D/v_i) in order to maintain charge neutrality. (The charge separation is very small.) The electron path length ℓ then becomes

$$\ell = \frac{Dv_e}{v_i} = \frac{c}{e} \frac{Mv_i}{2 \langle B \rangle} , \qquad (13)$$

$$= 1/2 \text{ ion Larmor radius.}$$

This result could have been predicted on the basis that the Lorentz force impulse on the electrons must correspond to that required to accelerate an ion by v_i. In a magnetic field B, this requires that an equal charge be displaced a distance equal to the ion Larmor radius across the magnetic field. It is evident that this displacement is independent of the thickness of the layer, provided only that the ions are accelerated by an electrostatic field.

COLLISION BROADENING OF A STRONG SHOCK LAYER

The condition for doubling the thickness of a layer one electron Larmor radius thick by scattering requires one collision in the path ℓ:

$$\ell = \lambda = \frac{1}{N\sigma} = \frac{c}{e}\frac{Mv_i}{2 < B >}, \tag{14}$$

or

$$\sigma = \frac{2 < B > e}{NMv_i c},$$

where σ is the electron scattering cross section at the velocity v_e.

Since the electron scattering leads to the equivalent of a diffusion of magnetic flux, condition (14) can be derived on the basis of a resistivity resulting in a magnetic skin depth 2D at a diffusion velocity v_i. In other words, this current layer cannot be localized to less than the diffusion depth x_D for a given resistivity and velocity.

To demonstrate this, the skin depth x_D in a time t is:[5]

$$x_D = \left[\frac{\eta t}{4\pi}\right]^{1/2} \quad (\eta \text{ in cgs units}), \tag{15}$$

or, defining a diffusion velocity $x_D/t = v_i$,

$$x_D = \frac{\eta}{4\pi v_i}. \tag{16}$$

Using the classical resistivity,[5]

$$\eta = \frac{mc^2 \nu}{Ne^2} = \frac{mc^2 N\sigma v_e}{Ne^2} = \frac{mc^2 \sigma v_e}{e^2} \tag{17}$$

where the electron collision frequency $\nu = N\sigma v_e$. Therefore

$$x_D = 2D = \frac{\eta}{4\pi v_i} = \frac{mc^2 \sigma v_e}{4\pi e^2 v_i} \tag{18}$$

or

$$\sigma = \frac{4\pi e^2 \left[\frac{mc^2}{8\pi Ne^2}\right] v_i e^2 < B >}{mc^2 \, cMv_i^2} \tag{19}$$

or

$$\sigma = \frac{2e\langle B\rangle}{NMv_i},$$

which is identical to the condition (14) derived on a single scattering basis. The layer therefore has a minimum thickness D, provided that the electron scattering cross section is less than (19), or is diffusion-broadened to a thickness given by

$$x_D = \frac{\eta}{4\pi v_i}. \tag{20}$$

However, once the layer is broader than D, the electron drift velocity is no longer given by (11); that is, the electric field extends over a dimension $x_D \gg D$, so that the electron drift velocity becomes

$$v_{eD} = \frac{c}{e}\,\frac{Mv_i^2}{2x_D\langle B\rangle} = v_{e\,max}\left[\frac{x_D}{D}\right]^{-1}. \tag{21}$$

However, when $x_D > D$, there must necessarily be electron collisions, which will heat the electrons. If electrons are drifting at velocity v_{eD} through essentially stationary heavy ions, then the electrons gain a velocity increment v_{eD} randomly per collision. This dynamical friction heating of the electrons is given accurately by Spitzer;[5] but, for the present required accuracy, a random walk analysis would say that after n collisions the velocity spread will be

$$v_{eth} = v_{eD}\, n^{1/2} \tag{22}$$

where v_{eth} is the electron thermal velocity, and the width of the layer

$$x_D = D\,n^{1/2} \tag{23}$$

Therefore, by (21)

$$v_{eth} = v_{eD}\frac{x_D}{D} = v_{e\,max}\,. \tag{24}$$

This implies that the electrons are heated by collisions to the same energy they would have had in the layer if there were no collisions. In other words, the electrons acquire the same energy as the change in kinetic energy of the ions regardless of layer thickness, provided only that the collisions are elastic and the mass ratio infinitely large. Of course, the electrons do exchange energy with the ions after M/m elastic collisions, or by (23), when the thickness of the layer is

$$x_D = D\,(M/m)^{1/2} = a_i\,. \tag{25}$$

This is also the condition of the limit of validity of the electron drift velocity (12) because (25) defines the ion Larmor radius, since D alone (by (7)) is the electron Larmor radius at the ion energy. When the layer is broadened by diffusion to a thickness greater than the ion Larmor radius, the ions are then accelerated by a magnetic field in addition to the electrostatic field of charge separation, and the primary assumption of layer structure becomes invalid. This limit also corresponds to the electron collision frequency equaling the electron cyclotron frequency, i. e., $\omega_{ce}\,\tau = 1$. To show this, the number of the electron cyclotron frequency is $(M/m)\,\omega_{ci}$. But the time to cross the layer is one ion cyclotron period, so that one electron collision occurs per electron cyclotron period.

COLLISION BROADENING OF A WEAK SHOCK LAYER

For a weak shock or magnetic pulse where the thickness D (by Eq. (11)) is $2\left[B^2/\Delta(B)^2\right](v_s/v_i)$ electron Larmor radii thick, the cross section for scattering to broaden the layer and the diffusion heating are the same as for the strong shock case - as it must be from the laws of irreversible magnetic diffusion.

To demonstrate this result in terms of collisions and random walk, assume (as in the strong shock case) a cross section σ such that in n collisions the layer is broadened by diffusion to a thickness D. We wish to show that the electrons will be heated to an energy corresponding to the ion kinetic energy and that the resistivity corresponds to that required to give a skin depth D at a diffusion velocity v_s: namely, the rate at which magnetic flux is being compressed.

By Eq. (22), the electron thermal velocity after n collisions is increased by $n^{1/2}$. Therefore, the Larmor radius of the scattered electrons becomes (by Eq. (11))

$$a_{eth} = n^{1/2}\,a_{eo} = (1/2)n^{1/2}\,D\,\frac{\Delta(B)^2}{\langle B\rangle^2}\,\frac{v_i}{v_s}\,. \tag{26}$$

The random walk diffusion of n steps a_{eth} long becomes

$$x_D = n^{1/2}\,a_{eth} = nD/2\,\frac{\Delta(B)^2}{\langle B\rangle^2}\,\frac{v_i}{v_s}\,, \tag{27}$$

or for $x_D = D$

$$n = 2 \frac{\langle B \rangle^2}{\Delta(B)^2} \frac{v_s}{v_i} .$$

The final electron thermal energy by Eqs. (22) and (9) becomes

$$\frac{mv_{eth}^2}{2} = \frac{m}{2}(n^{1/2} v_{eD})^2$$

$$= (1/2) \frac{Mv_i^2}{2} \frac{v_i}{v_s} \frac{\Delta(B)^2}{\langle B \rangle^2} \frac{v_s}{v_i} \frac{\langle B \rangle^2}{\Delta(B)^2}$$

$$= (1/2) \frac{Mv_i^2}{2} \tag{28}$$

in agreement with the strong shock case (Eq. (24)).

The resistivity corresponding to n collisions occurring within the ion traversal time of the layer D/v_s is by Eq. (17),

$$\eta = \frac{mc^2}{Ne^2} \frac{n v_s}{D} , \tag{29}$$

giving a diffusion thickness at the velocity v_s the shock speed of

$$x_D = \frac{\eta\beta}{4\pi v_s} = \frac{n\beta\, mc^2}{4\pi Ne^2 D} \frac{v_s}{v_i} = 2n\beta D , \tag{30}$$

where β is the usual ratio of particle pressure to magnetic field pressure $8\pi NkT/B^2$. For the modification of the usual diffusion equation (16), for low particle pressure, see Rosenbluth and Kaufman.[6]

From Eq. (28)

$$\beta = \frac{Nmv_{eth}^2}{2} \frac{8\pi}{\langle B \rangle^2} \tag{31}$$

$$= 1/4\, NMv_i^2 \Big/ \frac{\langle B \rangle^2}{8\pi} ,$$

or, by Eq. (8),

$$\beta = \frac{1}{4} \frac{\Delta(B)^2}{8\pi} \frac{v_i}{v_s} \frac{8\pi}{\langle B \rangle^2} .$$

Therefore, Eq. (30) becomes

$$x_D = \frac{1}{2} n \frac{\Delta (B)^2}{\langle B \rangle^2} \frac{v_i}{v_s} D = D, \tag{32}$$

thus confirming the resistive broadening of the current layer.

The diffusion heating of the electrons to a temperature equal to the change in the ion kinetic energy is evident on the basis of conservation of energy. Whenever a step function of magnetic field diffuses into a conductor (provided that the velocity is less than that of light) the process is irreversible and the irreversible work done becomes $p\Delta V$. Since the change in magnetic pressure is $\Delta B^2/8\pi$, this must be the irreversible work dissipated per unit volume which, in turn, is just the change in kinetic energy of the mass density.

SUMMARY OF THE LAYER STRUCTURE

For very low resistivity, electrons are accelerated in the charge separation field (α electron Larmor radii thick) to a kinetic energy equal to $1/\alpha$ of the change in kinetic energy of the ions (α being the ratio of final magnetic energy density to the change in ion kinetic energy density). At higher resistivity the layer broadens by resistive diffusion, and the electrons reach the same temperature by joule heating as the change in kinetic energy of the ions. When the layer becomes broader than an ion Larmor radius, both the charge seperation field and the temperature reached in joule heating become less.

IONIZATION

It has been pointed out by Alfven[7] that partially ionized plasma flow through a magnetic field is strongly stabilized in velocity at precisely the value where the kinetic energy of motion corresponds to the ionization potential of the neutrals. Let us consider that a current layer corresponding to the above change in velocity is formed, and then ask under what conditions the probability of ionization within the layer is high.

Let M = mass of deuteron. Then

$$Mv_i^2/2 = 15 \text{ ev (includes molecular breakup)},$$

$$v_i = 3.9 \times 10^6 \text{ cm/sec},$$

$$\sigma_{\text{electron-neutral}} = 6 \times 10^{-15} \text{ cm}^2,$$

$$\eta = 0.05\, T_e^{-3/2} + \frac{0.0015(1 - f)}{f} \text{ ohm cm},$$

where f = fractional ionization. The thickness of the layer becomes (by substituting in (20))

$$x_D = \frac{0.05\, T^{-3/2} + [0.0015\,(1 - f)]/f}{4\pi \times 3.9 \times 10^6 \times 10^{-9}}\,, \tag{33}$$

$$= T_e^{-3/2} + \frac{0.03\,(1 - f)}{f} \quad .$$

Provided that x_D is less than an ion Larmor radius a_i, then $T_e = E_i = 15$ ev, in which case for f = 50% ionized $x_D = 0.05$ cm, provided that $\beta \cong 1$ and $x_D \leqslant a_i$.

The density at which there exists 50 per cent probability for ionization of a neutral during its traversal of the layer is defined when the ionization time equals the traversal time. This time is

$$\frac{1}{N\sigma v_{eth}} = \frac{x_D}{v_i} = \frac{0.05}{3.9 \times 10^6} = 1.3 \times 10^{-8} \text{ sec},$$

where σv_{eth} for ionization at 15 ev temperature $\simeq 2 \times 10^{-8}$ per sec,

$$\therefore N_e = 4 \times 10^{15} \text{ electrons/cc}$$

for $\beta = 1$, B = 1500 gauss.

Since the layer thickness is proportional to (1 - f)/f and the ionization rate is proportional to f, the ionization probability remains roughly constant. Therefore, 100 microns pressure of initial gas density should result in a high enough ionization probability in a current layer for the rate of change of ionized mass to stabilize the velocity.

HIGH NEUTRAL DENSITY

If the neutral density is high enough for a number of neutral ion collisions to occur within the layer thickness, then the electric field stress needed to change the velocity of the ions by a given amount becomes greater. In other words, if we determine a given velocity change in the fluid flow by a given potential between two electrodes across a given magnetic field, then the electric field stress per ion required to change the velocity becomes greater as the effective mass per ion increases. Ion-neutral collisions essentially couple the mass of the neutrals to the electric charge of the ion, so that the electric field stress must equal the ion-neutral collisional stress. This collisional stress is a function of the ion slip -- the mean relative velocity between ions and neutrals. If the ions undergo n_i neutral collisions in traversing the layer of fractional ionization f, the effective stress τ will be increased by

$$\tau \cong \tau_o \left[1 + n_i \frac{M_o}{M_i}\right] \quad \text{if } n_i \ll \frac{1}{f}\frac{M_o}{M_i}, \tag{34}$$

and

$$\tau \cong \tau_o \frac{1}{f}\frac{M_o}{M_i} \qquad \text{if } n_i \gg \frac{1}{f}\frac{M_o}{M_i}, \tag{35}$$

where the collisionless stress $\tau_o = NM_i v_i v_s$, and M_o and M_i are the neutral and ion atom masses, respectively.

In other words, when the number of collisions are fewer than are required to thermalize the ions to the neutrals within the layer (34), then the additional stress is just proportional to the few relatively large energy collisions that take place. On the other hand, if a sufficiently large number of collisions occur so as to thermalize the neutrals to the ions at each point in the layer, then the ions will behave as if they had a larger mass by just the neutral-to-ion mass ratio. At small fractional ionization, the former case is the more likely since a sufficiently high density to thermalize the ions will also result in $\omega_e \tau_e \geqslant 1$ and therefore small charge-separation.

As an example, consider an MHD generator, where the potential is shorted in a single stage. Assume that

$$N_o = 10^{17} \text{ argon atoms/cc;}$$

$$B = 10^4 \text{ gauss;}$$

$$\sigma \text{ (electron neutral)} \cong 10^{-16} \text{ cm}^2;$$

$$\therefore \omega\tau = 10.$$

Further assume that

$$v_i = 2 \times 10^5 \text{ cm/sec;}$$

$$\eta = 0.05\, T_e^{-3/2} + \left[\frac{1-f}{f}\right] 2.5 \times 10^{-5} \text{ ohms cm;}$$

$$x_D = 20\, T_e^{-3/2} + \left[\frac{1-f}{f}\right] 1 \times 10^{-2} \text{ cm.}$$

Assuming that the electron temperature will be limited by the ionization potential of argon at 15 ev, then for $f = 10^{-2}$, $x_D = 1.5$ cm.

For an alkali metal ion like Cs^+, the effective scattering cross section on argon is σ $(Cs^+ - A) \cong 10^{-15}$ cm^2.

Therefore in moving 1. 5 cm, a Cs^+ ion will undergo

$$n_i = (1.5/N_o\sigma) = 150 \text{ collisions ,}$$

which is enough, by (34) and (35), to couple the neutral gas fraction to the ions, giving an effective mass:

$$NM_i \text{ (effective)} \simeq 100 \text{ A atoms.}$$

Since

$$\frac{M_A v_i^2}{2} = 0.8 \text{ volts,}$$

the potential of the layer, which is the integral of the stress, becomes larger by the number of neutrals per ion or 80 volts across the layer. The electron temperature will not, of course, reach this value due to elastic collisions, line excitation, and ionization. The number of elastic electron neutral collisions that occur in traversing the layer, assuming that the electron temperature is limited by ionization to about 10 ev, is

$$c = \frac{x_D}{v_i} N\overline{\sigma v} = 3 \times 10^4 \text{ collisions.}$$

The energy lost to neutrals by elastic collisions will be

$$w_e = c \frac{m}{M} kT_e = 4 \text{ ev.}$$

This is negligible compared to the available heat energy (namely, 80 ev per electron) and so this energy will go into ionization and excitation. Assuming that no more neutral cesium is available (only argon remaining), roughly equal energy goes into excitation and ionization, so that 2-1/2 atoms of argon should be ionized in passage through the layer. In addition, the cesium should remain ionized regardless of the ambient gas temperature. Therefore, the possibility exists that sufficient nonequilibrium ionization can be maintained to couple the gas to the magnetic field effectively, yet have a low stream temperature.

INSTABILITY BROADENING

Finally, it should be pointed out that the collisionless current layer structure is not realistic from the standpoint of electron stream instabilities. The state of a high-energy monoenergetic electron stream traversing relatively cold ions is an exceedingly unstable situation -

due to both plasma oscillations growth as described by Buneman,[8] and to Helmholtz (or velocity shear) instability as described by Northrop.[9] The effective electron collision frequency for the nonlinear amplitude growth has been shown by Buneman to be of the order of one-fifth the plasma frequency, which in most cases is high compared to the electron cyclotron frequency - resulting in a very broad current layer. However, once the layer is more than a few electron Larmor radii thick due to any collisions, either cooperative or single-particle, the electron velocity distribution is close to thermal and so instability growth should be limited. The result is the probability that no current layer can exist less than a few electron Larmor radii thick, and in the presence of additional collisions will become broader according to the laws of magnetic field diffusion. The irreversible heat generated among the electrons will always correspond to the change in kinetic energy of the ions, provided only that $\omega\tau < 1$.

This discussion has been partly based upon a series of lectures on magnethohydrodynamic generators given in the Electrical Engineering Department of the University of California, Berkeley, California. The work also was partly performed under the auspices of the U. S. Atomic Energy Commission.

REFERENCES

1. M. Rosenbluth, *Magnetohydrodynamics*, (R.K.M. Landshoff, Ed.) (Stanford, Calif: Stanford Univ. Press, 1957) pp.57-69.

2. J. H. Adlam and J. E. Allen, *2nd International Conference on Peaceful Uses of Atomic Energy*, Vol. 31, p. 221.

3. C. S. Gardner, et al., *2nd International Conference on Peaceful Uses of Atomic Energy*, Vol. 31, p. 230.

4. P. L. Auer, H. Hurowitz and L. Kilb, *Bull. Am. Phys. Soc.*, Vol. II, No. 5, p. 353 (1960); and Vol. II, No. 6, p. 197 (1961).

5. L. Spitzer, *The Physics of Fully Ionized Gases* (New York: Interscience 1956).

6. M. Rosenbluth and A. N. Kaufman, *Phys. Rev.*, Vol. 109, p. 1 (1958).

7. H. Alfven, *Rev. Mod. Phys.*, Vol. 32, No. 4, p. 710 (1960).

8. O. Buneman, *Phys. Rev.*, Vol. 115, No. 3, p. 503 (1959).

9. T. G. Northrop, "The Guiding Center Approximation to Charged Particle Motion," UCRL-5708-T, University of California.

OBLIQUE SHOCK WAVES IN STEADY TWO-DIMENSIONAL HYDROMAGNETIC FLOW

Jack Bazer
Institute of Mathematical Sciences, New York University

W. B. Ericson
Grumman Aircraft Engineering Corporation

A method is presented for determining the orientation and strength of oblique-shock waves in steady two-dimensional (planar) hydromagnetic flow. The medium is assumed to be an infinitely conducting, nonviscous, ideal polytropic gas. The method employs the results of an earlier paper by the authors in which it was shown that the velocities relative to the shock, the excess density ratio, excess pressure ratio, etc., can be expressed as simple algebraic functions of h, the magnitude of the jump in magnetic field across the shock, and the angle, ω, which the shock makes with upstream field.

Attention is focused chiefly on the aligned fields case where the results are especially easy to assess and are directly applicable to problems involving flow around wedges and corners. In this case the ranges for the slow and fast shock angles are easily delimited in terms of the turning angle and the upstream sound to Alfven speed ratio. Moreover, the dependence of the shock angle, ω on h, and hence of all the characteristics of the downstream flow, are readily determined in terms of the characteristics of the upstream flow.

I. FORMULATION OF THE PROBLEM

In this paper, we study oblique shock waves in steady two-dimensional hydromagnetic flow. It is assumed throughout that the medium is an infinitely conducting, nonviscous, polytropic ideal gas, and that the conservation laws of F. de Hoffmann and E. Teller[1] and R. Lüst [2] apply. We are concerned chiefly with the aligned-fields case in which the magnetic field is everywhere in the direction of the velocity field. Our results are immediately applicable to flow around corners and wedges.

As parameters for the problem, we have chosen the following:

$A_o = V_o/b_o$ = the upstream Alfven number;

$s_o = a_o^2/b_o^2$ = the upstream speed ratio;

θ = the turning angle of the magnetic field;

ω = the shock angle.

Presented at the Symposium on Electromagnetics and Fluid Dynamics of Gaseous Plasma, Polytechnic Institute of Brooklyn, April 4, 5, 6, 1961

Here, $\underline{V}_0$ is the upstream flow velocity* which we suppose is horizontal and directed from left to right; a_0 is the upstream sound speed; $b_0 = \sqrt{\mu H_0^2 \rho_0^{-1}}$ is the upstream Alfven disturbance speed parallel to the upstream magnetic field, $\underline{H}_0$; ρ_0 and μ are the upstream density and specific inductive capacity.** The subscript "1" is used in place of "o" to identify the corresponding quantities behind the shock, i. e., on the downstream side. The angles ω and θ are measured from the direction of the upstream magnetic field $\underline{H}_0$ (see Fig. 1(a)).

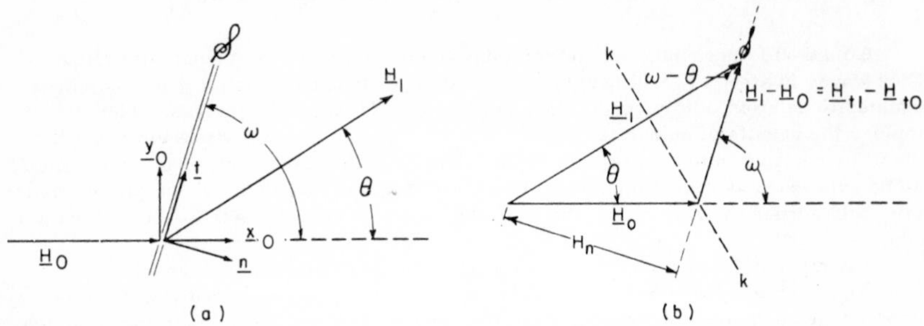

Figure 1 Transition of $\underline{H}$ through a fast shock

In terms of these quantities, the problem may be formulated as follows. For fixed values of the turning angle θ and the upstream speed ratio s_0, determine the dependence of the shock angle ω on the upstream Alfven number A_0. In attacking this problem, we address ourselves specifically to the task of determining: 1) the ω ranges in which one may expect slow and fast shocks to be present; 2) the subranges in which these shocks are thermodynamically stable; † 3) the subranges in which these shocks are both thermodynamically stable and stable to small perturbations; 4) the ranges of ω and A_0 associated with hyperbolic and elliptic flow in front and behind. In addition, we briefly describe how the over-all picture changes as the speed ratio s_0 is varied while the turning angle is held fixed, and vice versa. Finally, we indicate how our discussion can be extended to deal with the problem of nonaligned fields.

Our approach to these problems is partly analytical, partly graphical and numerical. The analytical part is based on our previous papers[4, 5] in which the analysis of propagating shocks was the main

*In this paper, a dash beneath a letter signifies a vector. The same letter without the dash denotes the absolute value of that vector.

**It is assumed that μ is everywhere constant. The MKS Giorgi system of units is used throughout the paper.

† Thermodynamically stable shocks are those in which the entropy behind is greater than or equal to the entropy in front.

concern. In these works we showed that the state behind the shock and the normal flow velocities (relative to the shock) are expressible in terms of the jump in the tangential component of the magnetic field $[H_t] = H_{t1} - H_{t0}$, the cosine of the shock angle ω, the upstream speed ratio s_0, and the adiabatic exponent γ by means of simple algebraic formulas. * With the aid of these formulas, we then demonstrated that one could eliminate all thermodynamically unstable shocks, explicitly delimit the range of $[H_t]$ in which thermodynamically stable shocks exist, and classify all compressive shocks as slow or fast according to the sign of $[H_t]$, or equivalently according to the relation in the region behind the shock of the normal flow velocity (relative to shock) to the normal Alfven disturbance speed. The link between this analysis and the present one is contained in Eq. (6) of Section II of this paper, where $[H_t]$ is related to the basic parameters ω and θ. Owing chiefly to the simple form of this relationship, the above results and others in references 4 and 5 find immediate application in the present work; they simplify the analysis considerably and enable one to obtain precise qualitative information about the various shocks under consideration.

Graphical and numerical methods enter the analysis in determining the shock angle ω from a relation of the form $A_0 = f(\omega, \theta, s_0, \gamma)$ where f is a known function of ω, θ, s_0, γ. Our graphical method essentially consists of plotting A_0 against ω for fixed θ and s_0, and reading off the value of ω which corresponds to a given value of A_0. Once ω is known, all remaining quantities may be calculated from explicit formulas.

Oblique hydromagnetic shocks in steady two-dimensional flow, have been studied by H. Cabannes,[7] and M. I. Kiselev and N. I. Kolosnitzyn.[8] Cabannes' work is a numerical study of the aligned-fields case. The work of Kiselev and Kolosnitzyn is a partly analytical, partly graphical study of the general nonaligned-fields case in which the shock angle is obtained by iterative graphical methods. Most studies of hydromagnetic shocks have dealt with propagating shocks. The papers by H. L. Helfer,[9] R. Lust,[2, 3] and K. O. Friedrichs[10] in addition to the works mentioned earlier, fall into this category.

II. SURVEY OF PREVIOUS WORK: LIMITATIONS ON THE ω RANGE

In this section we shall summarize those results and definitions from our previous work which have a direct bearing on the problem under discussion In addition, at appropriate stages of the discussion we shall, successively:(1) map out in a rough way the ω ranges in which one may expect the various categories of hydromagnetic shocks

* In the numerical part of our analysis, γ is taken to be 5/3.

to be present; 2) delimit these ranges further by specifying precisely which shocks in each category are thermodynamically stable; and finally, 3) explicitly establish the (usually) smaller subranges of ω in which the thermodynamically stable shocks are stable to small perturbations.

A. Definitions, Notation and Preliminary Remarks

Let $\underline{x}_o$ and $\underline{y}_o$ denote the unit vectors along the horizontal x axis and the vertical y axis and let the vectors

$$\underline{n} = \sin\omega\,\underline{x}_o - \cos\omega\,\underline{y}_o, \tag{1}$$

$$\underline{t} = \cos\omega\,\underline{x}_o + \sin\omega\,\underline{y}_o, \tag{2}$$

be respectively, the unit normal and tangent to the shock front, (see Fig. 1). If $\underline{Q}$ is any vector, then we shall refer to the scalars $Q_n = \underline{Q} \cdot \underline{n}$ and $Q_t = \underline{Q} \cdot \underline{t}$ as the normal and tangential components of $\underline{Q}$, and the vectors $\underline{Q}_n = Q_n\underline{n}$ and $\underline{Q}_t = Q_t\underline{t}$ as the normal and tangential projections of $\underline{Q}$. Throughout, it is to be understood that the terms normal and tangential refer to the shock front.

As earlier, the subscripts o and 1 distinguish values of the same physical quantity in front of and behind the shock. In particular, Q_{no}, Q_{to}, and Q_{n1}, Q_{t1} denote the tangential and normal components of $\underline{Q}$ in front of and behind the shock.

By "shock" we mean, at this stage, a stationary planar discontinuity in the flow across which mass flows. The region into which the mass flows is then termed the region *behind** the shock.

Shocks as defined above may be separated into two main families: those in which the density ρ is continuous across the shock; and those across which ρ suffers a jump. The first family is, of course, the Alfven shocks (abbreviated, A-shocks). As is well-known, in A-shocks the tangential projection $\underline{H}_t$ of the magnetic field undergoes a rotation through an arbitrary angle on crossing the shock. With one exception, it is clear that these shocks can play no role in the ensuing analysis, which is concerned solely with planar flow. The exceptional case is the so-called 180° A-shocks in which $\underline{H}_t$ turns through 180°, i. e., $\underline{H}_{t1} = -\underline{H}_{to}$. The shocks of the second family ($\rho_1 \neq \rho_o$) fall naturally into two classes called "fast" and "slow" according to the relation of the tangential projection of the magnetic field $\underline{H}_{t1}$ behind, to the corresponding projection $\underline{H}_{to}$ in front.** Specifically, a member of this family is said to be "fast" shock (abbreviated, f-shock) if: (1) $\underline{H}_{t1}$

*As soon as thermodynamically unstable shocks have been eliminated, the region behind the shocks becomes the region of higher entropy, density, and pressure.

**It is important to recall here that $\underline{H}_{t1}$ is parallel to $\underline{H}_{to}$ in all members of this family.

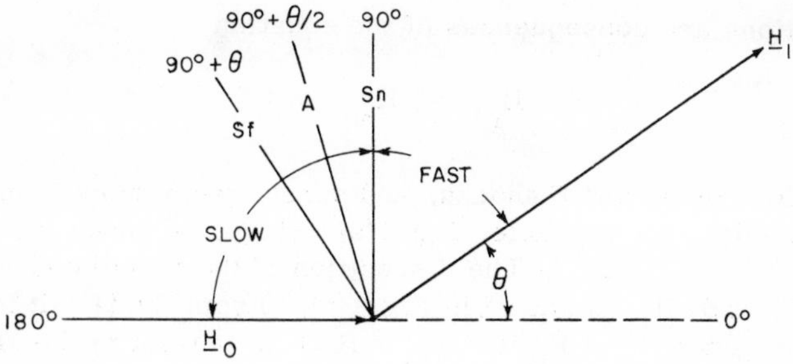

Figure 2 The orientation of s, f, Sf and Sn shocks with respect to the upstream magnetic field

is in the same direction as $\underline{H}_{to}$; and 2) $\underline{H}_{t1}$ exceeds $\underline{H}_{to}$ in magnitude. If either or both of these conditions are violated, the shock is said to be a "slow" shock* (abbreviated s-shock). The 180° A-shock may be regarded as a limiting form of slow shock with $\rho_1 = \rho_o$. The so-called "switch-off" shocks (abbreviated, Sf-shocks) are also special slow shocks. Sf-shocks are characterized by the relations $\underline{H}_{t1}=0$, $\underline{H}_{to}\neq 0$. In Sf-shocks, the shock front is evidently perpendicular to the direction of $\underline{H}_1$, the magnetic field behind the shock. Finally, mention should be made of "switch-on" shocks (abbreviated, Sn-shocks) which are characterized by the relations $\underline{H}_{t1} \neq 0$, $\underline{H}_{to} = 0$. Here, the shock front is perpendicular to the magnetic field in front.

We can now begin to map out in a rough way the ω ranges within which the various categories of shocks may be found. We maintain (see Fig. 2) that

$$\omega_{Sf} = 90^o + \theta,$$

$$\omega_{Sn} = 90^o,$$

$$\theta < \omega < 90^o \text{ in fast shocks,} \tag{3}$$

$$90^o < \omega < 180^o \text{ in slow shocks,}$$

$$\omega_A = 90^o + \theta/2,$$

where ω_{Sf}, ω_{Sn}, and ω_A are the angles of the Sf, Sn, and A-shocks. The first two equations follow directly from the fact that Sf and Sn-shock fronts are respectively perpendicular to $\underline{H}_1$ and $\underline{H}_o$. The last

*Switch-on shocks are by themselves neither fast nor slow (see Reference 4). They exist only when the parameter s_o is less than unity, and then only if the pressure ratio is sufficiently small.

three relations are consequences of the equation

$$H_{n1} = H_{no}, \tag{4}$$

the definitions of s and f-shocks, and purely geometrical considerations. Consider, for example, Fig. 1(a), where the shock front is in the range $\theta^o < \omega < 90^o$. The disposition of the associated magnetic vectors $\underline{H}_o$ and $\underline{H}_1$ is shown in Fig. 1(b). From Eq. (4), it follows that the difference $\underline{H}_1 - \underline{H}_o$ (= $\underline{H}_{t1} - \underline{H}_{to}$) is tangent to the shock front. The angle between this vector and $\underline{H}_o$ is therefore ω and the angle between $\underline{H}_1$ and $\underline{H}_1 - \underline{H}_o$ is $\omega - \theta$, as shown. If we now project $\underline{H}_1$ and $\underline{H}_o$ onto the direction of the shock front, we find that $\underline{H}_{t1}$ is necessarily in the same direction as $\underline{H}_{to}$ and exceeds this vector in magnitude; thus shocks in the range $\theta < \omega < 90^o$ are necessarily fast. Note, in addition, that the components of $\underline{H}_o$ and $\underline{H}_{t1} - \underline{H}_{to}$ onto any line k perpendicular to $\underline{H}_1$ are equal in absolute value (see Fig. 1(b)). Setting

$$h = |H_{t1} - H_{to}|/H_o, \tag{5}$$

we accordingly arrive at the equation

$$W(\theta): \ h = \frac{\sin\theta}{\sin(\omega-\theta)}\ . \tag{6}$$

Entirely analogous arguments show that shocks in the range $90^o < \omega < 180^o$ * are slow, that $\omega_A = 90^o + \theta/2$, and that Eq. (6) also holds for s-shocks.

The above results specify the orientation of the shock front with respect to $\underline{H}_o$ and apply whether or not the velocity field is aligned with the magnetic field. If the fields are aligned** we may say that f-shocks tilt downstream and s-shocks tilt upstream. The existence of upstream tilting shocks and waves of small amplitude has already been observed by many writers, among whom may be mentioned J. E. McCune and E. L. Resler, Jr.[11] and M. N. Kogan.[12]

For fixed θ, Eq. (6) is the equation of a line denoted by $W = W(\theta)$, in the polar co-ordinates (h, ω); h is measured along the radial direction and ω measured counterclockwise from the positive x-axis. This line is shown in Fig. 3(a) and 3(b). It makes an angle θ with the polar axis and intersects this axis at the point $h = 1$, $\omega = 180^o$.

*At $\omega = 180^o$, an s-shock reduces to a contact discontinuity with the property that $\underline{H}_1 = 0$.

**It is merely necessary to assume alignment in front, for from the shock relation $\underline{V}_o \times \underline{H}_o = \underline{V}_1 \times \underline{H}_1$, it follows that $\underline{V}_1$ is aligned with $\underline{H}_1$ behind.

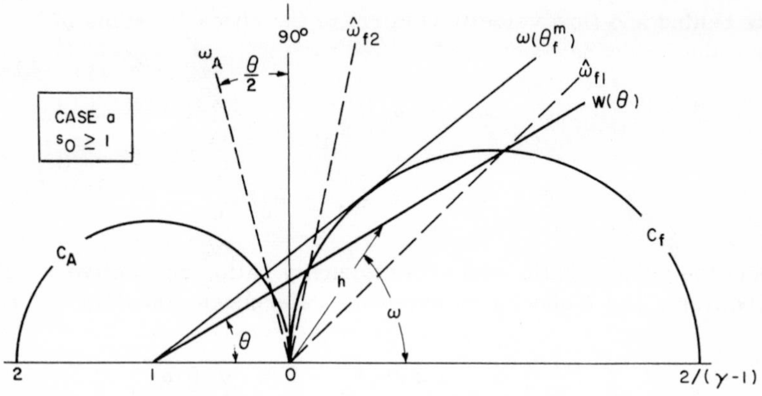

(a)

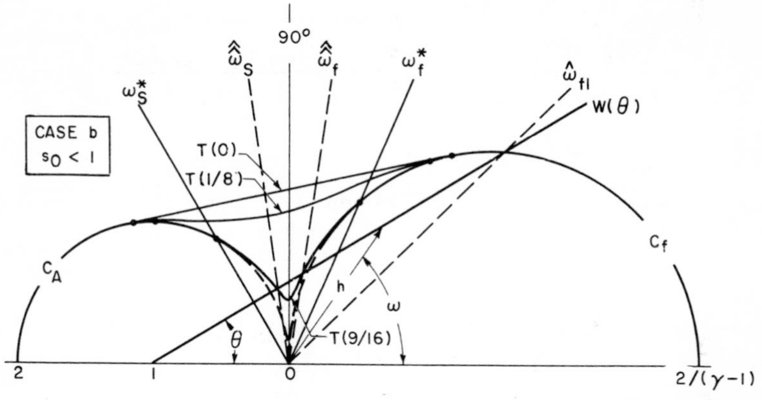

(b)

Figure 3 (a) Regions of thermodynamic stability in the (h, ω) polar diagram when $s_0 \geq 1$. The regions in the upper half-plane bounded by the semicircles C_f and C_A are the regions of thermodynamic stability. In the complementary region, shocks either do not exist or are thermodynamically unstable. Thermodynamically stable f-shocks exist for values of ω between $\hat{\omega}_{f1}$ and $\hat{\omega}_{f2}$. Thermodynamically stable slow shocks exist in the range $90^o + \theta / 2 \leq \omega < 180^o$. (b) Regions of thermodynamic stability on the (h, ω) polar diagram when $s_0 < 1$. The region in the upper half-plane bounded by the arcs C_f, $\omega_f^* \geq \omega \geq 0$; $T(s_0)$, $\omega_s^* \geq \omega \geq \omega_f^*$; C_A, $180^o \geq \omega \geq \omega_s^*$; is the region of thermodynamic stability. In the complementary region, shocks either do not exist or are thermodynamically unstable. The angles ω_f^*, $\hat{\hat{\omega}}_f$, $\hat{\hat{\omega}}_s$, ω_s^* are shown for the case $s_0 = 9/16$, $\theta_{Sn}^m < \theta < \theta_f^m$.

In every shock mentioned above, whether thermodynamically stable or not, the pair (h, ω) must be a point of W.

The formulas* mentioned in the introductory section relating the

*A derivation of these formulas from the basic shock relations of de Hoffman and Teller is given in the Appendix of Reference 5.

state behind and flow velocity relative to the shock in terms of h, ω, s_o, γ are the following: Let

$$\eta = \rho_1/\rho_o \tag{7}$$

and

$$\bar{\eta} = \eta - 1 = (\rho_1 - \rho_o)/\rho_o \tag{8}$$

denote the density ratio and excess density ratio, respectively. Then for both s and f-shocks we have (see references 4 and 5):

$$\bar{\eta} = h \left[\frac{-\frac{\gamma}{2} h \cos\omega + s_o - 1 \pm \sqrt{R(h)}}{2s_o \cos\omega - (\gamma-1)h} \right], \tag{9a}$$

$$\frac{p_1 - p_o}{p_o} = \frac{\gamma}{s_o} \left\{ -\frac{h^2}{2} + h \left[\frac{\bar{\eta}/h - \cos\omega}{1 - (\bar{\eta}/h)\cos\omega} \right] \right\}, \tag{9b}$$

$$\frac{V_{no}}{\sqrt{\eta}\, b_{no}} = \left[1 - (\bar{\eta}/h)\cos\omega\right]^{-1/2} = \frac{V_{n1}}{b_{n1}}, \tag{9c}$$

$$\frac{V_{n1} - V_{no}}{b_{n1}} = -\bar{\eta}\left[1 - (\bar{\eta}/h)\cos\omega\right]^{-1/2}, \tag{9d}$$

$$\frac{V_{t1} - V_{to}}{b_o} = \frac{h}{\sqrt{\eta}}\left[1 - (\bar{\eta}/h)\cos\omega\right]^{1/2}, \tag{9e}$$

where p denotes the pressure, R(h) is defined by

$$R(h) = h^2 \left[\frac{\gamma^2 \cos^2\omega}{4} - (\gamma-1) \right] + h\cos\omega\,(2-\gamma)(1+s_o)$$

$$+ 4s_o \cos^2\omega + (1-s_o)^2, \tag{10}$$

and

$$b_n = \sqrt{\mu H^2 \rho^{-1}} = b \sin\omega \tag{11}$$

denotes the Alfven disturbance speed along $\pm\underline{n}$. The above formulas yield fast shocks for values of ω in the range $0 < \omega < 90^o$, and slow shocks for values of ω in the range $90^o < \omega < 180^o$. Note that the values of all the left members of Eq. (9) may be calculated as soon as the parameters h, ω, s_0 and γ are prescribed.

B. Thermodynamically Stable Shocks*

The above equations do not distinguish between thermodynamically stable and thermodynamically unstable shocks. To distinguish between these two, it is necessary to make use of the fact that in thermodynamically stable shocks the entropy behind the shock exceeds the entropy ahead if and only if the excess pressure ratio and excess density ratio are both positive (for a proof see Ref. 6). Evidently, values of h and ω which lead to negative values of either the excess density or excess pressure ratio must be eliminated. But, these values have already been eliminated in our earlier work (see Refs. 4 and 5); accordingly we may confine ourselves to a statement of the results.

For this purpose it is convenient to distinguish two cases in which $s_0 \geqslant 1$, and, $s_0 < 1$.

Case 1: $s_0 \geqslant 1$:

Here, all values (h, ω) associated with thermodynamically stable fast shocks must be within the semicircle

$$C_f: \qquad h = \frac{2}{\gamma-1} \cos \omega \equiv \hat{h}_f(\omega); \qquad 0^o \leqslant \omega \leqslant 90^o, \tag{12}$$

while all points (h, ω) associated with thermodynamically stable slow shocks must be within the semicircle

$$C_A: \qquad h = 2|\cos \omega| \equiv \hat{h}_s(\omega); \qquad 90^o \leqslant \omega \leqslant 180^o. \tag{13}$$

Moreover, for (h,ω) within C_f or C_A only the branch associated with the positive sign in Eq. (9a) yields thermodynamically stable solutions.

C_f and C_A have been plotted together with $W(\theta)$ in Fig. 3(a). Note that points on C_A correspond to 180° A-shocks. This follows from the definition of 180° A-shocks and the fact that for such shocks $h = 2|H_{to}|/H_0 = 2|\cos \omega|$. It is also easy to prove by substituting $h = 2 \cos \omega/(\gamma-1)$ into the appropriate formulas, Eqs. (9a) through (9c), that $(p_1 - p_0)/p_0$, V_0 and V_1 are infinite on C_f.

*It is assumed in the following that values of h and ω which lead to imaginary values in Eq. (9a) have been eliminated.

The points of intersection of $W(\theta)$ with C_f and C_A yield the extreme values of ω between which thermodynamically stable s-and f-shocks exist. For f-shocks we find that

$$\theta < \hat{\omega}_{f2} < \omega < \hat{\omega}_{f1} , \tag{14}$$

where

$$\hat{\omega}_{f1} = \text{arc cos} \left[\left[\frac{1 - \gamma \sin^2 \theta + \cos \theta \sqrt{1 - \gamma^2 \sin^2 \theta}}{2} \right]^{\frac{1}{2}} \right] \tag{15}$$

and

$$\hat{\omega}_{f2} = \text{arc cos} \left[\left[\frac{1 - \gamma \sin^2 \theta - \cos \theta \sqrt{1 - \gamma^2 \sin^2 \theta}}{2} \right]^{\frac{1}{2}} \right] \tag{16}$$

The corresponding relation for s-shocks is

$$\hat{\omega}_s = \omega_A = 90^o + \theta/2 \leqslant \omega < 180^o. \tag{17}$$

Evidently, when $s_0 \geqslant 1$, s-shocks first appear at $\omega = 90^o + \theta/2$ as 180° A-shocks, and then, with increasing ω, pass continuously over, at $90^o + \theta$, to Sf-shocks, and finally at $\omega = 180^o$ to contact discontinuities.

Observe that there is a largest turning angle, denoted by θ_f^m, such that whenever $\theta > \theta_f^m$, $W(\theta)$ no longer intersects the circle C_f. From Fig. 3(a), or directly from Eq. (15) and (16), we find this angle to be

$$\theta_f^m = \text{arc sin}\,(\gamma^{-1}). \tag{18}$$

The corresponding shock angle ω_f^m is given by the expression

$$\omega_f^m = \theta_f^m/2 + 45^o . \tag{19}$$

A comparision of $\hat{\omega}_{f1}$, $\hat{\omega}_{f2}$, ω_f^m and θ_f^m with the corresponding gas dynamic quantities reveals that they are identical. This is to be expected since f-shocks approach the behavior of gas shocks as the flow velocities become infinite.

While there is no limitation on θ in thermodynamically stable s-shocks, it will follow from the discussion in Section III that s-shocks, which are both thermodynamically stable and stable to small perturbations, exist only when $\theta < 90^o$.

It should be noted that it is possible to map out the regions of thermodynamic stability in this way only because the maximum values of h limiting the regions of thermodynamic stability are independent of the parameters A_0 and θ. For $s_0 \geqslant 1$ we have the added simplification on independence of s_0 (see Eqs. (12) and (13)). When $s_0 < 1$, it becomes necessary to specify the value of s_0 to determine the regions of thermodynamic stability.

Case 2: $s_0 < 1$.

In this case, thermodynamically stable s and f-shocks exist only in the (h,ω) domain bounded by the horizontal axis and the circular arcs

$$\hat{C}_f: \quad h = \frac{2}{\gamma-1} \cos \omega \equiv \hat{h}_f(\omega), \qquad 0 \leqslant \omega \leqslant \omega_f^* \leqslant 90^\circ, \tag{20}$$

$$\hat{C}_A: \quad h = 2|\cos \omega| \equiv \hat{h}_s(\omega), \qquad \omega_s^* \leqslant \omega \leqslant 180^\circ, \tag{21}$$

and the arc $T(s_0)$

$$T(s_0): \quad h = \hat{\hat{h}}(\omega, s_0)$$

$$\equiv \left| \frac{1}{2(\gamma-1) - \gamma^2 \cos^2 \omega/2} \left\{ (1+s_0)(2-\gamma)\cos\omega + 2\sin\omega \sqrt{(\gamma-1)(1-s_0)^2 + s_0\gamma^2\cos^2\omega} \right\} \right|, \tag{22}$$

$$\omega_f^* \leqslant \omega \leqslant \omega_s^*, \tag{23}$$

(see Fig. 3(b)). The angles ω_f^* and ω_s^* are defined by

$$\omega_f^* = \operatorname{arc\,cos}\left[\sqrt{\frac{\gamma-1}{\gamma}(1-s_0)}\right], \tag{24}$$

$$\omega_s^* = \operatorname{arc\,cos}\left[-\sqrt{(1-s_0)/\gamma}\right]. \tag{25}$$

For fixed ω, $0 < \omega < \omega_f^*$ the greatest value that h can achieve in thermodynamically stable f-shocks is $2\cos\omega/(\gamma-1)$. Similarly, for fixed ω, $\omega_s^* < \omega < 180^\circ$ the greatest value that h can achieve in thermodynamically stable slow shocks is $2|\cos\omega|$. For fixed ω, in the range $\omega_f^* \leqslant \omega < 90^\circ$, the greatest value that h can achieve in thermodynamically stable f-shocks is $\hat{\hat{h}}(\omega, s_0)$. Furthermore, for fixed ω in the range $90^\circ < \omega \leqslant \omega_s^*$, the same function furnishes the greatest value that h may assume in thermodynamically stable s-shocks. The function $h = \hat{\hat{h}}(\omega, s_o)$ is found by solving for the positive root of $R(h) = 0$, (see Eq. (10)). For values of $h > \hat{\hat{h}}$, $\omega_f^* \leqslant \omega \leqslant \omega_s^*$, $R(h) < 0$ and all quantities in the left-hand side of Eq. (9) are complex valued. The expressions for ω_f^* and ω_s^*, Eqs. (24) and (25), are obtained by equating $\hat{\hat{h}}(\omega, s_o)$ defined in Eq. (22) to, respectively, $\hat{h}_f(\omega)$ defined in Eq. (20) and $\hat{h}_s(\omega)$ defined in Eq. (21). For values of $\hat{\hat{h}} > h \geqslant \hat{h}_f$, $\omega_f^* \leqslant \omega \leqslant 90^o$, or $\hat{\hat{h}} > h \geqslant \hat{h}_s$, $90^o \leqslant \omega \leqslant \omega_s^*$, $R(h) > 0$ and both positive and negative signs before $\sqrt{R}$ in Eq. (9a) yield thermodynamically stable shock solutions. Thus each point (h, ω) on the $W(\theta)$ line which lies outside the semicircles the C_f($\hat{h}_f(\omega)$ - curve) and the C_A ($\hat{h}_s(\omega)$ - curve) and underneath the $T(s_o)$ ($\hat{\hat{h}}(\omega, s_o)$ - curve) corresponds to two thermodynamically stable shocks.* Within the semicircles C_f and C_A, each point on $W(\theta)$ yields only one thermodynamically stable shock, i. e., the one corresponding to the choice of the positive sign before the radical in Eq. (9a).

In Fig. 3(b), we have pictured the arcs T(1), T(9/16), T(1/8) and T(0). With the aid of Eq. (22), it is easy to show that T(0) is the segment, between the points of tangency, of the line which is tangent to both C_A and C_f, and that T(1) is a single point -- the origin. The arcs T(9/16) and T(1/8) are typical curves in the range $0 < s_o < 1$.

Let us examine the cases $s_o = 9/16$ and $s_o = 1/8$ in greater detail. Consider first the case $s_o = 9/16$. Referring to Fig. 3(b), there are within the family of lines $W(\theta)$, $0^o < \theta < 90^o$, two lines, $W(\tilde{\theta})$ and $W(\tilde{\tilde{\theta}})$, which are tangent to the T(9/16) curve. Let $\tilde{\theta}$ be the smaller of the two angles. When $0^o < \theta \leqslant \tilde{\theta}$; the ω range is $\hat{\omega}_{f1} < \omega < 180^o$, with $\hat{\omega}_{f1}$ defined as in Eq. (15). As ω increases from $\hat{\omega}_{f1}$, f-shocks continuously pass over, through Sn-shocks, at $\omega = 90^o$, to thermodynamically stable slow shocks. On the other hand, when $\tilde{\theta} < \theta < \tilde{\tilde{\theta}}$, a gap appears between the ω ranges of the s and f-shocks. In this case, thermodynamically stable f-shocks exist in the range

$$\hat{\omega}_{f1} < \omega \leqslant \hat{\hat{\omega}}_{f2} \tag{26}$$

and thermodynamically stable s-shocks in the range

$$\hat{\hat{\omega}}_s \leqslant \omega < 180^o, \tag{27}$$

(see Fig. 3(b)). The picture here is the same as that described in Case 1, except that $\hat{\hat{\omega}}_{f2}$ is somewhat larger than $\hat{\omega}_{f2}$ (see Eq. (16)) and

*In References 4 and 5 thermodynamically stable shocks that lie within the angular region $\omega_f^* \leq \omega \leq \omega_s^*$ were called shocks of Type 2 and those that lie outside this region shocks of Type 1.

$\hat{\hat{\omega}}_s$ is somewhat smaller than $\hat{\omega}_s \equiv \omega_A$ (see Eq. (17)). The values of $\hat{\hat{\omega}}_s$, $\hat{\hat{\omega}}_f$ and $\tilde{\theta}$, $\tilde{\tilde{\theta}}$ are best determined graphically. Note that in the present case, $\tilde{\tilde{\theta}}$ is only slightly larger than θ_f^m defined in Eq. (18), while $\tilde{\theta}$ is approximately equal to the angle θ_{Sn}^m defined by

$$\theta_{Sn}^m = \text{arc tan}\left[\hat{\hat{h}}(90^0, s_o)\right] = \text{arc tan}\left[\frac{1 - s_o}{\sqrt{\gamma - 1}}\right] \tag{28}$$

(see Eq. (23)). Note that when $\theta = \theta_{Sn}^m$, $W(\theta)$ intersects $T(s_o)$ at the point $\left[\hat{\hat{h}}(90^0, s_o)\right]$ and that θ_{Sn}^m is the largest angle beyond which Sn-shocks are no longer available to effect the turning of the flow.

Referring again to Fig. 3(b), we see that when $s_o = 1/8$, the ω range of thermodynamically stable shocks is always connected, whatever the value of θ; i. e., there are no gaps. The lower end-point in the f-shock ω range is once more $\hat{\omega}_{f1}$ (see Eq. (15)) provided that θ is less than the angle θ_{f1}^* defined by

$$\theta_{f1}^* = \tan^{-1}\left[\frac{2}{\gamma + 2(1 - s_o)}\sqrt{\frac{(1 - s_o)\left[1 + s_o(\gamma - 1)\right]}{\gamma - 1}}\right] \tag{29}$$

In geometrical terms, θ_{f1}^* may be defined as follows: At $\theta = \theta_{f1}^*$, $W(\theta_{f1}^*)$ intersects $T(s_o)$ at its right end-point; here $\hat{\omega}_{f1}$ is equal to ω_f^* (see Eq. (24)). When θ lies within the range $\theta_{f1}^* < \theta < \theta_{Sn}^m$, the lower end-point of the f-shock ω range exceeds $\hat{\omega}_{f1}$ (see Eq. (15)), and is most easily determined by graphical means, i. e., by finding the intersection of $W(\theta)$ with $T(s_o)$. Observe that for $\theta > \theta_{Sn}^m$, only slow shocks are available to effect the turning of the flow.

In general, when $s_o < 1$, it is necessary to know $T(s_o)$ if one is to be successful in establishing the ω ranges of thermodynamically stable f- and s-shocks. However, s_o is close to one, and θ satisfies the relation

$$\theta \geqslant \text{arc cos}\left[1 - 2(1 - s_o)/\gamma\right], \tag{30}$$

then the knowledge of $T(s_o)$ is superfluous. This is true because in this case $W(\theta)$ lies entirely above $T(s_o)$ and the ω ranges may be determined as in Case 1, where $s_o \geqslant 1$.

III. ADDITIONAL STABILITY CONSIDERATIONS HYPERBOLICITY, ELLIPTICITY

In the following, when we refer to stable shocks* we shall mean shocks which are both thermodynamically stable and stable to small perturbations. The word shock without qualification will be reserved for the larger class of thermodynamically stable shocks. Unless otherwise mentioned, all points (h, ω) which play a role in the ensuing discussion are assumed to be on the line $W = W(\theta)$ and within the regions of thermodynamic stability mapped out in Fig. 3(a) and 3(b).

Since $\bar{\eta}$ and h are positive, it follows from Eq. (9c) that

$$V^f_{n1} > b_{n1}, \qquad \theta < \omega < 90^o \tag{31}$$

in f-shocks, and that

$$V^s_{n1} < b_{n1}, \qquad 90^o < \omega < 180^o \tag{32}$$

in s-shocks. In other words, the normal flow velocity in f-shocks is super-Alfven behind, while the normal flow velocity in s-shocks is sub-Alfven behind. In statements of this kind, it is to be understood that the Alfven speed is in the normal direction. Also, relations (31) and (32) can serve as alternative definitions of f-and s-shocks.

If we let ω approach 90° in Eq. (9c), we find that in Sn-shocks

$$V^{Sn}_{n1} = b_{n1}, \qquad \omega = 90^o . \tag{33}$$

These shocks exist only if $s_o < 1$, and then only if $h < (1-s_o)/\sqrt{\gamma-1}$ (cf. Eq. (28)). From the mass conservation relation

$$\rho_1 V_{n1} = \rho_o V_{no}, \tag{34}$$

and from relation (31) and the fact that $\rho_1 > \rho_o$, it follows that in f-shocks

$$V^f_{no} > b_{no}, \qquad \theta < \omega < 90^o. \tag{35}$$

In s-shocks the situation is more complicated. As was shown in Refs. 4 and 5, for each ω in the range $90^o < \omega < 180^o$ we must have

$$V^s_{no} < b_{no} \tag{36}$$

*Our "stable" shocks correspond precisely to R. V. Polovin's evolutionary shocks.

as long as $$h < |\cos\omega| ,\qquad (37)$$

while the opposite inequality,

$$V^{s}_{no} \geqslant b_{no} ,\qquad (38)$$

holds whenever $$h \geqslant |\cos\omega| ,\qquad 90^{o} < \omega < 180^{o} .\qquad (39)$$

In addition, it can be shown that the equality holds in Eq. (37) only when (h, ω) is a point of the semicircle

$$C_A: \quad h = 2|\cos\omega| ,\qquad 90^{o} \leqslant \omega \leqslant 180^{o},\qquad (40)$$

introduced earlier (cf. Eq. (13)), or when (h, ω) is a point of the semicircle

$$C_{Sf}: \quad h = |\cos\omega| ,\qquad 90^{o} \leqslant \omega \leqslant 180^{o}.\qquad (41)$$

It was shown in Section II that points of C_A corresponds to 180° A-shocks. In the same way it can be shown that points on C_{Sf} correspond to Sf-shocks.

Now it has been demonstrated by S. I. Syrovatskii[13], and A. I. Akhiezer, G. Ia. Liubarskii, and R. V. Polovin[14] that hydromagnetic shocks are stable to various small perturbations only if one of the following three pairs of relations are satisfied:

$$V_{no} > b_{no} \text{ and } V_{n1} > b_{n1},\qquad (42a)$$

$$V_{no} = b_{no} \text{ and } V_{n1} = b_{n1},\qquad (42b)$$

$$V_{no} < b_{no} \text{ and } V_{n1} < b_{n1}.\qquad (42c)$$

If we compare these relations with the relations (31), (35), and (32), (36), and (38), we find that all fast shocks are stable while slow shocks are stable if and only if (h, ω) lies within C_{Sf} or is a 180° A-shock.* By finding the intersections of the line $W(\theta)$ with C_{Sf}, we can now easily determine the extreme angles between which stable slow shocks exist. These angles are seen to be $\omega = 180^{o}$ and $\omega = \omega_{Sf} = 90^{o} + \theta$, so that stable s-shocks exist in the range

$$90^{o} + \theta < \omega < 180^{o},\qquad (43)$$

*The 180° A-shock (see Eq. (42b)) was shown by Syrovatskii to be stable to Alfven disturbances only. It is quite possible that perturbation by slow and fast disturbances will reveal an instability. However until this is rigorously demonstrated we here follow Syrovatskii in classifying 180° A-shocks as stable. Currently there also appears to be some difference of opinion about the stability or instability of Sn-shocks (see the discussion at the end of Reference 15).

and at $$\omega = \omega_A = 90^\circ + \theta/2. \tag{44}$$

On the other hand, all s-shocks associated with values of ω satisfying the relation

$$90^\circ \leqslant \omega \leqslant 90^\circ + \theta \tag{45}$$

are thermodynamically stable but, with the exception of the 180° A-

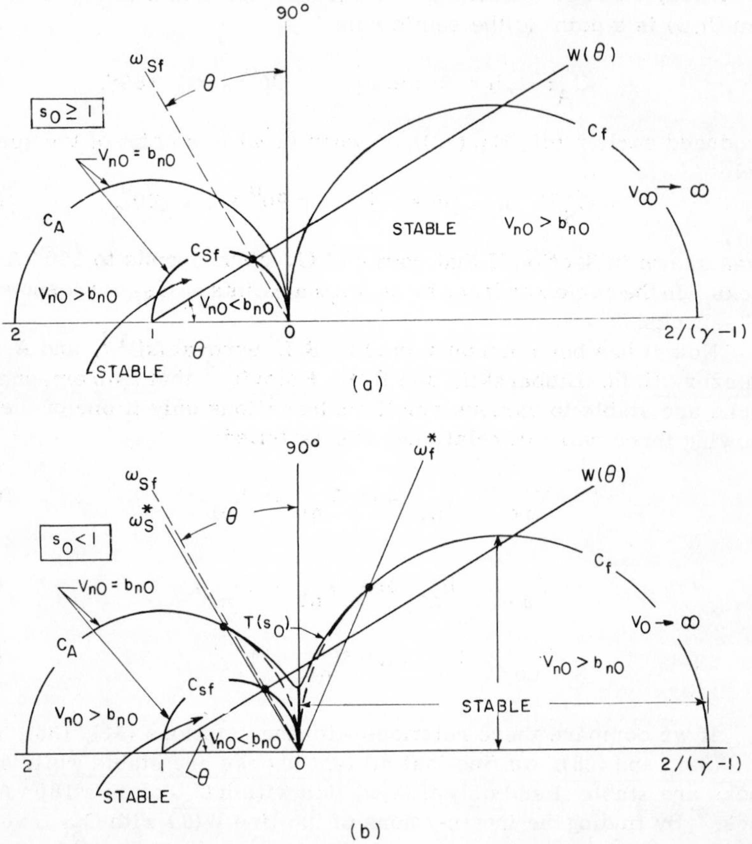

Figure 4 (a) Regions of stability in the (h, ω) polar diagram when $s_0 \geq 1$. The regions in the upper half-plane bounded by the semicircles C_{Sf} and C_f are the regions of stability. The crescent-shaped region between the semicircles C_A and C_{Sf} corresponds to shocks which are thermodynamically stable but not stable to small perturbations. On C_A and C_{Sf}, $V_{no} = b_{no}$, within C_{Sf}, $V_{no} < b_{no}$ and within the crescent-shaped region, $V_{no} > b_{no}$. In C_f, $V_{no} > b_{no}$. (b) Regions of stability in the (h, ω) polar diagram when $s_0 < 1$. In the first quadrant the region in the upper half-plane bounded by the circular arc, C_f, $\omega_f^* \geq \omega \geq 0$, the curve $T(s_0)$, $90^\circ \geq \omega \geq \omega_f^*$, and the ray $\omega = 90^\circ$ is the region of stability for f-shocks. The semicircular region under C_{Sf} is the region of stability for s-shocks. The region bounded by C_A, $180^\circ \geq \omega \geq \omega_s^*$, $T(s_0)$, $\omega_s^* \geq \omega \geq 90^\circ$, and the ray $\omega = 90^\circ$ which lies exterior to C_{Sf}, corresponds to shocks which are thermodynamically stable but unstable to small perturbations.

shock, unstable to small hydromagnetic disturbances.* Specifically, Sf, Sn and all shocks "between" (with the exception of the 180° A-shocks) are unstable. The basic facts of the above discussion are summarized in Fig. 4(a) and 4(b).

The above results are valid whether or not the fields are aligned. From now on, unless otherwise mentioned, it will be assumed that the fields are aligned.

Let a be the local sound speed, $b = \sqrt{\mu H^2 \rho^{-1}}$ be the local Alfven disturbance speed along $\underline{H}$, and V be the local fluid velocity. We shall call the flow "hyperbolic-fast" whenever

$$\max\{a, b\} < V, \tag{46}$$

and "hyperbolic-slow" whenever

$$\frac{ab}{\sqrt{a^2 + b^2}} < V < \min\{a, b\} \tag{47}$$

and "elliptic" whenever either of the following relations is satisfied:

$$V \leqslant \frac{ab}{\sqrt{a^2 + b^2}}, \tag{48a}$$

or

$$\min\{a, b\} \leqslant V \leqslant \max\{a, b\}. \tag{48b}$$

Here, $\min\{x, y\}$ denotes the smaller of the quantities x and y while $\max\{x, y\}$ denotes the larger. It is readily verified that the hyperbolic and elliptic regions as here defined are the hyperbolic and elliptic regions found by J. McCune and E. L. Resler,[11] and T. Taniuiti[17] in their treatments of steady aligned-fields flow. Now it can be shown (Ref. 4) that in f-shocks

$$V^f_{no} > c_{fo}(\underline{n}), \tag{49}$$

and that in slow shocks

$$V^s_{no} > c_{so}(\underline{n}), \tag{50}$$

where

$$c_{fj}(\underline{n}) = b_j \left[\frac{1 + s_j + \sqrt{(1+s_j)^2 - 4s_j \sin^2 \omega_j}}{2} \right]^{1/2} \quad (j = 0, 1) \tag{51}$$

*R. V. Polovin[16] suggests that these shocks are most appropriately termed "non-evolutionary". Polovin maintains that non-evolutionary shocks "can exist only for an instant as intial conditions" and that they must be distinguished from " unstable" discontinuities.

is the fast disturbance speed along the direction $\underline{n}$ in the region j; and that

$$c_{sj}(\underline{n}) = b_j \left[\frac{1 + s_j - \sqrt{(1+s_j)^2 - 4s_j \sin^2 \omega_j}}{2} \right]^{1/2} \quad (j = 0, 1) \tag{52}$$

is the slow disturbance speed along $\underline{n}$ in the region j. The angle ω_j is the angle that the wave front makes with $\underline{H}_j$. From Eqs. (51) and (52), we derive the following set of useful relations:

$$\frac{a_j b_j \, |\sin \omega_j|}{\sqrt{a_j^2 + b_j^2}} \leqslant c_{sj}(\underline{n}) \leqslant \min \left\{ a_j, \, b_{nj} \right\} , \tag{53a}$$

$$\max \left\{ a_j, \, b_j \right\} \leqslant c_{fj}(\underline{n}). \tag{53b}$$

With the aid of Eqs. (53)and (49) we find that

$$V_0^f > \max \left\{ a_0, \, b_0 \right\} , \tag{54}$$

so that ahead of f-shocks the flow is hyperbolic-fast. The situation here is entirely analogous to that of gas dynamics where the velocity ahead is supersonic.

In describing the flow ahead of s-shocks it is convenient to consider the parameter ranges $s_0 \geqslant 1$ and $s_0 < 1$ separately. We confine our discussion to stable slow shocks. Consider first the case $s_0 \geqslant 1$ $(a_0 \geqslant b_0)$. Since $v_{no}^s < b_{no}$, or equivalently, $V_0^s < b_0$, in stable slow shocks, we find that $V_0^s < b_0 \leqslant a_0$. From relations (50) and (53a), it then follows that the flow ahead of all stable s-shocks is hyperbolic-slow when $s_0 \geqslant 1$. When $s_0 < 1$, it follows from analogous arguments that the flow ahead of stable s-shocks is hyperbolic-slow when $V_0^s < a_0$ and elliptic when $a_0 \leqslant V_0^s \leqslant b_0$.*

The problem of determining the character of the flow behind slow and fast shocks is more difficult In this region a_1 and b_1 are not fixed parameters of the problem; unlike a_0 and b_0 they are functions of ω. At the end of Section IV, we shall analyze a few typical cases by graphical means.

IV. GRAPHICAL METHODS - ALIGNED FIELDS

This part of our discussion is based on the equation

$$\ell(A_0): \qquad q \sin \omega = 1/A_0 , \tag{55}$$

*See the paper presented by W. R. Sears in this publication.

where $q = q(\omega, \theta, s_o, \gamma)$ is the expression*

$$q \equiv \left[\frac{V_{no}}{b_o}\right]^{-1} = \frac{\eta^{-1/2}\left|1 - (\bar{\eta}/h)\sin\omega\right|^{1/2}}{\sin\omega} \qquad (56)$$

With q defined as in Eq. (56), Eq. (55) follows immediately from Eq. (9c) and Eq. (1). Observe that for fixed θ, s_o and γ, the Alfven number A_o may be calculated directly from Eqs. (55) and (56). To obtain ω explicitly as a function of A_o is a more difficult problem. H. Cabannes[7] has shown, for example, that $\tan\omega$ satisfies a quintic equation whose coefficients depend upon A_o, $\tan\theta_o$, s_o and γ. One may, of course, tabulate A_o against ω for fixed values of θ, s_o and γ and use interpolation to obtain ω for a given value of A_o. However, for presenting a concrete picture of the full range of possibilities, graphical methods, based on Eq. (55), are preferable.

We again employ polar co-ordinates with the shock angle ω as the angular co-ordinate. However, we now choose q to be the radial co-ordinate. The choice of q as the radial co-ordinate might appear to be somewhat artificial; however, such a choice makes possible a polar diagram that has many points in its favor. Among these are:

1) The graph of Eq. (55) is a horizontal line, which we denote, by $\ell(A_o)$, whose distance from the x axis is A_o^{-1} and whose points of intersection with the graph of Eq. (56) furnish the shock angles associated with A_o. This remark is the basis of our graphical method.

2) The shock fronts lie along rays through the origin whose angular position with respect to the horizontal is the same as that of the shock fronts in physical space.

3) The curves which form the boundaries of the regions of stability and of hyperbolicity and ellipticity ahead of the shock are horizontal lines.

4) In the weak shock limit this polar diagram is equivalent to the Friedrichs' diagrams[10, 18] and moreover, better suited for numerical work.[19]

Let us first examine the situation for weak shocks. Assuming that $\omega \neq 0^o$, 90° or 180°, and letting θ (and hence h) approach zero, we find that Eq. (56) reduces to

$$0^o \text{ f-polar:} \qquad q = \frac{1}{c_{fo}/b_o}, \qquad 0 < \omega < 90^o \qquad (57)$$

*The variable h depends on θ and ω alone, but η and $\bar{\eta}$ depend upon ω, θ, s_o and γ (see Eq. (9)).

$$0^{\circ} \text{ s-polar:} \qquad q = \frac{1}{c_{so}/b_{o}}, \qquad 90^{\circ} < \omega < 180^{\circ} \; * \tag{58}$$

where $c_{fo} = c_{fo}(\underline{n})$ and $c_{so} = c_{so}(\underline{n})$ are the fast and slow disturbance speeds in the direction $\underline{n}$ ahead of the shock (see Eqs. (51) and (52)).

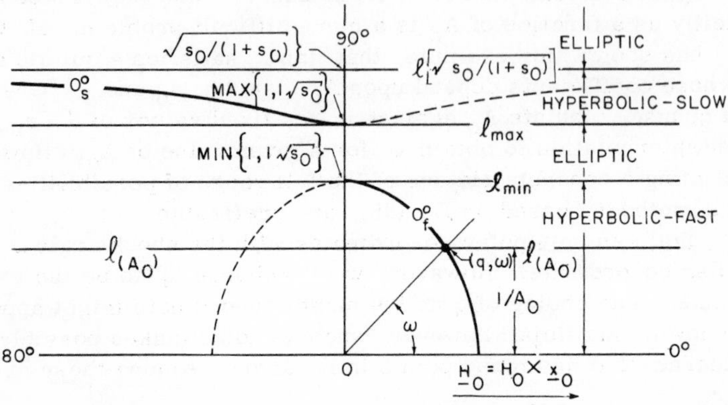

Figure 5 Zero degree fast and slow polars in the (q, ω) plane ($\omega \neq 0^{\circ}, 90^{\circ}, 180^{\circ}$)

Figure 5 shows the graphs of these curves in the angular range $0^{\circ} < \omega < 180^{\circ}$. Only the solid portions of these curves are of concern to us here. The 0° s-polar (see Eq. (58)) lies below the line given by the equation $\ell\left(\sqrt{s_o/(1+s_o)}\right)$

$$\ell\left(\sqrt{\frac{s_o}{1+s_o}}\right): \qquad q \sin \omega = \sqrt{\frac{1+s_o}{s_o}} \tag{59}$$

and above the horizontal line ℓ_{max} defined by

$$\ell_{max}: \qquad q \sin \omega = \max\left\{1, 1/\sqrt{s_o}\right\}. \tag{60}$$

The 0° s-polar is asymptotic to $\ell\left(\sqrt{s_o/(1+s_o)}\right)$ as ω increases toward 180° and becomes tangent to ℓ_{max} as ω decreases toward 90°. The 0° f-polar (see Eq. (57)) lies below the line ℓ_{min} defined by

*The portion of the 0° limit curve which is approached when $\omega = 90^{\circ}$ comprises the set of points on the 90° ray between the origin and the point $(1/\sqrt{s_o}, 90^{\circ})$. Each point of this segment corresponds to a pure gas shock.

$$\ell_{min}: \qquad q \sin \omega = \min \left\{1, 1/\sqrt{s_o}\right\}, \qquad (61)$$

and becomes tangent to this line as ω increases toward 90°.

With the aid of the relations (45) through (47), it is easy to verify that the flow ahead is hyperbolic-fast when $\ell(A_o)$ is below ℓ_{min}, hyperbolic-slow when $\ell(A_o)$ is above ℓ_{max} and below $\ell(\sqrt{s_o/(1+s_o)})$, and elliptic in the remaining regions of the (q, ω) diagram, (see Fig. 5).

In Section III, we showed that all f-shocks are stable while s-shocks are stable only when $V_o < b_o$. It follows that the stability region for the s-shocks lies above the line ℓ (1). In Fig. 5, ℓ (1) is ℓ_{min} when $s_o < 1$ $(a_o < b_o)$ and ℓ_{max} when $s_o \geqslant 1$ $(a_o \geqslant b_o)$.

Turning now to the case of finite θ, we show in Figs. 6(a) through 6(d), in addition to the 0°-polars just discussed, the (q, ω) polars of Eq. (56) which correspond to a turning angle θ of 30°. In Fig. 6(a), $s_o = 1/8$; in Fig. 6(b), $s_o = 9/16$; in Fig. 6(c), $s_o = 1$; and in Fig. 6(d), $s_o = 2$. Note that along each ray the 30° f-polars and 30° s-polars lie closer to the origin than the corresponding 0° polars. This fact is true for arbitrary values of θ, as one can easily verify with the help of relations (48) and (49).

Figure 6(a) ($s_o = 1/8$) illustrates the situation previously described in Section II-B (see Fig. 3(b)). The ω range of f-shocks is connected to the ω range of s-shocks at $\omega = 90^o$. In Fig. 6(b) ($s_o = 9/16$), θ exceeds the angle θ^m_{Sn} defined in Eq. (28) and as noted in Section II-B, the ω range of f-shocks and the ω range of s-shocks are separated by an ω range where no shocks are present. In Fig. 6(c) ℓ_{max} coincides with ℓ_{min} since $s_o = 1$. The 30° gas dynamical polar is also shown here for comparison. Note the close similarity in appearance of the fast polar and the gas dynamical polar. The curves of Figs. 6(c) and 6(d) are typical of those in the parameter class $s_o \geqslant 1$; the f-polars form a closed loop and the ω ranges of f-shocks and s-shocks are disjoint. In Figs. 6(a) and 6(b), q is a double-valued function of ω in parts of the s- and f-shock ω ranges. These are the ω ranges referred to earlier (Section II-B) in which the ratios $(\rho_1-\rho_o)/\rho_o$, $(p_1-p_o)/p_o$ become double-valued functions of ω. The portions of the s-polars shown as dotted lines correspond to those s-shocks which, with the exception of the 180° A-shock at $\omega=(\theta/2)+90^o$, are unstable to small disturbances*. Although it is not possible to illustrate this fact on Figs. 6(a) through 6(d), the s-polars reach a maximum in the vertical direction and then decrease steadily. At $\omega = 180^o$ all s-curves return to the horizontal line whose distance from the polar axis is unity, i. e., to the line ℓ_{min} if $s_o < 1$ and to ℓ_{max} if $s_o \geqslant 1$. When $s_o < 1$, there exist, (see Section III), stable s-shocks for which the flow is elliptic ahead. In fact, all points above the line ℓ (1) on the 30° s-polars shown in Figs. 6(a) and 6(b) corre-

*See footnote on page 403.

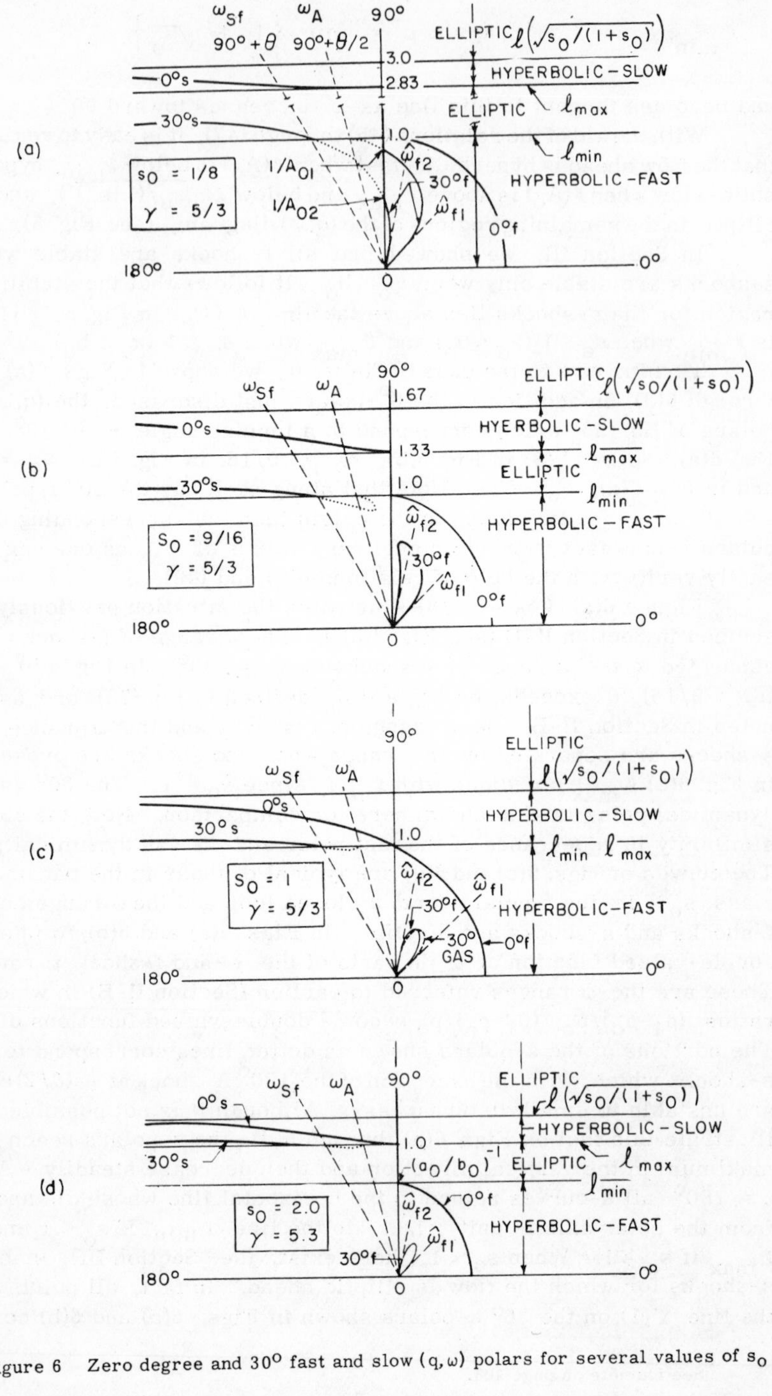

Figure 6 Zero degree and 30° fast and slow (q, ω) polars for several values of s_0

spond to stable s-shocks which are elliptic ahead.

Referring to Fig. 6(a), ($s_0 < 1$), we note that there are two fast branches issuing from the origin at $\hat{\omega}_{f1}$ and $\hat{\omega}_{f2}$. These branches terminate on the 90^0 ray at the point (A_{o1}^{-1}, 90^0) and (A_{o2}^{-1}, 90^0). The shocks corresponding to these points are Sn-shocks, as we have seen earlier. Assuming that $A_{o2} > A_{o1}$ and setting $\omega = 90^0$ in Eq. (56), we find that

$$A_{o1,2} = \left[\frac{\gamma - s_0 \pm \sqrt{(1 - s_0)^2 - (\gamma - 1)\tan^2\theta}}{\gamma - 1} \right]^{1/2}.$$

Here, A_{o2} is to be paired with the positive sign of the right member of this equation, and A_{o1} with the negative sign. Now when A_o exceeds A_{o2}, the line $\ell(A_o)$ intersects the f-polars twice. When, however, A_o satisfies the relation $A_{o2} \geqslant A_o > A_{o1}$, there is only one fast shock angle associated with a given value of ω. In the stable s-shock region, for A_o less than unity but greater than a certain minimum value, $\ell(A_o)$ will intersect the s-polars twice.

The picture for the f-shocks changes radically when $s_0 \geqslant 1$ or when θ is sufficiently large (see Figs. 6(b) through 6(d)). In these figures, the f-polars are no longer connected to the s-polars; instead they form closed loops. For A_o exceeding a certain minimum value, two f-shocks are possible. In the stable s-shock region, the picture is the same as before: For A_o less than unity, but greater than a certain minimum value, $\ell(A_o)$ intersects the s-polar twice.

The possibility of having two different shocks to effect the same turning of a given upstream flow is not new. It also occurs in the study of gas dynamics. In any given problem some additional condition is required to single out that shock which is expected to occur. In the problem of flow past a wedge, one may insist that for fixed A_o the s and f-polars continuously pass over into the weak shock polars as θ approaches zero. This condition selects the smaller-angle fast and slow shocks and eliminates those stable slow shocks for which the flow is elliptic ahead. The angles corresponding to the shocks so selected decrease as A_o increases.

Figure 7 depicts the variation of the (q, ω) polars with the turning angle θ, when s_0 is assumed to be 1/8. Observe that the s- and f-polars for small θ lie in the vicinity of the corresponding 0^0 polars. When θ approaches zero, the steeper portions of the s- and f-polars in the neighborhood of the ray $\omega = 90^0$ approach the part of this ray which lies between the origin and the point ($1/\sqrt{s_0}$, 90^0). Points on this segment correspond to pure gas shocks. The remaining portions of the s and f-curves coincide in the 0^0 limit with the weak shock s and f-polars discussed earlier in connection with Fig. 5. This description of the limiting process may be confirmed analytically by letting θ

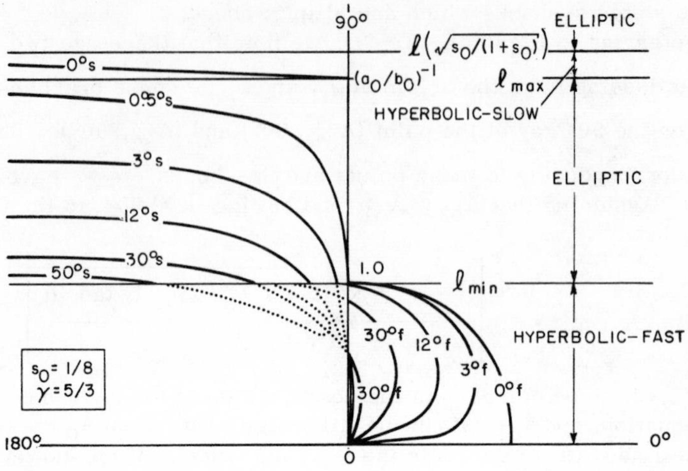

Figure 7 Fast and slow (q, ω) polars for $s_o = 1/8$ and several values of θ

approach zero in the right-hand side of Eq. (56), after substituting for h and $\overline{\eta}/h$ the expressions in the right-hand side of Eqs. (6) and (9a), respectively. For other values of s_o the details of the analysis will differ, but the final results are the same as those presented here.

In Figs. 8(a), 8(b), and 8(c), for $s_o = 1/8$, 9/16 and 1, respectively, we have plotted on a rectangular grid the functions $V_1/b_1 \equiv A_1$, $s_1 = a_1/b_1$ and $\sqrt{s_1/(1+s_1)}$ against the shock angle ω.* These figures serve to characterize the nature of the flow (i. e., whether it is elliptic or hyperbolic) behind s-and f-shocks. The angle θ is 30° in all cases. The portions of the $(\omega,\ V_1/b_1)$ curves that correspond to elliptic and hyperbolic flow are indicated on the figures. Now in f-shocks, the relation $V_1^f < b_1$ is always satisfied when the fields are aligned (cf. Eq (41)). Thus, in view of Eqs. (46) and (48b) the flow will be hyperbolic-fast or elliptic behind f-shocks according to whether it is super or subsonic behind. We saw earlier that two shocks were possible for a given A_o. Calculations reveal that as a rule, the smaller-angle shock is hyperbolic behind and the larger one is elliptic behind. This is precisely the situation in gas dynamics.

Behind s-shocks, the relation $V_1^s < b_1$ is always satisfied when the fields are aligned (c. f. ,Eq. (32)). Thus according to Eq. (47), the flow behind s-shocks is hyperbolic-slow if it is subsonic and satisfies the relation

$$V_1^s > \frac{a_1 b_1}{\sqrt{a_1^2 + b_1^2}} = b_1 \sqrt{\frac{s_1}{1 + s_1}} .$$

*The functions $A_1 = A_1(\omega;\theta,\ s_o,\ \gamma)$ and $s_1 = s_1(\omega;\theta,\ s_o,\ \gamma)$ are found with the aid of Eqs(9).

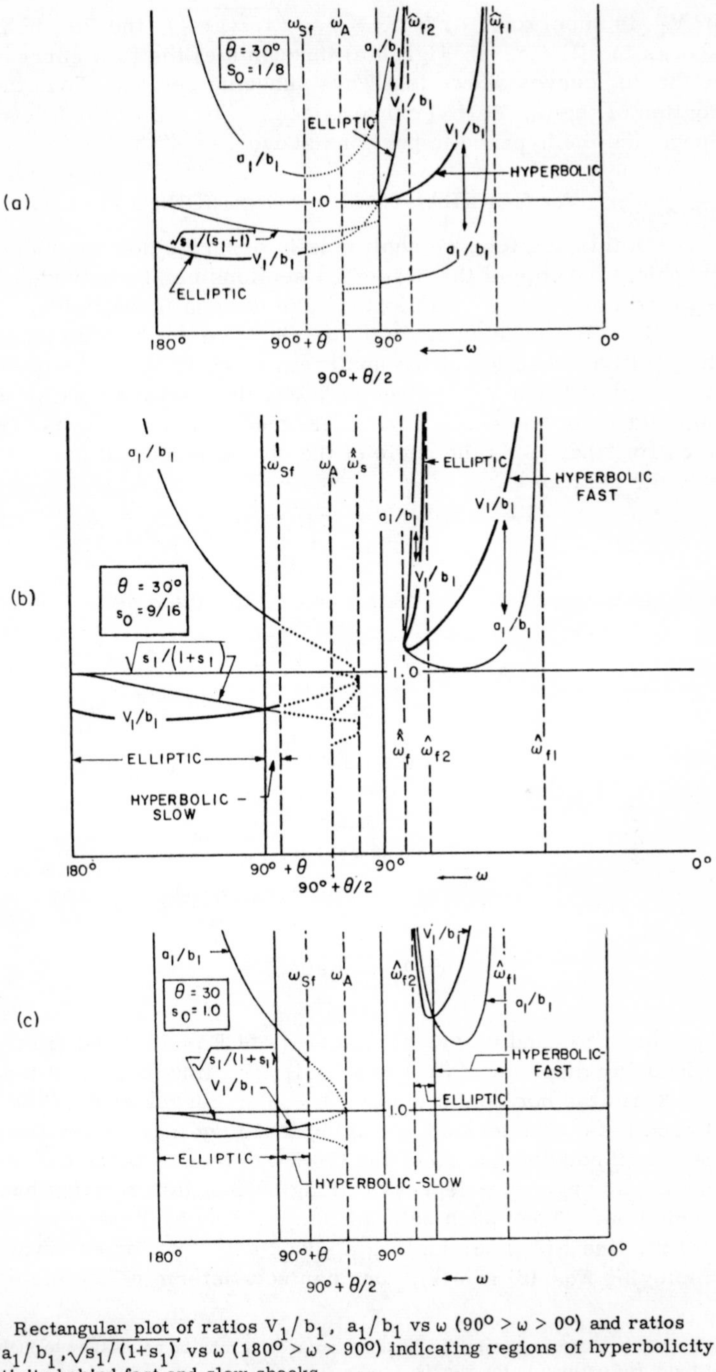

Figure 8 Rectangular plot of ratios V_1/b_1, a_1/b_1 vs ω ($90^\circ > \omega > 0^\circ$) and ratios V_1/b_1, a_1/b_1, $\sqrt{s_1/(1+s_1)}$ vs ω ($180^\circ > \omega > 90^\circ$) indicating regions of hyperbolicity and ellipticity behind fast and slow shocks

If V_1^s is supersonic or if $V_1^s < b_1 \sqrt{s_1/(1+s_1)}$, the flow behind s-shocks is elliptic. In Figs. 8(a) through 8(c) the flow corresponding to the 30° curves shown is always subsonic behind. Thus the elliptic portion of the $(\omega, V_1/b_1)$ curve is seen to be below the $(\omega, \sqrt{s_1/(1+s_1)})$ curve and the hyperbolic portions above.

V. GENERAL CASE - NONALIGNED FIELDS

In this section, we shall briefly describe how the numerical and graphical scheme of the preceding sections can be extended to deal with the much more complicated case of nonaligned fields.

Let $\underline{H}_o$ make an angle of α, $-90^o < \alpha < 90^o$, with respect to the positive direction of the upstream velocity $\underline{V}_o$. As previously, it is assumed that $\underline{V}_o$ is directed along the positive x axis. In addition, let, $\bar{\omega}$ be the shock angle measured counterclockwise from $\underline{V}_o$. Recalling that ω is the angle of the shock measured from $\underline{H}_o$, we note the relation

$$\omega = \bar{\omega} - \alpha . \tag{62}$$

Now, in terms of $\bar{\omega}$, Eq. (9d) may be expressed as

$$A_o \sin \bar{\omega} = \frac{1}{q\left[\bar{\omega}-\alpha;\ \theta,\ s_o,\ \gamma\right]} , \tag{63}$$

where $q\left[\omega;\ \theta,\ s_o,\ \gamma\right]$ is the function of ω, θ, s_o and γ defined in Eq. (56). Putting

$$\bar{q} = q\left[\bar{\omega}-\alpha;\ \theta,\ s_o,\ \gamma\right] , \tag{64}$$

we may rewrite Eq. (63) as

$$\bar{\ell}\,(A_o):\ \bar{q} \sin \bar{\omega} = \frac{1}{A_o} . \tag{65}$$

Equations (64) and (65) are the analogs of Eqs. (55) and (56). In the $(\bar{q}, \bar{\omega})$ polar diagram, $\bar{\ell}\,(A_o)$ is a horizontal line located at a distance A_o^{-1} from the horizontal axis. The polar curves of Eq. (64) (see Fig. 7) are best characterized by saying that they may be obtained from the corresponding polars of Eq. (56)* by rotating these curves rigidly through an angle of α degrees. Imagine that this rotation has been carried out. Then each point of intersection at these rotated curves with the line $\bar{\ell}\,(A_o)$ determines a shock angle ω for each value of θ. Employing Eqs. (6) and (9), one can now determine the state behind

*In problems, in addition to these polars, it may be necessary to include parts of their reflections in the x-axis.

the shock corresponding to this ω. It must be stressed, however, that while it is natural to prescribe s_0, γ and α, the situation may be otherwise with the parameter θ. There are of course, cases where θ is the natural parameter to prescribe, but frequently it is θ_V, the angle between $\underline{V}_0$ and $\underline{V}_1$, that one wishes to prescribe.

To complete the solution of the problem when not θ, but θ_V is prescribed, it becomes necessary to supplement Eq. (63), which relates A_0 to θ, $\bar{\omega}-\alpha$, α, s_0 and γ, by a similar equation for θ_V. Without going into details, we may mention that it is relatively easy to isolate θ_V and express it in the form

$$\theta_V = \Theta_V\left[\theta,\ \bar{\omega}-\alpha;\ \alpha,\ s_0,\ \gamma\right]. \tag{66}$$

Such a relation may be derived, for example, by first eliminating V_1 between the equation $\underline{V}_0 \times \underline{H}_0 = \underline{V}_1 \times \underline{H}_1$ and Eq. (9e), and then eliminating A_0 from the resulting expression by means of Eq. (63).

Equation (66) and Eq. (63), which may be cast into the form

$$A_0 = f(\bar{\omega}-\alpha;\ \theta,\ s_0,\ \gamma), \tag{67}$$

furnish two equations for A_0 and θ_V in terms of $\omega-\alpha$, and θ; the parameters α, θ, s_0, and γ are here assumed fixed. To obtain the numerical values of $\bar{\omega}-\alpha$ and θ associated with given values of A_0 and θ_V, iterative graphical procedures must be resorted to. One such procedure is the following: Make rectangular plots of A_0 and θ_V against $\bar{\omega}-\alpha$ for several values of θ and obtain two families of curves, each indexed by θ. Given A_0 and θ_V, determine (in general by trial and error) the value of $\bar{\omega}-\alpha$ with the property that $(\bar{\omega}-\alpha, A_0)$ and $(\bar{\omega}-\alpha, \theta_V)$ fall on curves indexed by the same value of θ. This procedure is a natural extension of that employed earlier. It shows that it is possible to make use of the analytical results of the aligned fields case to obtain analogous results for the present case.

REFERENCES

1. F. De Hoffmann and E. Teller, *Phys. Rev.*, Vol. 80, p. 692 (1950).
2. R. Lüst, *Z. Naturforsch*, Vol. 8a, p. 277, (1953).
3. R. Lüst, *Z. Naturforsch*, Vol. 10a, p. 125 (1955).
4. W. B. Ericson and J. Bazer, *Hydromagnetic Shocks*, Report No. MH-8, New York University, Institute of Mathematical Sciences, Division of Electromagnetic Research, (1958).
5. J. Bazer and W. B. Ericson, *Astrophys. J.*, Vol. 129, p. 758 (1959).
6. W.B. Ericson and J. Bazer *Phys. Fluids*, Vol.3, p.631 (1960).
7. H. Cabannes, *Revs. Modern Phys.*, Vol. 32, p. 973 (1960).

8. M. I. Kiselev and N. I. Kolosnitzyn, *Doklady Akademii Nauk SSSR*, Vol. 131, p. 773 (1960).

9. H. L. Helfer, *Astrophys. J.*, Vol. 117, p. 177 (1953).

10. K. O. Friedrichs, *Nonlinear Wave Motion in Magnetohydro-dynamics*, LAMS 2105 (Physics) (1957). [See also a later version of this report by K. O. Friedrichs and H. Kranzer, *Nonlinear Wave Motion*, Report No. MH8 (Sherwood Group), Institute of Mathematical Sciences, New York University, (1958).]

11. J. E. McCune and E. L. Resler, Jr., *J. Aero/Space Sciences*, Vol. 27, p. 493 (1960).

12. M. N. Kogan, *Prikladnaia matematika i mechanika*, Vol. 23, p. 70 (1959).

13. S. I. Syrovatskii, *Soviet Phys., JETP*, Vol. 35, p. 1024 (1959).

14. A. I. Akhiezer, G. Ia. Lizubarskii and R. V. Polovin, *Soviet Phys. JETP*, Vol. 35, p. 507 (1959).

15. P. Germain, *Revs. Mod. Phys.*, Vol. 32, p. 951 (1960).

16. R.V. Polovin, *Soviet Physics, Uspelehi* Vol.3 p.677, 1961

17. J. Taniuti, *Progr. Theoret. Phys.*, Vol. 19, p. 749 (1958).

18. W. R. Sears, *Revs. Modern Phys.*, Vol. 32, p. 701 (1960).

19. J. Bazer, "Reflection and Refraction of Weak Hydromagnetic Discontinuities," Research Report No. MH-11. Division of Electromagnetic Research, Institute of Mathematical Sciences, New York University (1961).

ELECTROMAGNETIC DIFFUSION INTO A CYLINDRICAL PLASMA COLUMN

Joseph L. Neuringer, Lester Kraus, and Herbert Malamud
Plasma Propulsion Laboratory, Republic Aviation Corporation
Farmingdale, New York

The diffusion of electromagnetic energy into a cylindrical plasma column due to the discharge of the energy stored in a capacitor is formulated, taking into a account the effects of the capacitance and inductance of the discharge circuit. The discharge circuit reflects the linear pinch geometry in that the energy source is a charged condenser and the return lead is a perfectly conducting cylindrical shell concentric with and surrounding the plasma column. The plasma properties enter the formulation through an extended Ohm's law which includes the time rate of change of current density. Under the assumption that changes in the ionization density and collision frequency may be neglected, Maxwell's equations lead to a third-order linear partial differential equation for the diffusion current. An exact solution is obtained by Laplace transform techniques, using appropriate initial and boundary conditions which take into account the finite external circuitry. The spatial and temporal behavior of the current density distribution as functions of the parameters that characterize both the circuit and the plasma are discussed and compared with that of an ordinary conductor obeying the simple Ohm's law.

INTRODUCTION

Increasing the effectiveness and efficiency of many devices whose basic operational mechanism depends on the pinch effect requires a clear understanding of the various phases of the discharge taking place before the onset of the phase characterized by magnetically driven gross plasma motions. To illustrate, it is well known that unless conditions are correctly chosen, an electric discharge will not always give rise to the current sheath so essential to the entire mechanism of plasma acceleration, but may produce a glow discharge or some other diffuse current path between the electrodes. Therefore, to utilize the discharge as a plasma-accelerating mechanism, it is essential that one have some knowledge of the physics of current sheath formation and the minimal requirements necessary for its production. This is particularly true for marginal or weak-pinch devices whose initial capacitor energy is limited, e. g. , the low-thrust, high-specific-impulse pinch plasma engine for space propulsion. [1]

The sequence of phases that take place in the time between the closing of the switch and the time when gross plasma motion actually

---

Presented at the Symposium on Electromagnetics and Fluid Dynamics of Gaseous Plasma, Polytechnic Institute of Brooklyn, April 4, 5, 6, 1961

begins is called the pinch initiation process. During this time the following phases may be distinguished:

1) An electrostatic field is built up across the electrodes in a few milli-microseconds or less.

2) The electrons in the discharge tube corresponding to the initial electron density are accelerated by the electrostatic field up to the point when the average electron kinetic energy equals the ionization energy. This phase is characterized by the beginning of a current sheath of small current density with very little increase in electron density and collision frequency.

3) When the average electron energy exceeds the atom ionization energy, the rate of rise of the current in the sheath increases tremendously due to the sudden increase of the ionization rate. Also, because of the increase of energy dissipation in the sheath as compared with that further toward the core, the sheath temperature and pressure rise rapidly during this phase.

4) With increase of pressure in the sheath, compression signals propagate inward at the local sound speed. With increasing temperature, succeeding pressure waves travel at higher and higher speeds, catching up with the preceding waves. These waves thus coalesce into a hydrodynamic shock.

5) The shock is then driven by the magnetic piston.

It should be emphasized that this separation into discrete temporal phases is only for the purpose of aiding the understanding of a very complex process. Obviously the phases overlap, and some take place continuously throughout the initiation process.

A theoretical treatment encompassing all five phases in a single formulation is exceedingly difficult, if not impossible. Each phase must be analyzed independently with the initial and boundary conditions judiciously chosen so that they match the asymptotic temporal and spatial behavior of the previous phase. Phase (5) is a case in point. This phase has been treated exhaustively using various gas dynamical models,[2] all of which, in the last analysis, reduce to the concept of a magnetic piston driving a hydromagnetic shock formed near the skin during the later stages of phase (4). The other phases, however, have received very little treatment. Wyld and Watson[3] treated a part of phase (3), i. e., the variations of ionization, resistivity, and thermodynamic state with time of a plasma carrying a uniform current. Killeen, Gibson, and Colgate,[4] extending the analysis of Reference 3 to include the spatial behavior of current density, and treating phases (2) and (3) as one, investigated the build-up of the current sheath for thermonuclear pinch processes. Their analysis was necessarily a numerical one, since the differential equations describing the processes of current sheath build-up, ionization, and heating taking place in phase (3) are highly nonlinear and coupled. The nonlinearity and coupling arise because the ionization, temperature, and therefore conductivity, depend on the current distribution penetrating the plasma, and this in turn depends on the value of the conductivity.

Examination of Fig. 5 of Reference 4, which is representative of the results obtained, shows that up to the time that the electron energy reaches the ionization energy: a) the fractional degree of ionization remains constant; b) the resistivity decreases only by a factor of two or three; c) the rate of current density rise is exceedingly large. At least during the formative stages of the pinch initiation process, i. e., phase (2), these results indicate, first, that the inertia term must be included in Ohm's law, since it is of the same order of magnitude as the accelerating force $\vec{E}$ or the frictional force $\eta' \vec{J}$, and, second, that the process of electromagnetic diffusion into the plasma is fairly linear, since the transport properties of the plasma, of which the resistivity is representative, change very little in time.

Once linearity of the electromagnetic diffusion process is accepted, the distribution of current density, for example, inside the plasma is amenable to exact analytical treatment. In this paper, we shall assume that such is the case and consider an analysis of the current density distribution developed in a plasma during an early stage of pinch initiation, i. e., phase (2). The analysis will include and will be based on the following special features:

1) Inclusion of the electron inertia term in Ohm's law.

2) A plasma in the form of a cylindrical column of finite radius with a finite current return in the form of a perfectly conducting shell concentric with and surrounding the plasma column.

3) A voltage source whose instantaneous value is intimately related to the time integral of the total current passed through the plasma, e. g., an initially charged capacitor.

Features (2) and (3) are deliberately chosen in order to conform closely to the plasma shape, external circuitry, and energy source used in linear pinch experiments.

In summary, our aim will be to obtain the spatial and temporal behavior of the current density distribution as functions of the parameters that characterize both the plasma and the circuit, and compare this behavior with that of an ordinary conductor obeying the usual Ohm's law.

II. FORMULATION OF THE PROBLEM

A. Derivation of the Diffusion Equation

Consider a cylindrical plasma conductor of radius a and height ℓ. An infinitely conducting return cylindrical shell of radius b, concentric with and surrounding the plasma conductor, is connected to it by perfectly conducting circular flanges at the base and at the top. To complete the series circuit, a capacitor of capacitance C and initial charge q_0 is symmetrically connected through a switch to the inner and outer cylinders. The problem is to find the spatial and temporal distribution of the current density in the inner plasma cylinder when the switch is closed. A schematic diagram is shown in Fig. 1.

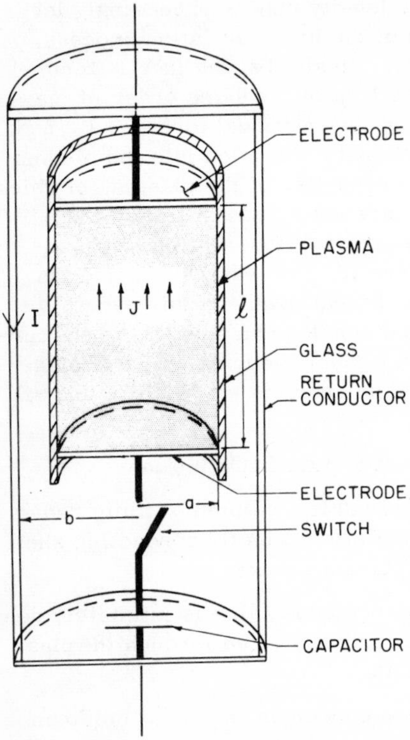

Fig. 1 Schematic of cylindrical pinch geometry: diffusion stage

The field equations, neglecting the displacement current, are

$$\nabla \times \vec{E} = -\mu \partial \vec{H}/\partial t \tag{1}$$

$$\nabla \times \vec{H} = \vec{J}, \tag{2}$$

where $\vec{E}$ is the electric intensity, $\vec{H}$ the magnetic intensity, $\vec{J}$ the current density and μ the permeability. Ohm's law, modified to include the electron inertia term, is

$$\vec{E} = \delta \partial \vec{J}/\partial t + \eta' \vec{J}, \tag{3}$$

where η' is the resistivity, assumed constant during the diffusion, and it is also assumed that δ, defined as the "inertia" constant, does not vary. As can be seen from Eq. (3), δ has the dimensions of ohms-length-time and varies inversely with the electron density. In the case of a fully ionized gas, δ and η' are simply related, i. e., $\eta'/\delta = \nu$ where ν is the collision frequency between electrons and ions.[5] Because we are concerned here only with an early stage of the diffusion process, when the magnetic field and the changes of the gas dynamical state of the plasma are small, all other terms in the full Ohm's law, i. e., Hall current term, electron pressure gradient term, etc., are neglected. We consider only the axi-symmetric diffusion of the longitudinal component of the current density and assume no variation in the axial direction. Symbolically, let us call this component J(r, t).

Taking the curl of (1) and the partial derivative of (2) with time, eliminating $\vec{H}$ from (1) using (2), and then eliminating $\vec{E}$ using (3), we obtain, in cylindrical coordinates, the following third-order partial differential equation for the longitudinal component of the diffusion current.

$$\left[\frac{\partial^2}{\partial r^2} + \frac{1}{r}\frac{\partial}{\partial_r}\right]\left[\delta\frac{\partial J}{\partial t} + \eta' J\right] = \mu\frac{\partial J}{\partial t} . \tag{4}$$

B. Initial and Boundary Conditions

The relationship between the instantaneous charge on the capacitor and the current density flowing in the plasma cylinder is

$$\frac{dq}{dt} = -2\pi\int_0^a \xi J(\xi, t)\, d\xi = -I ,$$

where I is the total current flowing in the circuit. Integrating, using the initial value of the charge, we obtain

$$q(t) = q(0) - 2\pi\int_0^t d\tau\int_0^a \xi J(\xi, \tau) d\xi . \tag{5}$$

For the initial condition, we take

$$J(r, 0) = 0 . \tag{6}$$

The boundary condition at $r = 0$ requires,

$$J(0, t) \text{ finite and continuous.} \tag{7}$$

The boundary condition at the plasma surface, $r = a$, requires some consideration. Subdivide the cylindrical plasma conductor into n concentric shells. Using lumped circuit theory, one can consider the original continuum as being replaced by n conducting shells connected in parallel to a common capacitor. Consider, in particular, the closed surface circuit, i. e. , the circuit consisting of the cylindrical shell of current flowing at $r = a$ through the return at $r = b$ and back to the capacitor. Using Kirchoff's law, we have

$$\frac{q}{C} = \ell\sum_{k=1}^{n} L_{1k}\frac{dI_k}{dt} + \ell\eta' J(a, t) + \ell\delta\left(\frac{\partial J}{\partial t}\right)_{r=a} \tag{8}$$

The term on the left represents the instantaneous capacitor voltage. The summation on the right represents the total voltage drop due to the self-inductance of, and the mutual inductance of all the current-carrying inner shells with, the surface shell (L_{11} is defined as the self-inductance per unit length of the surface shell). The next term is the ohmic drop, and the last term represents the inertial drop. From the definition of self and mutual inductance, and from the cylindrical circuit geometry, we have

$$L_{11} = L_{12} = \cdots = L_{1n} = L = \frac{\mu}{2\pi} \ln\left(\frac{b}{a}\right)$$

Also, since $I_k = 2\pi r_k J(r_k, t) \Delta r$,

$$\lim_{n\to\infty} \ell \sum_{k=1}^{n} L_{1k} \frac{dI_k}{dt} = 2\pi \ell L \frac{d}{dt} \int_0^a \xi J(\xi, t) d\xi \; .$$

By substituting for q from (5), the boundary condition (8) finally becomes

$$\frac{q_o}{\ell C} = \frac{2\pi}{\ell C} \int_0^t d\tau \int_0^a \xi J(\xi, \tau) d\xi + 2\pi L \frac{d}{dt} \int_0^a \xi J(\xi, t) d\xi$$
$$+ \eta' J(a, t) + \delta \left(\frac{\partial J}{\partial t}\right)_{r = a} . \qquad (9)$$

We now require a solution of (4) subject to the conditions (6), (7), and (9).

III. EXACT, ASYMPTOTIC, AND SPECIAL SOLUTIONS

A. Exact Solution

Using the Laplace transform defined as

$$\mathfrak{J}(r, s) = \int_0^\infty e^{-st} J(r, t) \, dt \quad ,$$

and using the initial condition (6), Eq. (4) becomes

$$\frac{d^2\tilde{J}}{dr^2} + \frac{1}{r}\frac{d\tilde{J}}{dr} - \frac{\mu s}{\delta s + \eta'}\tilde{J} = 0 .$$

A solution of the above, satisfying the finiteness condition at $r = 0$, is

$$\tilde{J}(r, s) = \beta(s)\, I_0\left[r\sqrt{\frac{\mu s}{\delta s + \eta'}}\right], \tag{10}$$

where I_0 is the modified Bessel function of order zero, and $\beta(s)$ is a function of s to be determined from the boundary condition at $r = a$. Again using the initial condition (6), the transformed boundary condition at $r = a$ is

$$\frac{q_0}{\ell Cs} = \frac{2\pi}{\ell Cs}\int_0^a \xi\tilde{J}(\xi, s)d\xi + 2\pi Ls\int_0^a \xi\tilde{J}(\xi, s)d\xi + \eta'\tilde{J}(a, s) + \delta s\tilde{J}(a, s) \tag{11}$$

Substituting (10) into (11), using the identity,[6]

$$\int_0^a \xi I_0\left[\xi\sqrt{\frac{\mu s}{\delta s + \eta'}}\right]d\xi = a\sqrt{\frac{\delta s + \eta'}{\mu s}}\; I_1\left[a\sqrt{\frac{\mu s}{\delta s + \eta'}}\right],$$

and solving for $\beta(s)$, we obtain

$$\beta(s) = \frac{q_0}{2\pi a\ell CL\sqrt{\eta}} \times$$

$$\frac{\sqrt{s}}{\sqrt{\frac{\delta s}{\eta'} + 1}\left[(s^2 + A)I_1\left[a\sqrt{\frac{\mu s}{\delta s + \eta'}}\right] + Bs^{3/2}\sqrt{\frac{\delta s}{\eta'} + 1}\; I_0\left[a\sqrt{\frac{\mu s}{\delta s + \eta'}}\right]\right]}$$

where I_1 is the modified Bessel function of order one and $A = (\ell CL)^{-1}$, $B = \mu\sqrt{\eta}\,/(2\pi aL)$, and $\eta = \eta'/\mu$. Substituting for $\beta(s)$ in Eq. (10), we find that the solution of the transformed problem becomes

$$\tilde{J}(r, s) = \frac{q_o}{2\pi a \ell CL\sqrt{\eta}} \times$$

$$\frac{I_o\left[r\sqrt{\frac{\mu s}{\delta s + \eta'}}\right]}{\sqrt{\frac{\delta s + \eta'}{\eta' s}}\left\{(s^2 + A) I_1\left[a\sqrt{\frac{\mu s}{\delta s + \eta'}}\right] + Bs^{3/2}\sqrt{\frac{\delta s + \eta'}{\eta'}}\, I_o\left[a\sqrt{\frac{\mu s}{\delta s+\eta'}}\right]\right\}} \tag{12}$$

Using the inversion integral, the formal solution of (12) is given by

$$J(r, t) = \frac{1}{2\pi i} \int_{Br.} \tilde{J}(r, s) e^{st} ds \tag{13}$$

where the Bromwich path, Br., in the complex s-plane is the imaginary axis if all the singularities of the integrand lie to its left. It is difficult to work directly with the variable s in order to determine the exact nature of the singularities involved in (12), because square roots of s are involved in a most complicated manner. Therefore, we introduce a new integration variable, γ, defined by

$$\gamma^2 = a^2 \mu s/\delta s + \eta'. \tag{14}$$

Thus,

$$s = \frac{\eta'}{a^2\mu}(\gamma^2/1 - G\gamma^2) \text{ where } G = \delta/a^2\mu.$$

By substituting (12) into (13) and using (14), Eq. (13) becomes, in terms of the new integration variable,

$$J(r, t) = \frac{q_o}{\pi \ell CL\eta} \frac{1}{2\pi i} \int_{Br.'} \left[\frac{\gamma^2 I_o(\frac{r}{a}\gamma) \exp\left[\frac{\eta}{a^2}\left[\frac{\gamma^2}{1 - G\gamma^2}\right] t\right]}{\left[\gamma^4 + E\left\{1 - G\gamma^2\right\}^2\right] I_1(\gamma) + F\gamma^3 I_o(\gamma)}\right] d\gamma \tag{15}$$

where $E = a^4/\ell CL\eta^2$, $F = \mu/2\pi L$, and Br.' is the transformed Bromwich path. The integrand is now recognized as meromorphic and therefore contributes to the integral only through its poles, i. e., zeros of the denominator.

We proceed to examine the nature of the Bromwich path, Br.', and the region or regions in the γ-plane containing the zeros of the denominator. The s-plane Bromwich path is $s = is_2$, where $-\infty < s_2 < \infty$ (for simplicity we take $s_1 = 0$). Let $\gamma = \gamma_1 + i\gamma_2 = \rho e^{i\theta}$. Substituting this into the transformation (14) and equating real and imaginary parts yields

$$\gamma_1^2 - \gamma_2^2 = \rho^2 \cos 2\theta = \frac{a^2 \mu \delta s_2^2}{\eta'^2 + \delta^2 s_2^2} \tag{16}$$

and

$$2\gamma_1\gamma_2 = \rho^2 \sin 2\theta = \frac{a^2 \mu \eta' s_2}{\eta'^2 + \delta^2 s_2^2} . \tag{17}$$

Eliminating the parameter s_2, we obtain in polar form,

$$\rho^2 = \frac{a^2 \mu}{\delta} \cos 2\theta = \frac{1}{G} \cos 2\theta , \tag{18}$$

a two-cusped lemniscate. Because the transformation (14) is quadratic, the entire s-plane maps into the right half γ-plane so that the right cusp alone constitutes the entire mapping of Br. into Br.', (see Fig. 2). We determine the direction in which the lemniscate is transversed by examining the set (16) and (17) in its rectangular representation. We proceed along the s-plane Bromwich from $is_2 = -i\infty$ to $is_2 = +i\infty$, where $s_2 = -\infty$ corresponds to point 2 on the lemniscate and s_2 negative corresponds to $\gamma_1\gamma_2$ negative. This means that γ_1 and γ_2 have opposite signs, so that the radius vector generating the lemniscate moves from point 2 to 3 to the origin. At the origin, $s = 0$. When s_2 becomes positive, γ_1 and γ_2 have the same sign and the radius vector moves from the origin to 1 and back again to 2. The lemniscate is traversed in the clockwise direction, so that the region inside the cusp corresponds to the entire right half-plane of s. The shaded left half-plane of s, where all the contributing s-plane zeros lie, corresponds to the shaded region in γ, where all the γ contributing zeros lie. In the case of a conductor obeying the simple Ohm's law, i. e., $\delta = 0$ or $G = 0$, the lemniscate grows into a wedge bounded by the straight lines $\theta = \pm\, \pi/4$. The contributing zeros in this case lie in the regions $\pi/2 \geqslant \theta \geqslant \pi/4$ and $-\pi/2 \leqslant \theta \leqslant -\pi/4$. Except for the region bounded by the lemniscate, the contributing zeros γ_n cover the entire right half γ-plane. However, because of the particular transformation (14), the corresponding zeros in the s-plane are bounded and lie in the circle of radius η'/δ centered at $-\eta'/\delta$.

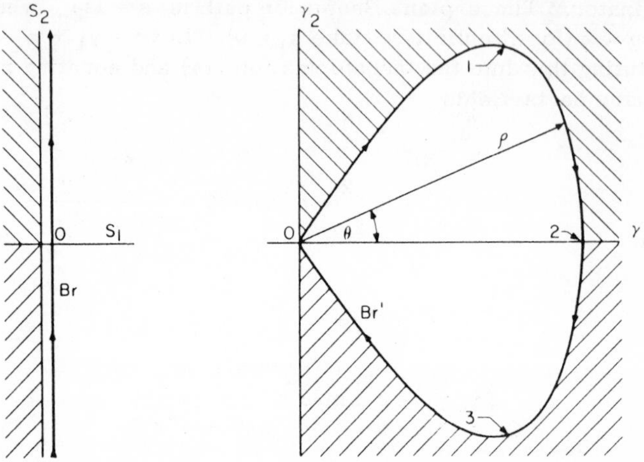

Fig. 2 Transformation from s-plane to γ-plane

Having once determined that the zeros of the denominator of the integrand of Eq. (15) are poles, the integral can be evaluated using the theory of residues. As aids in evaluating Eq. (15), the following facts are established:

1) If the denominator has complex roots, they occur in conjugate pairs. Proof: Let the denominator be denoted by the function $\phi(\gamma)$ and let $\gamma_n = \gamma_{1n} + i\gamma_{2n}$ be one of its complex roots with $\overline{\gamma}_n = \gamma_{1n} - i\gamma_{2n}$ its conjugate. Then

$$\phi(\gamma_n) = \phi_1(\gamma_{1n}, \gamma_{2n}) + i\phi_2(\gamma_{1n}, \gamma_{2n}) = 0,$$

or

$$\phi_1(\gamma_{1n}, \gamma_{2n}) = \phi_2(\gamma_{1n}, \gamma_{2n}) = 0 .$$

Since $\phi(\gamma)$ is a power series in γ with real coefficients,

$$\phi(\overline{\gamma}_n) = \phi_1(\gamma_{1n}, \gamma_{2n}) - i\phi_2(\gamma_{1n}, \gamma_{2n}).$$

But $\phi_1(\gamma_{1n}, \gamma_{2n}) = \phi_2(\gamma_{1n}, \gamma_{2n}) = 0$. Hence $\phi(\overline{\gamma}_n) = 0$ is also a root. Since, as we shall prove in the next section, $\phi(\gamma)$ has only one real root (i. e., $\gamma = 0$, which is non-contributing unless $E = 0$), we can multiply Eq. (15) by two and replace the contribution of every complex pair by the real part of one of them.

2) The above multiplication by two is cancelled out by virtue of the transformation from the s- to the γ-plane, i. e., because of the quadratic transformation, the argument in s is twice that in γ, so that in evaluating the contribution of a simple pole in the γ-plane we go around half the circle about the pole. Now,

$$\phi(\gamma) = (\gamma^4 + E\{1 - G\gamma^2\}^2)I_1(\gamma) + F\gamma^3 I_0(\gamma)$$

so that

$$\frac{d\phi}{d\gamma} = \left\{ 4\gamma^3 - 4GE\gamma(1 - G\gamma^2)\right\} I_1(\gamma)$$

$$+ \left\{\gamma^4 + E(1 - G\gamma^2)^2 \right\} I'_1(\gamma) + 3F\gamma^2 I_0(\gamma) + F\gamma^3 I'_0(\gamma),$$

where primes denote differentiation with respect to γ.

Using $\phi(\gamma) = 0$ in conjunction with the identities $I'_0(\gamma) = I_1(\gamma)$ and $\gamma I'_1(\gamma) = \gamma I_0(\gamma) - I_1(\gamma)$, we can rewrite $d\phi/d\gamma$ in terms of only one modified Bessel function, i. e., Eq. (19). Evaluating the residues, using the above expression for $d\phi/d\gamma$, the exact solution finally has the form of Eq. (20), where γ_n are the roots of

$$\phi(\gamma) = \left[\gamma^4 + E\left\{1 - G\gamma^2\right\}^2\right] I_1(\gamma) + F\gamma^3 I_0 = 0 \qquad (21)$$

located in the shaded region of the upper right quarter of the γ-plane.

B. Asymptotic Small Time Solutions

The exact solution given by Eq. (20) is essentially a long-time solution, i. e., the larger the time, the fewer the number of terms required in the sum. We now obtain asymptotic solutions valid for small time. Since small t implies large s, small-time solutions can be obtained to any desired degree of approximation by inverting the solution of the transformed problem (12) after suitable modification when s is made large. When $s \to \infty$, the arguments of the modified Bessel functions in the denominator reduce to the constant $a\sqrt{\mu/\delta}$, and A is negligible compared to s^2. The numerator $I_0\left[r\sqrt{\mu s/\delta s + \eta'}\right]$ can be expanded in a series, and for small enough time, be expressed adequately by the first two terms. Thus,

$$\frac{d\phi}{d\gamma} = \frac{\left\{\left[1 + G^2\left\{2E + E^2\right\}\right]\gamma^8 - \left[F^2 + G\left\{FE + E^2\right\}\right]\gamma^6 + \left[2E - 4GEF + 6E^2G^2\right]\gamma^4 + \left[4EF - 4GE^2\right]\gamma^2 + E^2\right\} I_o(\gamma)}{\gamma^4 + E(1 - G\gamma^2)^2} \tag{19}$$

$$J(r, t) = \mathrm{Re}\,\frac{q_o}{\pi \ell C L \eta} \sum_{n=1}^{\infty} \left[\frac{\gamma^2\left[\gamma^4 + E\left\{1 - G\gamma^2\right\}^2\right] I_o\left(\frac{r}{a}\gamma\right) \exp\left[\frac{\eta}{a^2}\left[\frac{\gamma^2}{1 - G\gamma^2}\right] t\right]}{\left\{\left[1 + G^2\left\{2E + E^2\right\}\right]\gamma^8 - \left[F^2 + G\left\{FE + E^2\right\}\right]\gamma^6 + \left[2E - 4GEF + 6E^2G^2\right]\gamma^4 + \left[4EF - 4GE^2\right]\gamma^2 + E^2\right\} I_o(\gamma)} \right]_{\gamma = \gamma_n} \tag{20}$$

$$I_0\left[r\left\{\frac{\mu}{\delta}\,\frac{1}{1+\eta'/\delta s}\right\}^{1/2}\right] \simeq I_0\left[r\sqrt{\frac{\mu}{\delta}}\left\{1-\frac{\eta'}{2\delta s}\right\}\right]$$

$$\simeq I_0\left[r\sqrt{\frac{\mu}{\delta}}\right] - \frac{1}{s}\left[\frac{r^2\eta'^2\mu}{4\delta^3}\right]^{1/2} I_1\left[r\sqrt{\frac{\mu}{\delta}}\right]$$

and Eq. (12) reduces to

$$\tilde{J}(r,s) \simeq \frac{q_0}{2\pi a\ell CL}\sqrt{\frac{\mu}{\delta}}\;\frac{1}{\left[I_1\left[a\sqrt{\frac{\mu}{\delta}}\right]+\frac{\sqrt{\delta\mu}}{2\pi aL}\,I_0\left[a\sqrt{\frac{\mu}{\delta}}\right]\right]}\times$$

$$\left\{\frac{I_0\left[r\sqrt{\frac{\mu'}{\delta}}\right]}{s^2} - \frac{1}{s^3}\left[\frac{r^2\eta'^2\mu}{4\delta^3}\right]^{1/2} I_1\left[r\sqrt{\frac{\mu'}{\delta}}\right]\right\}.$$

Taking the inverse transform, we get, to order t^2,

$$J(r,t) \simeq \frac{q_0}{2\pi a\ell CL}\sqrt{\frac{\mu}{\delta}}\;\frac{\left\{I_0\left[r\sqrt{\frac{\mu'}{\delta}}\right]t - \frac{1}{2}\left[\frac{r^2\eta'^2\mu}{4\delta^3}\right]^{1/2} I_1\left[r\sqrt{\frac{\mu'}{\delta}}\right]t^2\right\}}{I_1\left[a\sqrt{\frac{\mu'}{\delta}}\right]+\frac{\sqrt{\delta\mu}}{2\pi aL}\,I_0\left[a\sqrt{\frac{\mu'}{\delta}}\right]} \tag{22}$$

Equation (22) should be compared with the small-time solution obtained for a conductor obeying the simple Ohm's law. With the inertia term missing, i. e., $\delta = 0$, Eq. (12) takes the following form for large s:

$$\tilde{J}(r,s) \simeq \frac{q_0}{2\pi a\ell CL\sqrt{\eta}}\sqrt{\frac{a}{r}}\;\frac{e^{-(a-r)\sqrt{s/\eta}}}{s^{3/2}},$$

where the modified Bessel functions have been replaced by the first term of their asymptotic expansion for large argument.[7] The inverse transform yields[8]

$$J(r,t) \simeq \frac{q_0}{2\pi a\ell CL\sqrt{\eta}}\sqrt{\frac{a}{r}}\left[2\sqrt{\frac{t}{\pi}}\,e^{-\frac{(a-r)^2}{4\eta t}} - \frac{(a-r)}{\sqrt{\eta}}\,\frac{2}{\sqrt{\pi}}\int_{\frac{(a-r)}{2\sqrt{\eta t}}}^{\infty} e^{-\beta^2}\,d\beta\right].$$

Further, since t is small, we may use the asymptotic formula

$$\int_x^\infty e^{-y^2}\,dy = e^{-x^2}\left[\frac{1}{2x} - \frac{1}{4x^3} + \frac{3}{8x^5}\cdots\right],$$

valid for large x. Insertion of this in the above yields

$$J(r,t) \simeq \frac{q_0}{\pi^{3/2}\, a\ell CL\sqrt{\eta}}\sqrt{\frac{a}{r}}\left[\frac{2\eta t^{3/2}}{(a-r)^2}\, e^{-\frac{(a-r)^2}{4\eta t}}\right] \tag{23}$$

The asymptotic form (23) does not converge for $r \to 0$. This is because $I_0(r\sqrt{s/\eta})$ cannot be replaced by its asymptotic form,

$$\frac{e^{r\sqrt{s/\eta}}}{\left[2\pi r\sqrt{s/\eta}\right]^{1/2}}$$

when $r \to 0$. The small time asymptotic solution near $r = 0$ is obtained instead by first expanding $I_0(r\sqrt{s/\eta})$ about the origin, replacing I_0 and I_1 in the denominator by their asymptotic forms and then taking the inverse transform of the resulting power series in r. To order r^2, we have

$$\tilde{J}(r,s) \simeq \frac{q_0}{2\pi a\ell CL\sqrt{\eta}}\left[\frac{2\pi a}{\eta^{1/2}}\right]^{1/2}\left\{s^{-5/4}\, e^{-a\sqrt{\frac{s}{\eta}}}\left[1 + \frac{1}{4}\frac{r^2}{\eta}\, s\right]\right\},$$

the inverse transform of which is[9]

$$J(r,t) \simeq \frac{q_0}{\pi a^{1/2}\ell CL\,(2\eta)^{3/2}}\, t^{-3/2}\left[\left[\frac{\eta^{1/2}}{a}\right]^{3/4}\int_0^\infty \zeta^{5/2}\, e^{-\zeta^2/4t}\, \times\right.$$

$$\left. J_{3/2}\left[\sqrt{\frac{4a\zeta}{\eta^{1/2}}}\right]d\zeta + \frac{r^2}{4\sqrt{a\eta}}\int_0^\infty \zeta^{3/2}\, e^{-\zeta^2/4t}\, J_1\left[\sqrt{\frac{4a\zeta}{\eta^{1/2}}}\right]d\zeta\right]. \tag{24}$$

Since t is assumed small, we may simplify this formula asymptotically. Changing variables slightly in the above formulae, we recognize them as being Laplace transforms. Therefore, the behavior for small t (i.e., large $1/4t$) is determined by the behavior of the integrals for small ζ. Now,

$$J_{3/2}(x) \sim \frac{x^{3/2}}{2^{3/2}\,\Gamma(5/2)} = \sqrt{\frac{2}{\pi}}\,\frac{x^{3/2}}{3}$$

and $J_1(x) \sim x/2$ for small x, so that we have

$$J(r,t) \simeq \frac{q_o}{\pi a^{1/2} \ell CL(2\eta)^{3/2}}\, t^{-3/2} \left[\frac{4}{3\sqrt{\pi}} \int_o^\infty \zeta^{13/4}\, e^{-\zeta^2/4t}\, d\zeta \right.$$

$$\left. + \frac{r^2}{4\eta^{3/4}} \int_o^\infty \zeta^2\, e^{-\zeta^2/4t}\, d\zeta \right],$$

and these integrals can be evaluated exactly in terms of Γ-functions. The result is

$$J(r,t) \simeq \frac{q_o}{\pi a^{1/2} \ell CL(2\eta)^{3/2}} \left[\frac{3\Gamma(\frac{1}{8})}{2^{3/4}\sqrt{\pi}}\, t^{5/8} + \frac{r^2\sqrt{\pi}}{2\eta^{3/4}} \right]. \qquad (25)$$

Note that these asymptotic formulae are meant to hold over different ranges. In all cases one must be somewhat sophisticated as to where they are valid. The most anomalous behavior appears in the last quoted formula for $J(r,t)$, which does not reduce to zero even when t is set equal to zero. The point is that a formal setting of $t = 0$ is unjustified, since for fixed t, the formula is valid for small r (the smallness evidently dependent on t); thus, $t \to 0$ implies $r \to 0$, and this explains the behavior.

C. Special Solutions

It is seen that the limit $q_o/C \to 1$ as $C \to \infty$, everything else remaining constant, corresponds to the case of a unit dc applied source. In this case, $E \to 0$ and the integrand given by Eq. (15) reduces to

$$\frac{I_o(\frac{r}{a}\gamma)\exp\left[\frac{\eta}{a^2}\left[\frac{\gamma^2}{1-G\gamma^2}\right]t\right]}{\gamma\left\{\gamma I_1(\gamma) + F I_o(\gamma)\right\}},$$

where $\gamma = 0$ is now a contributing pole. The roots of $\gamma I_1(\gamma) + FI_0(\gamma)$ are also poles and will be shown later to be pure imaginary. Again, using residue theory, Eq. (15) becomes

$$j(r, t) = \frac{1}{\pi L \eta \ell} \left[(2F)^{-1} + \sum_{n=1}^{\infty} \left[\frac{I_0(\frac{r}{a}\gamma) \exp\left[\frac{\eta}{a^2} \left[\frac{\gamma^2}{1 - G\gamma^2} \right] t \right]}{(\gamma^2 - F^2) I_0(\gamma)} \right]_{\gamma = \gamma_n} \right] \tag{26}$$

where j represents the unit dc solution and γ_n are the pure imaginary roots of $\gamma I_1(\gamma) + FI_0(\gamma) = 0$, with only one of each pair being counted. The contribution of the pole at the origin is $(2F)^{-1}$ which represents $j(r, t)$ as $t \to \infty$. In fact, $j(r, \infty) = 1/\pi L\eta\ell \cdot 1/2F = 1/\ell\eta'$. The total current $i(\infty) = \int_0^a 2\pi j(r, \infty) r dr = \pi a^2/\ell\eta'$, but $\ell\eta'/\pi a^2 = R$, the total resistance of the cylindrical conductor, and thus $i(\infty)R = 1$, as we should expect.

Since Eq. (26) represents the unit source solution, the solution for any arbitrarily applied voltage $V(t)$, using the convolution integral, becomes

$$J(r, t) = \int_0^t V(\tau)\, j(r, t - \tau)\, d\tau . \tag{27}$$

IV. THE CHARACTERISTIC EQUATION

Let us call the three parameter transcendental equation (21), whose roots are sought, the "characteristic" equation. By rewriting (21), using the Bessel functions of the first kind with real arguments, the nature of its zeros as functions of the positive parameters E, F, and G are easily determined qualitatively. Introducing the variable $\lambda = -i\gamma$ and defining the functions

$$Y(\lambda) = \frac{J_1(\lambda)}{J_0(\lambda)} \quad \text{and} \quad Z(\lambda) = \frac{F\lambda^3}{\lambda^4 + E\{1 + G\lambda^2\}^2},$$

Eq. (21) becomes

$$\frac{J_1(\lambda)}{J_0(\lambda)} = \frac{F\lambda^3}{\lambda^4 + E\{1 + G\lambda^2\}^2} . \tag{28}$$

The roots λn of (28), corresponding to the intersections of the two functions $Y(\lambda)$ and $Z(\lambda)$, are $-i$ times the roots of (21). We now examine qualitatively the nature of the intersections of these functions as E, F, and G vary.

For simplicity, we examine the simple Ohm's law case, i. e., $G = 0$. The $G \neq 0$ cases have the same qualitative features and so require no special consideration. Shown in Fig. 3 are the graphs of $Y(\lambda)$ and $Z(\lambda)$ as functions of positive λ only (since both functions are odd, the negative λ intersections are symmetric to those of positive λ and therefore, require no special treatment). The func-

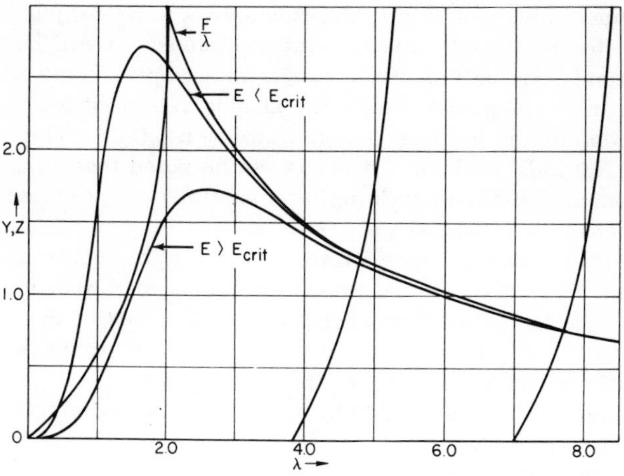

Fig. 3 Graphical description of nature of the roots of the characteristic equation as functions of E and F; G = 0

tion $Y(\lambda)$ essentially behaves like the tangent function, with each branch asymptotically approaching infinity at the corresponding zero of $J_0(\lambda)$ and cutting the axis at the corresponding zero of $J_1(\lambda)$. The function $Z(\lambda)$ starts at zero with zero first and second derivatives, increases to a maximum at $\lambda = (3E)^{1/4}$ with a value of $3^{3/4}F/4E^{1/4}$, and then decreases hyperbolically to zero like F/λ.

For a given F and $E < E_{crit}$ (to be defined later), $Z(\lambda)$ intersects the first branch of $Y(\lambda)$ three times (once at the origin), and every succeeding branch only once. The roots λ_n are therefore all real. (Except for the root at the origin, the roots λ_n are pure-imaginary whose conjugates are generated by the negative λ_n intersections.) These $E < E_{crit}$ cases correspond to the overdamped or aperiodic solutions of (20). For the chosen F, as E increases, all succeeding curves of $Z(\lambda)$ lie inside one another so that no envelope exists. It is also seen from the above formulas for the location and magnitude of the maximum, that as E increases, the magnitude of the maximum decreases while its location moves to the right. Consequently, the intersections that generate the two non-zero first branch roots begin to approach one another until a critical value of E is reached where the two curves become tangent to each other at the coalesced double root. The $E = E_{crit}$ case, whose value in terms of F can be obtained by eliminating γ from the parametric set $\phi(\gamma, E, F) = \phi'(\gamma, E, F) = 0$, corresponds to the critically damped solution of Eq. (20). As E becomes greater than E_{crit}, $Z(\lambda)$ altogether avoids a non-zero first branch intersection with $Y(\lambda)$, so that the double root suddenly generates a complex pair (not conjugate to each other) corresponding to the imaginary intersection of the two curves. Correspondingly, the negative λ intersections also generate a complex pair, which will be later shown to be conjugate to the pair generated by the λ positive intersections. It will be further shown that only one pair of these conjugate complex roots (i. e., that pair which in γ-language lies in the shaded region of the right half γ-plane) contributes to the solution given by Eq. (20) The other pair lies in the left half γ-plane. It is also to be noted that no matter what value E assumes, the remaining intersections of $Z(\lambda)$ with the other branches of $Y(\lambda)$ are all real.

From the above considerations, we state the following theorem. For a given F and G, there exists an E_{crit} such that for all $E \leqslant E_{crit}$, all the roots of Eq. (21), except the root at the origin, are conjugate pure-imaginary. For $E > E_{crit}$, there exist two and only two pairs of conjugate complex roots with non-zero real parts, with the remainder of the roots, except for the root at the origin, remaining conjugate pure-imaginary.

We consider two limiting cases:

1) $E = 0$ and any F and G.

2) $F = 0$ and any E and G.

The case $G = 0$ has already been discussed, and corresponds to neglect of the electron inertia term.

In case (1), $Z(\lambda)$ degenerates into the hyperbola F/λ. The intersections of this curve with $Y(\lambda)$ are all real (see Fig. 3). This proves the conjecture made in the special solution section (III, C) that the roots of the γ-language characteristic equation, corresponding to a dc source, i. e., $E = 0$, are all pure-imaginary. Incidentally, an analytical proof of the above conjecture is given in Section 15.25 of Reference 7.

We approach the situation in case (2) as follows: F acts simply as a multiplier in $Z(\lambda)$, raising or lowering the value of its ordinate as F increases or decreases. Starting originally with an E and F which causes two non-zero real intersections with the first branch of $Y(\lambda)$, then as F continuously goes to zero, the value of $Z(\lambda)$ soon becomes everywhere less than the first branch of $Y(\lambda)$, thus avoiding real intersections. The two real intersections now transform into

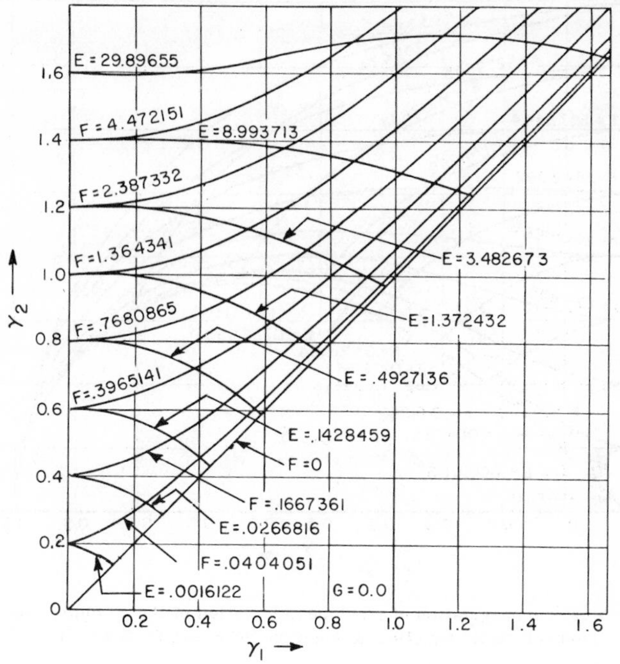

Fig. 4 Graphical representation of machine calculation of the complex roots of the characteristic equation as functions of E and F ; G = 0

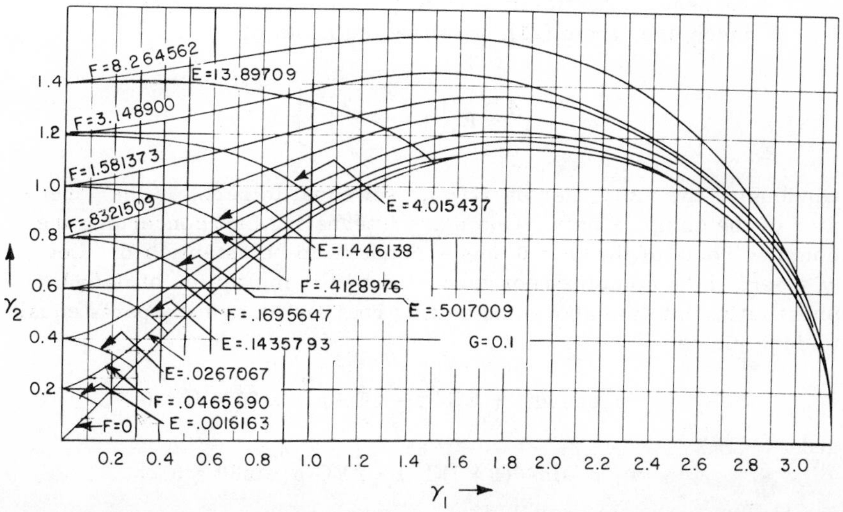

Fig. 5 Graphical representation of machine calculation of the complex roots of the characteristic equation as functions of E and F ; G = 0.1

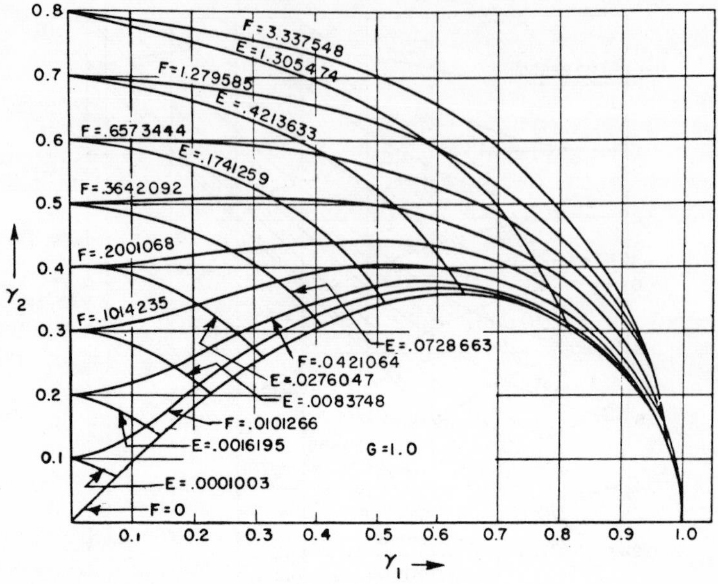

Fig. 6 Graphical representation of machine calculation of the complex roots of the characteristic equation as functions of E and F; G = 1.0

a complex pair depending only on the values of E and G. In the limit, as $F \to 0$, $Z(\lambda) \to 0$, so that besides the two complex roots, the intersection of the horizontal axis with $Y(\lambda)$ yields the remaining roots which are seen to be the roots of $J_1(\lambda)$.

Expressed analytically and in γ-language, the roots of the $F = 0$ cases are, from (21), given by the roots of

$$\left\{ \gamma^4 + E\left[1 - G\gamma^2\right]^2 \right\} I_1(\gamma) .$$

Obviously, the multiplier of $I_1(\gamma)$, set equal to zero, is the generator of the complex pair. One more interesting fact concerning the complex roots of the $F = 0$ cases remains to be established. Let $\gamma = \rho e^{i\theta}$ be a complex root generated by the multiplier of $I_1(\gamma)$. Substituting into the above and setting real and imaginary parts equal to zero yields

$$\rho^4 \cos 4\theta (1 + EG^2) - 2EG\,\rho^2 \cos 2\theta + E = 0$$

and

$$\rho^4 \sin 4\theta (1 + EG^2) - 2\,EG\,\rho^2 \sin 2\theta = 0 .$$

Eliminating the parameter E yields $\rho^2 = 1/G \cos 2\theta$, i. e., the same lemniscate of Section III. Thus, the bounding curve in the

γ-plane which delineates the regions described in Section III is generated by the complex roots of the $F = 0$ cases.

The roots of Eq. (21) were obtained on Republic Aviation Corporation's IBM 7090 computer. We concentrated on obtaining the contributing conjugate complex pair, which, of course, generates the periodic solutions of Eq. (20). Figures 4, 5 and 6 are plots of the real and imaginary parts of only one of these roots, i. e., the root with the positive imaginary part, as continuous functions of E and F for specific values of G. As was pointed out in Section III, the bounding curve for $G \neq 0$ is the lemniscate of Eq. (18) which degenerates into the wedge $\theta = \pm\pi/4$ as $G \rightarrow 0$. All the other conjugate pure-imaginary roots of Eq. (21) correspond to a certain discrete set of points on the imaginary axis.

Certain features concerning the nature of the roots are very aptly described by examining conditions in the complex γ-plane. Consider any G curve. For a given F and $E < E_{crit}$, all the roots are conjugate pure-imaginary lying on the imaginary γ-axis with the particular two pairs corresponding to the four non-zero intersections of $Z(\lambda)$ with the first branch of $Y(\lambda)$ (we include the negative λ intersections) lying closest to the origin. As $E \rightarrow E_{crit}$, the two imaginary roots above the origin merge to form a double pure-imaginary root, as do the pair below the origin. When $E > E_{crit}$, each pair of double imaginary roots split off the axis, with one in each pair falling to the left and one to the right of the imaginary axis. Those that fall to the left of the imaginary axis do not contribute (as was pointed out in Section III). Those that fall to the right are conjugate to each other. The one with the positive imaginary part becomes one of the points depicted in the particular G-figure chosen.

V. DISCUSSION AND CONCLUSIONS

The principal novel feature of the diffusion problem treated above was the inclusion of the inertia term in Ohm's law. Its effect on the solution is manifested through the parameter δ or G. In this section, we shall concentrate on examining the effect of the inertia term on both the overall circuit characteristics and the current density distribution in the plasma.

A critically damped circuit is characterized by the existence of a double root. In the language of Section IV, this requires

$$\phi(E, F, G, \gamma) = \phi'(E, F, G, \gamma) = 0 .$$

By eliminating the parameter γ, a surface in the E, F, G space is generated which may be interpreted as delineating the region or regions where the circuit behavior is periodic or aperiodic. With G acting as parameter, the results of this calculation are shown in Fig. 7.

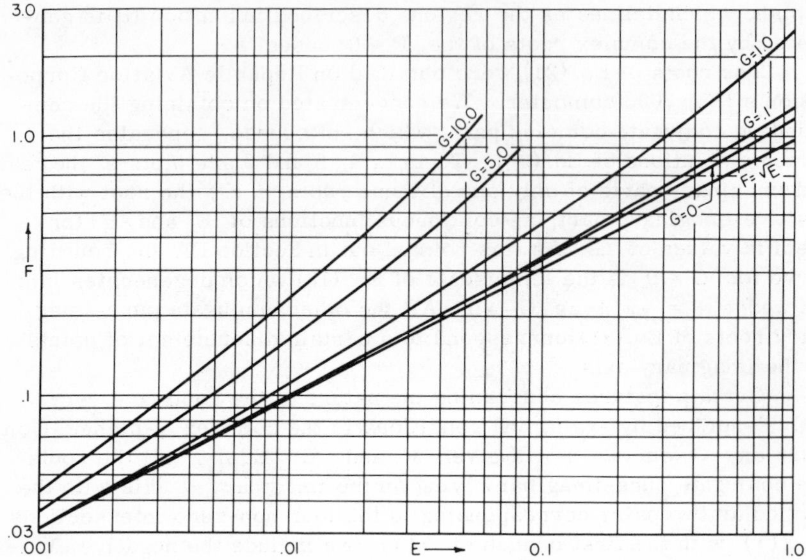

Fig. 7 Delineation of the regions in E, F-space of periodic and aperiodic solutions for various values of G.

For comparison purposes, the curve $F = \sqrt{E}$ is also plotted. This curve represents the critically damped condition in E, F language of an ordinary lumped R, L, C series circuit with the inertia term absent. All points below a given G curve correspond to the periodic solutions and those above it to the overdamped solutions. It is seen that the effect of increasing G is to increase the area corresponding to the periodic solutions at the expense of the aperiodic ones. Further, for operating values of E and F in the wedge-shaped area between the $G = 0$ and $G = G$ curves, circuits deemed aperiodic by omission of the inertia term become periodic if it is included.

We now examine the asymptotic small-time behavior given by Eq. (22). We observe the following five properties:

1) The introduction of δ does not change the essential features of normal electromagnetic diffusion. That is, the magnitude of the current density is still smallest at the center and increases as $I_0(x)$ toward the surface.

2) The dependence of the current density build-up rate on δ is more easily examined by considering the surface station $r = a$ of a plasma cylinder of small radius. In this case, $J(a, t) \sim q_0/\ell C \cdot t/\delta$. The rate of increase of current density is inversely proportional to δ (and varies approximately in the same manner for all other radial stations in the column). On physical grounds, this behavior is to be expected. Because of the time derivative in the mechanical inertia

term, $\delta \partial J/\partial t$, it is of the same form and acts in much the same way as the inductive or electromagnetic inertia term in the differential equation. In fact, by considering the plasma column once again broken up into concentric shells in parallel and connected to the capacitor as in Section II, it is seen that the main effect of the $\delta \partial J/\partial t$, term is to increase the effective self-inductance of each shell of the column, thus reducing the rate of current density rise everywhere.

3) $J(r, t)$ is practically independent of the external inductance L, with the inductive effects supplied primarily by the mechanical inertia term.

4) Comparing (22) with the $\delta = 0$ solution (23), it is seen that for very small times, $J(r, t)$ varies linearly with time, while $J(r, t)$ varies essentially negative-exponentially in (23). This difference in temporal behavior should be expected, since the order of the equation whose solution is (22) is increased by one over that whose solution is (23), the higher order arising from an extra time derivative.

5) If we consider, in particular, the time behavior of the current density at the surface, then from Eq. (23), $J(a, t)$ varies as $t^{1/2}$ when $\delta = 0$. The initial rate of current rise is therefore infinite as compared to the finite rate of current rise when inertia is included. This behavior may partially explain the disagreement between experiment and the numerical results of Killeen, Gibson and Colgate. Their results predict a temporal behavior of the plasma and electrical variables during the pinch initiation process, which is one to two orders of magnitude faster than observed experimentally. They present the following example: for an electric field to pressure ratio of 3,000 with a current return 1 cm from the plasma surface, their analysis predicts complete ionization at the surface in about 0.1 μsec, whereas experiments indicate about 25 μsec.

Consider the large time solutions (20). We take time sufficiently large so that the solution is well represented by the first term of the series, and then examine the damped periodic solutions. The temporal behavior of a pure damped periodic motion is characterized by two parameters, i.e., frequency and damping factor. If we denote the complex root associated with the periodic solution by $\gamma = \gamma_R + i\gamma_I$ and substitute this into the coefficient of t in the exponential (20), then the circular frequency ω is given by the imaginary part and the e-fold time or damping factor t_e by the absolute value of the reciprocal of the real part. Carrying out the calculation gives

$$\omega^* = \frac{\omega\eta}{a^2} = \frac{2\gamma_R \gamma_I}{1 - 2G(\gamma_R^2 - \gamma_I^2) + G^2(\gamma_R^2 + \gamma_I^2)^2} \tag{29}$$

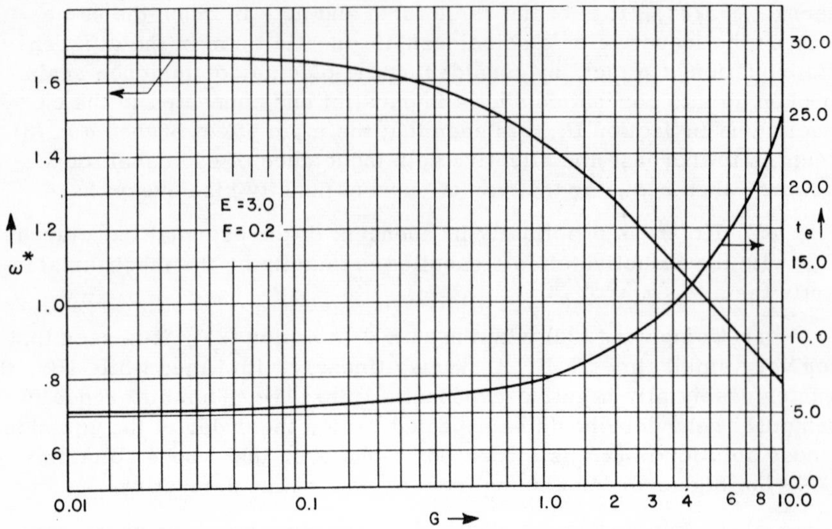

Fig. 8 Variation of dimensionless frequency and damping factor as a function of G for the case E = 3.0, F = 0.2.

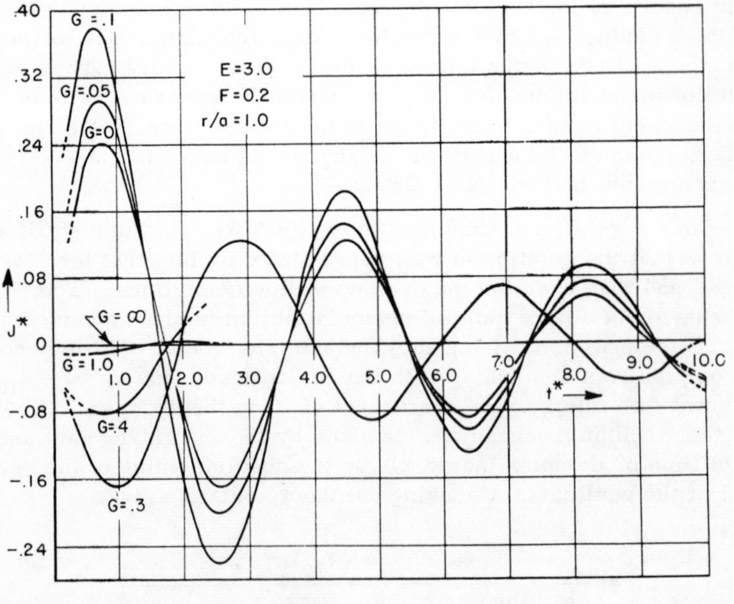

Fig. 9 Variation of current density with time at plasma surface for various G, for the case E = 3.0, F = 0.2

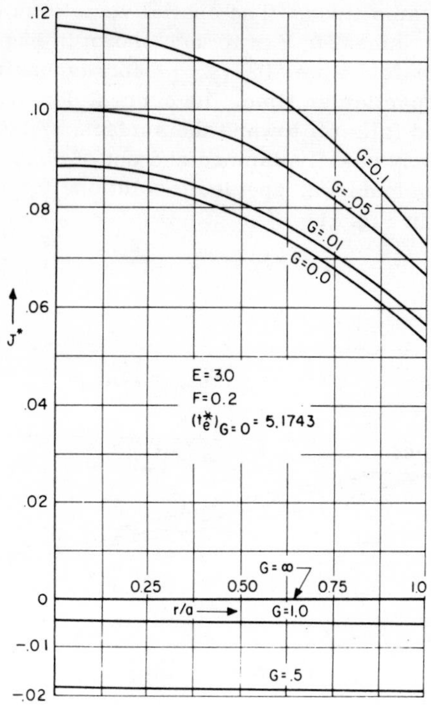

Fig. 10 Variation of current density with radial position at $(t_e^*)_{G=0} = 5.1743$, for various G ; E = 3.0, F = 0.2

$$t_e^* = \frac{t_e \eta}{a^2} = \left| \frac{1 - 2G(\gamma_R^2 - \gamma_I^2) + G^2(\gamma_R^2 + \gamma_I^2)^2}{(\gamma_R^2 - \gamma_I^2) - G(\gamma_R^2 + \gamma_I^2)^2} \right| \tag{30}$$

The variation of the dimensionless quantities ω^* and t_e^* with G for a given E, F pair is shown in Fig. 8. The frequency decreases and the damping increases with G, which again points to the conclusion reached in the examination of the small time solutions: i. e., the inertia term is inductive in its behavior.

Define the dimensionless current density $J^* = (\pi \ell CL\eta/q_o)J$. The variation at the surface of J^* with t^* for a given E, F pair and for various values of G are shown in Fig. 9. Since each curve represents a one-term solution of (20), the values of J^* near the origin are left open. Note particularly the effect of G on the frequency, damping and amplitude. The spatial variation of J^* for different G and for the same E, F pair are shown in Fig. 10. The time chosen was the e-fold time $(t_e^*)_{G=0}$ corresponding to the G = 0 case. At this particular time, the current density is a maximum at the center and falls off toward the surface. Also, the large G solutions are already heavily damped and out of phase with those for small G. For comparison, aperiodic solutions for three different G values are shown in Fig. 11.

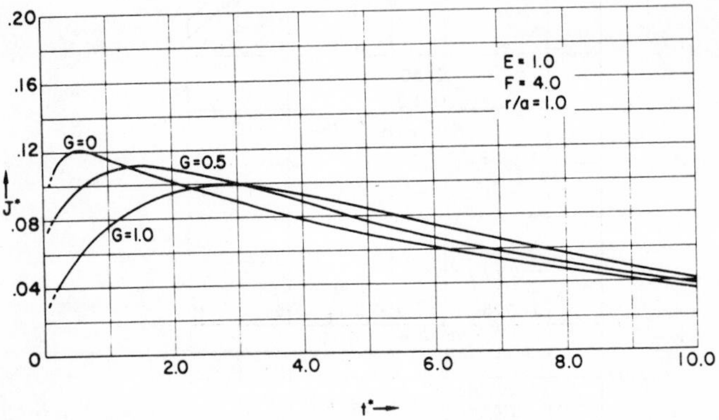

Fig. 11 Variation of current density with time at plasma surface for various G, for the case E = 1.0, F = 4.0 (aperiodic case)

ACKNOWLEDGMENTS

It is a pleasure to thank Professor Donald J. Newman of Yeshiva University for many helpful discussions. Thanks are also extended to Mr. Lionel W. Levin and Mr. Clark Squire for their kind help in performing the numerical calculations.

This research was supported in part by the U. S. Air Force through the Air Force Office of Scientific Research.

REFERENCES

1. A. E. Kunen and W. McIlroy, *Proceedings of the Third Biennial Gas Dynamics Symposium* (Evanston, Ill: Northwestern Univ. Press, 1960) p. 176.

2. See for example, J. K. Wright and M. C. Black, *J. Fluid Mech.*, Vol. 6, Pt. 2, p. 289 (1959); V. P. Korobeinikov and E. V. Riazanov, *J. Appl. Math. and Mech.*, Vol. 24, No. 1, p. 144 (1960); and B. T. Chu, "An Analytical Approach to the Problem of Pinch Dynamics," Tech. Rept. No. PPL-TR-60-9 (185), Republic Aviation Corp. (November 1960).

3. *Conference on Controlled Thermonuclear Reactions*, Gatlinburg, Tennessee, June 1956.

4. J. Killeen, G. Gibson and S. A. Colgate, *Phys. Fluids*, Vol. 3, p. 387 (1960).

5. L. Spitzer, Jr., *Physics of Fully Ionized Gases* (New York: Interscience, 1956).

6. H. S. Carslaw and J. C. Jaeger, *Conduction of Heat in Solids* (London: Oxford Univ. Press, 1950), 2nd Impression, p. 173.

7. G. N. Watson, *Theory of Bessel Functions* (London: Cambridge Univ. Press, 1952), Reprint of 2nd Ed., p. 203.

8. R. V. Churchill, *Modern Operational Mathematics in Engineering* (New York: McGraw-Hill, 1944) 1st Ed., p. 299.

9. A. Erdelyi et al., *Table of Integral Transforms* (New York: McGraw-Hill, 1954), Vol. 1, p. 247.

MAGNETOHYDRODYNAMIC SHOCK WAVES IN LOW-DENSITY IONIZED GAS

R. Z. Sagdeev
Kurchatov Institute, U. S. S. R.

This paper considers several types of plasma instabilities that occur within the front of so-called collision-free shock waves propagating perpendicular to a magnetic field in a rarified plasma.

The thickness of the front of a weak shock wave in a rarified plasma can be described from the point of view of two-fluid dynamics if the pressure of the plasma is considerably less than the pressure of the magnetic field, i. e.,

$$n\,T \ll H_o^2/8\pi\ .$$

This condition is necessary so that the Larmor radius of the electrons can be considered small in comparison with the characteristic length (c/ω_o) which arises in the problem; this is the length of the oscillations within the front of the shock wave. Under the present approximations (if trapping of the particles is neglected) the only dissipative mechanism is joule dissipation. The behavior of the parameters characterizing the plasma within the front of the shock wave can be described as follows.

Let us introduce a coordinate system in which the wave front is at rest, with the magnetic field along the z-axis. Let the wave propagate along the x-direction. The structure of the front will be described by a system of equations expressing for the plasma the laws of conservation of mass, momentum and energy, and Maxwell's equations for the electromagnetic field. This system of equations is materially simplified by the assumption of quasi-neutrality for the plasma and by neglecting the displacement current. For a low-pressure plasma, $n\,T \ll H_o^2/8\pi$. In the final analysis, these equations may be written as a single second-order differential equation for the magnetic field:

$$-a^2 H'' = H_o - H + H\,\frac{H^2 - H_o^2}{8\pi\, m_i\, n_o\, u^2} + \frac{a^2}{u}\,\nu\, H'\ . \qquad (1)$$

Presented at the Symposium on Electromagnetics and Fluid Dynamics of Gaseous Plasma, Polytechnic Institute of Brooklyn, April 4, 5, 6, 1961

Here, $a^2 = m_e c^2/4\pi n_0 e^2$, n_0 = the undisturbed density of the number of ions and electrons, u = the velocity of the shock wave relative to the undisturbed plasma, and ν = the average frequency of collisions of the electrons with the ions (which enters into the determination of the mobility of the electrons). The right-hand side of Eq. (1) owes its presence to the inclusion of the inertia of the electrons in the direction perpendicular to the propagation of the wave. This calculation takes into account the important dispersive effect usually absent in magnetohydrodynamics.

Equation (1) is the equation of motion of a harmonic oscillator in the presence of friction, with the role of a generalized coordinate being played by H, and that of time by x. The form of the "effective" potential well is determined by the potential

$$V(H) = \frac{1}{2}(H - H_0)^2 \left[\frac{(H + H_0)^2}{16\pi n_0 m_i u^2} - 1 \right] \qquad (2)$$

The form of V(H) is shown graphically in Fig. 1. V is a minimum when

$$H = H^* = -\frac{H_0}{2} + \sqrt{8\pi n_0 m_i u^2 + \frac{H_0^2}{4}} .$$

The analogy with an oscillator allows the profile of H within the front of the shock wave to be easily established. H oscillates about the value of H* with decreasing amplitude until it reaches H = H*, which conditions correspond to the magnetic field behind the front of the shock wave.

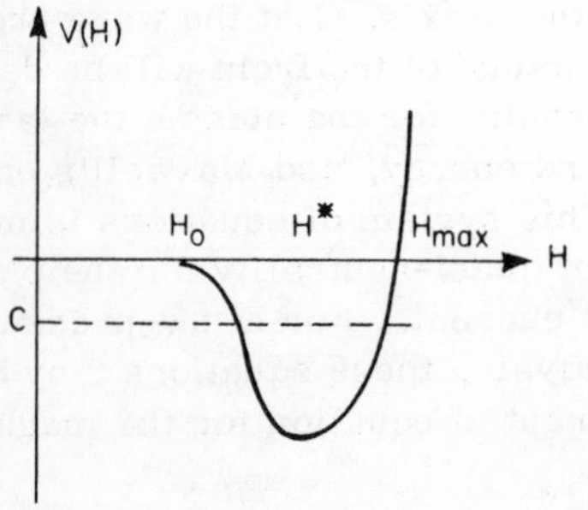

Figure 1

For H_0 to correspond to the minimum of the magnetic field in the wave (i. e., for V(H) to possess the form shown in Fig. 1), it is necessary that the following condition be fulfilled:

$$u^2 > H_0^2/4\pi n_0 m_i .$$

When $\nu \rightarrow 0$, the maximum amplitude attained at the end of the first half-period of oscillation is

$$H_{max} = 4u\sqrt{\pi n_0 m_i} - H_0 .$$

In the absence of friction, the motion of the "particle" in our potential well can be determined with the aid of a single constant, C, representing the total energy level of the particle (see Fig. 2). For small C, the solution has the form

$$H \cong H_o \left[1 + 2\,(M-1)\ \mathrm{sech}^2\ \frac{x}{a}\sqrt{M-1} \right],$$

$$M^2 = \frac{4\pi\, n_o\, m_i\, u^2}{H_o^2}\ . \tag{3}$$

For large C, when the amplitude of oscillation has noticeably decreased in comparison with the initial amplitude, the oscillation becomes damped harmonic:

$$H - H^* \sim e^{(\nu/u)x}\ \sin\left[\frac{1}{\sqrt{2}}\ \sqrt{M-1}\ \frac{x}{a}\right]. \tag{4}$$

The profile of the variation of H within the wave front can finally be represented as follows: At first an isolated wave appears in an undisturbed plasma. At the crest of this wave the magnetic field attains its maximum value. As a consequence of the presence of irreversible dissipation (friction), the state of the plasma will be slightly altered after the passage of the wave. At an interval of order

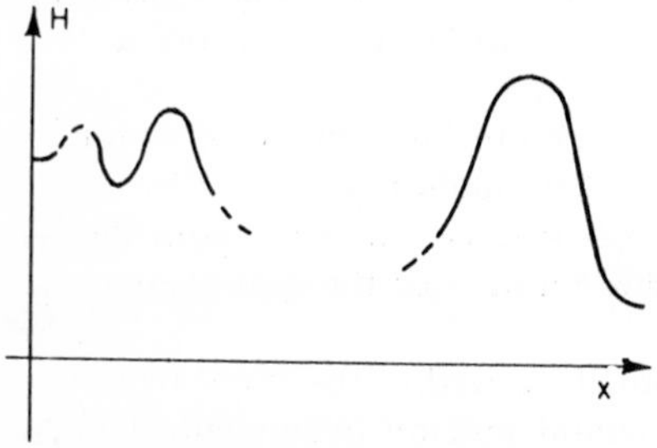

Figure 2

$$\frac{a}{\sqrt{M-1}}\ \ell n\ \frac{a}{\nu\, a}\ \sqrt{M-1}$$

after the first wave, a second wave appears, and so on. Subsequent waves possess a diminishing amplitude, and the interval between two neighboring "crests" of the magnetic field is shortened to $a/\sqrt{M-1}$ when the series of crests and troughs are an attenuated sinusoidal wave. The attenuation length of the oscillator will be of the order

$$\frac{u}{\nu} \approx \sqrt{\frac{H^2}{8\pi\, nT}}\ \sqrt{\frac{m_e}{m_i}}\ \lambda\ ;\quad (\lambda \sim \sqrt{T/m_e}/\nu) \tag{5}$$

This is clearly seen to be the thickness of a small-amplitude shock wave.

From Eq. (5) it can be seen that the width of the shock-wave front can be considerably smaller than the mean-free path (in the extreme case, by a factor of $\sqrt{m_e/m_i}$). This is natural, since under joule heating both the increase in temperature and the relaxation time of the electrons are considerably less than those of the ions due to the larger velocity of the electrons.

When the amplitude of the magnetic field in the wave approaches a value three times larger than its initial value, the qualitative picture described above no longer holds, and a "turning over" takes place. In several regions, the ions which originally move slowly overtake and pass the forward ones. The velocity profile at this moment is triple-valued.

An analogous phenomenon has been well investigated in the theory of waves of finite amplitude on the surface of a heavy liquid in a channel of finite depth. In this case nonlinear, steady motion exists in the form of isolated or periodic waves. With sufficiently large amplitude, such waves disintegrate as a result of the "turning over."

Let us now turn to the initial question of stability within the wave front. It is well known that a plasma existing sufficiently far from a state of thermodynamic equilibrium (in other words, having a non-Maxwellian velocity distribution) becomes unstable as regards self-excitation of different kinds of oscillations. For example, it is clear that the multiple-velocity current which arises after a "turning-over" must be unstable.

It is interesting to note that in a wave on the surface of water a similar instability (contrary current) also takes place; this is simply an instability of a tangential discontinuity, arising from the collision of the incident current with the surface of the quiescent liquid.

In principle, however, the instabilities within the front of the shock wave can appear before much current motion is formed, i. e., for $M < 2$. For example, let us consider a steady isolated wave, propagating across a magnetic field in a "cold" plasma

$$(nT \ll H^2/8\pi).$$

In the direction of the wave's propagation, both the ions and the electrons move with the same velocity. However, the electric field in the direction perpendicular to the direction of propagation of the wave and the magnetic field consist principally of electrons. As is well known, in a homogeneous plasma, the presence of an appreciable relative motion of the ions and electrons leads to instability.

It is clear that an analogous effect can be expected in this case. The problem is simplified if, when considering small deviations from the stationary picture of an isolated wave, we neglect those terms which take into account undisturbed motion of the plasma in the x direction. It is evident that this is justified because the time required for the instability to develop is significantly less than the time of "passage" of the isolated plasma wave region.

For simplicity, let us consider the disturbed motion of the ions and electrons as the motion of two fluids with adiabatic behavior under a change of pressure, and neglect the influence of the magnetic field on the disturbed motion, so that we limit ourselves to those oscillation frequencies considerably larger than the Larmor frequency of the electrons (eH/m_eC). Now after fulfilling the usual linearization procedure, it is possible to exclude all variables except n_e, the disturbed density of the electrons. In the case where the derivatives in the x direction of the disturbed quantities are much greater than those of the undisturbed ones (quasi-classical approximation), the system of equations for the disturbed motion reduces to one second-order differential equation in the quantity n_e:

$$S_o^2 n_e'' + \left[(\omega + K v_o)^2 - S_o^2 K^2 - \frac{\omega_o^2}{1 - \Omega_o^2/\omega^2} \right] n_e = 0; \tag{6}$$

where

$$\omega_o^2 = 4\pi n_o e^2/m_e; \qquad \Omega_o^2 = 4\pi n_o e^2/m_i.$$

We immediately choose the dependence of the disturbed quantities in the form $\phi(x) \cdot \exp\left[i(\omega t + ky)\right]$. The quantities v_o, S_o^2, and n_o are repectively, the undisturbed average velocity of the electrons along the y axis, the square of the thermal velocity of the electrons, and the plasma density, depending on x.

Equation (6) describes local instabilities, the criteria for whose appearance almost coincide with the case of an inhomogeneous plasma. It is necessary that there exist within the wavefront a region where $v_o > S_o$. As is well known, the increments of accumulation of such an instability are of the order of Ω_o.*

The amplitude of v_o increases with an increase in Mach number. Finally, for a certain value of Mach number, $M = M^*$, the amplitude of v_o will exceed the average thermal velocity of the electrons. For a "cold" plasma, the critical Mach number is

*In a plasma of "zero" temperature, the maximum increment is still larger: $\Omega_o (m_i/m_e)^{2/3}$.

$$M^{*} \cong 1 + \frac{3}{4}\left[\frac{8\pi nT}{H^2}\right]^{1/3} \qquad (7)$$

The action of such a type of instability can, in the known sense, be treated as a frictional force of the electrons on the ions, having a "collective" nature. It seems reasonable to take into account the dissipating effect of this frictional force, in Eq. (1), which determines the profile of the variation of H within the shock wave front. If, in Eq. (1), we replace ν (the collision frequency of the electrons with the ions), with the maximum increment of the determined instability, then the character of the variation of H in terms of the "effective potential well," V(H), will be as shown in Fig. 3. As long as the frictional force is very large, the "motion" will be aperiodic. Then when the amplitude of v_o decreases (and the electrons warm up), the instability disappears and the motion becomes oscillatory.

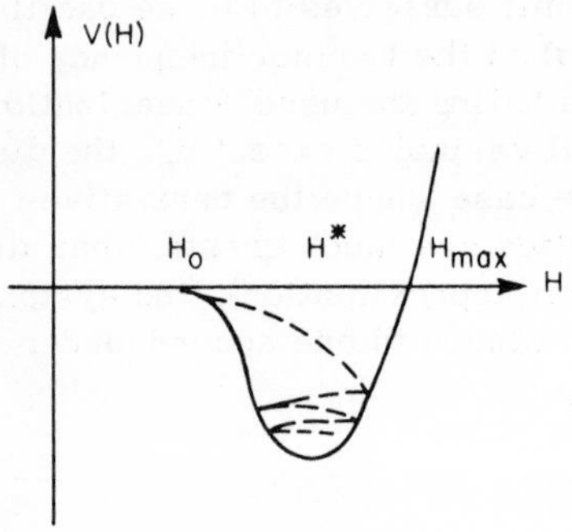

Figure 3

In the entire profile H for $M > M^{*}$ may be represented as shown in Fig. 4. The region of anomalous dissipation, where H varies aperiodically, possesses a thickness of order $(c/\omega_o)(H^2/8\pi\, nT)^{1/2}$.

In the preceding discussion we have not taken into account dependence on the spatial coordinate z parallel to the magnetic field H. This dependence is related to both the stationary and excited solutions. Let us briefly state several preliminary results pertinent to this question.

Consider first the stationary solutions, which represent the profile of a shock wave propagating along an angle nearly perpendicular to the magnetic field. If the condition of small amplitude of the shock wave is satisfied, and if the normal to the shock wave front makes an angle θ with the plane perpendicular to the magnetic field ($\sqrt{m/M} \ll \theta \ll 1$), it can easily be shown that the equation describing the variation of the magnetic field within the shock wave front has the form:

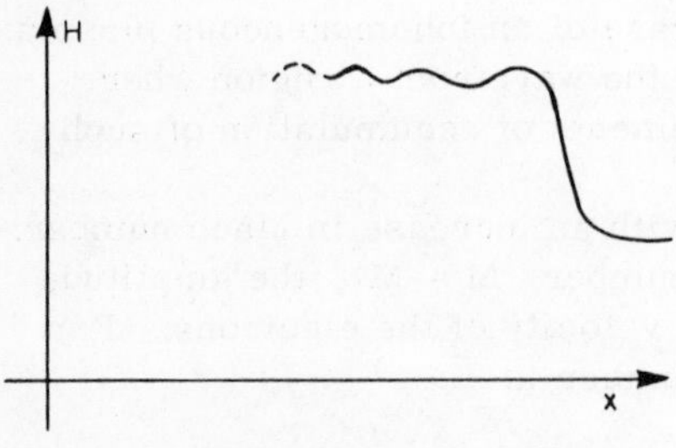

Figure 4

$$b^2 H'' = -\frac{d}{dH} V(H); \qquad (8)$$

where

$$b^2 = \frac{c^2}{\Omega_o^2} \theta^2, \quad \Omega_o^2 = \frac{4\pi ne^2}{M}.$$

Note that this equation recalls the form of Eq. (1). However, in contrast to Eq. (1), on the left side of Eq. (8) there is a positive coefficient before the second derivative.

The difference in sign of the coefficients results from the difference in the behavior of the dispersion for small-amplitude waves propagating strictly perpendicular to a magnetic field;

$$\omega^2 \cong \frac{H^2}{\sqrt{4\pi\, nM}} (1 - a^2 K^2); \qquad (9)$$

and at a small angle to the perpendicular,

$$\omega^2 \cong \frac{H^2}{\sqrt{4\pi\, nM}} (1 + b^2 K^2). \qquad (10)$$

Equation (8), in the absence of dissipation, has in quality of solutions, in particular, the isolation of a wave of rarefaction. In the general case it describes the profile of a shock wave front which is inverted and reflected (see Fig. 4).

Let us now consider the question of the stability of shock waves in relation to disturbances depending on the direction along the magnetic field. If we omit instabilities of the kind considered previously, the possibility of a breakdown into faster transverse waves is the most dangerous type of instability.

In usual magnetohydrodynamics, when the front of a disturbance is considered as a mathematical surface, the proof of the instability for this case reduces to a calculation of the number of unknown constants determining the amplitude of the disturbance and the number of conditions at the discontinuity. If a disturbance exists having a velocity exceeding the velocity of a given wave, the number of constants is greater than the number of conditions. In such a case, the solution of the Cauchy problem is not unique. In particular, it is possible to construct an unstable solution with as large an increment as one pleases.

This has served as the foundation on which several authors have classified cases similar to the above as "unevolutionary" rather than unstable. Also, one usually says that, in contrast to the usual problem in stability, here, because of the terminal interval of time, the amplitude of the disturbance considered in the linear approximation rotates endlessly, which, in general, testifies to the inapplicability of the linear approximation.

In our case, however, a similar linear scheme of treatment cannot be used, due to the fact that the front cannot be considered very thin in comparison with c/Ω_o. It is now necessary to solve the extremely cumbersome problem of stability of a continuous distribution. For simplicity, let us consider an idealized model, which is very close to the original one. The equation for the model is:

$$\frac{\partial V}{\partial t} + V\frac{\partial V}{\partial x} = -\frac{\partial}{\partial x}\frac{H^2}{8\pi} - \frac{\partial}{\partial x}\left[a^2\frac{\partial}{\partial x^2} - b^2\frac{\partial}{\partial z^2}\right]H,$$

$$\frac{\partial M}{\partial t} + \frac{\partial}{\partial x} VH = \beta^2 \Delta H; \quad (\beta = c^2/4\pi\sigma). \tag{11}$$

The solution must vanish at $\pm\infty$. The condition at $+\infty$ for an unstable wave ($e^{i\omega t}$, Im $\omega < 0$), can be satisfied only for $\omega/K_x > u$.

For this solution to vanish at $-\infty$ also, there must exist a point at which the phase changes sign: $K_x' = 0$. From the condition it is possible to find the increments (in the quasi-classical approximation), and the sufficient condition for stability (Im $\omega > 0$) has the form

$$nmc^2 > \frac{H}{8\pi}(M-1)(\omega_o \tau_e)^2 \tag{12}$$

where M = Mach number and τ_e = collision time.

ROUND TABLE DISCUSSION*

Moderator: N. Marcuvitz
Polytechnic Institute of Brooklyn

I. B. Bernstein, Princeton University
O. Buneman, Stanford University
A. Busemann, NASA, Langley Research Laboratory
A. Ferri, Polytechnic Institute of Brooklyn
A. Kantrowitz, AVCO Research Laboratory
A. C. Kolb, U. S. Naval Research Laboratory
R. K. M. Landshoff, Lockheed Missile Space Division
L. Sedov, Academy of Sciences, U. S. S. R.

In keeping with tradition, the symposium endeavored to serve the twofold purpose of providing both a review of the present state of research in the plasma field and a forum for discussion of recent outstanding advances of interest to engineers, mathematicians, and physicists involved in plasma research. The program concluded with a critical summary of the symposium presentations.

OPENING REMARKS

Dr. Marcuvitz: The organizers of this symposium have attempted to arrange a marriage between the electromagneticists, who are gradually entering the field of plasma physics, and the fluid-mechanicists. From the papers given at the symposium, it is apparent that while the marriage is agreed upon on both sides, it will perhaps be of the shotgun variety.

Abandoning the metaphor, there is a major problem involved for those who have attempted to enter this common area of interest from backgrounds that are, to some extent, quite different, with a resulting difference in terminology and language, and frequently in point of view. In the course of this panel discussion we will attempt to seek out from some of the topics either explicitly discussed or implicit in the symposium papers, those subjects which we hope would attempt to cross the boundary line between the interests of the two groups.

The subjects in question can be classified as either theoretical or experimental in nature. In the former instance, we have heard a number of papers concerned with presenting the relevant equations of plasma fluid dynamics. These presentations have been somewhat different and applicable in different ranges, the range of interest for the symposium being the non-thermonuclear range. The reason for this

*This report, summarizing the round table discussion at the Symposium on Electromagnetics and Fluid Dynamics of Gaseous Plasma, Polytechnic Institute Of Brooklyn, April 4, 5, and 6, 1961 was prepared by Professor Enrico Levi, Co-Chairman of the Symposium.

constraint in interest is that we already have an abundance of discussion on the thermonuclear aspects of plasma.

On the theoretical side, there is a sort of duality of approach to the question of what is an acceptable set of equations applicable to a range of phenomena within a prescribed area. On one hand we have the moment approach, which is very much akin to the macroscopic treatment familiar to fluid-dynamicists; while on the other hand we have the distribution function approach. The equations themselves have been applied to the solution of a number of dynamical problems. The significance of boundaries is a problem which has been touched upon, but the "well-putting", so to speak, of these problems is still an open question. The question of techniques, either linear or non-linear, applicable in this region has come up explicitly and implicitly.

On the experimental side, there has been a correspondingly wide range of interest, from problems concerning those interested in communications: transmission, reflection, propagation properties associated with plasmas, to the more energetic type of consideration associated with ponderomotive forces: questions concerning the significance of plasma in lift, drag, thrust effects, and, inversely, the question of energy conversion from the dynamical form into electrical energy of one form or another. Also touched upon have been a number of experimental plasma problems of astrophysical interest including the question of the fireball.

EQUATIONS OF PLASMA DYNAMICS

To open the discussion, I would like to start with the question of what is an appropriate form for the equations of plasma dynamics which are applicable over the non-thermonuclear range? What are the virtues of the moment approach vs the distribution function approach?

Dr. Bernstein: The scope of the phenomena mentioned by Dr. Marcuvitz is so large that I would hesitate to say that there is any one set of equations that would cover them all and still remain tractable and familiar. However, the equations of interest to this panel and this meeting fall into two major groups. First are those in which aerodynamicists and those who propose to generate magnetohydrodynamic power might be interested. This is substantially a collision-dominated domain, and the equations are the familiar equations of fluid dynamics modified by electromagnetic terms. In principle, we can treat them by the methods of kinetic theory of Chapman, Cowling and Enskog*. Gases, of course, tend to be complex, they tend to be mixtures, the chemistry is uncertain, etc. However, within these limits, we feel we have a good handle on the problem. As the ionization den-

*S. Chapman and T.C. Cowling, *Mathematical Theory of Non-Uniform Gases* (Cambridge University Press, 1952) sity increases to the point where the interactions among the charged particles (i. e., Coulomb collisions) begin to dominate, we begin to leave the well established, familiar, and usual realm of phenomena. We reach one where the kinetic equation must be modified, collision integrals must be replaced by Fokker-Planck terms, and the rationality of all of this is not yet well established. Finally, if we permit the ionization to go up to completion and the temperatures to rise very high, we end up in a domain where the representation of phenomena by transport coefficients and simple moment equations ceases to be legitimate. In this domain one must resort to the kinetic equation.

Consider as an example the magnetohydrodynamic generator. Posing the problem is quite simple, because for most of the feasible pressure and temperature ranges the conductivities are low, the electromagnetic interactions are weak, and one can very easily and readily adapt familiar dynamical considerations -- channel flows, nozzle flows, etc. At the opposite extreme, the field of traveling-wave tubes and microwave-beam tubes is also very well established and well developed. Here, collisions are usually negligible, temperature effects small, and -- at least qualitatively -- we believe we have an understanding of the phenomena, albeit in general it is derived from small-amplitude considerations. However, in the intermediate region, there is much to be done. In particular, nonlinear phenomena and wave propagation problems in density gradients are essentially wide-open fields.

Dr. Buneman: In a variety of places a fairly clear relation has been established between moment and distribution function approaches, and we know what the moment method can do and what it cannot. The moment method is of use even at the extreme of the collision-free region. There are applications in which this method can be used and relied upon, although there are, of course, certain things that it misses. Under a variety of conditions, for example, when the phenomena become rather supersonic, one can still use MHD.

I would like to bring a new element into the discussion by pointing out that we may hope to use MHD even more and even further without even worrying about such details as transport coefficients and Fokker-Planck terms -- namely, we are looking for an alternative to collisions for establishing something like a regime of thermal equilibrium. It is the basis of all hydrodynamics that one does not deviate from equilibrium too much; that there are plenty of collisions to bring one near the most probable condition of equilibrium.

I think we have an alternative to collisions; in fact, we have so many that there is a bit of a quarrel about which is the right one. We have the instabilities which can develop without collisions and which will aid a plasma in its desire to approach thermal equilibrium. We can never get very far from it because as soon as we deviate too much some instability will arise, which, at a rate much faster than collisions, will see the plasma back into equilibrium. This has been pointed out in several of the papers given at this symposium, particularly in those on shocks. What is the type of instability that changes the entropy in a shock, for instance? What is the type of instability that produces something nearer to thermal equilibrium than the rather abstract models of shocks where particles are extremely cold and just follow the Newton laws?

DYNAMICAL EQUATIONS CONTAINING THE EFFECTS OF LANDAU DAMPING

Dr. Marcuvitz: Since the moment approach is really a means of integrating out velocity effects, can another approach be devised which will have the virtues implicit in the moment approach of obtaining a set of true dynamical equations resembling those of fluid dynamics but which will contain the effects of Landau damping?

Dr. Bernstein: Simple physical considerations suggest that it might be difficult to get anything closely resembling a normal moment approach which would serve this purpose, because the phenomenon of Landau damping is effectively a resonance phenomenon. It is a question of the interaction of the wave with those particles that are moving close to the phase velocity of the wave. In order to describe such particles you must give their distribution function. You cannot characterize them by giving only a few moments, and if you have to give more than a few the moment approach fails and you had much better work directly with kinetic theory.

Dr. Buneman: I have tried to smuggle a Landau damping term into the ordinary magnetohydrodynamics equations, that is, the equations that deal with local properties, and have failed. I thought there might be something like a pseudo-viscosity that one might get in, but it just didn't work. I got the phase factor wrong. I couldn't really put it right; there seemed to be no local property that would help me get some Landau damping in. I think the reason is that which Dr. Bernstein just mentioned: in one case you have an integral over all space, and in the other you have only local properties to deal with.

Dr. Landshoff: One of the papers delivered here at the symposium, "On a Variational Principle for Plasmas," by Dr. Gartenhaus, seems to have possible germs of a method for treating such matters as this. He suggested the possibility of putting into the equation types of parameters other than the usual moments, and using a variational principle. I could very well imagine that when we are looking for a solution which is damped like $e^{-\lambda T}$, we can put this into the solution and then look for it. I can probably write down a distribution function which looks like a shock, and then try to adjust the parameters so that it will be a shock.

Dr. Kantrowitz: There is a point to be made for an approach reminiscent of the moment approach of kinetic theory which can be used in high-temperature gases and fully ionized gases. Instead of concentrating on the individual particles one concentrates on the waves present. The positions of all the particles can then be described by describing the amplitudes and phases of a sufficient number of waves; this approach was used many years ago in the theory of solids. One obtains something like a Boltzman equation for waves (which has been derived by Dr. Petscheck*). This leads, for slightly disturbed conditions, to a situation reminiscent of the moment approach to the ordinary Boltzmann equation. When collisions cease to be the important phenomena and collective interactions become the important factor, the situation closely parallels that in the solid state where heat conductivity and all kinds of transport properties are calculated from the point of view of the motion of phonons; again, we can look forward to this kind of approximation being significant in the case of a fully ionized plasma.

Dr. Bernstein: I would like to point out some of the difficulties of this very interesting way of approaching the problem. In the theory of solids you deal with situations close to thermal equilibrium, in which damping processes are small. You therefore have ways of arriving at the amplitude of the individual wave. However, in fully ionized high-temperature plasmas, you usually have a random-wave field, superposed on a pseudo-steady state far from thermal equilibrium, and the difficulty is essentially that of determining the power spectrum of the waves. This is very much more difficult than any problem close to thermal equilibrium.

Dr. Kantrowitz: This method of dealing with states far from equilibrium has been approached before. For example, it works out beautifully in ordinary kinetic theory. The states available to a gas are divided into two groups, one of which is classified as accessible and the other as inaccessible. It is not yet clear how to make such classifications in terms of plasma wave quantities. One might hope that this classification into accessible and inaccessible regions will make it possible to use statistics similar to those used so successfully in kinetic theory.

M. S. Sodha (Armour Research Foundation): I have a question referring to the applicability of the magnetohydrodynamic equations to highly ionized gases. Even if we disregard the motion of the gas and consider only a stationary gas, we find that the generalized Ohm's law that everybody uses is only applicable if the collision frequency is constant, that is, if it does not depend on electron velocity. However, in the case of a fully ionized gas, or even a strongly ion-

*M.M. Litvak, "A Transport Equation for Magnetohydrodynamic Waves," Avco-Everett Research Laboratory, Research Report 92, August 1960.

M. Camac, A.R. Kantrowitz, M.M. Litvak, R.M. Patrick, and H.E. Petschek, "Shock Waves in Collision-Free Plasmas," paper presented at the International Atomic Energy Conference on Plasma Physics and Controlled Nuclear Fusion Research, Salzburg, Germany, September 4-9, 1961.

ized gas, this is not so. How do we justify using the MHD equations for these cases?

Dr. Buneman: In a general sense, Ohm's law states what currents flow when an electric field is given. One can calculate the current by applying MHD methods, e. g., the moment method, to an ordinary plasma, provided one studies electrons and ions separately. This is one of the provisos that I am applying when I say that one can study collision-free or nearly collision-free plasmas by MHD methods. Then the currents that flow will come out of the MHD analysis -- that is, two-fluid MHD.

Dr. Marcuvitz: What about the rapid velocity dependence of the collision frequencies?

Dr. Buneman: I was talking about the extreme of the rare collisions when one does not worry about collisions at all. The large-scale collisions, that is, the collisions of charge in bulk, are taken into account in the Vlasov equation from which one starts.

M. S. Sodha: To make my point clear: what I am against is using just one conductivity and using it in the generalized Ohm's law.

Dr. Buneman: It is a tensor conductivity we are talking about. In this case, if you take into account the density gradients that occur in the gases and the consequent variation in the collision frequency, the MHD description is more complicated than the description by a distribution function and nothing is gained.

Dr. Bernstein: Lyman Spitzer's* derivation of the generalized Ohm's law is based on the assumption of weak collisions and small currents and velocities; in that range it is a phenomenological theory which is qualitatively correct. In the limit of strong collisions, one can devise an equivalent, very similar-appearing Ohm's law. When a magnetic field is present, this theory is characterized by a tensor conductivity and is certainly legitimate in that region. A third instance in which you can get a similar-looking Ohm's law is in the limit of a very strong magnetic field and no collisions. All of these Ohm's laws look very much alike, although they are based on essentially different physical regimes. This should be borne in mind. When these regimes occur, the appropriate rules are applicable and a much simpler description is obtained, in the sense of a smaller number of variables, than if the Boltzmann equation must be solved directly.

PRECISION OF PLASMA EXPERIMENTS

Dr. Marcuvitz: We now switch to the experimental side of the problem, which is designed to ascertain the basic processes

*L. Spitzer, *Physics of Fully Ionized Gases* (New York: Interscience, 1956)

and whether or not their quantitative measure is adequate. The following question is of great importance to an experimentalist: what precision is potentially available from the plasma experiments insofar as they bear on the properties of plasma which the experiments are designed to measure?

Dr. Kolb: The question of the precision required in a plasma experiment will depend partially on the subtlety of the question asked. If the question is whether the plasma is at one electron volt or ten electron volts, then perhaps a crude spectroscopic observation could answer it. The situation where the plasmas are collision-dominated is the simplest, albeit difficult. In this case, you have the advantage of being able to calculate concentrations using a mass-action law. In this limit, the ionization by electron impact is balanced by three-body recombination. Therefore, if the density is not too low and the temperature not too high, one can achieve quite remarkable precision in measuring plasma properties: namely, degree of ionization, excitation temperatures, ionization temperatures, and electron and ion density. This is true because, in these plasmas, even though you may be dealing with a transient situation, you can make time-resolved photoelectric observations of line radiation and continuous radiation. If you work with gases where the quantum mechanics is tractable, say atomic hydrogen, or some of the simplest lines of helium, it is possible to make really precise temperature measurements. Recently, E. A. McLean of the U. S. Naval Research Laboratory has measured temperature behind shock fronts in He with a precision better than 1.5 per cent at 40,000 degrees*. Once the spectroscopic temperature is known, the mass-action law or the Saha equation can be used to predict the intensities of other ion and neutral spectral lines. This can also be looked at spectroscopically and the agreement is within the experimental accuracy. Knowing the electron temperature and *assuming* that there is equilibrium, one can then calculate the densities of ions, electrons and neutrals. It is interesting now to check the question of whether or not equilibrium actually exists by measuring the density by an independent technique which does not rely on the equilibrium assumption. One possibility is to measure the absolute intensity of the continuous radiation which depends mainly on the density; another is to measure the detailed profiles of spectral line which are broadened by the first and second-order Stark effect caused by ion and electron microfields. In both cases, the theory is sufficiently accurate so that one can determine densities in a collision-dominated plasma at temperatures up to 50,000 degrees with an accuracy of about 10 per cent. This is a regime where you can really talk about a unique ionization, excitation and electron temperature,

*E.A. McLean, C.E. Faneuf, A.C. Kolb and H.R. Griem, *Physics of Fluids*, Vol. 3, p. 843 (1960)

and therefore a unique Boltzmann factor. The plasma then has a well defined state.

One of the virtues of shock waves for the production of high-density plasmas is that, although the time scale of the experiment is quite short, there is no time for demixing to occur (if more than one gas is present) or for wall effects to dominate the situation, and you can really learn something from precision measurements of the emitted radiation. As you move up in temperature, the real controversy, which is born from the scarcity of experimental data, basically arises when one moves from the collision-dominated regime to the collision-free regime. The astrophysicists work in a steady-state regime (for example, in the low-density corona where the temperature is about one million degrees) where the densities are low and there is no balance of ionization by electron impact and three-body recombination. Here there is a balance between radiative recombination and ionization by electron impact which is described by the famous corona formula of Elwert*. This is the extreme opposite of a high-density plasma where radiative processes are not so important. The interpretation of laboratory spectroscopic data in this temperature regime really becomes difficult because a plasma is not born at one million degrees -- it must be heated up and generally there is no steady state. Therefore, an experiment may start in a condition which is initially collision-dominated and ultimately end in a state which is collision-free and not in equilibrium. One would like to learn something about the heating rates in the intermediate stages. This subject is still in its infancy, but I think that with the spectroscopic techniques available now, a great deal can be learned by watching ionization rates. However, the subject of non-equilibrium plasma physics is too new to say much about the precision of different experimental methods.

MEASUREMENT OF THICKNESS

Dr. Marcuvitz: In the area of shock waves, what measurement of thickness are important to determine whether collision effects are present or not and in what degree?

Dr. Kantrowitz: The shock tube has provided us with a most important tool for studying high-temperature gases. For a number of years we have been attempting to extend its usefulness to the range of collision-free gases as well. The key thing that can be studied in this connection is the shock front itself, its thickness, and ultimately, perhaps, its profile. This is a useful thing to do because it can be a relatively clean experiment in the sense that you know what you started out with and you can easily measure the velocity of

*G. Elwert, Z. *Naturforschung*, Vol. 13a, p. 941(1958)

the wave and the pressure that is driving it with great precision. Therefore, we have almost all the same great advantages that we had with ordinary chemical shock tubes in studying the properties of gases in the range from 10,000 to 50,000 degrees Kelvin. I would like to urge others to consider this field of experimental research, that is, measuring the properties of shock waves in the collision-free regime.

Dr. Kolb: I whole-heartedly support the last statements by Dr. Kantrowitz. The question of the existence of a collision-free shock wave is a very important one. After first showing their existence, questions arise about its state, etc. In connection with the experimental aspects, the importance of the question is so great that one must try to make these measurements redundant. In other words, if one is measuring a physical effect that may depend on more than one parameter (say, something that depends on the magnetic field, the density, the temperature, and perhaps the velocity), it is useful to make independent measurements as a cross-check on the conclusions of one measurement. I would like to ask Dr. Kantrowitz if he expects that interferometric techniques like those used by Alpher and White* for collision-dominated shock waves may give independent information on the density and compression ratio. Or may it be useful to look at the shape of He II spectral lines whose width depends quite insensitively on the temperatures; this may give an independent check on the density at the front. Does Dr. Kantrowitz have in mind other measurements that may support the conclusion that there is a compression at the front of a collision-free plasma wave, as was deduced from the earlier measurements of the continuous radiation measurements?

Dr. Kantrowitz: As the audience probably has been able to detect, Dr. Kolb has been challenging us to demonstrate that we (AVCO-Everett Research Laboratory) have produced collision-free shocks as we have claimed for years now. I will simply summarize the evidence at this time without going into great detail.

The first evidence was the fact that these shocks moved with a velocity determined by the conservation of momentum; this checks. The second point, the density measured by Bremsstrahlung,** also

*R. Alpher and D.R. White, *Physics of Fluids*, Vol. 2, p. 153 (1959); Vol. 2, p. 162 (1959)

** R.M. Patrick, "High Speed Shock Waves in a Magnetic Annular Shock Tube," *Physics of Fluids*, Vol. 2, p. 589 (Nov. - Dec. 1959).

G.S. Janes, and H. Koritz, "Numerical Calculation of Absolute Bremsstrahlung Intensity for Fully Ionized Fully Dissociated Hydrogenic Gas," *J. Appl. Phys.* Vol. 31, p. 525 (March 1960)

M. Camac, et. al, *op.cit.*

checks with various magnetic fields giving various calculated density ratios; this variation is observed. The correct density increase is obtained, so we have conservation of momentum and conservation of mass on our side, and they both work pretty well, indicating that the description has some elements of truth in it.

As far as the thickness of these waves is concerned, there are three points. First, by measuring the rate at which the electron density builds up, we can obtain a thickness. We have recently succeeded in using a magnetic probe and have obtained another measure of the rate at which the magnetic field builds up which agrees with the rate at which the Bremstrahlung builds up. The density measurements that are made by considering the over-all change in magnetic field also agree with the density measurements made by Bremsstrahlung. The thickness measured agrees with that of the order of magnitude of an ion cyclotron radius. We derived this some years ago and it was also obtained by Sagdeev, as shown in his fine paper at this symposium ("MHD Shock Waves in Low Density Ionized Gas"). It varies with density and with Mach number precisely as calculated.

It would really be difficult to take each of these bits of evidence and call them into question to such an extent that one could doubt the entire structure. However, we all agree that somebody else should try to do this independently and experimentally.

EXPERIMENTS FOR TESTING VALIDITY OF EXISTING MHD EQUATIONS

Dr. Marcuvitz: Along the same lines, I would like to pose a slightly more general question: Rather than concerning ourselves with measurements of specific properties, is it possible to suggest or devise definitive experiments for testing the validity of some existing equations?

Dr. Buneman: I owe my career as a theoretician to a very simple experiment carried out by Sayers and Sixmith in 1942.* They observed and measured the rate of rotation of the space-charge cloud in the magnetron. I would suggest that all of you who are making shocks, glow discharges and pinches, or PIG's** in tubes of cylindrical geometry carry out experiments on the cylindrical geometry of your apparatus and the phenomena that go on inside. Put a few probes around in azimuth. Look for azimuthal variations and measure the phase difference in azimuth. With all these theories of instabilities this would be extremely helpful. We have already seen numerous examples of cylindrical symmetrical devices not remaining cylindrically symmetrical.

*British Admiralty CVD Magnetron report.

**PIG -- abbreviation for Phillip's ionization gauge and for an ion source based on the same principle..

Mr. Hess (NASA, Langely Research Lab.): We have just observed such asymmetries. I would like to ask whether or not the instabilities in the PIG discharge are not in some way related to the possible instabilities in the shock front. In a PIG discharge, which is a cylindrical symmetric structure with a cathode inside and a magnetic field in the direction of the cathode, the electrons, in going across the field, are deflected in one direction, whereas the ions, because of their high mass, go straight across. This picture looks somewhat like a shock front where the mass comes in and the electrons drift because of their greater mobility. In the PIG discharge we note instabilities which, by the way, produce ion oscillations. You can observe frequencies which have to do with the ion oscillations. The shock mentioned by Dr. Kantrowitz is also related to ion oscillations and waves. Can he comment on this?

Dr. Kantrowitz: Restating the question: is it conceivable that ion cyclotron oscillations, which we think are important inside the shock, are also important in other situations? The purpose of studying a shock wave was to create a situation where you know that dissipative phenomena must exist and to give the plasma a chance to exhibit that dissipative phenomena by which it prefers to dissipate the required amount of energy. It is also true that waves in this frequency range are significant and that they can transfer momentum between electrons and ions. Thus they can be significant in determining the conductivity of the gas. Dr. Petschek has been working on this and is going to report on the results in conductivity in the near future.

Dr. Kolb: As far as the question of the validity of the MHD equations for the cylindrical geometry is concerned, the main problem from the point of view of the experimentalist who for the past years has been doing experiments with supposedly symmetrical plasmas confined by pinch fields or axial magnetic fields, is the following: One can accumulate a great deal of experimental information, but there are few realistic theoretical calculations to compare with the data. K. Hain at the Max Planck Institute and K. Roberts at Harwell have recently done a remarkable job in coding the complete two-fluid MHD equations for the cylindrical geometry for digital computers.* The ions and electrons are allowed to have different temperatures, and a relaxation term due to collisions is included in the energy equations. Thermal conductivity and a tensor electrical conductivity, which depend on the mean electron velocity or local temperature, and therefore on the spatial coordinate, are also taken into account. Consequently, this is the calculation of the motion of a plasma cylinder in a pulsed magnetic field with the theoretically derived transport coefficient as they now exist and without unwarranted approximations

*K. Hain, G. Hain, K.V. Roberts, S.J. Roberts, Z. *Naturforschung*, Vol. 15a, p. 1039 (1960)

to the MHD equations.

This code now works, that is, is numerically stable. This does not mean that the plasma will be stable, but it is going to be very interesting to examine for example, the radial density, temperature and magnetic field distributions now that we have the numerical solution of the full nonlinear problem, in order to check just how good these equations are. We can start with experiments at very high densities in a regime where the plasma is collision-dominated and decrease the densities or increase the plasma energies and look for differences between the calculated and the experimental results.

WELL POSED PROBLEMS

Dr. Marcuvitz: The equations of plasma dynamics are local equations which are frequently applied in a consistent way to infinite media. The question arises of what is a well posed problem and how can the effects of finite boundaries be taken into account in a self-consistent or other procedure.

Dr. Bernstein: Apart from work on cylinders and the like, the bulk of the theoretical work that has been done on plasma has been confined to infinite homogeneous media, of which very few exist in nature; the question of solving problems in general bounded geometries is wide open. At one extreme we might contemplate performing microwave scattering experiments in plasma. This would essentially involve solving wave equations or equations similar to wave equations, and computing scattering amplitudes, etc. At the other extreme, we might want to perform experiments within cavities. As is usual in microwave electronics, we would like to know the shifts of the resonant frequencies as we couple in and out of cavities or change their shapes from some simple geometric shape. All of this implies that we must solve the appropriate equations subject to physically reasonable boundary conditions. The notions gleaned from infinite homogeneous media may be very much modified by the fact that wavelengths have to fit into geometry and that boundaries can reflect and otherwise complicate the phenomena we are investigating. Taking this into account, I feel that cavity measurements and scattering measurements are potentially useful tools for gathering further information about plasmas. Certainly, one of the most signal needs of all plasma physics is the need for reliable diagnostic methods, unambiguously related to the phenomena we are attempting to investigate.

Dr. Buneman: I should like to address the following remark to Dr. Grad, who, in his talk, raised a question of well-posedness. Dr. Grad, I noticed that the difficulty you encountered with the Chew-Goldberger-Low* set of pressures disappears if one allows a completely anisotropic pressure tensor. The constraint that the two pres-

*C.F. Chew, F.E. Low, M.L. Goldberger, *Proc. Royal Soc.*, (London) Vol. A236, p. 112 (1956) sures across the magnetic field should be the same is the cause of the lack of well-posedness.

Dr. Grad: Whether or not a problem is well posed has nothing to do with physics. The proper boundary conditions for a set of equations are determined by the equations and not by the problems from which they arose. For example, although when two people look at the same problem in ordinary fluid dynamics, one may think viscosity is important and the other that it is not very important, it is nevertheless the same problem. One of these people will use a set of equations requiring more boundary conditions than will the other because he happens to put viscosity in. Therefore, the reason why the physics is needed is to suggest equations; they can never even hint at whether or not the equations are good ones. This is why one must look for existence theorems. I think that the belief that one can decide, on the basis of a physical intuition, whether or not some equations are good is a fallacy resulting from the 19th century success of the potential and wave equations. Relying on such an intuition, one may drop from the equations some terms which are small but without which the equations are mathematically meaningless. This is unfortunate but true. Many of the equations we come across in MHD unfortunately have no theory, so we are just in our infancy in trying to discover which of them are local and which are not.

Coming back to what Dr. Buneman just mentioned, I do not think that one can say whether or not it is surprising that the Low equations are well posed or not in some circumstances. One can only suspect that it is because of the stress tensor, but it is very important to make sure.

Dr. Busemann: In the last fifty years, mathematical aerodynamics consisted in finding ways to get solutions. The mathematicians have provided the engineers with a lot of integrable cases, mainly in two ways. The first narrows the boundaries in such a way that from the many variables only one remains, for instance, by creating a channel flow. This procedure leads to ordinary differential equations when it succeeds. The second method pushes as many portions of the boundaries as possible to infinity in order to isolate the remaining problem from too many arbitrary inputs. Only for the simplified problem can one hope to find a closed form or at least a manageable solution. Thus, even in cases where the real problem does not extend to infinity, the achievable simplification is sufficient reason for the early investigations to consider infinite extensions of the flow field. These infinities in turn lead most obviously to the question "what is a well-posed problem?" Conditions removed to infinity may still exert an important influence on the solution. Disturbances, though created in the finite, may not leave the whole infinity unaffected. It may sometimes be the forward initial velocity and sometimes the rearward velocity which remains unchanged while sometimes a certain type of disturbance all around the infinity must be accepted.

Very often there is the additional difficulty that the integration is rather indirect and furnishes more or less isolated particular solutions while no detailed information about neighboring flow can be derived. In that respect, we welcome the effort of the mathematicians to show very early in magnetofluiddynamics the interpretation of those particular solutions which are easy to find. The only alternate source of information is to rely on the engineer' s intuition. The engineer is bound to have some idea how the flow should react when certain obstacles are put in its path. This intuition, being developed by experimental experience, works as long as the equations express the laws of nature. Many times, however, the equations must be mutilated for convenience by neglecting effects considered as small. Occasionally nature relies on the smaller effects in critical areas and thus the mutilated equation becomes an independent problem not open for engineer's intuition.

Take the question of observable magnetofluiddynamic shock waves, "do they have to face only backward, or perhaps only forward, or both?" This morning, I asked W. R. Sears after the presentation of his paper, "Some Paradoxes of Sub-Alfvenic Flow of a Compressible Conductive Fluid," if he knew in his work how to discriminate between the particular solutions or whether he still uses cut and try methods as we did when nobody knew what transonic meant or how the practical problems in supersonics were related to well-posed problems. He admitted that he is still in this preliminary state; by finding more and more complete solutions, the wealth of solution gives enough hints to connect the solutions with the proper boundary conditions. I think this is the direction in which we have to proceed, that is, trying to find enough particular solutions to be able, by intuition, or whatever mathematical information is available, to apply them properly. The idea of avoiding infinite extensions of the flow in space and time and to achieve in this manner a rather obvious interpretation should not be forgotten, but only very exceptional problems will allow us to get even a single quantitative solution. The more promising method therefore remains of finding particular solutions of infinite extent and then to find their relation to a well-posed problem, either by the wealth of solutions or by intuition or mathematics and, if nothing else works, perhaps by a qualitative investigation of flows with finite extent.

Dr. Bernstein: I think that what we need in plasma physics is essentially phenomena; that is, we must know which are the important phenomena and which are not. We will be happy for the time being to get the right answer, even if for the wrong reason.

CURRENT RESEARCH IN THE SOVIET UNION

Dr. Marcuvitz: In his talk (see Foreword) in which he briefly described some of the work done in this field at the U. S. S. R. Academy of Sciences, Professor Sedov mentioned the subject of fireballs. I would now like to ask Dr. Sedov to elaborate a bit about the particular work being done in the Soviet Union on this question.

Dr. Sedov: I would like to say a few words about the work being done in my country in connection with the solutions of MHD equations.

First of all, I would like to note that (as far as we mechanicists connected with the dynamics of gas now understand) the question of the construction of a model for the motion of plasma is still an open one. It seems to me that not only are the kinetic theories presented here fundamental, but the macroscopic theories may also be found useful. Multicomponent systems with a variable number of particles must now be made a subject of study and research by taking into account radiation, with modified forms of Ohm's law. At present, we have the classical equations of MHD, in relation to which many results have been obtained. In particular, I want to mention the following qualitative conclusion.

In studying the flow around bodies, the possibility of the squeezing off of the flow by the magnetic field has been established. Also established is the possibility of forward propagation in the presence of supersonic velocities. The properties of the equations' characteristics were investigated, and in many cases they differ significantly from the usual characteristics of the dynamics of gases. A large number of investigations on not-steady flows and "jumps of density" have been carried out. The nonlinear problem of the disintegration of any discontinuity and the problem of the piston have been solved.

Concerning the influence of finite conductivity on unsteady flows, much work has been done at Moscow University. I remember only one work on finite conductivity, that is, the propagation of ionizing shock waves; in that case the propagation of shock waves depends on the dissipation mechanism behind the shock wave.

As far as the "fireball" lightening problem is concerned, I do not know whether this problem is really related to actual fireballs. The relaxation due to finite conductivity was not included in the study, and this may very well preclude the possibility of applying the results to that case.

What I would like to speak about is the solution of a problem dealing with a system of toroidal currents which is associated with the motion of a fluid. The fluid motion and its interaction with the magnetic field is most significant in this case. The exact solution is available for a torus in which currents flow and the hydrodynamic pressure inside is higher than in the surrounding space. Since the pressure is higher, there is a possibility of obtaining substantial pressures inside, which in turn will result in a large energy concentration. This toroidal solution was tested for stability and was found to be stable in many instances. The motion of a system of thin toroids was investigated. The problems of motion of such toroidal currents near the wall have been solved. The qualitative effects of changes in the radius of the torus as well as its velocity have been clarified. The qualitative picture of the motion of such toruses is very similar, according to many published observations, to a fireball. In particular, when approaching a wall, it is possible for the torus to contract to a point and, in the presence of a keyhole in the wall, it may pass through it. There also exist many other effects which are described in the original paper on the subject by Ladikov. *

Dr. Kolb: As a result of the calculations, you said that the densities are substantial. What kind of densities? What kind of magnetic fields are involved? What are the temperatures? What do calculations say the conditions of this fireball are?

Dr. Sedov: I do not know what the temperatures and densities in the fireball are. With regard to the solution of the problem, it was made for an incompressible fluid; therefore, the results must be looked on as qualitative.

Dr. Kantrowitz: If you make the solutions only for an incompressible fluid, can you assure yourself of the possibility that in a real fluid the structure will just expand and lower the density and the temperature while maintaining its geometry and angles -- that this will occur in the real case and the fireball will dissipate in the same manner?

Dr. Sedov: This will not occur because of the pressure. As to the effect of the temperature, this question is connected with the movement of the gas. These may be secondary effects if the primary effects include the dynamic interaction and pressure distributions.

AERODYNAMICISTS POINT OF VIEW

Dr. Marcuvitz: The question of the significance of plasmas on such problems as lift, drag and thrust, for some of the vehicles of the future in the inner reaches of outer space, is one which has a variety of answers. We would like to hear an aerodynamicist's point of view on this controversial subject.

Dr. Ferri: I would first like to make a statement that is not connected with MHD. When I started work in supersonic flow in 1935, I was asked if I thought that supersonic aerodynamics would be of any use and where. I became interested in it, but at that stage I had no quick answer.

I assume that we are now in the same position regarding the creation of forces in the electromagnetic field. The possibility of creating thrust is accepted by everybody; without question, electromagnetic thrust can be obtained and will play a very important part in space investigation. However, at the present time we are too anxious to get engines that can be used for space investigation and are probably by-

*Y.P. Ladikov, *Applied Mathematics and Mechanics*, (U.S.S.R.) Vol. 24, No. 5, pp. 897-905 (1960).

passing some fundamental points that should be considered more carefully. In connection with external forces (lift and drag) and the problem of modifying heat transfer, I believe that MHD can be advantageously applied. However, being an aerodynamicist, I am tempted to solve the same problems in a classical way which is easier for me and which at the present time is adequate, although this may not be true in the future. However, independently of the problems of lift and drag, the study of MHD is important because we will certainly find some other applications of it which we cannot now foresee. However, I would be very cautious about relying exclusively on MHD for immediate application in space flight.

Dr. Buneman: Is there any hope of lifting, pushing or dragging a space vehicle smaller than the size of the mean free path of the surrounding plasma?

Dr. Kantrowitz: The mean free path is not really the relevant dimension. In this kind of situation, the ion Larmor radius is more relevant and it is possible to apply forces even when the Debye length is the only dimension comparable with the vehicle.

Dr. Kantrowitz: There is a certain amount of evidence that satellites going through the upper regions of the ionosphere have their drag increased by the accumulation of charges and by the deflection of particles that are within the Debye sphere of the satellite. The Debye sphere is on the order of meters, so it can, for small enough satellites (e. g., a meter or so) increase the drag noticeably. There is at least good theoretical evidence of this, although I do not know how clear it is experimentally.

Dr. Sedov: Studies show that the movement of the center of the mass, that is, the effects of the interaction of electrical forces with the magnetic forces of the environment, are not very significant to the movement of the center of mass of the satellite. The effects on the spinning or rotation of the mass may imply a great deal of force. Through the changing of orientation with which the satellite passes through the air, the forces within the Debye length may in some way change the movement of the center of mass. But up to now this is not very significant because most of the cosmic equipment is made such that they keep their orientation.

Dr. Kantrowitz: This is a negative experimental view, although not a negative theoretical view; there is such an electrical effect on the drag.

Dr. Sedov: The effect is not big for a cosmic apparatus.

Dr. Marcuvitz: I have heard Dr. Kantrowitz say that the effect is very large in certain circumstances.

Dr. Busemann: I agree with Dr. Ferri's remark. With respect to internal aerodynamics, we have already conceded that we can definitely do many things better with ionized gases than without ionization. The only question left, "do we or do we not break the ionic barrier?" concerns the external aerodynamics. In this restricted field, the Mach number is limited and the altitude in which problems arise is also limited. In this range, we may be able to manage by stretching every fluid-mechanical resource one more notch, which is sufficient and probably quicker, but we may perhaps get some help from ionization utilized by magnetofluid mechanical means. Remembering the past, I think that a choice between old and new methods is not a matter of knowledge alone but of wisdom, even if it may sound like a fraud. For instance, the Germans would not have spent the money for the development of jet propulsion if their proponents had not claimed that propeller efficiency would deteriorate completely when the tips approach the speed of sound. In reality, the propeller could have been improved up to a Mach number of 1. 2 or higher. Furthermore, the airplane speeds for which they could propose to develop the jets had to stay inside the limits considered reasonable at that time, even though the performance of a jet at these speeds is so poor that only a propeller caught in transonic troubles could have done worse. What would have been the result of a more "scientific" appraisal? We would have been exactly ten years behind in jet development.

Dr. Ferri: I would like to stress that we still have a problem from the negative point of view. The presence of plasma can create very serious difficulties for communications and problems of this kind, and the problem of the window is certainly a problem of fluid dynamics.

Dr. Kantrowitz: Very early in considering the re-entry of a nose cone, we (AVCO) made some analyses of the application of lift and drag to hypersonic problems. We considered the possibility of slowing it down magnetically, and decided that that could be done but that there are better ways. I still think that we were right, but I have recently been forced to alter my point of view slightly because of the advent of superconducting coils. The superconducting coil makes the application of MHD to flight a much more interesting question, and I feel very strongly that at the present time we should proceed to the study of this much more seriously.